Flood Estimation Handbook

Volume 4

Flood Estimation Handbook

Volume 4

Restatement and application of the Flood Studies Report rainfall-runoff method

Helen Houghton-Carr

Institute of Hydrology

ISBN for complete set of 5 volumes: 978-1-906698-00-3
ISBN for this volume: 978-1-906698-04-1

Originally published by the Institute of Hydrology 1999

Centre for Ecology & Hydrology
Maclean Building, Benson Lane, Crowmarsh Gifford
Wallingford, Oxfordshire OX10 8BB
UK

General and business enquiries: 01491 692562
E-mail: enquiries@ceh.ac.uk
Website: www.ceh.ac.uk

Cross-referencing

Cross-references to other parts of the Handbook are usually abbreviated. They are indicated by the relevant volume number preceding the chapter, section or sub-section number, with the volume number in bold (e.g. **4** 2.2 refers to Section 2.2 of Volume 4). Cross-references conventionally prefixed by Chapter, Section or § are to the current volume.

The Flood Estimation Handbook should be cited as:
Institute of Hydrology (1999) Flood Estimation Handbook (five volumes).
Centre for Ecology & Hydrology.

This volume should be cited as:
Houghton-Carr, H. A. (1999) Restatement and application of the Flood Studies Report rainfall-runoff method. Volume 4 of the Flood Estimation Handbook.
Centre for Ecology & Hydrology.

Contents

Preface

The research for the Flood Estimation Handbook was undertaken at the Institute of Hydrology, Wallingford, Oxfordshire. The Institute is an integral part of the Centre for Ecology and Hydrology, and a component institute of the Natural Environment Research Council. The research programme ran from 1994 to 1999.

Contributors

The core research team comprised Duncan Reed (team leader), Adrian Bayliss, Duncan Faulkner, Helen Houghton-Carr, Dörte Jakob, David Marshall, Alice Robson and Lisa Stewart. David Jones acted as an internal consultant, advising on all aspects of the research. The WINFAP-FEH software package was principally developed by Lawrence Beran, and the FEH CD-ROM was designed and developed by Kevin Black. The Handbook is dedicated in memory of Tanya Jones, a team member whose contribution to hydrological research was tragically cut short by cancer.

Major contributions were also made by David Morris, Susan Morris, Christel Prudhomme and Robert Scarrott, with additional contributions by Val Bronsdon, Victoria Edmunds, Beate Gannon, Stephanie Hills and Nick Reynard.

The team was supported by 1-year Sandwich Course Students from Luton and Sheffield Hallam Universities, including: Mark Bennett, Robert Brookes, Russell Brown, Louisa Coles, Nick Davie, Philip Davies, David Hewertson, Catriona Kelly, Marina Syed Mansor and Paul Nihell.

Sponsors

The research programme was funded by the Ministry of Agriculture Fisheries and Food (MAFF), the Environment Agency, the Department of Agriculture Northern Ireland, and a consortium led by the Scottish Office. The budget for the programme totalled about £1.7m. Indirect support was provided by the Centre for Ecology and Hydrology, the Meteorological Office and river gauging authorities. Costs of final editing and publication of the Handbook, and development of the WINFAP-FEH software, were met by the Institute of Hydrology.

Advisers

The research was reviewed by the Flood Estimation Handbook Advisory Group, comprising:

David Richardson, MAFF Flood and Coastal Defence *(Chair)*
Linda Aucott, Environment Agency
Alan Burdekin, Scottish Office
John Clarke, Department of Agriculture, Northern Ireland
Christopher Collier, University of Salford
Conleth Cunnane, University College Galway, Ireland
John Goudie, MAFF Flood and Coastal Defence *(Technical Secretary)*
Richard Harpin, Sir William Halcrow and Partners
David MacDonald, Binnie Black and Veatch
Andrew Pepper, Consultant to the Environment Agency *(Observer)*
Duncan Reed, Institute of Hydrology
Richard Tabony, Meteorological Office
Howard Wheater, Imperial College

Testers

The main participants in the user test programme were:

David Archer, Consultant to Jeremy Benn Associates
Alan Barr and Grace Glasgow, Kirk McClure and Morton
Don Burn, University of Waterloo, Canada
Jonathan Cooper, Owen Bramwell and Brian Darling, WS Atkins North West
Con Cunnane and Savithri Senaratne, University College Galway
Steve Dunthorne, Sir Alexander Gibb and Partners
Jim Findlay, Murray Dale, Stuart King and Birol Sokmenor, Babtie Group
Mark Futter, Montgomery Watson
Malcolm MacConnachie, Scottish Environment Protection Agency
David MacDonald, Binnie, Black and Veatch
Ian Rose, Emma Blunden and Rob Scarrott, Halcrow
Peter Spencer and David Rylands, Environment Agency
Peter Walsh, Bullen Consultants Ltd
Paul Webster and Anna Lisa Vetere Arellano, University of Birmingham
Howard Wheater and Christian Onof, Imperial College

Acknowledgements

The Flood Estimation Handbook is a product of strategic research funding at the Institute of Hydrology in the 1990s. It would not have happened without the lead shown by MAFF, in particular by Reg Purnell and David Richardson. The dedication of Advisory Group members and the testers is gratefully acknowledged. Alan Gustard (IH) is thanked for managerial assistance in a research programme that did not fit a standard mould.

General thanks go to all those who exchanged ideas with members of the team during the research programme. Those having greatest impact on the course of the research were Don Burn and Jon Hosking. A more general acknowledgement is to all earlier researchers in UK rainfall and flood frequency estimation. It would be invidious to list some and not others.

More specific acknowledgements to individuals and organisations co-operating in the research are made in the relevant volume.

Volumes

1 Overview
2 Rainfall frequency estimation
3 Statistical procedures for flood frequency estimation
4 Restatement and application of the *Flood Studies Report* rainfall-runoff method
5 Catchment descriptors

Notation

The following are the main symbols and abbreviations used throughout this volume of the FEH. Other symbols have just a local meaning and are defined where they occur. All units are metric except where otherwise stated.

ANSF	Average non-separated flow or baseflow ($m^3 s^{-1}$)
API5	5-day antecedent precipitation index (mm)
AREA	Catchment area (km^2)
ARF	Areal reduction factor
α	Attenuation ratio
BF	Baseflow or average non-separated flow ($m^3 s^{-1}$)
BFI	Baseflow index
BNCOLD	British National Committee on Large Dams
CIRIA	Construction Industry Research and Information Association
CWI	Catchment wetness index (mm)
CWI′	Catchment wetness index with snowmelt contribution (mm)
D	Duration (hours)
D_{CRIT}	Critical duration (hours)
DANI	Department of Agriculture, Northern Ireland
DPLBAR	Mean drainage path length (km)
DPR	Dynamic percentage runoff (%)
DPR_{CWI}	DPR component attributable to CWI (%)
DPR_{RAIN}	DPR component attributable to catchment rainfall (%)
DPSBAR	Mean drainage path slope ($m\ km^{-1}$)
EM-Dh	Estimated maximum D-hour rainfall (mm)
EM-2h	Estimated maximum 2-hour rainfall (mm)
EM-24h	Estimated maximum 24-hour rainfall (mm)
EM-25d	Estimated maximum 25-day rainfall (mm)
EMa	Estimated maximum antecedent precipitation (mm)
EMP	Estimated maximum precipitation (mm)
FEH	Flood Estimation Handbook
fse	Factorial standard error
FSR	Flood Studies Report
FSSR	Flood Studies Supplementary Report
h	Water level or water depth (m)
HOST	Hydrology Of Soil Types (soil classification)
$HOST_x$	Fraction of catchment in HOST class x
ICE	Institution of Civil Engineers
IH	Institute of Hydrology
IHDTM	Institute of Hydrology Digital Terrain Model
IUH	Instantaneous unit hydrograph
LAG	Time from the centroid of rainfall profile to the runoff peak or centroid of peaks (hours)
MAFF	Ministry of Agriculture, Fisheries and Food
Met. Office	Meteorological Office
MLURI	Macaulay Land Use Research Institute
MORECS	Met. Office Rainfall and Evaporation Calculation System
MRLAG	Mean reservoir lag (hours)
MSL	Main stream length (km)

MT/M5	Growth factor
MT-Dh	T-year return period rainfall of duration D hours (mm)
M5-Dh	5-year return period rainfall of duration D hours (mm)
M5-2d	2-day rainfall of 5-year return period (mm)
M5-60min	60-minute rainfall of 5-year return period (mm)
NERC	Natural Environment Research Council
OS	Ordnance Survey
p	Rainfall depth in time interval ΔT hours (mm)
P	Total rainfall depth (mm)
P'	Total rainfall depth with snowmelt contribution (mm)
PMF	Probable maximum flood ($m^3 s^{-1}$)
PMP	Probable maximum precipitation (mm)
PR	Percentage runoff (%)
PR_{RURAL}	Rural percentage runoff (%)
PROPWET	Proportion of time when SMD was below 6 mm during the period 1961-90
q	Rapid response runoff ($m^3 s^{-1}$)
Q	Flow ($m^3 s^{-1}$)
Q_T	T-year return period flood peak ($m^3 s^{-1}$)
r	Jenkinson's r (M5-60min) / (M5-2d)
RC	Routing coefficient
RLAG	Reservoir lag (hours)
RSMD	1-day rainfall of 5-year return period less effective mean soil moisture deficit (mm)
r^2	Correlation coefficient
S_{100}	100-year snow depth water equivalent (mm)
SAAR	Standard average annual rainfall (1961-90) (mm)
$SAAR_{4170}$	Standard average annual rainfall (1941-70) (mm)
see	Standard error of estimate
SMa	Snowmelt contribution to antecedent rainfall (mm)
SMp	Snowmelt contribution to event rainfall (mm)
SMD	Soil moisture deficit (mm)
$SMDBAR_{FSR}$	Effective mean soil moisture deficit (mm)
SOIL	Soil index, being a weighted sum of SOIL1, ..., SOIL5
$SOIL_X$	Fraction of catchment in WRAP class x
SPR	Standard percentage runoff (%)
SPRHOST	SPR derived from HOST soil classification (%)
SPR_X	SPR of HOST class x (%)
SSLRC	Soil Survey and Land Research Centre
S1085	10-85% main channel slope ($m\ km^{-1}$)
T	Return period (years)
T_F	Return period of flood peak (years)
T_R	Return period of design rainfall depth (years)
T_S	Return period of snowmelt event (years)
TB	Unit hydrograph time base (hours)
Tp	Unit hydrograph time-to-peak (hours)
Tp(0)	Instantaneous unit hydrograph time-to-peak (hours)
$Tp(\Delta T)$	Time to peak of ΔT-hour unit hydrograph (hours)
ΔT	Time interval or data interval (hours)
U or u	Unit hydrograph response ($m^3 s^{-1}$ / 10 mm)
UH	Unit hydrograph

Up	Unit hydrograph peak ($m^3 s^{-1}$ / 10 mm)
$URBAN_{FSR}$	Fraction of catchment in urban development
$URBAN_{50K}$	Fraction of catchment in urban development on 1:50 000 OS map
URBEXT	Extent of urban and suburban land cover
WRAP	Winter Rainfall Acceptance Potential (soil classification)
y	Gumbel reduced variate

Chapter 1 Introduction

1.1 Overview

Volume 4 of the Flood Estimation Handbook aims to enhance practical interpretation of the Flood Studies Report (FSR) rainfall-runoff method, one of the principal methods used in the UK for estimating the magnitude of the flood of given frequency of occurrence. All information about the FSR rainfall-runoff method has been brought together, including relevant aspects of the basic methodology, supplementary research and recommendations, and specialist guidance on aspects of use to provide a comprehensive technical restatement of the method. The recommended methodology is presented as a succinct set of rules and worked examples in convenient form; background information is provided as necessary. The volume aims to provide greater clarity and ease of use, and thereby do away with the need for users to refer to numerous documents.

1.1.1 Introduction to the FSR rainfall-runoff method

In the FSR rainfall-runoff method, a rainfall input is converted to a flow output using a deterministic model of catchment response. The model used is the unit hydrograph and losses model, which has three parameters. The parameters relate to the catchment response to rainfall (unit hydrograph time-to-peak), the proportion of rainfall which directly contributes to flow in the river (percentage runoff), and the quantity of flow in the river prior to the event (baseflow). Where possible, the model parameters are derived from observed rainfall and runoff records. However, if no records exist, the model parameters may be estimated from physical and climatic descriptors of the catchment.

Once the model parameters have been derived for a catchment, the method may be used to estimate the total flow from any rainfall event. The rainfall will be in the form of a hyetograph, defined by a duration, depth and profile. The rainfall may be a statistically-derived design event to produce a flood of a specific return period (the T-year flood), or may be a probable maximum precipitation (PMP) to produce a probable maximum flood (PMF). Alternatively, the rainfall may be an observed event, the aim being to simulate a notable flood.

In the T-year design case, the duration of the design storm is related to the speed of catchment response, and the point rainfall depth is estimated for a return period which depends on the return period of the design flood. An areal reduction factor is applied to give the catchment rainfall depth. This is subsequently transformed into a hyetograph by a standard time profile. Estimation of the PMF follows a similar procedure, with conservative assumptions regarding catchment response and the rainfall, and possibly snowmelt, inputs. For reconstruction of an event, direct estimation of catchment rainfall from observed data is possible.

In each case, the proportion of rainfall which directly contributes to flow in the river (the effective or net rainfall) is adjusted according to the runoff potential of the catchment, the rainfall total and the antecedent catchment wetness. Again, conservative assumptions about runoff potential and antecedent catchment wetness are made for estimation of the PMF, and direct estimation of antecedent condition from observed data is made for simulation of an event. The effective rainfall is combined with the catchment unit hydrograph (a process known as convolution) to form the rapid response runoff hydrograph. Finally, the flow in the river prior to the event is added, to complete the design flood.

1.1.2 Development of the FSR rainfall-runoff method

Since NERC published the FSR in 1975, there have been many developments in flood hydrology. Several of these have had direct relevance to the FSR rainfall-runoff method, although the basic philosophy has remained unchanged.

Between 1977 and 1988, IH published a series of 18 Flood Studies Supplementary Reports (FSSRs). The recommendations in some of the FSSRs superseded those given in the original report. In terms of the FSR rainfall-runoff method, the most important of the FSSRs was FSSR16 (IH, 1985) which presented revised model parameter estimation equations, though FSSR5 (IH, 1979a) which considered flood estimation on catchments subject to urbanisation, and FSSR13 (IH, 1983c) which rationalised suggestions for the use of local data in flood estimation, were also of consequence.

Since 1988, specific recommendations for national application arising from current research within IH have appeared in the IH Report series, and in relevant journals and conference proceedings. In particular, IH Report 124 (Marshall and Bayliss, 1994) and IH Report 126 (Boorman *et al.*, 1995) presented further revisions of the model parameter estimation equations.

At the request of the Flood Estimation Handbook Advisory Group, some of the model parameter estimation equations have been further updated by IH to use catchment information available in digital form. Therefore, all users should note that this volume includes specific new equations for key parts of the method, which supersede all previously published equations (see §§2.2.3, 2.2.4 and 2.3.1).

Research has also been conducted by other organisations, in particular: the Met. Office in conjunction with Salford University, who investigated new estimation methods for probable maximum precipitation and flood (Austin *et al.*, 1995), the ICE, who recently published a third edition of their engineering guide to floods and reservoir safety (ICE, 1996), and CIRIA, who updated their guide for the design of flood storage reservoirs (Hall *et al.*, 1993).

1.1.3 Guide to Volume 4

The contents of each chapter and appendix making up Volume 4 are described in more detail below, and the linkages between chapters are indicated in Figure 1.1 which provides a diagrammatic overview of the volume. New users of the FSR rainfall-runoff method are recommended to read Chapters 1, 2 and 3, and work through the example in §6.2, before attempting to apply the methods. The notation list and index will help to identify and locate unfamiliar abbreviations and hydrological terms. Experienced users will be familiar with much of the material contained in the early parts of the volume. However, they should benefit from the fresh presentation of the method, and the discussion of topics not covered comprehensively in the FSR or subsequent reports.

Chapter 2: Unit hydrograph and losses model

The unit hydrograph and losses model lies at the heart of flood estimation by the FSR rainfall-runoff method. This chapter presents the model, assumptions and limitations, and discusses and compares the various methods for model parameter estimation. The chapter is illustrated throughout with worked examples.

Chapter 3: *T*-year flood estimation

The rainfall input to the unit hydrograph and losses model may be in the form of

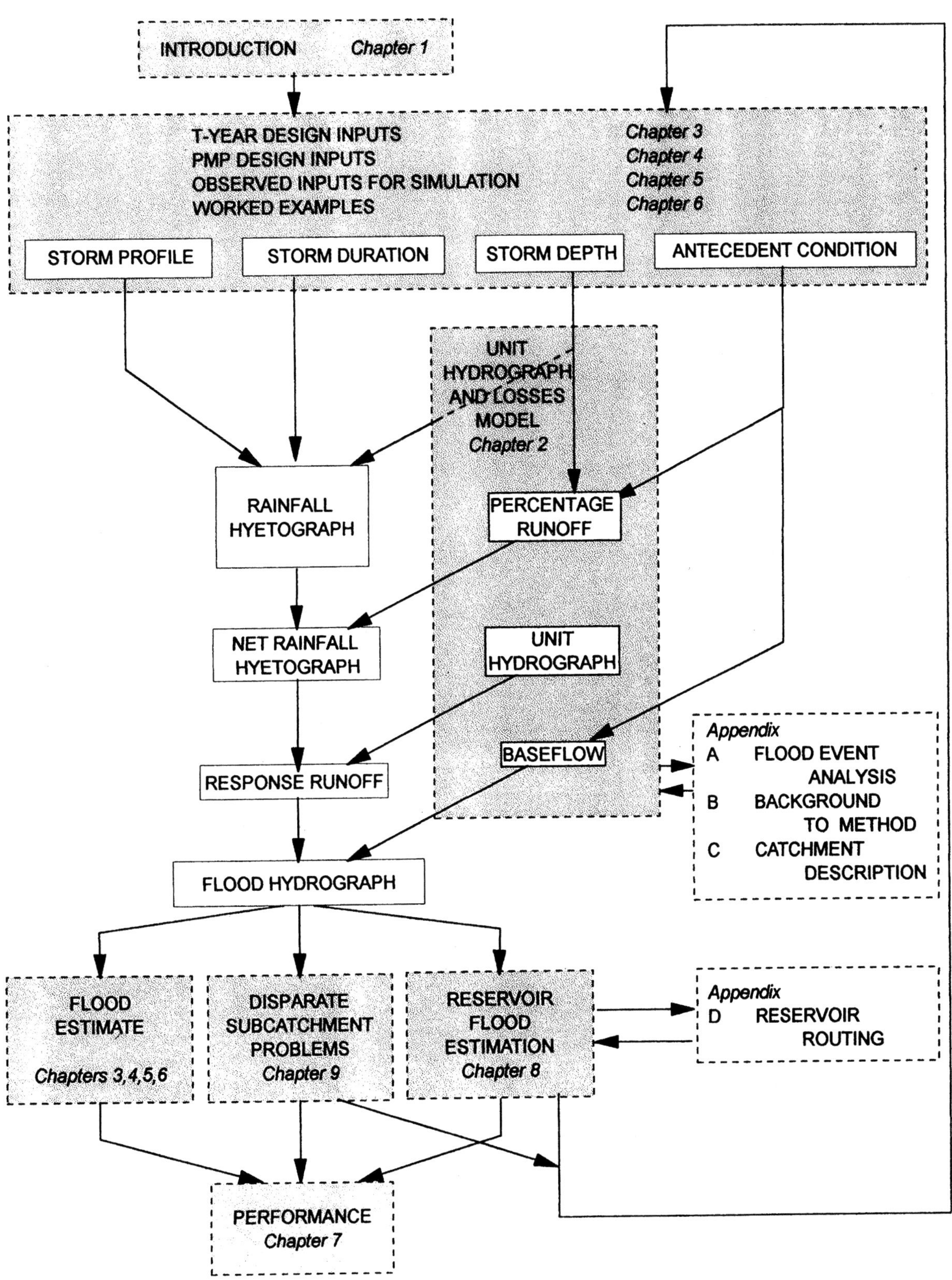

Figure 1.1 *Overview of Volume 4*

an event of a specific return period to produce a *T*-year flood. This chapter describes the simulation exercise behind the design rainfall input package and presents the method for deriving the *T*-year flood, together with worked examples.

Chapter 4: Probable maximum flood estimation

An alternative rainfall input to the unit hydrograph and losses model is a PMP to produce a PMF. This chapter describes the current recommendations for PMP derivation and PMF estimation, together with worked examples. A method for linking a flood frequency curve to the PMF is also included.

Chapter 5: Simulation of a notable event for return period assessment

The FSR rainfall-runoff method is frequently applied to simulate an observed event, and assess its return period. Recommendations for information gathering are presented. The simulation procedure, and return period assessment, are illustrated with worked examples.

Chapter 6: Worked examples

The methodologies from Chapters 2, 3, 4 and 5 are brought together to illustrate flood estimation and event simulation by the FSR rainfall-runoff method.

Chapter 7: Performance of the FSR rainfall-runoff method

The performance of the FSR rainfall-runoff method is briefly reviewed. The preferred choice of method for tackling particular problems and the issue of reconciling flood estimates from different methods are discussed.

Chapter 8: Reservoir flood estimation

The presence of a reservoir or balancing pond can cause complications in flood estimation e.g. an iterative approach may be required to determine design storm duration, or a single catchment approach may not be suitable. Worked examples are provided to illustrate the recommended procedures.

Chapter 9: Disparate subcatchments and land-use effects

Other wider, and highly topical, applications of the FSR rainfall-runoff method are covered, including flood estimation on urbanised catchments and at river confluences, and the effects of afforestation and agricultural drainage on river flows.

References

The reference list aims to encompass all relevant documentation, ranging from the background to the FSR, through literature associated specifically with the FSR rainfall-runoff method and applications of the method, to the results of more recent associated research.

Appendix A: Flood event analysis

Analysis of observed flood events is described, including event selection, data requirements and sources, and guidelines on evaluation of catchment average rainfall and pre-event catchment wetness. Unit hydrograph derivation software is provided.

Appendix B: Background to the FSR rainfall-runoff method

The main body of the text presents the most up-to-date equations and statistics for use with the FSR rainfall-runoff method. For reference, this appendix includes all the previous equations and statistics.

Appendix C: Catchment characteristics and descriptors

A major part of this appendix is concerned with introducing the HOST classification of soils. For reference, the appendix also includes a summary of manually-derived catchment characteristics and digitally-derived catchment descriptors.

Appendix D: Reservoir routing

Chapter 8 considers flood estimation in reservoirs and balancing ponds. Here, the formulation of the reservoir routing solution schemes is presented. Reservoir routing software is provided.

1.2 Summary of the FSR rainfall-runoff method

Application of the FSR rainfall-runoff method can be extremely complex, with several options available at some steps in the procedure. This section summarises the method, in its most basic form, as an introduction to new users. Equation numbers identify the appropriate chapter, to which the user should turn for guidance about the techniques and their limitations. This section is not intended to replace the recommendations and examples given in the individual chapters. For reference, Figure 1.2 summarises flood estimation using the FSR rainfall-runoff method.

1.2.1 FSR unit hydrograph and losses model

Conventionally, a flow hydrograph is split into quick and slow response components, known as rapid response runoff and baseflow, respectively. The rapid response runoff caused by a unit depth of effective rainfall falling in unit time is known as the unit hydrograph. Effective rainfall is the proportion of total rainfall which becomes rapid response runoff i.e. rainfall minus evapotranspiration, changes in storage and baseflow contributions. When the duration of the unit depth of effective rainfall tends to zero time, the rapid response runoff is known as the instantaneous unit hydrograph IUH. A three-component unit hydrograph and losses model based on these concepts forms the core of the FSR rainfall-runoff method. The model components are:

- The unit hydrograph, which characterises the catchment response to the effective rainfall input; the FSR unit hydrograph has a simple triangular form, where the unit hydrograph peak and time base are both functions of the time-to-peak;
- The percentage runoff, which is the ratio of effective to total rainfall i.e. the proportion of the total rainfall input which becomes rapid response runoff in the river;
- The baseflow, which represents the flow in the river prior to the event and the start of the slow response component of the event itself.

Where possible, the model components should be derived from rainfall and runoff records. However, the unit hydrograph time-to-peak, percentage runoff and baseflow can be estimated, via multiple regression equations, from physical and climatic descriptors of the catchment. This enables flood estimates to be made at

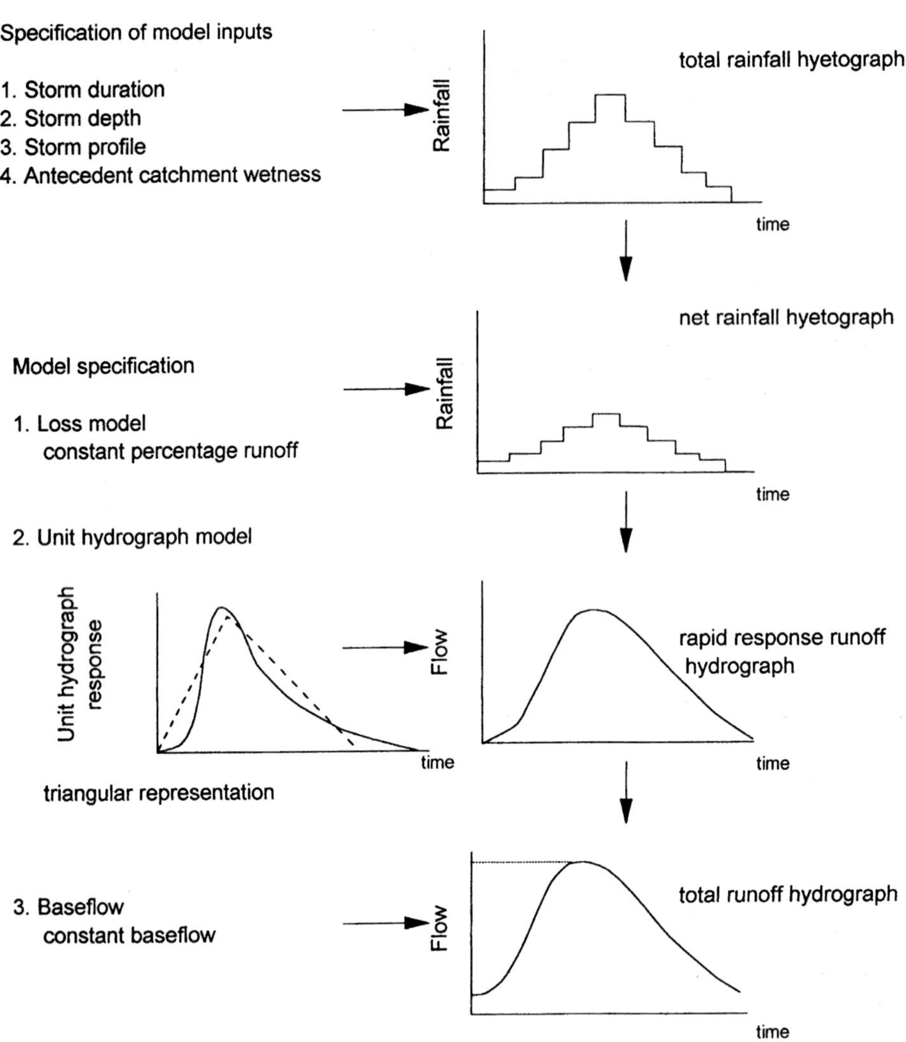

Figure 1.2 *Flood estimation using the FSR rainfall-runoff method*

ungauged sites. The multiple regression equations were developed using a database of model parameter values, derived from observed runoff and rainfall data, and physical and climatic descriptors. However, such estimates may be refined using observed data local to the site of interest.

Unit hydrograph time-to-peak

Where records exist, unit hydrograph time-to-peak should be estimated by deriving a unit hydrograph from records of rainfall and runoff (§2.2.2). Alternatively, time-to-peak of the IUH $Tp(0)$, can be estimated from observed values of the catchment lag (the time from the centroid of rainfall to the runoff peak, or centroid of runoff peaks; see §2.2.3) by:

$$Tp(0) = 0.879\ LAG^{0.951} \qquad (2.9)$$

Where there are no records, time-to-peak of the instantaneous unit hydrograph may be estimated from catchment descriptors (§2.2.4) by:

$$Tp(0) = 4.270\ DPSBAR^{-0.35}\ PROPWET^{-0.80}\ DPLBAR^{0.54}\ (1 + URBEXT)^{-5.77} \quad (2.10)$$

The effective rainfall input to the unit hydrograph and losses model will be in block form, with each block having a data interval ΔT. Therefore, however estimated, $Tp(0)$ must be adjusted to provide the unit hydrograph time-to-peak for the appropriate data interval ΔT by:

$$Tp\ (\Delta T) = Tp(0) + \Delta T/2 \quad (2.4)$$

In general, $Tp(\Delta T)$ is subsequently referred to simply as Tp. The unit hydrograph peak Up and the time base TB are derived from Tp, and a triangular unit hydrograph can be drawn up from these three parameters (§2.2.1). Ordinates of the unit hydrograph U_t can be read off the plot at ΔT-hourly intervals, or calculated in terms of Tp, Up, and TB.

Percentage runoff

The percentage runoff model synthesises percentage runoff from the natural part of the catchment PR_{RURAL} in two parts: a *standard* part SPR representing the normal capacity of the catchment to generate runoff, and a *dynamic* part DPR representing the variation in the runoff depending on the state of the catchment prior to the storm and the storm magnitude itself. The relationship is given by:

$$PR_{RURAL} = SPR + DPR_{CWI} + DPR_{RAIN} \quad (2.13)$$

The standard component is fixed for a particular catchment, and it is the standard component which is the true model parameter. Where rainfall and runoff records exist, SPR should be derived at the same time as unit hydrograph time-to-peak (§2.3.2), or from the catchment baseflow index BFI (§2.3.3) by:

$$SPR = 72.0 - 66.5\ BFI \quad (2.16)$$

Where there are no records, SPR may be estimated from catchment descriptors (§2.3.4) by:

$$\begin{aligned} SPR = SPR_{HOST} &= \Sigma_1^{29} SPR_i\ HOST_i \quad (2.17) \\ &= SPR_1\ HOST_1 + SPR_2\ HOST_2 + \dots + SPR_{29}\ HOST_{29} \end{aligned}$$

The dynamic components vary between storms, depending on catchment wetness index CWI and catchment rainfall P:

$$DPR_{CWI} = 0.25\ (CWI - 125) \quad (2.14)$$

$$DPR_{RAIN} = \begin{cases} 0 & [\text{for } P \leq 40 \text{ mm}] \\ 0.45\ (P - 40)^{0.7} & [\text{for } P > 40 \text{ mm}] \end{cases} \quad (2.15)$$

The total percentage runoff is estimated by adjusting PR_{RURAL} for the effects of catchment urbanisation by:

$$PR = PR_{RURAL} (1.0 - 0.615\ URBEXT) + 70\ (0.615\ URBEXT)$$

The urban adjustment assumes that 61.5% of the urbanised area is impervious and gives 70% runoff, whilst the other 38.5% of the urbanised area acts as natural (i.e. rural) catchment.

Baseflow

Where rainfall and runoff records exist, baseflow *BF* should be estimated during unit hydrograph and losses derivation (§2.4.2). Where there are no records, baseflow may be estimated from catchment descriptors (§2.4.3) by:

$$BF = \{33\ (CWI - 125) + 3.0\ SAAR + 5.5\}\ 10^{-5}\ AREA \qquad (2.19)$$

Flood estimation using the FSR rainfall-runoff method

Once a unit hydrograph, a percentage runoff and a baseflow have been derived for a catchment, an estimate of the total runoff hydrograph from any rainfall input may be obtained. Chapter 3 describes how a rainfall of a particular return period is used to produce a flood peak of the required return period, or T-year flood (in general, the rainfall and flood return periods are not the same e.g. the 81-year return period rainfall is used to produce the 50-year return period flood peak); similarly, in Chapter 4, a PMP is used to produce a PMF. The rainfall may also be an observed event to simulate a notable flood, as explained in Chapter 5.

1.2.2 T-year flood estimation

For estimation of the flood of a required return period, the FSR package of design inputs (§3.1.1) provides a set of rules for choosing the rainfall duration, depth and profile, and the antecedent catchment wetness, for use with the unit hydrograph and losses model.

Design storm duration

The duration *D* of the design storm depends on unit hydrograph time-to-peak and the standard average annual rainfall *SAAR* (§3.2.1) by:

$$D = Tp\ (1 + \frac{SAAR}{1000}) \qquad (3.1)$$

In reservoir flood estimation, the characteristic catchment response time Tp is extended by the lag time imposed by the reservoir storage (§8.2.1), and in other cases it may be appropriate to try a number of storm durations (§9.2.2).

Design storm depth

The return period of the design storm T_R is deduced from the return period of the design flood T_F (§3.2.2). This relationship between design storm and flood return periods is the result of a statistical sampling exercise (§3.1.1). It is not suggested that storms with, for instance, an 81-year return period will necessarily (or even typically) produce the 50-year return period flood peak. However, it is simply that the particular complete package of inputs specified here i.e. the storm duration, depth, profile and antecedent conditions, will give the best estimate. The mean point rainfall of duration *D* and return period *T* is abstracted from the rainfall duration-depth-frequency statistics in Volume 2. This point rainfall is reduced to the catchment rainfall P using an areal reduction factor ARF (§3.2.2).

Design storm profile

The catchment rainfall *P* of duration *D* is distributed in time by the standard profile (§3.2.3).

Antecedent catchment wetness

Finally, the appropriate catchment wetness index *CWI* is estimated from the standard average annual rainfall *SAAR* (§3.2.4).

Synthesis of the flood frequency curve

Given the values of catchment rainfall *P* and catchment wetness index *CWI*, the percentage runoff and baseflow calculations in §1.2.1 may be completed (§3.3.1). The percentage runoff is applied to the design storm to give the effective rainfall hyetograph (§3.3.2). The effective rainfall is then combined with the unit hydrograph (§3.3.3), and the baseflow allowance added (§3.3.4), to give the *T*-year flood hydrograph. *T*-year flood peaks can be plotted against their corresponding return period to produce a flood frequency curve for the catchment.

1.2.3 Probable maximum flood estimation

For PMFs, a worst possible scenario is assumed, with extreme conditions combined to give a maximum flood. Conservative assumptions are made regarding catchment response, runoff potential and antecedent catchment wetness, and the storm inputs.

Changes to the unit hydrograph and losses model

Time-to-peak *Tp*(0) is reduced by one-third to represent the more rapid and intensive response that may occur in exceptional conditions (§4.2.1). Optional changes to the percentage runoff calculation allow for higher than normal runoffs from frozen ground (§4.2.2).

Storm duration, depth and profile and antecedent catchment wetness

Storm duration (§4.3.1) is calculated in essentially the same way as for the *T*-year flood. However, there are differences to the derivation of storm depth and profile (§4.3.2), and an allowance for snowmelt may be added (§4.3.4). Catchment wetness *CWI* is also determined in a different way to that for the T-year flood (§4.3.3).

1.2.4 Simulation of a notable event

For the reconstruction of a notable observed flood event, the rainfall duration, depth and profile, and the antecedent catchment wetness will ideally be observed values, which will be input to the unit hydrograph and losses model.

Storm duration, depth and profile

The duration, depth and profile of the design storm will be given by the best estimate of the catchment average event rainfall (§5.2.1). This might be based on one recording raingauge, or derived from several daily and recording raingauges (Section 4.1 of Appendix A).

Antecedent catchment wetness

The catchment wetness index *CWI* is estimated from the observed antecedent precipitation index *API*5 and pre-event soil moisture deficit *SMD* (§5.2.2) by:

$$CWI = 125 + API5 - SMD \tag{A.1}$$

*API*5 is derived from daily rainfalls on the five days prior to the event, whilst SMD is based on daily values from soil moisture monitoring sites or from the Met. Office Rainfall and Evaporation Calculation System (MORECS) squares (Thompson *et al.*, 1981; Hough *et al.*, 1997; Hough and Jones, 1997). More detail is given in Section 4.2 of Appendix A.

Chapter 2 Unit hydrograph and losses model

2.1 Introduction

2.1.1 Rainfall-runoff models

Rainfall-runoff modelling for design flood estimation has conventionally been based on the modelling of individual events. At the most rudimentary level, all that is required to reproduce the catchment-scale relationship between storm rainfall and stream response to climatic inputs is a volumetric loss, to account for hydrological processes such as evaporation, soil moisture storage and groundwater recharge, and a time distribution function, to represent the various dynamic modes of catchment response. However, the quality and definition of the rainfall-runoff relationship is very much related to scale, both spatial and temporal. For instance, the relationship between annual rainfall and runoff for a small, homogeneous catchment may be very simple, whilst the relationship between hourly rainfall and runoff on a large heterogeneous catchment may be extremely complex. This ability to lump together various hydrological processes rather than explicitly include them, and to identify and isolate the event response, together with the simplicity of model application, accounts for the widespread use of event-based modelling.

Event-based rainfall-runoff modelling was reviewed by Wheater *et al.* (1993) within the broader topic of rainfall-runoff modelling generally. More general discussions are provided by standard texts, such as Shaw's *Hydrology in Practice* and Wilson's *Engineering Hydrology*. Within event-based rainfall-runoff modelling, several techniques for determining either the peak flow alone or the total flow hydrograph resulting from a given rainfall event exist, including the rational formula (variously attributed to Mulvaney, 1850; Kuichling, 1889; Lloyd-Davies, 1906), the unit hydrograph model (Sherman, 1932) and the TRRL method (Watkins, 1962). It is the unit hydrograph model, or more strictly the unit hydrograph and losses model, which is used in the FSR rainfall-runoff method to convert a storm rainfall input into a stream response output. The FSR unit hydrograph and losses model has three parameters, which are concerned with aspects such as the catchment response to rainfall (unit hydrograph time-to-peak), the proportion of rainfall which directly contributes to flow in the river (percentage runoff), and the quantity of flow in the river prior to the event (baseflow).

An alternative approach to event-based modelling is continuous simulation, whereby a rainfall-runoff model which is capable of simulating the catchment water balance continuously is applied (Reed, 1994a). With such a model, the total flow hydrograph is calculated, so baseflow separation is not an issue, and soil moisture accounting continues between events, thus avoiding the problems of antecedent conditions. Flood frequency analysis can then be performed on the simulated hydrograph. However, whilst having the advantages stated, continuous simulation also poses major challenges, such as the representation of the continuous inputs, the specification of the model parameters, and the ability to regionalise. Methods based on continuous simulation modelling are under development (Spijkers *et al.*, 1995; Calver and Lamb, 1996; Lamb, 1999; Calver *et al.*, in press).

2.1.2 FSR unit hydrograph and losses model

The FSR unit hydrograph and losses model, in which a rainfall input is converted to a flow output, is the main tool for the FSR catchment response and rainfall-runoff modelling studies. The model is based on the analysis of individually-

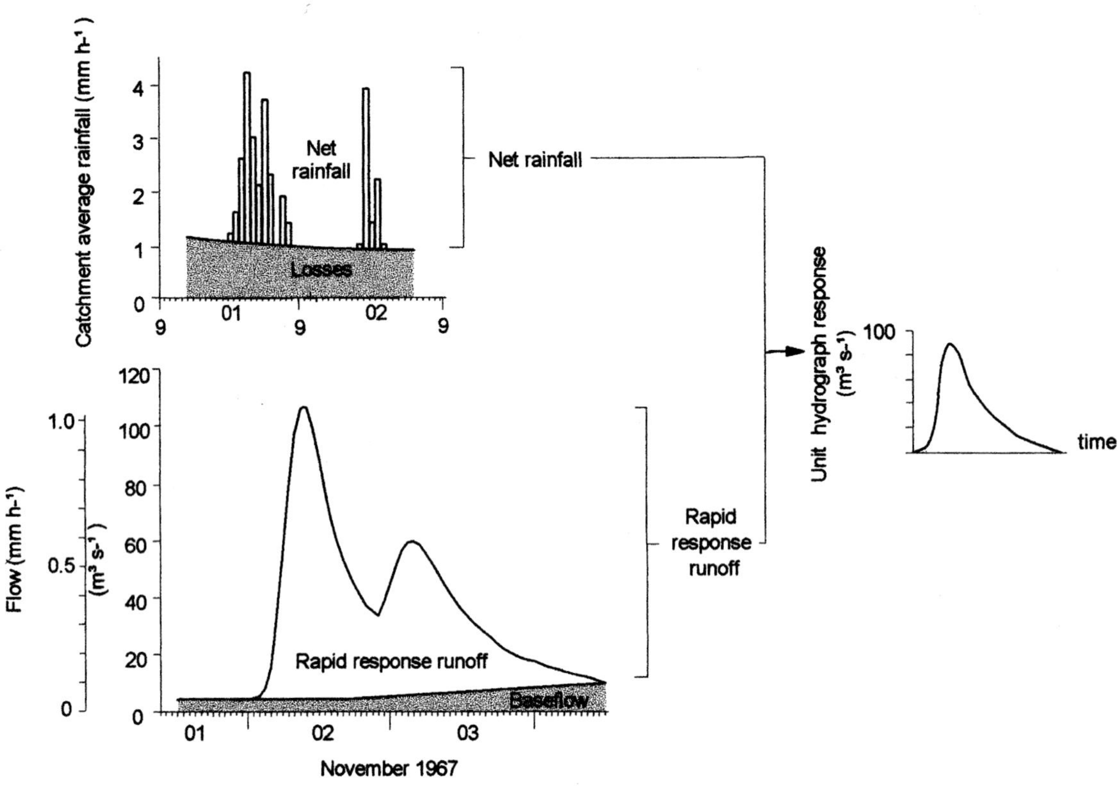

Figure 2.1 *Unit hydrograph and losses model in analysis (November 1967 event on River Almond at Craigiehall)*

recorded flood events, such as that in Figure 2.1 which shows a typical event for the River Almond at Craigiehall (19001). Hourly flow data are plotted against time for the event hydrograph, and hourly rainfalls are plotted as a catchment average hyetograph from four recording raingauges.

For each event, the total flow hydrograph is separated into runoff which is a direct response to the storm rainfall and runoff which is not. This latter runoff is the baseflow which represents the flow in the river before the event started, and to a lesser extent the start of the slow flow from the event itself; this is one of the model parameters. The difference between the rainfall volume and the direct response runoff volume is the loss. A percentage runoff term indicates the proportion of the total rainfall which is effective and becomes rapid response runoff; this is another model parameter. The effective rainfall and the rapid response runoff are jointly analysed to yield the unit hydrograph. The unit hydrograph is defined by a characteristic catchment response time called time-to-peak; this is the final model parameter.

Table 2.1 shows results from the analysis of five events on the Almond catchment, which are the minimum that should be successfully analysed for confidence in the results. The bold columns indicate the three model parameters. The first column shows the date of the event. Next are three columns of figures based on observed data: the catchment average rainfall depth P (see Section 4.1 of Appendix A), the storm duration D and the peak flow Q_P. Then there are two columns of derived values: the catchment lag *LAG* (see §2.2.3) and the baseflow

Table 2.1 Flood event analysis results: River Almond at Craigiehall

Date	P *mm*	D *h*	Q_P $m^3 s^{-1}$	LAG *h*	BF $m^3 s^{-1}$	SMD *mm*	API5 *mm*	CWI *mm*	R/O *mm*	PR *%*	SPR *%*	Tp(0) *h*
13 Aug 1966	41.6	20	149.40	9.4	**6.34**	1.5	4.9	128.4	23.5	56.5	**54.7**	**7.3**
1 Nov 1967	39.6	32	106.29	6.5	**7.79**	0.0	0.0	125.0	17.9	45.3	**44.8**	**5.5**
22 Dec 1967	18.3	21	113.86	6.6	**8.33**	0.0	4.4	129.4	10.0	54.8	**53.5**	**6.6**
4 May 1968	55.2	34	130.35	6.3	**11.61**	3.6	6.7	128.1	28.5	51.7	**47.5**	**5.1**
21 Nov 1989	57.5	29	169.77	14.8	**4.22**	16.0	2.9	111.9	33.8	58.7	**58.6**	**8.4**

BF (see §2.4.2). Next are three more columns of figures based on observed data: catchment wetness index *CWI* (see Section 4.2 of Appendix A), which is derived from soil moisture deficit (*SMD*) and antecedent precipitation index (*API* 5). There are then three more columns of derived values: the storm runoff in mm (*R/O*), as a percentage (*PR*), and converted to a standard percentage runoff *SPR* (discussed further in §2.3.2). The final column is the time-to-peak *Tp* (0) (see §2.2.2). The analysis procedure is described in detail in Section 5 of Appendix A.

The FSR unit hydrograph and losses model has become widely used in design practice for three principal reasons: firstly, it is relatively well understood; secondly, it can be easily and generally derived for use at any site; and finally, its simple structure permits the incorporation of local data in a relatively straightforward manner. The unit hydrograph itself is a unique descriptor of catchment response, and the loss model component is very flexible, percentage runoff being one of several possible loss models that could have been adopted. All the model parameters can be regressed on physical and climatic descriptors of the catchment for use at ungauged sites. Although primarily intended for use in design flood estimation (Chapters 3 and 4), the FSR unit hydrograph and losses model can also be used in simulation mode to reconstruct notable observed flood events from rainfall data (Chapter 5).

2.1.3 Estimation of FSR unit hydrograph and losses model parameters

The shape of the rapid response runoff hydrograph is influenced by the unit hydrograph, but percentage runoff is the most influential parameter because it has a direct scaling influence on the magnitude of the rapid response runoff flood peak. In contrast, baseflow is generally a relatively unimportant parameter. However, accurate estimation of the three parameters of the unit hydrograph and losses model is clearly essential. There are various methods available for estimating the model parameters:

- Direct estimation of the model parameters at the subject site from the analysis of observed flood event data;
- Indirect estimation of the model parameters at the subject site from the analysis of observed hydrometeorological data;
- Estimation of model parameters at the subject site from catchment descriptors;
- Estimation of the model parameters at the subject site by transfer of information from nearby gauged *donor* catchments.

Which approach to parameter estimation to adopt depends on the data available, as summarised in Figure 2.2.

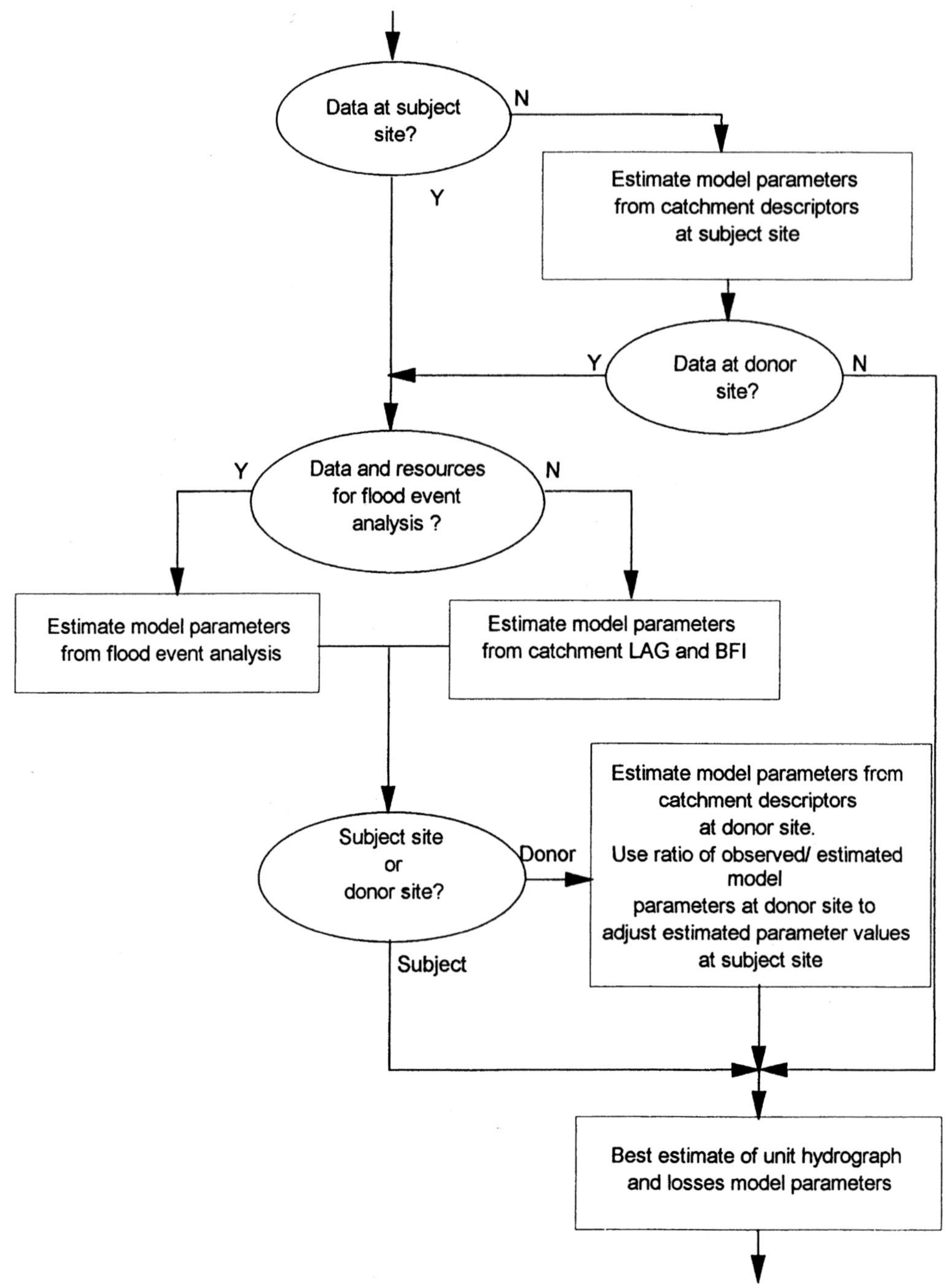

***Figure 2.2** Estimation of unit hydrograph and losses model parameters*

Estimation from observed flood event data

Direct estimation from flood event data at the subject site, as described in §2.1.2 and Appendices A.5 and A.6, is the best method. Estimation of unit hydrograph time-to-peak, percentage runoff and baseflow for a catchment from the analysis of flood events is described in §§2.2.2, 2.3.2 and 2.4.2, respectively.

Estimation from observed hydrometeorological data

If the subject site is gauged, but flood event analysis is not possible or practical because of data and/or logistic constraints, indirect estimation from hydrometeorological data at the subject site is the best alternative to flood event analysis. For instance, *Tp*(0) is closely related to catchment lag, which can be derived from inspection of rainfall and corresponding flow or level data (§2.2.3). Similarly, *SPR* is related to a low flow measure called baseflow index *BFI*, which can be obtained from a relatively short flow record (§2.3.3).

Estimation from catchment descriptors

Where there are no records at the site of interest, the model parameters can be estimated using physical and climatic descriptors of the catchment in multiple regression equations. Catchment-descriptor estimates of the model parameters are accompanied by relatively large errors due to imperfection of the regression equations, and should only be used when there is no alternative; they should *never* be the preferred option. It is recommended that a level recorder, and possibly one or more recording raingauges, are installed locally as soon as the need for a flood estimate at a site is foreseen; there is usually sufficient time between the project conception and final design for the collection of some useful data e.g. Jeffries *et al.* (1986). The equations for determining unit hydrograph time-to-peak, percentage runoff and baseflow from catchment descriptors are described in §§2.2.4, 2.3.4 and 2.4.3, respectively.

Estimation by transfer from donor catchments

Estimates of the model parameters made from catchment descriptors should only be used when there is no alternative and, where possible, should be refined using information from suitable gauged catchments nearby. In the Handbook, such catchments are referred to as *donor* catchments, and the information they provide is referred to as *local* data. These local data might be results from the analysis of flood event data or reliable estimates of catchment lag or BFI. It is strongly recommended that time is spent investigating what data are available for sites upstream or downstream of the site of interest, or in a neighbouring basin.

The refinement technique is based on the assumption that the performance of the catchment-descriptor method at the gauged donor site is indicative of the likely performance of the method at the subject site:

$$X_{s,adj} = X_{s,\,cds} \frac{X_{g,obs}}{X_{g,cds}} \tag{2.1}$$

where X is the model parameter, the subscripts s and g refer to the subject site and gauged site respectively, and the subscripts *cds*, *obs* and *adj* refer to the catchment-descriptor estimates at the gauged and subject sites, the observed value at the gauged site and the adjusted value at the subject site, respectively.

A more complicated adjustment may be appropriate where data are available from more than one donor site. For instance, a weighted adjustment may be called for, in which the weight w_i reflects the relative degree to which the *i*th gauged site is perceived to be similar to the subject site:

$$X_{s,adj} = X_{s,\,cds} \frac{\sum w_i X_{i,obs} / X_{i,cds}}{\sum w_i} \tag{2.2}$$

Application of this technique to refine catchment-descriptor estimates of unit hydrograph time-to-peak, percentage runoff and baseflow for a site is described in §§2.2.5, 2.3.5 and 2.4.4, respectively.

Choice of donor catchments

It is important that the gauged donor catchment is similar to the subject catchment, and there are several criteria for selecting suitable catchments; the criteria are necessarily subjective, and provide general guidance rather than definitive rules:

- The catchment descriptors should be *comparable*, in particular catchment areas should differ by less than a factor of 5. The reason for this is reasonably obvious: it is necessary to compare like with like;
- The catchment centroids should normally be separated by a distance of less than 50 km. The requirement for the catchments to be physically close arises because estimation errors in the generalised methods are not entirely random but tend to be spatially clustered i.e. they have a tendency to overestimate or underestimate flood potential in particular localities. Catchments that are physically close are also likely to have a similar climatic setting;
- The catchments should be substantially rural. This is a stringent criterion, with the purpose of discouraging transfer of information between principally rural and substantially urban catchments. In the event that both the subject site and gauged site are moderately or heavily urbanised, it is important to verify that the location and concentration of the urban area, and the underlying soil types, are broadly comparable. These subcriteria reflect the dominant influence of urbanisation on flood potential, and the fact that urban effects are complex and not fully indexed by the urban extent;
- Transfer of information between catchments within the same river basin is preferred, the ideal case being when the gauged site is upstream or downstream of the subject site. However, transfer from an otherwise suitable catchment in a neighbouring or nearby river basin is also useful.

An alternative method for refining hydrological parameters at ungauged sites, or sites at which only a limited flow record is available, entails classifying gauged catchments into groups according to their flow regime, assigning an ungauged catchment to a group based on the physical descriptors of that catchment, and using similarity measurements to transfer parameters from gauged to ungauged catchments (Burn and Boorman, 1992; 1993).

2.2 The FSR unit hydrograph and the time-to-peak parameter

2.2.1 Introduction

The unit hydrograph was introduced as a concept that might be useful in investigating drainage, flood control, water power and water supply (Sherman, 1932). The unit hydrograph is a flow hydrograph which accommodates a volume of water which corresponds to a unit depth of effective rainfall over a catchment. Each unit hydrograph relates to a specified time period ΔT, during which the generating rain falls uniformly, so that the ΔT-hour unit hydrograph defines the rapid response of a catchment to unit depth of effective rainfall in time ΔT hours, as depicted in Figure 2.3a. Thus, the 1-hour unit hydrograph represents the rapid response of the catchment to unit depth of effective rainfall in 1 hour. The unit hydrograph has various assumptions associated with it:

- There is a direct proportional relationship between the effective rainfall input and the catchment rapid response, known as linearity. Figure 2.3b shows how increasing, or decreasing, the effective rainfall causes the rapid response to increase, or decrease, by the same proportion;
- The rainfall-runoff relationship does not change with time so that the duration and quantity of the catchment rapid response are constant for a given duration and quantity of effective rainfall, known as time-invariance. Figure 2.3c shows how two identical blocks of effective rainfall, falling at different times, give identical rapid responses;
- Successive inputs of effective rainfall produce independent rapid responses which can then be summed to give the total catchment rapid response, known as superposition. Figure 2.3d shows how the individual responses to three different blocks of effective rainfall are added to give the total catchment response;
- The effective rainfall input is in block form, with each block of the same duration, and the rainfall input has a constant intensity within each duration block and falls uniformly over the entire catchment area.

If the unit hydrograph for a catchment can be found or estimated, the total catchment rapid response hydrograph due to any effective rainfall input may be obtained using the principles of linearity, superposition and time-invariance (Figure 2.4), which may be expressed as the convolution equation:

$$q_j = \Sigma_{i=1}^{j} p_i \, u_{j-i+1} \qquad \text{for } j=1, 2, 3, \ldots \qquad (2.3)$$

where q_j denotes the jth ordinate of the rapid response runoff hydrograph, p_i the ith effective rainfall, and u_k the kth ordinate of the ΔT-hour unit hydrograph. The value chosen for the data interval ΔT depends on the size of the catchment and its response time. To avoid this dependence on the subsequent choice of time period, the concept of the instantaneous unit hydrograph or IUH was developed. The IUH represents the response of the catchment to unit depth of effective rainfall falling instantaneously, rather than over a finite period.

The unit hydrograph approach was introduced to the UK in the late 1950s, and was developed in various investigations to ascertain its usefulness in application to ungauged basins. In UK practice, it became customary to use a unit depth of 10 mm (1 cm). In the Handbook (as in the FSR), the unit hydrograph is defined to represent the typical catchment response to 10 mm (or 1 cm) of effective rainfall. A general unit hydrograph study showed that the unit hydrograph could be derived directly from the records of rapid response runoff and effective rainfall, after separating baseflow and rainfall losses (Nash, 1960). Furthermore, in the absence of any flow and rainfall data, a conceptual unit hydrograph, derived from physical and climatic descriptors of the catchment and synthesised as a simple triangle, could be used (Nash, 1960; Gray, 1961; USDA, 1972). Since then, unit hydrograph techniques have matured further, and the concept has been widely applied. The theory has been well-covered and practical aspects have been detailed in many standard texts, such as *Hydrology in Practice* (Shaw, 1994) and *Engineering Hydrology* (Wilson, 1990).

The FSR unit hydrograph and estimation of *Tp*(0)

In the FSR rainfall-runoff method, the unit hydrograph is synthesised as a simple triangle of fixed shape, controlled by a single parameter: the time-to-peak *Tp*.

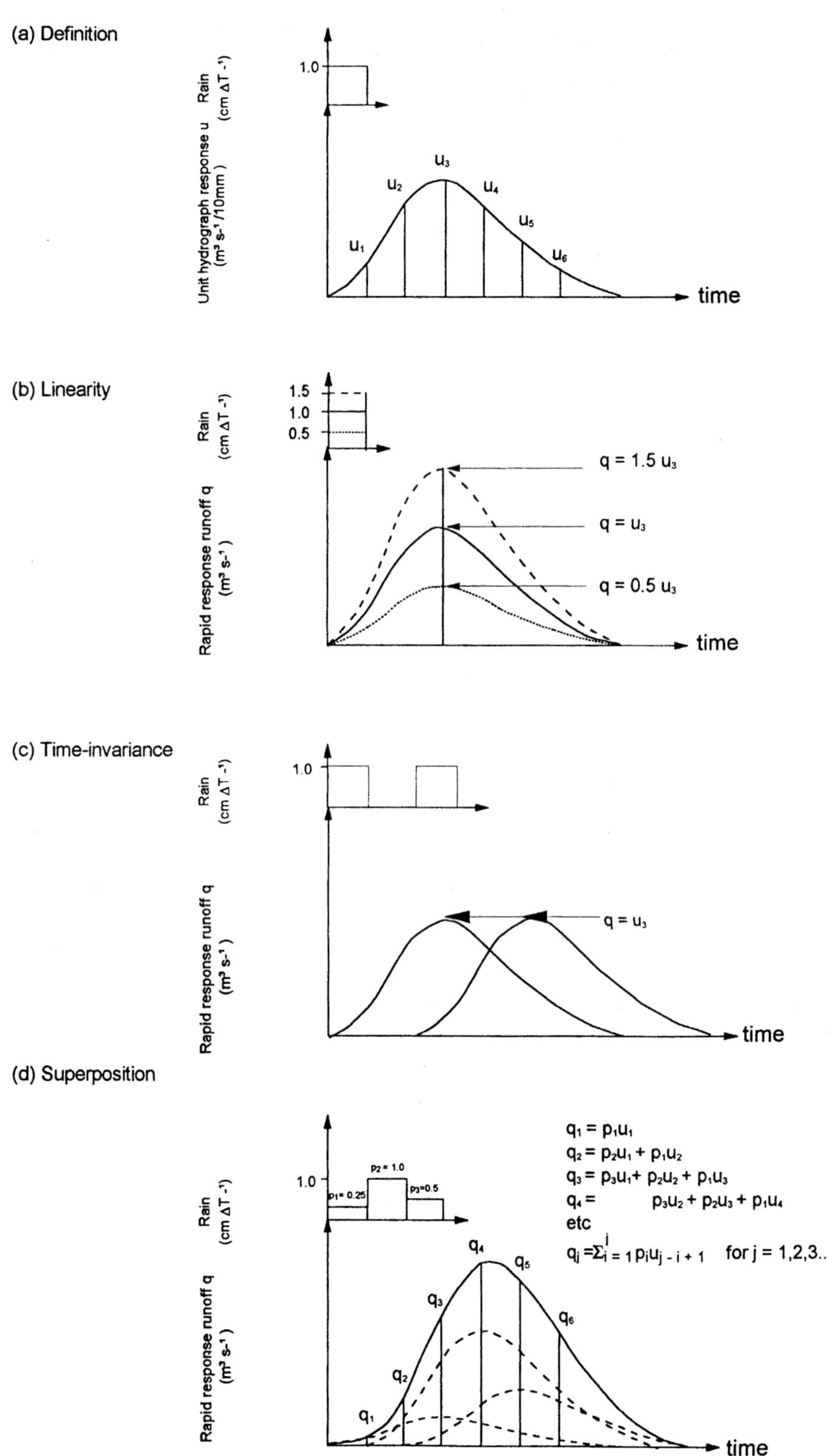

Figure 2.3 *Unit hydrograph theory*

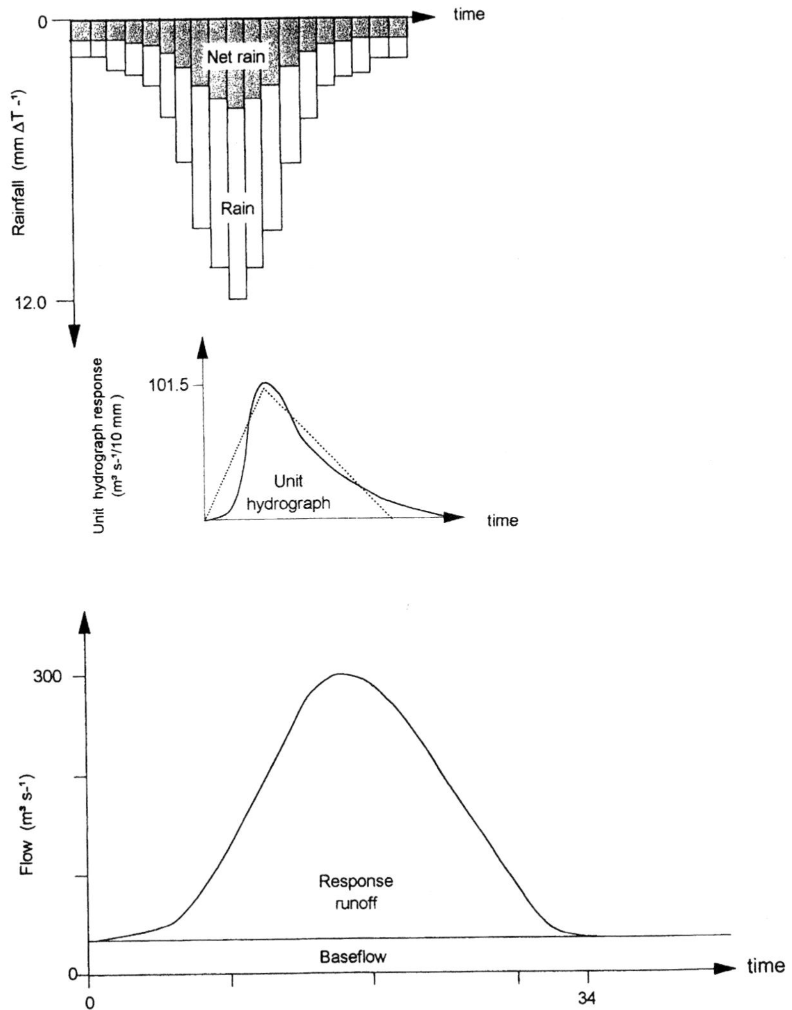

***Figure 2.4** Unit hydrograph and losses model in design and simulation (Design event on River Almond at Craigiehall)*

There is a strong interdependence between the unit hydrograph parameter values; the unit hydrograph peak *Up* and the time base *TB* are calculated as functions of time-to-peak, as illustrated in Figure 2.5.

Although the reduction of the FSR unit hydrograph to a triangle is a simplifying measure, it is important that the time-to-peak is estimated as accurately as possible, because the shape of the unit hydrograph determines how quickly the catchment responds to a rainfall input. If the time-to-peak estimate is inaccurate, the resulting flood hydrograph will have the correct volume, but will be too intense or too diffuse. For instance, an overestimate of time-to-peak will lead to a lower peak value and a longer time base value, and the derived rapid response runoff hydrograph will be overly long and subdued. Similarly, an underestimate of time-to-peak will lead to a higher peak value and a shorter time base, and the derived hydrograph will be overly short and peaky. The importance of a good

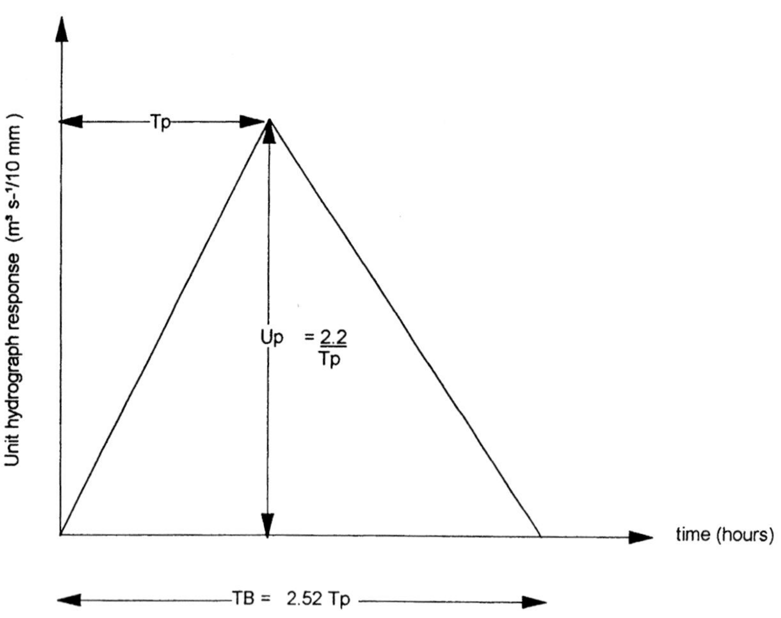

***Figure 2.5** FSR triangular unit hydrograph*

estimate of time-to-peak is amplified by the role that time-to-peak plays in determining the design storm duration in the *T*-year case, as described in §3.2.1. The unit hydrograph time-to-peak is initially estimated for the equivalent IUH, and is referred to as the time-to-peak of the instantaneous unit hydrograph or *Tp*(0). The various methods of estimating *Tp*(0) are covered in §§2.2.2 to 2.2.5.

Construction of the FSR unit hydrograph from *Tp*(0)

In the FSR rainfall-runoff method, the effective rainfall input to the unit hydrograph and losses model will be in block form, with each block having a duration ΔT. Therefore, the time-to-peak of the IUH *Tp*(0) must be adjusted to provide the unit hydrograph time-to-peak for this data interval ΔT, so that *Tp*(0) becomes $Tp(\Delta T)$ i.e. *Tp*(1) for the 1-hour unit hydrograph, *Tp*(0.5) for the ½-hour unit hydrograph, etc. The data interval should be fine enough that the design flood hydrograph is well-defined, but not so fine that excessive and unnecessary subdivision results. Using a fine-interval unit hydrograph gives a much smoother and more rounded response than using a coarse-interval one. In practice, a data interval of 10-20% of the value of *Tp*(0) is usually suitable. It is customary to adopt convenient values such as 0.25, 0.5, 1 or 2 hours. The adjustment is done using the equation:

$$Tp\,(\Delta T) = Tp(0) + \frac{\Delta T}{2} \qquad (2.4)$$

After this adjustment, $Tp(\Delta T)$ is generally referred to simply as *Tp*. It is possible to rearrange this equation in order to use it to change the data interval associated with $Tp(\Delta T)$:

$$Tp\,(\Delta T_{new}) = Tp\,(\Delta T_{old}) + \frac{\Delta T_{new} - \Delta T_{old}}{2} \qquad (2.5)$$

Alternatively, the S-curve method may be used to change the data interval of the ΔT-hour unit hydrograph (Section 6.2 of Appendix A).

The unit hydrograph peak *Up* and the time base *TB* are both derived from *Tp*, as a regression result and a continuity constraint, respectively:

$$Up = \frac{2.2}{Tp}\,\text{AREA} \qquad (2.6)$$

$$TB = 2.52\ Tp \qquad (2.7)$$

A triangular unit hydrograph can be drawn up from these three parameters. Ordinates of the unit hydrograph u_t can be read off the plot at ΔT-hourly intervals, or calculated in terms of *Tp*, *Up*, and *TB*:

$$u_t = \begin{cases} t\dfrac{Up}{Tp} & [\text{for } t \le Tp] \\ (TB - t)\dfrac{Up}{Tb - Tp} & [\text{for } Tp \le t \le TB] \end{cases} \qquad (2.8)$$

2.2.2 *Tp*(0) from observed flood event data

When the site is gauged, the preferred method of deriving estimates of IUH time-to-peak *Tp*(0) is by the analysis of observed flood events, by the procedure described in Sections 5 and 6 of Appendix A. Table 2.1 presented results from the analysis of five flood events from the River Almond at Craigiehall (19001). *Tp*(0) values for each event are given in column 13. It is usually sufficient to take the catchment average *Tp*(0), apply a data interval ΔT using Equation 2.4, and construct a triangular ΔT-hour unit hydrograph from this value using Equations 2.6 and 2.7, as illustrated in Example 2.1a. Use of a geometric mean (i.e. the antilogarithm of the arithmetic mean of the logarithms of the values) is more appropriate than an arithmetic mean because proportional changes rather than absolute changes are important. However, where considerable flood event data are available close to the subject site, a full flood event analysis can be carried out and a catchment average unit hydrograph derived (Section 5.3 of Appendix A).

2.2.3 *Tp*(0) from catchment lag

Tp(0) is closely related to catchment lag (*LAG*). Various definitions of catchment lag exist. The FSR defines lag as the time from the centroid of total rainfall to the runoff peak or centroid of runoff peaks (Snyder, 1938), as illustrated in Figure 2.6. Lag values can be abstracted during flood event analysis (Table 2.1), but may also be derived manually from inspection of rainfall and corresponding flow or level data. Hence, this technique is particularly appropriate where one or more years of water level data have been gathered to this specific end, without the expense of constructing a formal (i.e. rated) flow gauging station. It is possible to derive useful estimates of lag from as little as six months data on urbanised catchments, though on rural catchments a longer period of record (say 18 months) is usually necessary.

Table 2.1 presents results from the analysis of five flood events from the River Almond at Craigiehall (19001). Catchment lag values are given in column 5. A catchment average lag is estimated as the geometric mean of these values, and then substituted into the following equation to calculate *Tp*(0) (see Example 2.2a):

$$Tp(0) = 0.879\ LAG^{0.951} \qquad (2.9)$$

Derivation of Equation 2.9 is summarised in Section B.2. Derived values of $Tp(0)$ are not as reliable as those obtained from a full flood event analysis. However, they are based on data from the subject site, so they are preferred to estimates from catchment descriptors. Once $Tp(0)$ has been derived, an adjustment for the appropriate data interval can be made using Equation 2.4, and a triangular ΔT-hour unit hydrograph can be derived using Equations 2.6 and 2.7.

Example 2.1a
Estimation of *Tp*(0) and unit hydrograph from observed flood event data

Catchment: Almond at Craigiehall (19001) (Figure 1 of Appendix C)

Relevant catchment descriptors: $AREA = 386.19\ km^2$

The IUH time-to-peak $Tp(0)$ is derived from the flood event analysis results presented in Table 3 of Appendix A and, for this catchment, reproduced in Table 2.1.

The $Tp(0)$ values range from 5.1 to 8.4 hours, with a geometric mean of 6.47 hours:
$Tp(0) = 6.47$ hours

20% of 6.47 hours is 1.3 hours, so a 1-hour data interval is appropriate.
$Tp(0)$ is adjusted for the data interval ΔT using Equation 2.4: $\Delta T = 1.0$ hour

$Tp(\Delta T) = Tp(0) + \Delta T/2$ $\qquad Tp(1) = 6.47 + 1.0/2 = 6.97$ hours

$Tp(\Delta T)$ is hereafter referred to simply as Tp. The unit hydrograph peak Up and the time base TB are derived from Tp using Equations 2.6 and 2.7:

$Up = (2.2\ /\ Tp)\ AREA$ $\qquad Up = (2.2\ /\ 6.97)\ 386.19 = 121.90\ m^3\ s^{-1}$

$TB = 2.52\ Tp$ $\qquad TB = 2.52 \times 6.97 = 17.25$ hours

The triangular unit hydrograph may be drawn, and ordinates u_t can be read off at ΔT-hourly intervals or calculated using Equation 2.8.

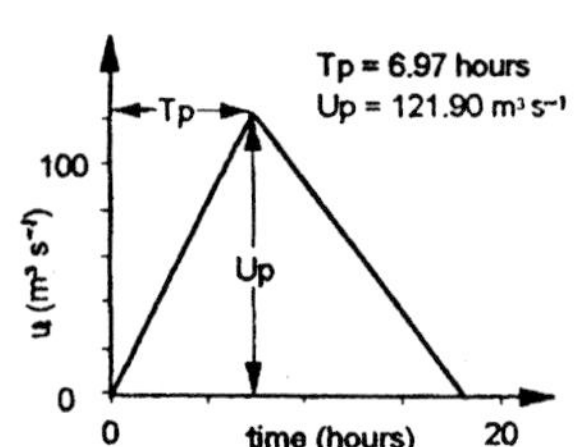

2.2.4 *Tp*(0) from catchment descriptors

Where there are no records at the site of interest, $Tp(0)$ is estimated from catchment descriptors using a generalised model derived by regression analysis. Such parameter estimates are not as reliable as parameter estimates based on analysis of

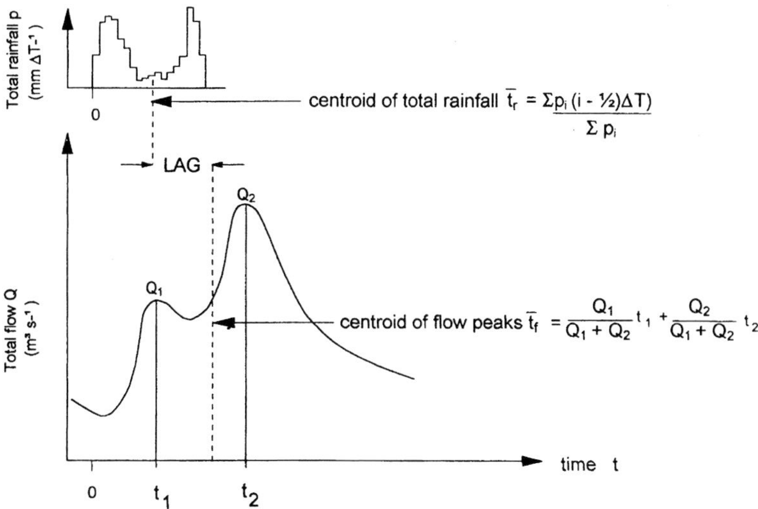

Figure 2.6 *Definition of catchment lag*

> ***Example 2.2a***
> **Estimation of *Tp*(0) from catchment lag**
>
> Catchment: Bourne at Hadlow (40006) (Figure 2 of Appendix C)
>
> The IUH time-to-peak *Tp*(0) is derived from the catchment lag results presented in Table 3 of Appendix A.
>
> The lag values range from 6.1 hours to 14.3 hours,
> with a geometric mean of 8.53 hours: *LAG* = 8.53 hours
>
> *Tp*(0) is derived from *LAG* using Equation 2.9:
>
> $Tp(0) = 0.879\ LAG^{0.951}$ $Tp(0) = 0.879\ (8.53)^{0.951} = 6.75$ hours
>
> 20% of 6.75 hours is 1.3 hours, so a 1-hour data interval is appropriate.
> *Tp*(0) is adjusted for the data interval ΔT using Equation 2.4: $\Delta T = 1.0$ hours
>
> $Tp(\Delta T) = Tp(0) + \Delta T/2$ $Tp(1) = 6.75 + 1.0 / 2 = 7.25$ hours
>
> $Tp(\Delta T)$ is hereafter referred to simply as *Tp*. The unit hydrograph peak *Up* and the time base *TB* are derived from *Tp* using Equations 2.6 and 2.7, and the triangular unit hydrograph may be drawn, and ordinates u_t read off at ΔT-hourly intervals or calculated using Equation 2.8, as in Example 2.1a.

rainfall and runoff records at or near the site, and should only be used when there are no observed data from which to derive more accurate values. However, whilst there may be no data at the site of interest, there may be data for a different point on the same river or in a nearby catchment, which can be used to improve a catchment-descriptor estimate of $Tp(0)$ at the subject site, as described in §2.2.5.

The equation currently used for estimating $Tp(0)$ from catchment descriptors is (see Example 2.3a):

$$Tp(0) = 4.270\ DPSBAR^{-0.35}\ PROPWET^{-0.80}\ DPLBAR^{0.54}\ (1+URBEXT)^{-5.77} \quad (2.10)$$

Derivation of Equation 2.10 is summarised in Section 2 of Appendix B. The equation reflects the view that the steeper, naturally wetter and more urbanised the catchment, the faster the characteristic response, whilst the larger or longer the catchment, the slower the response. *URBEXT* values for a given year can be updated using the urban growth model in §6.5.4 of Volume 5. Catchments where $URBEXT > 0.5$ are more appropriately treated by sewer design methods. Once $Tp(0)$ has been derived, an adjustment for the appropriate data interval can be made using Equation 2.4, and a triangular ΔT-hour unit hydrograph can be derived using Equations 2.6 and 2.7.

Example 2.3a
Estimation of *Tp*(0) from catchment descriptors

Catchment: Rhymney at Gilfach Bargoed (IHDTM grid ref. 315050 200250; Figure 3 of Appendix C)

Relevant catchment descriptors:
$DPSBAR = 101.40$ m km^{-1}, $PROPWET = 0.54$, $DPLBAR = 8.50$ km, $URBEXT = 0.026$

The IUH time-to-peak $Tp(0)$ is derived from catchment descriptors using Equation 2.10:

$$Tp(0) = 4.270\ DPSBAR^{-0.35}\ PROPWET^{-0.80}\ DPLBAR^{0.54}\ (1 + URBEXT)^{-5.77}$$

$$Tp(0) = 1.684\ (101.40)^{-0.18}\ (0.54)^{-1.05}\ (8.50)^{0.48}\ (1.026)^{-4.39}$$

$$= 3.80 \text{ hours}$$

20% of 3.80 hours is 0.8 hours, so a 0.5-hour data interval is appropriate.
$Tp(0)$ is adjusted for the data interval ΔT using Equation 2.4: $\Delta T = 0.5$ hours

$Tp(\Delta T) = Tp(0) + \Delta T/2$ $\qquad$ $Tp(0.5) = 3.80 + 0.5/2 = 4.05$ hours

$Tp(\Delta T)$ is hereafter referred to simply as Tp. The unit hydrograph peak Up and the time base TB are derived from Tp using Equations 2.6 and 2.7, and the triangular unit hydrograph may be drawn, and ordinates u_t read off at ΔT-hourly intervals or calculated using Equation 2.8, as in Example 2.1a.

2.2.5 *Tp*(0) by transfer from a donor catchment

Whilst there may be no rainfall and runoff records at the site of interest, there may be records at a different point on the same river or in a nearby similar catchment. Analysis of these records can provide observed values of $Tp(0)$ or LAG which can be used to improve a catchment-descriptor estimate of $Tp(0)$ at the subject site. The procedure for adjusting a $Tp(0)$ estimate is:

i Apply the catchment-descriptor method to estimate $Tp(0)$ at the (ungauged) subject site (this is $Tp(0)_{s,cds}$);

ii Apply the catchment-descriptor method to estimate $Tp(0)$ at the (gauged) donor site (this is $Tp(0)_{g,cds}$);

iii Analyse the observed flow data at the (gauged) donor site by an appropriate method to yield an observed value of $Tp(0)$ (this is $Tp(0)_{g,obs}$);

iv Adjust $Tp(0)_{s,cds}$ at the (ungauged) subject site accordingly; the equation for the transfer is:

$$Tp(0)_{s,adj} = Tp(0)_{s,cds} \frac{Tp(0)_{g,obs}}{Tp(0)_{g,cds}} \tag{2.11}$$

where the subscripts s and g refer to the subject site and the gauged site respectively, and the subscripts *cds*, *obs* and *adj* refer to the catchment-descriptor estimates at the gauged and subject sites, the observed value at the gauged site and the adjusted value at the subject site, respectively.

Example 2.4a (overleaf) illustrates the procedure. Once $Tp(0)$ has been derived, an adjustment for the appropriate data interval can be made using Equation 2.4, and a triangular ΔT-hour unit hydrograph can be derived using Equations 2.6 and 2.7. Alternatively, where considerable flood event data are available close to the subject site, a full flood event analysis can be carried out and a catchment average unit hydrograph derived (Section 5.3 of Appendix A). This can be transformed to the subject site using the extended S-curve method (Section 6.2 of Appendix A).

2.3 Percentage runoff and the standard percentage runoff parameter

2.3.1 Introduction

The proportion of the total rainfall input which becomes direct response runoff in the river is referred to as percentage runoff. Estimation of percentage runoff is probably the most important part of flood estimation using the FSR rainfall-runoff method. The percentage runoff parameter has a direct scaling influence on the magnitude of the resulting rapid response runoff flood peak, and so the ability to predict percentage runoff/losses properly is crucial (e.g. Gurnell and Midgley, 1987). Unfortunately, estimation of percentage runoff is also the most uncertain part of flood estimation, as it is difficult to collect data covering the full range of catchment type, catchment state and storm variability for calibration of the percentage runoff model. The usefulness of observed data in refining catchment percentage runoff estimates has long been recognised, and cannot be emphasised too strongly (e.g. Beran, 1973).

The FSR unit hydrograph and losses model assumes that percentage runoff is constant through an event, and is applied to each block of the total rainfall hyetograph i.e. a constant proportional loss model. However, in reality, percentage runoff will not be constant, but will increase as deficits are made up and soils become saturated.

Example 2.4a
Estimation of *Tp*(0) by transfer from a donor catchment

Subject catchment: West Lyn at Lynmouth (IHDTM grid ref. 272400 149450; Figure 4 of Appendix C). Donor catchment: Horner Water at West Luccombe (51002)

Relevant subject catchment descriptors:
DPSBAR = 112.14 m km^{-1}, *PROPWET* = 0.54, *DPLBAR* = 5.88 km, *URBEXT* = 0.004

Relevant donor catchment descriptors:
DPSBAR = 216.60 m km^{-1}, *PROPWET* = 0.54, *DPLBAR* = 6.31 km, *URBEXT* = 0.000

For the subject catchment, the IUH time-to-peak *Tp*(0) is derived from catchment descriptors using Equation 2.10:

$Tp(0)_{s,cds}$ = 3.41 hours

For the donor catchment, the IUH time-to-peak *Tp*(0) is derived from catchment descriptors using Equation 2.10: $Tp(0)_{g,cds}$ = 2.88 hours

For the donor catchment, the IUH time-to-peak *Tp*(0) is also derived from the flood event analysis results in Table 3 of Appendix A: the *Tp*(0) values range from 2.5 hours to 5.5 hours, with a geometric mean of 3.91 hours: $Tp(0)_{g,obs}$ = 3.91 hours

For the subject catchment, the IUH time-to-peak from catchment descriptors $Tp(0)_{s,cds}$ is refined by reference to the performance of the catchment descriptor method on the donor catchment using Equation 2.11:

$Tp(0)_{s,adj} = Tp(0)_{s,cds}\,(Tp(0)_{g,obs} \,/\, Tp(0)_{g,cds})$ $\qquad$ $Tp(0)_{s,adj} = 3.41\,(3.91 / 2.88)$
$= 4.63$ hours

20% of 4.63 hours is 0.9 hours, so a 0.5-hour data interval is appropriate.
Tp(0) is adjusted for the data interval ΔT using Equation 2.4: $\Delta T = 0.5$ hours

$Tp(\Delta T) = Tp(0) + \Delta T/2$ $\qquad$ $Tp(0.5) = 4.63 + 0.5/2$
$= 4.88$ hours

$Tp(\Delta T)$ is hereafter referred to simply as *Tp*. The unit hydrograph peak *Up* and the time base TB are derived from *Tp* using Equations 2.6 and 2.7, and the triangular unit hydrograph may be drawn, and ordinates u_t read off at ΔT-hourly intervals or calculated using Equation 2.8, as in Example 2.1a.

The percentage runoff model

The percentage runoff model used in the FSR rainfall-runoff method is as presented in FSSR16 (IH, 1985). Percentage runoff is made up of a standard term *SPR*, representing the normal capacity of the catchment to generate runoff, and dynamic terms representing the variation in runoff depending on the state of the catchment prior to the storm and the storm magnitude itself: DPR_{CWI} dependent on catchment wetness index *CWI* and DPR_{RAIN} dependent on storm depth *P*. The standard and dynamic terms are calculated for a completely rural catchment to give a PR_{RURAL}, and an urban adjustment is applied to this PR_{RURAL}:

$$PR = PR_{RURAL} (1.0 - 0.615\ URBEXT) + 70\ (0.615\ URBEXT) \tag{2.12}$$

where $PR_{RURAL} = SPR + DPR_{CWI} + DPR_{RAIN}$ (2.13)

and SPR is a standard term,

$$DPR_{CWI} = 0.25\ (CWI - 125) \tag{2.14}$$

and $$DPR_{RAIN} = \begin{cases} 0 & [\text{for } P \leq 40 \text{ mm}] \\ 0.45\ (P - 40)^{0.7} & [\text{for } P > 40 \text{ mm}] \end{cases} \tag{2.15}$$

The urban adjustment assumes that 61.5% of the urbanised area is impervious and gives 70% runoff, whilst the other 38.5% of the urbanised area acts as natural (i.e. rural) catchment (Kidd and Packman, 1980; Packman, 1980). Equation 2.12 derives from conversion of the FSSR16 PR model to use *URBEXT* in place of $URBAN_{FSR}$ (see Section 1 of Appendix B). The adjustment reflects the mixed natural and impervious areas that occur within urbanised areas, and makes the effect of the urbanisation dependent on the underlying soils.

SPR is fixed for all storms on a particular catchment, but varies between catchments, such that a chalk catchment will give a much lower runoff than a clay catchment. The *DPR* terms vary between storms on a particular catchment, causing an increase in percentage runoff with increasing catchment wetness and larger rainfall events i.e. a larger percentage response is produced by a large storm on a wet catchment than by a small storm on a dry catchment. The DPR_{CWI} component reflects the importance of antecedent conditions as an indicator of the greater variation in response between events on natural catchments than those on urban catchments. Determination of *CWI* is covered in §3.2.4 for the *T*-year case, §4.3.3 for the *PMF* case, and in §5.2.2 for the simulation of an observed flood event. The DPR_{RAIN} component is only applicable to substantial rainfall events (more than 40 mm of rain). Calculation of *P* is described in §3.2.2 for the *T*-year case, §4.3.2 for the PMF case, and in §5.2.1 for the simulation of an observed flood event. Because the dynamic components of percentage runoff vary from storm to storm, effort tends to concentrate on obtaining the best estimate of the *SPR* component, which is covered in the rest of this section. A better estimate of *SPR* is the most significant single improvement that can be made for flood estimation (FSR I.6.2.2).

2.3.2 *SPR* from observed flood event data

When the site is gauged, the preferred method of deriving estimates of standard percentage runoff *SPR* is by the analysis of observed flood events, by the procedure described in Sections 5 and 6 of Appendix A. Table 2.1 presents results from the analysis of five flood events from the River Almond at Craigiehall (19001). *SPR* values are given in column 12. The variability of *SPR* should be examined. Usually the catchment average *SPR* is taken as a simple arithmetic mean of the derived values, as illustrated in Example 2.1b. The catchment average *SPR* can then be substituted back into the percentage runoff model, together with the appropriate storm depth, catchment wetness index and urban fraction, to calculate percentage runoff for a particular event using Equations 2.12-2.15.

Example 2.1b
Estimation of *SPR* from observed flood event data

Catchment: Almond at Craigiehall (19001) (Figure 1 of Appendix C)

The standard percentage runoff *SPR* is derived from the flood event analysis results presented in Table 3 of Appendix A and, for this catchment, reproduced in Table 2.1.

The *SPR* values range from 44.8% to 58.6%, with an arithmetic mean of 51.8%:

SPR = 51.8%

2.3.3 *SPR* from baseflow index

SPR is closely related to baseflow index *BFI*. *BFI* measures the proportion of the river's long-term runoff that derives from stored sources, and typically ranges from 0.1 for relatively impermeable clay catchments to 0.99 for highly permeable chalk catchments. Figure 2.7 compares the hydrographs and *BFI* values for two catchments of contrasting geology. Although strictly a low flow index (IH, 1980; Gustard *et al.*, 1992), *BFI* is also a valuable index for flood estimation because the parameter (1 – *BFI*) is a measure of the rapid response runoff and therefore relates directly to *SPR*. In fact *BFI* and *SPR* are well correlated (r^2 = 0.75).

Determination of *BFI* for a catchment requires as little as one year of gauged daily mean flow data, and is not unduly sensitive to there being a high quality rating for flood flows. Furthermore, there is no requirement for rainfall data. The calculation entails separating the flow hydrograph into its rapid response runoff and baseflow components by the procedure described in *IH Report 108* (Gustard *et al.*, 1992). However, the common practice is to make use of published values of *BFI*, which exist for gauged sites in the UK. Catchment *BFI* is substituted into the following equation from FSSR16 to calculate *SPR* (see Example 2.2b):

$$SPR = 72.0 - 66.5\ BFI \qquad (2.16)$$

Derived values of *SPR* are not as reliable as those obtained from a full flood event analysis. However, they are based on data from the subject site, so are preferred to estimates from catchment descriptors. The *SPR* value can then be used in the percentage runoff model, together with the appropriate storm depth, catchment wetness index and urban fraction, to calculate percentage runoff for a particular event using Equations 2.12-2.15. Sources of *BFI* values include the Hydrometric Register and Statistics for 1991-95 (IH/BGS, 1998) and the Representative Basin Catalogue for Great Britain (IH, 1991b), and IH Report 108 (Gustard *et al.*, 1992). For Scotland, a *BFI* map (Gustard *et al.*, 1986) is also available.

2.3.4 *SPR* from catchment descriptors

Where there are no records at the site of interest, *SPR* is estimated from catchment descriptors using a generalised model derived by regression analysis. Such parameter estimates are not as reliable as parameter estimates based on analysis of rainfall and runoff records at or near the site, and should only be used when there are no observed data from which to derive more accurate values. However,

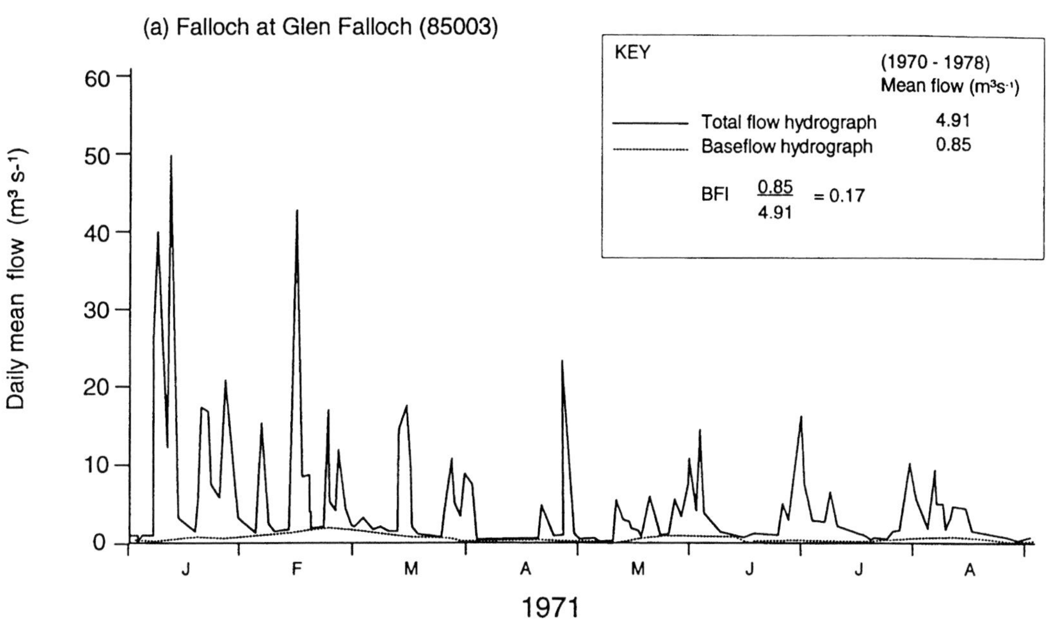

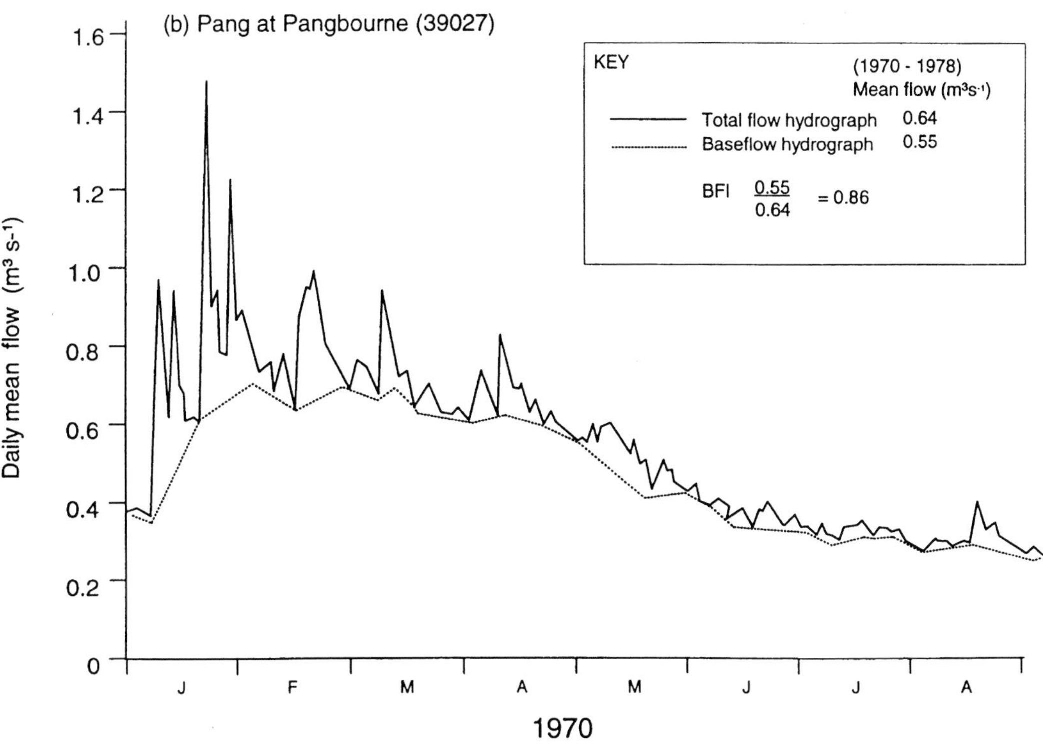

Figure 2.7 *Illustrative baseflow separation for (a) an impermeable catchment and (b) a permeable catchment*

Example 2.2b
Estimation of *SPR* from *BFI*

Catchment: Bourne at Hadlow (40006) (Figure 2 of Appendix C)

The standard percentage runoff *SPR* is derived from the published baseflow index *BFI* for the catchment (IH/BGS, 1998).

$BFI = 0.62$

SPR is derived from *BFI* using Equation 2.16:

$SPR = 72.0 - 66.5\ BFI$ $\qquad$ $SPR = 72.0 - 66.5\ (0.62) = 30.8\%$

whilst there may be no data at the site of interest, there may be data for a different point on the same river or in a nearby catchment, which can be used to improve a catchment-descriptor estimate of *SPR* at the subject site, as described in §2.3.5.

The equation currently used for estimating *SPR* from catchment descriptors is from IH Report 126 (Boorman *et al.*, 1995). *SPR* is estimated from HOST soil class fractions, using Equation 2.17 and the *SPR* values in Table 2.2 (see Example 2.3b):

$$SPR = SPRHOST = \sum_1^{29} SPR_i\, HOST_i = SPR_1\, HOST_1 + SPR_2\, HOST_2 + \ldots + SPR_{29}\, HOST_{29} \qquad (2.17)$$

Table 2.2 *Recommended SPR values for HOST classes*

HOST class	SPR %	HOST class	SPR %	HOST class	SPR %
1	2.0	11	2.0	21	47.2
2	2.0	12	60.0	22	60.0
3	14.5	13	2.0	23	60.0
4	2.0	14	25.3	24	39.7
5	14.5	15	48.4	25	49.6
6	33.8	16	29.2	26	58.7
7	44.3	17	29.2	27	60.0
8	44.3	18	47.2	28	60.0
9	25.3	19	60.0	29	60.0
10	25.3	20	60.0		

The equation allows *SPR* to vary between 2% and 60%, and better reflects the variation in runoff from different soil types than previous *SPR* models did. As well as providing a step forward towards more accurate estimation of *SPR*, the HOST classification presents a better way of selecting donor catchments for the transfer of local data. The catchment *SPR* should be used in the FSSR16 percentage runoff model, together with the appropriate storm depth, catchment wetness index and urban fraction, to calculate percentage runoff for a particular event using Equations 2.12-2.15.

Example 2.3b
Estimation of *SPR* from catchment descriptors

Catchment: Rhymney at Gilfach Bargoed (IHDTM grid ref. 315050 200250) (Figure 3 of Appendix C)

Relevant catchment descriptors:
$HOST_4$ = 19.17%, $HOST_6$ = 1.38%, $HOST_{10}$ = 4.71%, $HOST_{15}$ = 9.13%, $HOST_{17}$ = 10.69%, $HOST_{21}$ = 5.40%, $HOST_{24}$ = 11.37%, $HOST_{26}$ = 38.16%

The standard percentage runoff SPR is derived from catchment descriptors using Equation 2.17:

$SPR = SPRHOST = \sum_{1}^{29} SPR_i HOST_i$

$$\begin{aligned} SPR = \; & 0.1917\,(2.0) + 0.0138\,(33.8) \\ & + 0.0471\,(25.3) + 0.0913\,(48.4) \\ & + 0.1069\,(29.2) + 0.0540\,(47.2) \\ & 0.1137\,(39.7) + 0.3816\,(58.7) \\ & = 39.0\% \end{aligned}$$

2.3.5 *SPR* by transfer from a donor catchment

Whilst there may be no rainfall and runoff records at the site of interest, there may be records at a different point on the same river or in a nearby similar catchment. Analysis of these records can provide observed values of *SPR* or *BFI* which can be used to improve a catchment-descriptor estimate of *SPR* at the subject site. For *SPR*, the size and location restrictions for donor catchments are less relevant, as it is most essential that the catchments are similar in terms of soils and underlying geology, topography and land use. The procedure for adjusting an *SPR* estimate is:

i Apply the catchment-descriptor method to estimate *SPR* at the (ungauged) subject site (this is $SPR_{s,cds}$);

ii Apply the catchment-descriptor method to estimate *SPR* at the (gauged) donor site (this is $SPR_{g,cds}$);

iii Analyse the observed flow data at the (gauged) donor site by an appropriate method to yield an observed value of *SPR* (this is $SPR_{g,obs}$);

iv Adjust $SPR_{s,cds}$ at the (ungauged) subject site accordingly; the equation for the transfer is:

$$SPR_{s,adj} = SPR_{s,cds} \frac{SPR_{g,\,obs}}{SPR_{g,\,cds}} \tag{2.18}$$

where the subscripts *s* and *g* refer to the subject site and gauged site respectively, and the subscripts *cds*, *obs* and *adj* refer to the catchment-descriptor estimates at the gauged and subject sites, the observed value at the gauged site and the adjusted value at the subject site, respectively.

Example 2.4b illustrates the procedure. The adjusted value of *SPR* can then be used in the FSSR16 percentage runoff model, together with the appropriate storm depth, catchment wetness index and urban fraction, to calculate percentage runoff for a particular event using Equations 2.12-2.15.

Example 2.4b
Estimation of *SPR* by transfer from a donor catchment

Subject catchment: West Lyn at Lynmouth (IHDTM grid ref. 272400 149450; Figure 4 of Appendix C). Donor catchment: Horner Water at West Luccombe (51002)

Relevant subject catchment descriptors:
$HOST_4$ = 24.68%, $HOST_{15}$ = 45.55%, $HOST_{17}$ = 10.41%, $HOST_{21}$ = 4.99%,
$HOST_{22}$ = 1.47%, $HOST_{26}$ = 7.81%, $HOST_{29}$ = 5.09%

Relevant donor catchment descriptors:
$HOST_2$ = 0.01%, $HOST_3$ = 0.05%, $HOST_4$ = 41.64%, $HOST_5$ = 0.74%, $HOST_6$ = 0.03%,
$HOST_8$ = 0.29%, $HOST_{12}$ = 0.02%, $HOST_{15}$ = 40.11%, $HOST_{17}$ = 0.30%,
$HOST_{21}$ = 6.59%, $HOST_{26}$ = 7.75%, $HOST_{29}$ = 2.47%

For the subject catchment, the standard percentage runoff *SPR* is derived from catchment descriptors using Equation 2.17: $SPR_{s,cds}$ = 36.5%

For the donor catchment, the standard percentage runoff *SPR* is derived from catchment descriptors using Equation 2.17: $SPR_{g,cds}$ = 29.7%

For the donor catchment, the standard percentage runoff *SPR* is also derived from the flood event analysis results presented in Table 3 of Appendix A; the *SPR* values range from 12.0% to 36.7%, with an arithmetic mean of 20.2%:

$SPR_{g,obs}$ = 20.2%

For the subject catchment, the standard percentage runoff *SPR* from catchment descriptors $SPR_{s,cds}$ is refined by reference to the performance of the catchment descriptor method on the donor catchment using Equation 2.18:

$SPR_{s,adj} = SPR_{s,cds}\,(SPR_{g,obs} / SPR_{g,cds})$ $\qquad SPR_{s,adj}$ = 36.5 (20.2 / 29.7) = 24.8%

2.4 The baseflow parameter

2.4.1 Introduction

The final step in the formulation of the total flood hydrograph is the addition of a flow quantity to represent the flow in the river before the event started, and to a lesser extent the start of the slow response runoff from the event itself. This flow quantity is referred to as the baseflow *BF*. Strictly, it should be termed average non-separated flow *ANSF*, as a reminder that the flow hydrograph is separated as an expedient for analysis and does not necessarily represent a separation generated by different runoff processes. Baseflow is a relatively unimportant parameter compared to unit hydrograph time-to-peak and percentage runoff, as it is usually small compared with the magnitude of the rapid response runoff hydrograph.

In FSR design and simulation, baseflow is taken as constant through an event, and is added to each ordinate of the rapid response runoff hydrograph. However, in reality, baseflow will not be constant, but will vary as deficits are made up and soils become saturated.

2.4.2 *BF* from observed flood event data

When the site is gauged, the preferred method of deriving estimates of baseflow *BF* is by the analysis of observed flood events, by the procedure described in Sections 5 and 6 of Appendix A. Table 2.1 presents results from the analysis of five flood events from the River Almond at Craigiehall (19001). *BF* values for each event are given in column 6. Usually the catchment average *BF* can be taken as a geometric mean of these values, as shown in Example 2.1c. Once the *BF* value has been determined, it is added to all ordinates of the rapid response runoff hydrograph to produce the total flood hydrograph.

> ***Example 2.1c***
> **Estimation of *BF* from observed flood event data**
>
> Catchment: Almond at Craigiehall (19001) (Figure 1 of Appendix C)
>
> The baseflow is derived from the flood event analysis results presented in Table 3 of Appendix A and, for this catchment, reproduced in Table 2.1.
>
> The *BF* values range from 4.22 $m^3 s^{-1}$ to 11.61 $m^3 s^{-1}$, with a geometric mean 7.26 $m^3 s^{-1}$:
>
> $BF = 7.26\ m^3 s^{-1}$

2.4.3 *BF* from catchment descriptors

Where there are no records at the site of interest, *BF* is estimated from catchment descriptors using a generalised model derived by regression analysis. Such parameter estimates are not as reliable as parameter estimates based on analysis of flood event data at or near the site. However, since *BF* is usually very small relative to the magnitude of the flood peak, it is not as important model parameter as $Tp(0)$ and *SPR*, and efforts should be focused at refining these parameter estimates rather than *BF* estimates. However, whilst there may be no data at the site of interest, there may be data for a different point on the same river or in a nearby catchment, which can be used to improve a catchment-descriptor estimate of *BF* at the subject site, as described in §2.4.4.

The equation currently used for estimating *BF* from catchment descriptors is from FSSR16 (see Example 2.3c):

$$BF = \{33\ (CWI - 125) + 3.0\ SAAR + 5.5\}\ 10^{-5}\ AREA \qquad (2.19)$$

On some catchments, it is possible to obtain a slightly negative *BF* with Equation 2.19, in which case the *BF* should be set to zero. Determination of the *BF* is the final step in formulation of the total flood hydrograph, and the *BF* value is added to all ordinates of the rapid response runoff hydrograph.

2.4.4 *BF* by transfer from a donor catchment

Whilst there may be no rainfall and runoff records at the site of interest, there may be records at a different point on the same river or in a nearby similar catchment. Analysis of these records can provide observed values of *BF* which can be used to

> ***Example 2.3c***
> **Estimation of *BF* from catchment descriptors**
>
> Catchment: Rhymney at Gilfach Bargoed (IHDTM grid ref. 315050 200250, Figure 3 of Appendix C)
>
> Relevant catchment descriptors:
> $CWI^* = 124.5$ mm, $SAAR = 1507$ mm, $AREA = 58.31$ km^2
>
> The baseflow *BF* is derived from catchment descriptors using Equation 2.19:
>
> $$BF = \{33\,(CWI - 125) + 3.0\,SAAR + 5.5\}\,10^{-5}\,AREA$$
> $$BF = \{33\,(124.5 - 125) + 3.0 \times 1507 + 5.5\}\,10^{-5} \times 58.31$$
> $$= 2.63 \text{ m}^3\text{s}^{-1}$$
>
> * design event value of *CWI* used: see §3.2.4 for *T*-year case (design event), §4.3.3 for *PMF* case and §5.2.2 for event simulation.

improve a catchment-descriptor estimate of *BF* at the subject site. The procedure for adjusting a *BF* estimate is:

i Apply the catchment-descriptor method to estimate *BF* at the (ungauged) subject site (this is $BF_{s,cds}$);

ii Apply the catchment-descriptor method to estimate *BF* at the (gauged) donor site (this is $BF_{g,cds}$);

iii Analyse the observed flow data at the (gauged) donor site by an appropriate method to yield an observed value of *BF* (this is $BF_{g,obs}$);

iv Adjust $BF_{s,cds}$ at the (ungauged) subject site accordingly; the equation for the transfer is:

$$BF_{s,\,adj} = BF_{s,\,cds}\,\frac{BF_{g,\,obs}}{BF_{g,\,cds}} \tag{2.20}$$

where the subscripts *s* and *g* refer to the subject site and gauged site respectively, and the subscripts *cds, obs* and *adj* refer to the catchment-descriptor estimates at the gauged and subject sites, the observed value at the gauged site and the adjusted value at the subject site, respectively.

Example 2.4c illustrates the procedure. Determination of the *BF* is the final step in formulation of the total flood hydrograph, and the *BF* value is added to all ordinates of the rapid response runoff hydrograph.

Example 2.4c
Estimation of *BF* by transfer from a donor catchment

Subject catchment: West Lyn at Lynmouth (IHDTM grid ref. 272400 149450, Figure 4 of Appendix C). Donor catchment: Horner Water at West Luccombe (51002)

Relevant subject catchment descriptors:
CWI * = 124.6 mm, *SAAR* = 1543 mm, *AREA* = 24.08 km^2

Relevant donor catchment descriptors:
CWI * = 124.5 mm, *SAAR* = 1484 mm, *AREA* = 20.49 km^2

For the subject catchment, the baseflow *BF* is derived from catchment descriptors using Equation 2.19: $BF_{s,cds} = 1.11\ m^3s^{-1}$

For the donor catchment, the baseflow *BF* is derived from catchment descriptors using Equation 2.19: $BF_{g,cds} = 0.91\ m^3s^{-1}$

For the donor catchment, the baseflow *BF* is also derived from the flood event analysis results presented in Table 3 of Appendix A; the *BF* values range from 0.38 m^{3}s^{-1} to 1.70 m^{3}s^{-1}, with a geometric mean of 0.87 m^{3}s^{-1}: $BF_{g,obs} = 0.87\ m^3s^{-1}$

For the subject catchment, the baseflow *BF* from catchment descriptors $BF_{s,cds}$ is refined by reference to the performance of the catchment descriptor method on the donor catchment using Equation 2.20:

$BF_{s,adj} = BF_{s,cds}\ (BF_{g,obs}\ /\ BF_{g,cds})$ $\qquad BF_{s,adj} = 1.11\ (0.87\ /\ 0.91)$
$= 1.06\ m^3s^{-1}$

* design event value of *CWI* used: see §3.2.4 for *T*-year case (design event), §4.3.3 for PMF case and §5.2.2 for event simulation.

Chapter 3 *T*-year flood estimation

3.1 Introduction

The FSR rainfall-runoff method is used to estimate a flood peak of the required return period, known as the *T*-year flood, by applying an appropriate return period rainfall to the unit hydrograph and losses model. The rainfall is specified as part of the FSR design event method which provides a set of rules for choosing the rainfall duration, depth and temporal profile, and also the antecedent catchment wetness, to give the flood of the required return period. A different set of rules is provided for heavily urbanised catchments. A catchment flood frequency curve is obtained by plotting *T*-year flood peaks against their corresponding return periods.

This section outlines the simulation exercise which provides the basis of the FSR design event method, and considers the assumptions, limitations and weaknesses of the method. In Section 3.2, the design event method and the rules for choosing the storm characteristics and initial catchment state are considered in detail. Application of the design storm to the unit hydrograph and losses model to estimate the *T*-year flood is described in Section 3.3, and a short-cut method for estimating the design flood is presented in Section 3.4.

3.1.1 Foundation of the FSR design event method

The FSR rainfall-runoff method provides a way of synthesising a design flood hydrograph with peak of a given return period, from a single hypothetical rainfall event. It is of course possible, and indeed likely, that different combinations of storm characteristics and catchment state will produce flood peaks of similar magnitude. Furthermore, it is to be expected that the magnitudes of the derived flood peaks will be more sensitive to some of these input variables than to others e.g. rainfall depth is likely to affect flood peaks much more than its temporal profile. FSR I.6.7 describes a computer simulation exercise and various sensitivity analyses that were performed to examine the way in which the return period of the peak flow was affected by the input variables. The simulation exercise had two objectives. Firstly, it had to be proven that the technique of using a set of design inputs and an event-based model could successfully reproduce observed flood frequency curves. Once this was established, the second objective was to formulate a way of selecting a single set of inputs that would give the flood peak of the required return period. The following sections review these two phases of the simulation exercise, and discuss the resulting prescribed package of design inputs.

Reproduction of flood frequency curves

The four design variables that are required for T-year flood estimation using the FSR rainfall-runoff method are:

- Rainfall duration;
- Rainfall depth (or return period);
- Rainfall profile;
- Antecedent catchment wetness.

Each of these variables has a corresponding probability distribution which can be combined to yield an overall probability distribution of peak flow (statistically they are marginal distributions of a joint probability surface). The corresponding flow peak can be derived using the unit hydrograph and losses model. The probability of obtaining a flood magnitude in a given interval can then be found by summing all the joint probabilities for derived peaks in that interval. The flood frequency curve can be built up by performing this summation over successive intervals, and thereby covering the required range of flood peaks. The simulation exercise considered all combinations of the four variables, but was greatly simplified by defining just six to twelve sub-divisions to represent the entire range of each of the four variables. Figure 3.1 illustrates the procedure as a tree diagram with a particular set of choices indicated.

The simulations were carried out on 98 catchments for which unit hydrograph and losses model parameters, and a suitable length of annual maximum flows from which to derive a flood frequency curve, were available. Seventeen catchments were later rejected because their response was too flashy for successful simulation based on hourly rainfall. General comparisons were made between the flood frequency curve derived from annual maxima and the one resulting from the simulation process, though subsequent analysis was restricted to comparing observed and simulated values of the mean annual flood and the 10-year flood. Satisfactory comparisons led to the conclusion that "the probability distributions of floods from real catchments can be adequately predicted by the simulation technique" (FSR I.6.7.4).

Choice of a single set of design inputs

The second stage of the analysis involved selecting a single choice of variables for each flood return period. This was achieved by choosing suitable fixed values of the three less important variables, and then optimising the remaining variable such that the model reproduced the required flood magnitude.

Storm profile was found to be the least important variable influencing flood magnitude, and it was fixed to be the 75% Winter profile on rural catchments and the 50% Summer profile on urbanised catchments (see §3.2.3). These were the profiles which were on average more peaky than 75% of UK Winter storms and 50% of UK Summer storms, respectively.

Flood magnitude was less sensitive to storm duration than to either of the remaining variables (i.e. antecedent wetness and storm depth), and so the storm duration *D* was fixed to be the duration typically giving the largest flood magnitude, calculated from catchment response time (indexed by unit hydrograph time-to-peak) and *SAAR* (see §3.2.1).

Antecedent catchment wetness (represented by the catchment wetness index *CWI*) and storm depth were both found to be important in influencing flood peaks. When *CWI* was fixed, the relationship between flood return period and rainfall return period (and associated storm depth) was similar between catchments. The alternative strategy of fixing the rainfall depth by return period (i.e. so that the *T*-year storm produces the *T*-year flood) led to inconsistent values of *CWI* between catchments. Therefore, *CWI* was fixed, to be a median value estimated from *SAAR* (see §3.2.4), and the rainfall return period was chosen by optimisation. For each catchment, the return periods of rainfalls required to produce floods of various return periods were evaluated and plotted as a curve. An average curve (Figure 3.2) was recommended for selecting the appropriate storm return period to give the peak discharge of required return period when combined with the other variables. The design storm depth was determined from rainfall depth-duration-frequency relationships once the duration and return period of the storm were known (see §3.2.2).

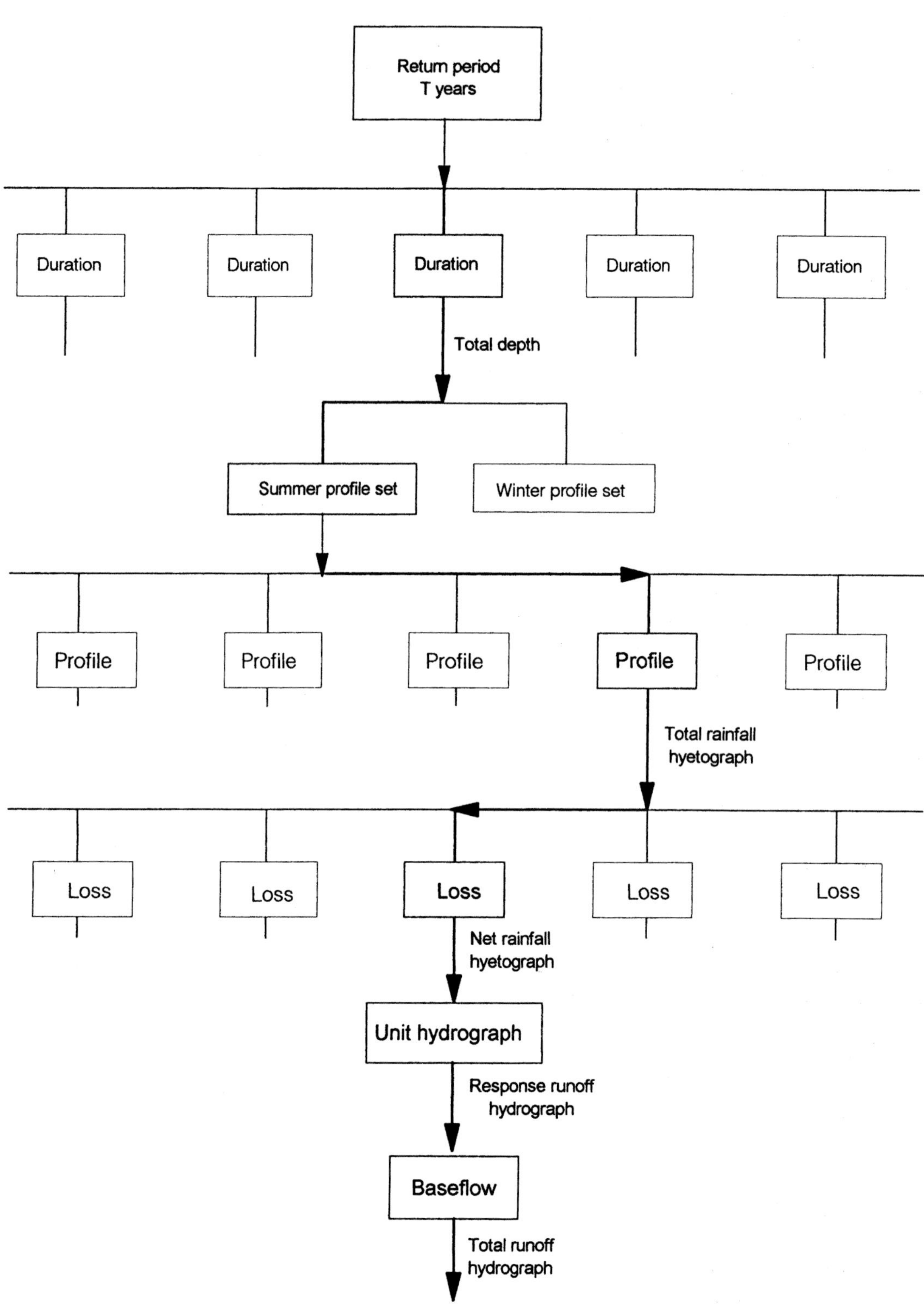

Figure 3.1 *Simulation procedure*

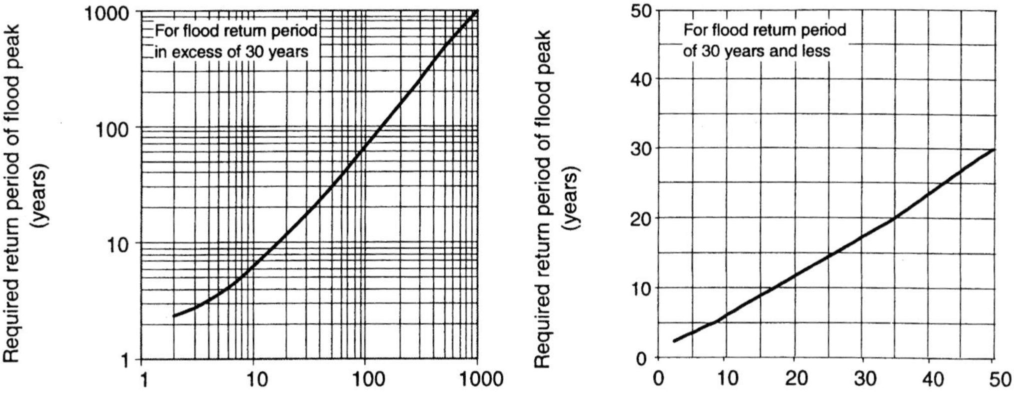

Figure 3.2 *Recommended storm return period to yield flood peak of required return period by design event method*

Several points in particular may be made about the second stage of the analysis. Firstly, in selecting the single choice of variables, a match was sought with the simulated flood frequency curves, rather than with those derived from annual maximum data. Thus, any regional deviations present in the simulations were built into the single choice of variables. Secondly, it is not clear how many catchments were used, and how much variability was present, when defining the relative return periods of design rainfall and peak flow. Results show considerable scatter in the relationship for seven catchments where the rainfall return period varies from 5 to 10 years for the 5-year flood, 12 to 27 years for the 10-year flood, and 60 to 128 years for the 50-year flood (FSR Figure I.6.54). The corresponding standard choices are 8, 17 and 81 years, respectively (Figure 3.2).

A recent review of flood-producing rainfalls confirmed rainfall rarity to be the most influential input variable, and antecedent catchment wetness and storm duration to be generally more influential than spatial and temporal features of the rainfall field. The review concluded that there was "nothing to suggest that there is anything inappropriate about the choices made in the FSR [rainfall-runoff] method" (Faulkner, 1997).

Discussion

The prescribed package of design inputs to the unit hydrograph and losses model provides an easy-to-use method for estimating the flood peak of a particular return period. However, it is possible to use the design event method without appreciating the critical assumptions on which it is based. Issues raised by use of the method are complex (Webster, 1998). The method has some fundamental weaknesses; for instance, several of the existing four design inputs are set in a manner that is not entirely satisfactory.

The unimodal, symmetrical design rainfall profiles are widely regarded as unrealistic (e.g. Kelway, 1977; Collier, 1992). Rainfall events which cause severe floods can have a wide variety of temporal and spatial profiles, and these (together with antecedent catchment wetness) can differ greatly from the design assumptions. However, in order to make the design event approach to flood frequency estimation work, it is necessary to have relatively simple rules, and it is not expected that any individual event will necessarily exhibit such a profile. The FSR design storm profiles attempt to characterise the typical variability of rainfall intensity during an event, which is very difficult to do because the precipitation process is highly variable. It is accepted that such profiles are unsuitable for long-duration events which typically comprise a series of storms. There has been some guidance about this, and new long-duration profiles relevant to spillway flood design on large, reservoired catchments have been developed for north-west Scotland (Stewart and Reynard, 1991). The approach uses the average variability method which successfully preserves the typically multi-peaked character of 3-day and longer accumulations (Pilgrim *et al.*, 1969; Pilgrim and Cordery, 1975; Cordery *et al.*, 1984). However, similar analyses in other parts of the country have shown significant differences, making generalisation of the method difficult (Reynard and Stewart, 1993). Furthermore, there is no formal mechanism by which to incorporate such profiles into the design event method. The commonly-proposed solution of a library of typical profiles from which to choose may indeed produce more realistic-looking storms and hydrographs, as can stochastic generation of storm profiles (Koutsoyiannis, 1994; Onof *et al.*, 1996), but use of a non-standard profile will not necessarily give a flood of the required return period.

Similarly, the design value of *CWI* is specified according to mapped SAAR values, and takes no explicit account of the differing drainage characteristics of the particular soils, slopes or land-uses. For example, antecedent groundwater level is highly relevant for runoff from chalk catchments but is almost insignificant for impermeable catchments, so *CWI* ought to be much more influential in the former case. Furthermore, no allowance is made for seasonal variation in catchment state. The very strong influence exerted by seasonal soil moisture deficits in many relatively permeable lowland catchments in the UK can cause the seasonal distribution of maximum floods to be diametrically opposed to that of maximum 1-day rainfalls (Reed, 1994b). Although it is a view that is not yet universally shared, this weakness may eventually lead to the use of the design event method being restricted to particular catchment types e.g. heavily urbanised catchments where soil moisture effects are less influential.

Perhaps the most general weakness of the method is the underlying assumption that a unique combination of four specific inputs will yield the flood peak of the required return period on all catchments. The rules for combining the inputs are only valid in some average sense, and there is no reason to expect that the combination of inputs deemed suitable will be equally appropriate on every catchment. Indeed, the rationale of pooling flood peak data from hydrologically similar catchments (**3** C6), argues against a method which imposes a unique combination of design inputs on all catchments. A good example of this latter point is snowmelt, which can be an important contributor to floods in parts of the UK, yet is not treated explicitly in the design event method. The recommended choice of design inputs makes implicit allowance for snowmelt events because the method is based on recorded floods, but its explicit inclusion would make the overall design package too complicated.

In the longer term, flood frequency estimation based on continuous simulation modelling of catchments appears a promising alternative to design event methods. Realistic accounting for soil moisture is seen as one of the key strengths of the continuous simulation modelling approach. However, some new problems remain to be resolved, particularly with respect to regionalisation. In the meantime, the FSR design event method continues to provide an easy-to-use prescribed package of design inputs for estimating the flood peak of a particular return period.

3.1.2 FEH rainfall statistics

The assessment of rainfall frequency is fundamental to design flood estimation using the FSR rainfall-runoff method. FSR II provided estimates of the rainfall depth corresponding to a given duration and return period, both at a point and over an area, together with a profile or time distribution of this rainfall. These statistics were incorporated in a computer-based model for determining rainfall depth-duration-frequency for any location in the UK (Keers and Wescott, 1977).

However, the FSR rainfall statistics were, like any other data analysis, subject to revision with regard to both the numerical values presented and the methodology adopted. Revisions to the rainfall statistics started on a regional level, prompted by the recognition that the FSR rainfall frequency methods were over generalised, and failed to adequately represent regional variation in rainfall growth rates (Bootman and Willis, 1981; Dales and Reed, 1989). For example, Reed and Stewart (1989) designed revised procedures for rainfall growth estimation, illustrated by derivation of 1-day rainfall growth curves in south-west England.

Volume 2 of the Handbook presents a new generalisation of rainfall depth-duration-frequency estimation. The techniques were developed and implemented following reworking of the county-wide rainfall data set, by arrangement with the Met. Office. Now that one of the four elements of the design input package has been updated, there is scope for future research to review the combination of design inputs. For completeness, the FSR rainfall statistics, which will only be of use if attempting to reproduce a previous flood estimate, are included in Section 3 of Appendix B.

3.2 FSR design input package

A rainfall of a given return period can produce a wide range of estimated design floods, depending on the storm duration, antecedent catchment wetness and, less critically in most cases, the temporal profile of the storm. The FSR design input package provides a way of selecting a single set of inputs to synthesise the flood peak of the required return period. Different recommendations for rural and urbanised catchments are sustained in the Handbook's restatement of the FSR rainfall-runoff model. However, it is important to note that the Handbook's use of a different definition of urban fraction leads to the breakpoint between *rural* and *urban* catchments being $URBEXT = 0.125$, rather than $URBAN_{FSR} = 0.25$. Where $URBEXT$ is close to the 0.125 breakpoint, it is recommended that both rural and urban input packages are considered separately to see which gives the largest flood. Cases where $URBEXT > 0.5$ are more appropriately treated by sewer design methods. Figure 3.3 shows the influence of the design inputs with respect to the steps in the calculation of the T-year flood.

3.2.1 Design storm duration

The design storm duration D is based on a formula which approximates the duration giving the largest flood magnitude, D_{CRIT}. The design storm duration D is calculated from unit hydrograph time-to-peak Tp and standard average annual rainfall $SAAR$ (see Example 3.1a):

$$D = Tp\,(1 + \frac{SAAR}{1000}) \tag{3.1}$$

Unit hydrograph time-to-peak is an index of catchment response time, i.e. the faster responding the catchment, the shorter the critical storm duration. $SAAR$

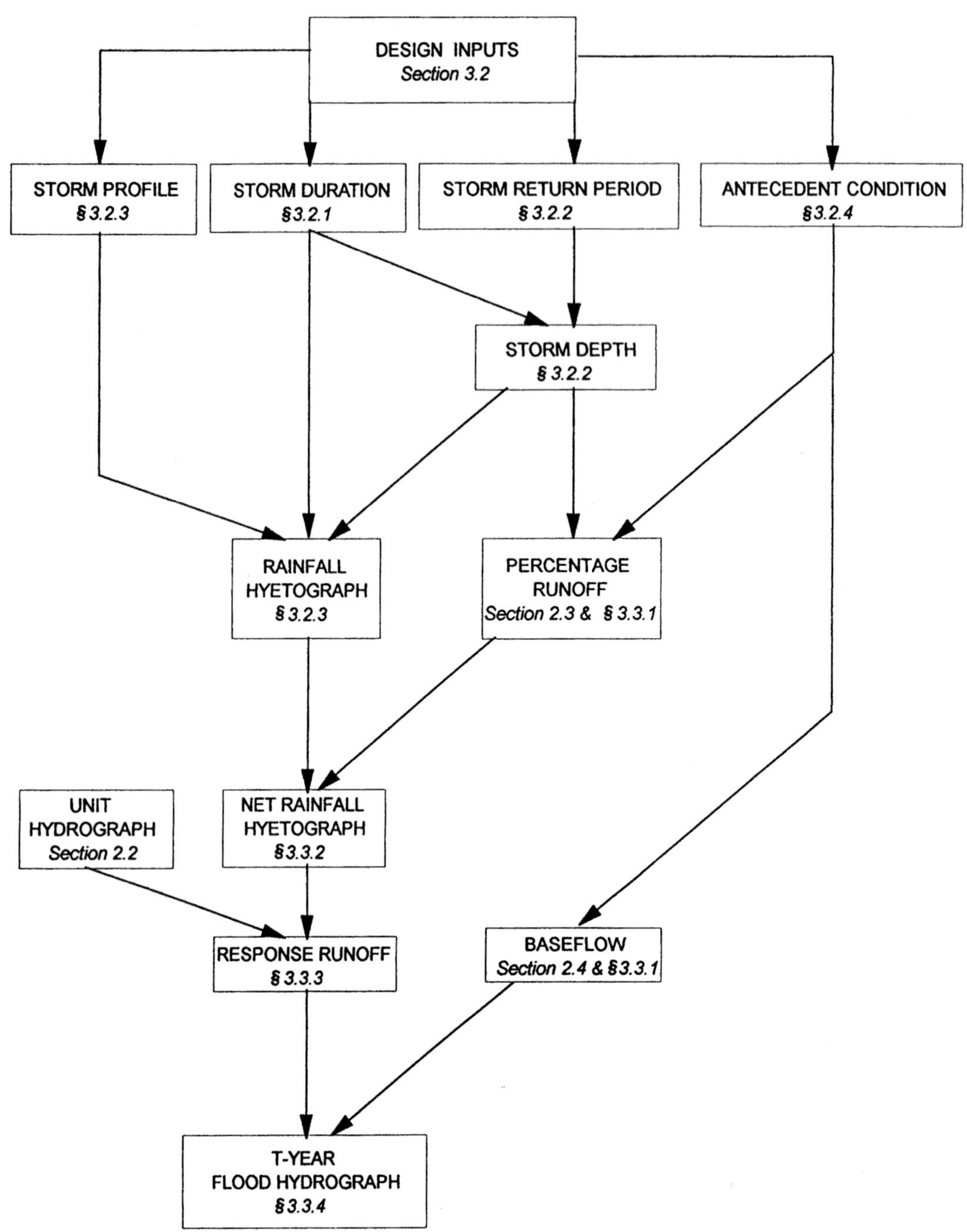

Figure 3.3 *Influence of design inputs and the steps in the calculation of the T-year flood*

represents important climatic effects; flood events are typically more prolonged on high *SAAR* catchments than catchment response times would alone indicate. One interpretation of this is the greater influence of *seeder-feeder* mechanisms in sustaining heavy rainfall in high *SAAR* areas (Hill *et al.*, 1981), and the more frequent role of short-duration convective storms in flood production in low *SAAR* areas.

Curves of flood magnitude against storm duration are generally flat, so the choice of storm duration is not usually critical for flood peak delineation (Reed and Field, 1992). However, in reservoired applications, the design storm duration is extended by adding the reservoir response time to the catchment response time (see §8.2.1), and in other situations, it may be appropriate to consider a range of design storm durations (see §9.2.2).

In the FSR design event method, it is necessary to have an odd number of rainfall blocks, for a reason explained in §3.2.3. Therefore, the computed value of storm duration is rounded, up or down, to the nearest odd integer multiple of the data interval ΔT (see Example 3.1a). For instance, with a 1-hour data interval, a calculated duration of 12.3 hours, would be rounded to 13 hours as 12 is an even integer multiple of the data interval (i.e. 12 × 1) and 13 is an odd integer multiple of the data interval (i.e. 13 × 1). Similarly, with a 2-hour data interval, a calculated duration of 12.3 hours, would be rounded to 14 hours as 12 is again an even integer multiple of the data interval (i.e. 6 × 2) and 14 is an odd integer multiple of the data interval (i.e. 7 × 2).

Example 3.1a
Calculation of design storm duration *D*

Catchment: Almond at Craigiehall (19001) (Figure 1 of Appendix C)

Relevant catchment descriptors and other information:
SAAR = 892 mm, ΔT = 1.0 hours (§2.2.2), $Tp(1)$ = 6.97 hours (§2.2.2)

The design storm duration D is calculated from Tp and SAAR using Equation 3.1:

$D = Tp\,(1 + SAAR / 1000)$ $\quad\quad$ $D = 6.97\,(1 + 892 / 1000) = 13.2$ hours

In this instance, ΔT = 1.0 hours so D is rounded down to 13 hours, the nearest odd integer multiple of ΔT: $\quad\quad$ $D = 13.0$ hours

3.2.2 Design storm depth

The design storm depth P is the T-year D-hour catchment rainfall. The storm depth P is determined from rainfall depth-duration-frequency relationships, once the duration and return period of the design storm are known, by the following procedure:

i Determine the appropriate rainfall return period, T_R;

ii Abstract the T-year D-hour point rainfall, *MT-Dh*;

iii Scale the point *MT-Dh* to the catchment *MT-Dh* or P.

The steps in the procedure are discussed below, together with relevant comment on related topics, and illustrated by Example 3.1b.

Determination of appropriate rainfall return period T_R

Determination of the appropriate rainfall return period depends on the degree of urbanisation of the catchment and the required return period of the flood. On rural or only moderately urbanised catchments (*URBEXT* < 0.125), the design rainfall return period T_R is determined from the design flood return period T_F using the graphs in Figure 3.2. Table 3.1 gives some common return period combinations abstracted from the graphs. Over the 10-year to 100-year design flood return periods, the design rainfall return period is typically about 1.7 times longer. However, it must be stressed that it is not suggested that all storms with, for instance, an 81-year return period will necessarily produce a 50-year flood peak, but rather that the complete package of design storm duration, depth, profile and antecedent conditions specified here will typically give the best estimate of the 50-year flood peak.

Table 3.1 *Recommended storm return period to yield flood peak of required return period by design event method*

Flood peak return period (years)	2.33	10	30	50	100	1000
Rainfall return period (years)	2	17	50	81	140	1000

On urban catchments (0.125 ≤ *URBEXT* ≤ 0.5), the design rainfall return period T_R is set equal to the design flood return period T_F, e.g. the 50-year flood is produced by the 50-year rainfall. The reasoning behind this is that for rural catchments, because of other factors (e.g. antecedent condition), not all extreme rainfalls generate equally extreme floods; however, urbanised catchments are generally less variable in their response, making a simpler choice of design conditions possible. For urban catchments, the use of equal return periods leads to a flatter flood frequency, which is borne out by observed data. Further discussion is provided in FSSR5 (IH, 1979a), and *IH Reports 61* (Kidd and Packman, 1980) and *63* (Packman, 1980).

Abstraction of *T*-year *D*-hour point rainfall *MT-Dh*

The point *MT-Dh* rainfall is abstracted from the rainfall depth-duration-frequency data presented on the CD-ROM (**2** 2).

Calculation of design storm depth *P*

The catchment *MT-Dh* rainfall or design storm depth *P* is calculated by scaling the point *MT-Dh* rainfall by an areal reduction factor *ARF*. The *ARF* used in the FSR rainfall-runoff method is defined as the ratio of the rainfall depth over an area to the rainfall depth of the same duration and return period at a representative point within that area. The *ARF* is read from Figure 3.4 which shows *ARF*s as percentages related to catchment area and storm duration. Thus:

$$P = MT\text{-}Dh\,(\text{catchment}) = ARF_D\; MT\text{-}Dh\,(\text{point}) \qquad (3.2)$$

The *ARF* simply relates the statistics of point rainfall (the scale at which gauge data are collected) to those of areal rainfall (the scale at which design takes place). However, the FSR concept and the use of *ARF* have caused considerable debate. This is partly because of confusion between the FSR definition and the alternative definition of a storm-centred *ARF*, which describes the way in which rainfall intensity decreases with distance from the centre of the storm in individual

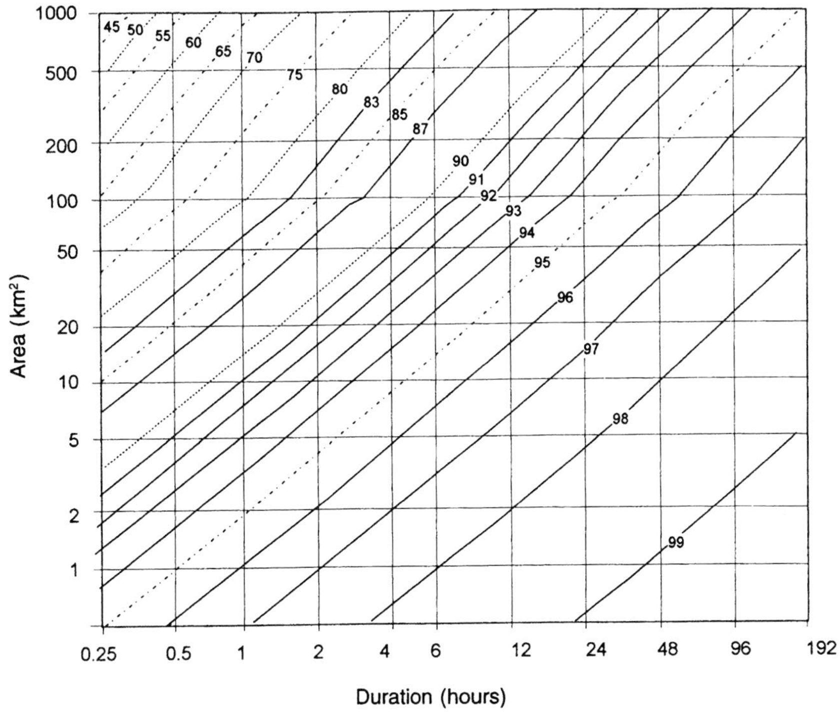

Figure 3.4 *Areal reduction factor (ARF) %, related to area AREA and duration D*

events. However, an investigation of ARF in rainfall frequency estimation confirmed that the FSR values of *ARF*s are appropriate for use in current design; if anything, they are slightly conservative (*IH Report 35* (Bell, 1976); FSSR1 (IH, 1977a)). Furthermore, subsequent research found no evidence for geographical variation in *ARF*s (Bell, 1976; Stewart, 1989). The tendency for *ARF* values to decrease slightly with increasing return period can be neglected for practical purposes, because such variations are small compared to the effects of the other simplifying assumptions in the design event method.

3.2.3 Design storm profile

The design storm depth P is distributed within the design storm duration D using the appropriate design storm profile according to whether the catchment is rural to moderately urbanised, or heavily urbanised. On predominantly rural catchments ($URBEXT < 0.125$), floods normally occur in winter so the appropriate design storm profile is the 75% winter profile, defined as the profile which is, on average, more *peaky* than 75% of UK winter storms. On urban catchments ($0.125 \leq URBEXT \leq 0.5$), floods normally occur in Summer so the appropriate profile is the 50% summer profile, defined as the profile which is, on average, more *peaky* than 50% of UK summer storms (FSSR5).

The profiles are symmetrical and bell-shaped, as shown in Figure 3.5a. Figure 3.5b shows the profiles as cumulative percentages of depth and duration related to storm peak. The 50% summer profile is seen to be peakier than the 75% winter profile, which is consistent with the typically more intense nature of convective storms which are more prevalent in summer. Use of the 50% summer

Example 3.1b
Calculation of design storm depth *P*

Catchment: Almond at Craigiehall (19001) (Figure 1 of Appendix C)

Relevant catchment descriptors and other information:
$URBEXT = 0.034$, $D = 13.0$ hours (§3.2.1), $AREA = 386.19$ km^2

Determining appropriate rainfall return period T_R:

Decide upon flood return period T_F: $T_F = 50$ years

$URBEXT < 0.125$ so the appropriate rainfall return period T_R is obtained from Figure 3.2/Table 3.1: $T_R = 81$ years

Abstracting *T*-year *D*-hour point rainfall *MT-Dh*:

MT-Dh(point) is abstracted from the CD-ROM: *M*81-13*h*(point) = 70.8 mm

Calculating design storm depth *P*:

The design storm depth *P* is the *T*-year *D*-hour catchment rainfall, calculated by scaling *MT-Dh*(point) by an areal reduction factor *ARF*. The *ARF* appropriate to the catchment area and storm duration is obtained from Figure 3.4:
$ARF_{13} = 0.896$

P is calculated using Equation 3.2:

$P = MT\text{-}Dh(\text{catchment}) = ARF_D\, MT\text{-}Dh(\text{point})$ $P = 0.896\,(70.8) = 63.4$ mm

profile, therefore, results in a somewhat higher peak discharge, other factors being equal. This profile was recommended in part for consistency with sewer design methods: further details may be found in *IH Reports 61* (Kidd and Packman, 1980) and *63* (Packman, 1980).

The design rainfall hyetograph is derived, somewhat cryptically, from the appropriate design storm profile, and it will now become clear why it was necessary to select the storm duration to be an odd integer multiple of the data interval.

For a *D*-hour storm, each ΔT-hour rainfall block has a duration equivalent to the fraction $\Delta T/D$ of the total storm duration. Furthermore, because the storm duration D is an odd integer multiple of the data interval ΔT, the storm is centred on the ΔT-hour rainfall block occurring between $\{D/2 - \Delta T/2\}$ and $\{D/2 + \Delta T/2\}$ hours after storm commencement. For example, each 1-hour rainfall block of a 5-hour storm will have a duration equivalent to 1/5 or 20% of the storm duration, and the storm will be centred on the 1-hour block occurring between 2 and 3 hours after the storm began.

Figure 3.6 shows just the 75% winter profile from Figure 3.5b. From Figure 3.6, the proportion of the total storm depth contained in the 20% of the duration

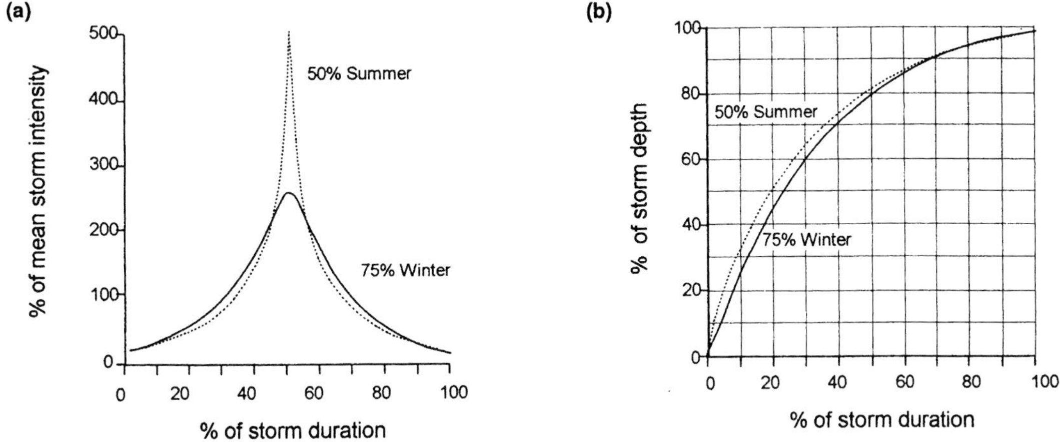

Figure 3.5 *Recommended design storm profiles, 75% winter and 50% summer: (a) in profile, (b) as cumulative percentages related to storm peak*

making up the 1-hour peak period in the centre of the storm is 45%. Similarly, the central 3 hours of the storm represent 60% of the storm duration; again from Figure 3.6, this will contain 85% of the total storm depth. Of this, 45% of the storm depth occurs in the central 1-hour block, so the remaining 40% of the depth (i.e. 85% – 45%) is divided equally between the two outer 1-hour periods, placing 20% of the storm depth in each. The complete 5 hours of the storm represent 100% of the storm duration; again from Figure 3.6, this will contain 100% of the total storm depth. Of this, 85% of the storm depth occurs in the central 3-hour block, so the remaining 15% of the depth (i.e. 100% – 85%) is divided equally between the two outer 1-hour periods, placing 7.5% of the storm depth in each.

To determine the design rainfall hyetograph, the percentage profile is converted into mm units by multiplying by the design storm depth *P*, as illustrated in Example 3.1c, which presents a slightly more complex case.

3.2.4 Design antecedent catchment wetness

The state of the catchment prior to the storm is referred to as the antecedent catchment wetness, and is indexed by the catchment wetness index CWI. CWI is an important factor influencing percentage runoff, and so has a considerable potential effect on flood magnitudes (Cordery, 1970). However, in the design event method, there is a need to make simplifying assumptions. The design CWI is estimated using Figure 3.7 which relates CWI to standard average annual rainfall SAAR (see Example 3.1d). CWI typically varies only between 120 mm and 130 mm, except on low SAAR catchments where it can fall to around 60 mm.

3.3 Derivation of T-year flood

The *T*-year flood is estimated from the input design storm and antecedent conditions by the following steps:

i Calculate the percentage runoff and baseflow, to completely specify the unit hydrograph and losses model;

ii Apply the percentage runoff to the total rainfall hyetograph to derive the net rainfall hyetograph;

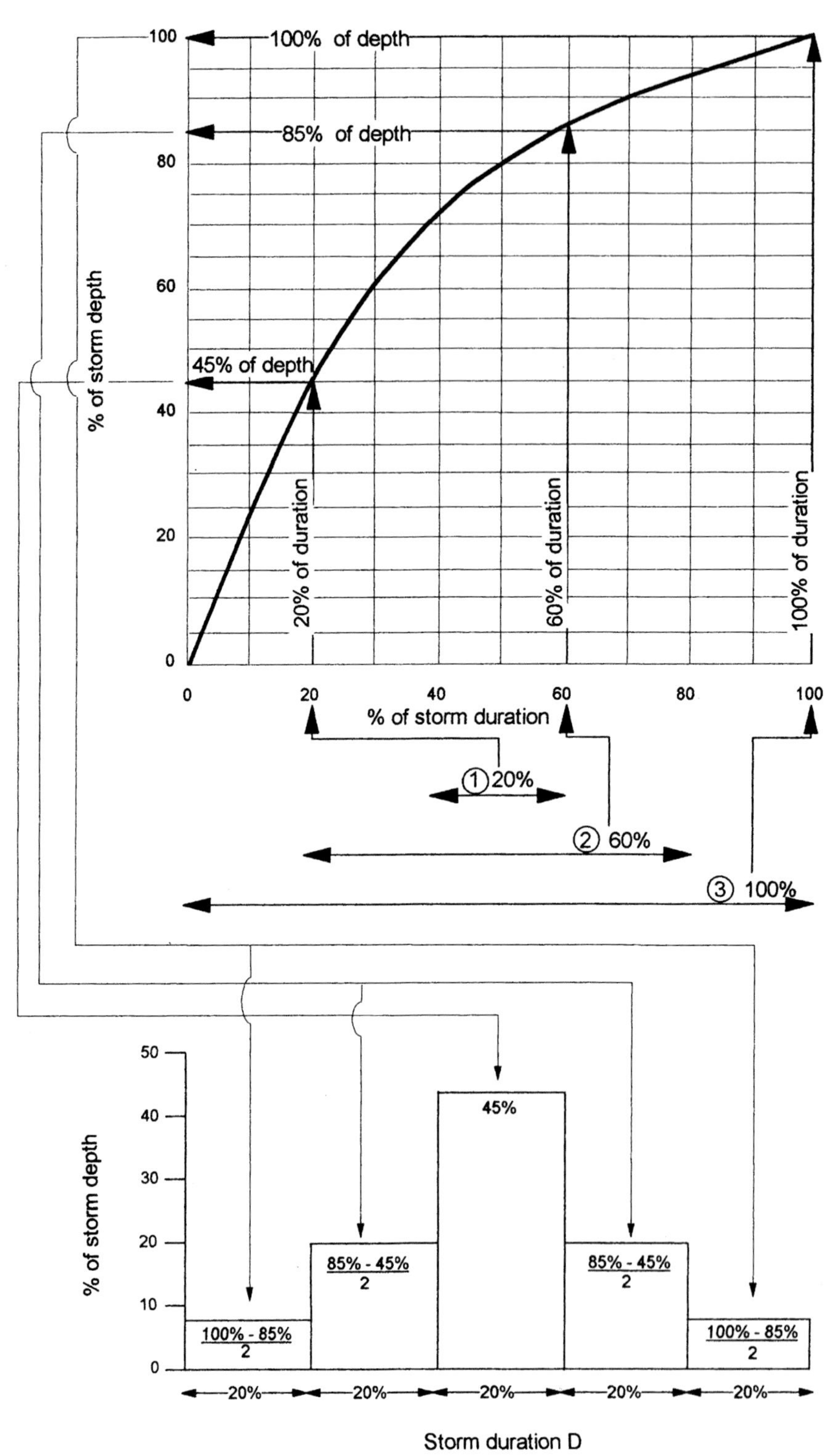

Figure 3.6 *Derivation of the winter design storm profile*

Example 3.1c
Derivation of design storm profile

Catchment: Almond at Craigiehall (19001) (Figure 1 of Appendix C)

Relevant catchment descriptors and other information:
ΔT = 1.0 hours (§2.2.2), D = 13.0 hours (§3.2.1), P = 63.4 mm (§3.2.2), *URBEXT* = 0.034

The design storm depth P is distributed within the design storm duration D using the appropriate design storm profile. *URBEXT* < 0.125 so the appropriate profile is the 75% Winter profile from Figure 3.5b:

% D	7.7	23.1	38.5	53.9	69.2	84.6	100.0
% P	20.0	49.5	69.0	82.0	90.5	96.2	100.0
Diff (%)	20.0	29.5	19.5	13.0	8.5	5.7	3.8
Diff (mm)	12.7	18.7	12.4	8.2	5.4	3.6	2.4

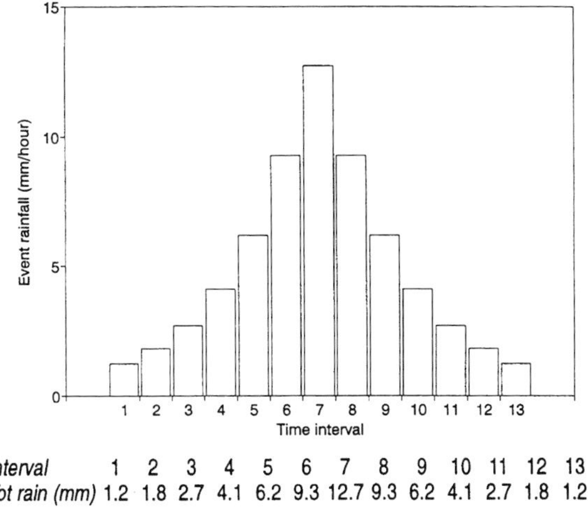

Interval	1	2	3	4	5	6	7	8	9	10	11	12	13
Tot rain (mm)	1.2	1.8	2.7	4.1	6.2	9.3	12.7	9.3	6.2	4.1	2.7	1.8	1.2

D = 13.0 hours and ΔT = 1 hour, so each rainfall block of interval 1-hour will have a duration equivalent to a fraction 1/13 or 7.7% of D.

The storm is centred on the 1-hour period occurring between 6 and 7 hours after storm commencement. This peak period represents 1/13 or 7.7% of D and the 75% winter profile specifies that this contains 20% of P.

The central 3 hours of the storm represent 3/13 or 23.1% of the storm duration. This contains 49.5% of P. Of this, 20% occurs in the central 1 hour, so the remaining 29.5% of the depth (i.e. 49.5% – 20%) is divided between the two outer 1-hour periods, with 14.7% of P in each.

The rest of the profile is constructed in a similar fashion, as illustrated.

iii Convolve the unit hydrograph with the net rainfall hyetograph to derive the rapid response runoff hydrograph;

iv Add the baseflow to the rapid response runoff hydrograph to derive the total runoff hydrograph.

T-year flood peaks can be plotted against their corresponding return period to produce a flood frequency curve for the catchment.

3.3.1 Calculation of percentage runoff and baseflow

The values of catchment wetness index *CWI* and storm depth P, determined in §3.2.4 and §3.2.2 respectively, can be substituted in Equations 2.14, 2.15 and 2.19 to calculate the percentage runoff and baseflow (if baseflow is being estimated from catchment descriptors), as shown in Example 3.1e.

Example 3.1d
Calculation of design antecedent catchment wetness *CWI*

Catchment: Almond at Craigiehall (19001) (Figure 1 of Appendix C)

Relevant catchment descriptors: *SAAR* = 892 mm

The design antecedent catchment wetness CWI is obtained for the appropriate value of *SAAR* from Figure 3.7: *CWI* = 121.8 mm

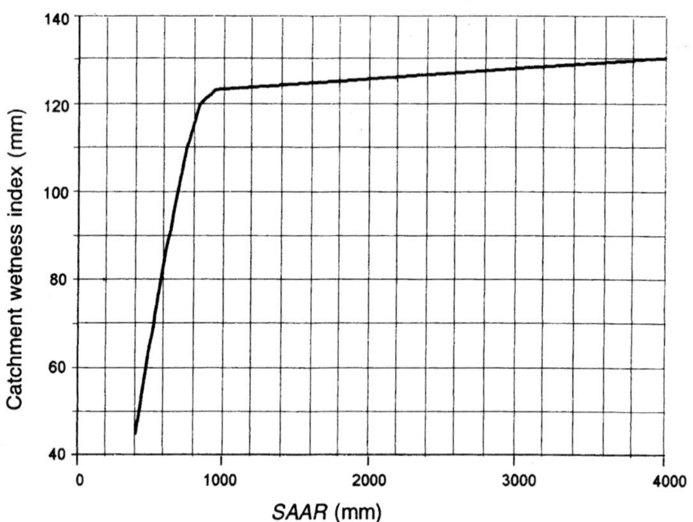

Figure 3.7 *Recommended design values for catchment wetness index CWI*

Percentage runoff

The percentage runoff from the natural part of the catchment PR_{RURAL} is estimated in two parts: a standard component *SPR* representing the normal capacity of the catchment to generate runoff, and a dynamic component *DPR* representing the variation in the response depending on the state of the catchment prior to the storm and the storm magnitude itself. *DPR* is, thus, made up of two components: DPR_{CWI} dependent on *CWI* and DPR_{RAIN} dependent on *P*:

$$PR_{RURAL} = SPR + DPR_{CWI} + DPR_{RAIN} \tag{2.13}$$

The various methods of estimating *SPR* are described in Section 2.3. The *DPR* equations are:

$$DPR_{CWI} = 0.25\ (CWI - 125) \tag{2.14}$$

and

$$DPR_{RAIN} = \begin{cases} 0 & [\text{for } P \leq 40 \text{ mm}] \\ 0.45\,(P-40)^{0.7} & [\text{for } P > 40 \text{ mm}] \end{cases} \qquad (2.15)$$

The total percentage runoff is estimated by adjusting PR_{RURAL} for the effects of catchment urbanisation:

$$PR = PR_{RURAL}\,(1.0 - 0.615\ URBEXT) + 70\,(0.615\ URBEXT) \qquad (2.12)$$

Baseflow

The various methods for estimating baseflow are discussed in Section 2.4. If baseflow is to be estimated from catchment descriptors, it is dependent on catchment area *AREA*, standard average annual rainfall *SAAR* and *CWI*:

$$BF = \{33\,(CWI - 125) + 3.0\ SAAR + 5.5\}\ 10^{-5}\ AREA \qquad (2.19)$$

In the design case, *CWI* is determined directly from *SAAR* using Figure 3.7. Therefore, baseflow is solely dependent on *SAAR*, and the value obtained from Equation 2.19 can be checked against the graphed relationship in Figure 3.8 which shows baseflow per unit area against *SAAR*. Note that this is only appropriate for the *T*-year flood; in the *PMF* case, *CWI* is a function of areal storm depth rather than *SAAR*.

Example 3.1e
Calculation of percentage runoff and baseflow

Catchment: Almond at Craigiehall (19001) (Figure 1 of Appendix C)

Relevant catchment descriptors and other information:
SPR = 51.8% (§2.3.2), *P* = 63.4 mm (§3.2.2), *CWI* = 121.8 mm (§3.2.4), *URBEXT* = 0.034

Percentage runoff
The percentage runoff *PR* appropriate to the design event is calculated using Equations 2.12 to 2.15:

$DPR_{CWI} = 0.25\,(CWI - 125)$ — $DPR_{CWI} = 0.25\,(121.8 - 125) = -0.8\%$

$DPR_{RAIN} = 0.45\,(P - 40)^{0.7}$ [as $P > 40$ mm] — $DPR_{RAIN} = 0.45\,(63.4 - 40)^{0.7} = 4.1\%$

$PR_{RURAL} = SPR + DPR_{CWI} + DPR_{RAIN}$ — $PR_{RURAL} = 51.8 - 0.8 + 4.1 = 55.1\%$

$PR = PR_{RURAL}\,(1.0 - 0.615\ URBEXT) + 70\,(0.615\ URBEXT)$

$PR = 55.1\,(1.0 - 0.615 \times 0.034) + 70\,(0.615 \times 0.034) = 55.4\%$

Baseflow
The baseflow *BF* was calculated in §2.4.3: $BF = 7.26\ m^3\,s^{-1}$

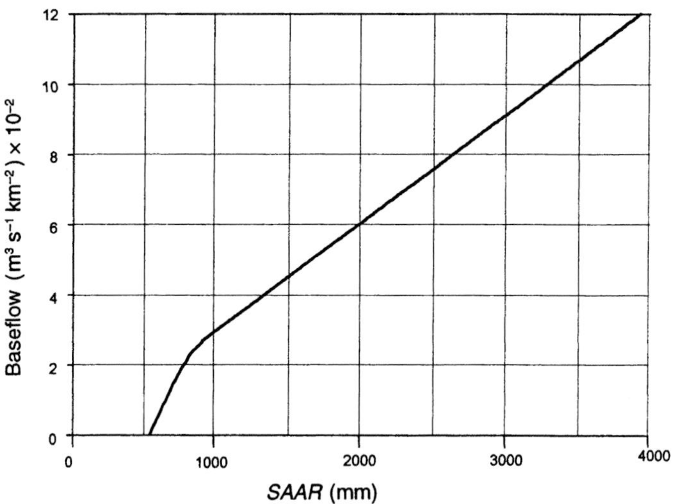

***Figure 3.8** Graphical representation of baseflow-SAAR relationship for design use*

3.3.2 Derivation of net rainfall hyetograph

Percentage runoff is applied as a constant proportional loss to each rainfall block through the storm event. The net (or effective) rainfall hyetograph is derived by multiplying each block of the total rainfall hyetograph (from §3.2.3) by the percentage runoff (from §3.3.1), as shown in Example 3.1f.

3.3.3 Derivation of rapid response runoff hydrograph

The rapid response runoff hydrograph is the product of convolving the unit hydrograph (from Section 2.2) with the net rainfall hyetograph (from §3.3.2). The theory behind the convolution procedure is described in §2.2.1. A typical convolution table is laid out in Example 3.1g. The ΔT-hourly ordinates of the ΔT-hour unit hydrograph are set out in the header row across the top of the table. The net rainfall values in cm per time step are set out in the column down the left-hand

Example 3.1f
Derivation of net rainfall hyetograph

Catchment: Almond at Craigiehall (19001) (Figure 1 of Appendix C)

Relevant information:
PR = 55.4% (§3.3.1)

The net rainfall hyetograph is derived by applying the percentage runoff *PR* to each block of the total rainfall hyetograph from §3.2.3:

Interval	1	2	3	4	5	6	7	8	9	10	11	12	13
Tot rain (mm)	1.2	1.8	2.7	4.1	6.2	9.3	12.7	9.3	6.2	4.1	2.7	1.8	1.2
Net rain (mm)	0.7	1.0	1.5	2.3	3.4	5.2	7.0	5.2	3.4	2.3	1.5	1.0	0.7

Example 3.1g
Derivation of rapid response runoff hydrograph and total runoff hydrograph

Catchment: Almond at Craigiehall (19001) (Figure 1 of Appendix C)

Rapid response runoff hydrograph

The convolution of the 1-hour unit hydrograph from §2.2.2 and the net rainfall hyetograph from §3.3.2 may be set out as a table. The 1-hour ordinates of the unit hydrograph are set out in the header row across the top of the table. The net rainfall values in cm are set out in the column down the left-hand side of the table. The first net rainfall value is applied
to each unit hydrograph ordinate in turn, and the product is written directly beneath, forming the first row of the table. The second rainfall value is applied to each unit hydrograph ordinate in turn, but the product entered is displaced one column to the right. The rest of the table is constructed in a similar fashion, as illustrated. The column sums give the rapid response runoff hydrograph.

Total runoff hydrograph

The total runoff hydrograph is obtained by adding the baseflow *BF* from § 3.3.1 to each ordinate of the rapid response runoff hydrograph. The 50-year design flood for the Almond at Craigiehall is estimated as 337.48 $m^3 s^{-1}$ and the complete hydrograph is also obtained.

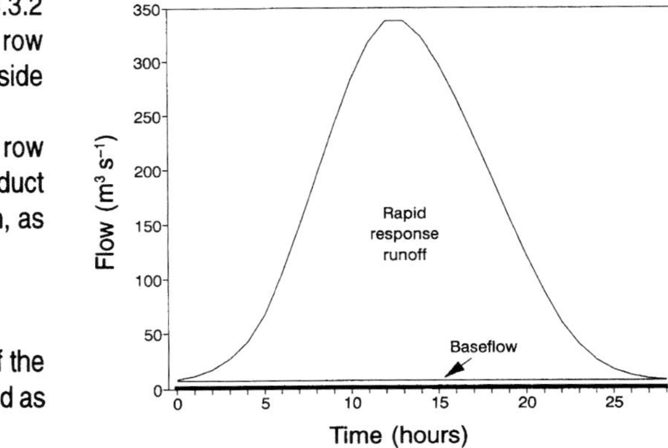

Net rain (cm)	Unit hydrograph response (cumecs)																												
	17.49	34.99	52.48	69.94	87.43	104.93	121.53	110.06	98.56	87.05	75.54	64.03	52.52	41.01	29.50	18.00	6.49												
0.07	1.22	2.45	3.67	4.90	6.12	7.34	8.51	7.70	6.90	6.09	5.29	4.48	3.68	2.87	2.07	1.26	0.45												
0.10		1.75	3.50	5.25	6.99	8.74	10.49	12.15	11.01	9.86	8.70	7.55	6.40	5.25	4.10	2.95	1.80	0.65											
0.15			2.62	5.25	7.87	10.49	13.12	15.74	18.23	16.51	14.78	13.06	11.33	9.60	7.88	6.15	4.43	2.70	0.97										
0.23				4.02	8.05	12.07	16.09	20.11	24.13	27.95	25.31	22.67	20.02	17.37	14.73	12.08	9.43	6.79	4.14	1.49									
0.34					5.95	11.90	17.84	23.78	29.73	35.68	41.32	37.42	33.51	29.60	25.68	21.77	17.86	13.94	10.03	6.12	2.21								
0.52						9.10	18.19	27.29	36.37	45.47	54.56	63.20	57.23	51.25	45.26	39.28	33.30	27.31	21.33	15.34	9.36	3.37							
0.70							12.25	24.49	36.74	48.96	61.20	73.45	85.07	77.04	68.99	60.93	52.88	44.82	36.77	28.71	20.65	12.60	4.54						
0.52								9.10	18.19	27.29	36.37	45.47	54.56	63.20	57.23	51.25	45.26	39.28	33.30	27.31	21.33	15.34	9.36	3.37					
0.34									5.95	11.90	17.84	23.78	29.73	35.68	41.32	37.42	33.51	29.60	25.68	21.77	17.86	13.94	10.03	6.12	2.21				
0.23										4.02	8.05	12.07	16.09	20.11	24.13	27.95	25.31	22.67	20.02	17.37	14.73	12.08	9.43	6.79	4.14	1.49			
0.15											2.62	5.25	7.87	10.49	13.12	15.74	18.23	16.51	14.78	13.06	11.33	9.60	7.88	6.15	4.43	2.70	0.97		
0.10												1.75	3.50	5.25	6.99	8.74	10.49	12.15	11.01	9.86	8.70	7.55	6.40	5.25	4.10	2.95	1.80	0.65	
0.07													1.22	2.45	3.67	4.90	6.12	7.34	8.51	7.70	6.90	6.09	5.29	4.48	3.68	2.87	2.07	1.26	0.45
Rapid response (cumecs)	1.22	4.20	9.80	19.42	34.98	59.64	96.49	140.37	187.24	233.72	276.06	310.14	330.22	330.16	315.18	290.43	259.07	223.76	186.53	148.74	113.06	80.59	52.93	32.16	18.55	10.01	4.84	1.91	0.45
Baseflow (cumecs)	7.26	7.26	7.26	7.26	7.26	7.26	7.26	7.26	7.26	7.26	7.26	7.26	7.26	7.26	7.26	7.26	7.26	7.26	7.26	7.26	7.26	7.26	7.26	7.26	7.26	7.26	7.26	7.26	7.26
Total flow (cumecs)	8.48	11.46	17.06	26.68	42.24	66.90	103.75	147.63	194.50	240.98	283.32	317.40	337.48	337.42	322.44	297.69	266.33	231.02	193.79	156.00	120.32	87.85	60.19	39.42	25.81	17.27	12.10	9.17	7.71

side of the table. They have been converted from millimetres to centimetres because the synthesised unit hydrograph refers to 10 mm or 1 cm input of net rainfall.

The convolution procedure starts by applying the first net rainfall value to each unit hydrograph ordinate in turn, the product being written directly beneath, thus forming the first row of the table. The process is repeated for the second net rainfall value forming the second row of the table, but the products entered are displaced one column to the right because the second rainfall value occurs one data interval after the first. The remaining net rainfalls are applied in the same way, and the columns are summed to give the rapid response runoff hydrograph, as illustrated.

3.3.4 Derivation of total runoff hydrograph

The total runoff hydrograph is obtained by simply adding the constant baseflow to each ordinate of the rapid response runoff hydrograph, as illustrated in Example 3.1g.

3.4 Short-cut method to unit hydrograph convolution

This section describes the FSSR9 (IH, 1979b) short-cut method to unit hydrograph convolution, which substantially reduces the amount of computation involved in estimation of the T-year flood peak and hydrograph.

3.4.1 Short-cut method

Computation of the design rapid response runoff hydrograph hinges on convolution of a triangular unit hydrograph with a design net rainfall hyetograph. The triangular unit hydrograph and the design net rainfall hyetograph are of fixed form and differ only in their time base or duration. Therefore, their convolution product will also be of fixed form, and the short-cut method produces a unique family of

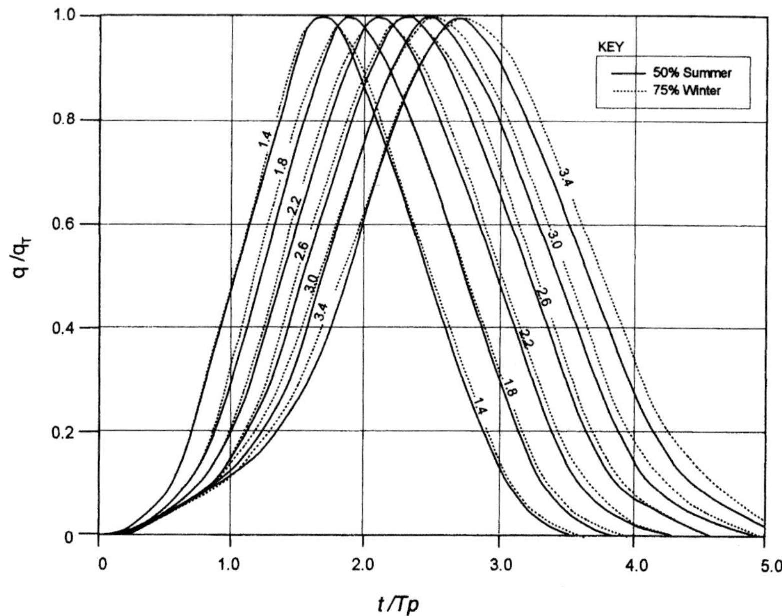

Figure 3.9 *Standard hydrograph shapes for stated values of D/Tp*

hydrograph shapes. These are shown in Figure 3.9 for the 75% winter and 50% summer profiles, appropriate for predominantly rural (*URBEXT* < 0.125) and urban (0.125 ≤ *URBEXT* ≤ 0.5) catchments, respectively. The shape of the rapid response runoff hydrograph is actually determined by the ratio *D/Tp*. Figure 3.9 shows the range of hydrograph shapes obtained for *D/Tp* ratios between 1.4 and 5.0. When *D* is relatively short compared to *Tp*, the hydrograph shape is more skewed resembling the unit hydrograph; when *D* is longer, the hydrograph shape tends more towards the rainfall profile.

The *T*-year rapid response runoff peak q_T is given by the equation:

$$q_T = RC \frac{PR}{100} \frac{P}{D} AREA \tag{3.3}$$

where *RC* is a routing coefficient whose value depends on the ratio *D/Tp*, and *PR*, *P*, *D* and *AREA* have their customary meaning. Figure 3.10 shows the relationship between *RC* and *D/Tp* for the 75% winter and 50% summer profiles.

The *T*-year rapid response runoff hydrograph is obtained from Figure 3.9 by sketching in a hydrograph for the appropriate *D/Tp* ratio, interpolating at intervals of *t/Tp*, and multiplying all the abstracted time abscissae by *Tp* and flow ordinates by q_T.

A baseflow must be added to the rapid response runoff peak and hydrograph, to give the *T*-year total runoff hydrograph. For the peak flow Q_T:

$$Q_T = q_T + BF \tag{3.4}$$

The procedure is illustrated in Example 3.2. Note that this is only appropriate for the *T*-year flood: the *PMP* hyetograph, although symmetrical, is not of a fixed structure (see §4.3.2), so the short-cut to unit hydrograph convolution cannot be used.

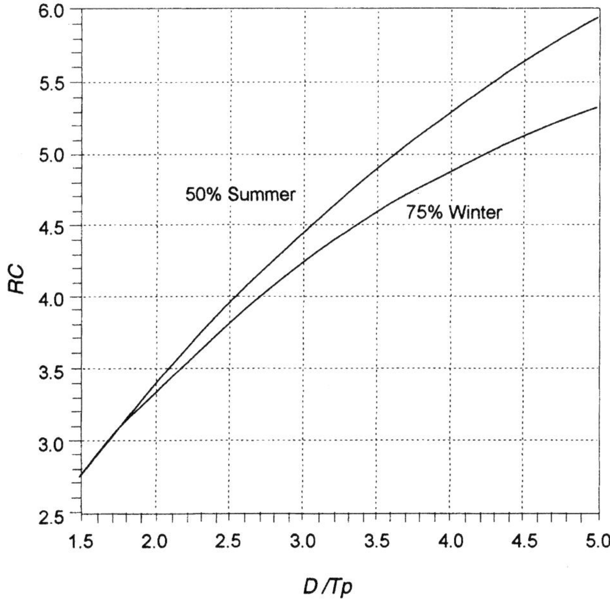

Figure 3.10 *Graphs of routing coefficient RC*

Example 3.2
Short-cut method

Catchment: Almond at Craigiehall (19001) (Figure 1 of Appendix C)

Relevant catchment descriptors and other information:
URBEXT = 0.034, *D* = 13.0 hours (§3.2.1), ΔT = 1.0 hours, *Tp*(1) = 6.97 hours (§2.2.2), *PR* = 55.4% (§3.3.1), *P* = 63.4 mm (§3.2.2), *AREA* = 386.19 km², *BF* = 7.26 m³s⁻¹ (§3.3.1)

With a recommended design storm profile, the rapid response runoff per unit area per unit net rainfall depends on the ratio *D/Tp* only. A routing coefficient *RC* appropriate to the ratio *D/Tp* (1.87) is obtained from Figure 3.10 (75% winter profile as *URBEXT* < 0.125):
RC = 0.32

The rapid response runoff flood peak q_T is calculated using Equation 3.3:

$q_T = RC\,(PR/100)\,(P/D)\,AREA$ $\qquad$ $q_{50} = 0.32\,(55.4/100)(63.4/13.0)\,386.19 = 333.89\ \mathrm{m^3\,s^{-1}}$

The total flood peak Q_T is calculated using Equation 3.4:

$Q_T = q_T + BF$ $\qquad$ $Q_{50} = 333.89 + 7.26 = 341.15\ \mathrm{m^3\,s^{-1}}$

The complete rapid response runoff hydrograph is obtained by sketching in a curve appropriate to the ratio *D/Tp* (1.87) on Figure 3.9, interpolating at intervals *t/Tp* and multiplying the abstracted time abscissae by *Tp* and the flow ordinates by *qT*. The total runoff hydrograph is obtained by adding the baseflow *BF* to each ordinate of the rapid response runoff hydrograph:

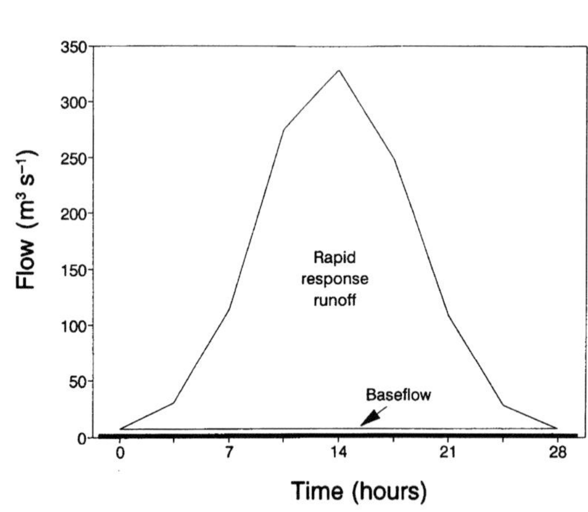

t/Tp (hours)	0.0	0.5	1.0	1.5	2.0	2.5	3.0	3.5	4.0
t (hours)	0.0	3.49	6.97	10.50	13.94	17.43	20.91	24.40	27.88
q/q$_T$ (m³ s⁻¹)	0.00	0.07	0.32	0.80	0.96	0.72	0.30	0.06	0.00
q (m³ s⁻¹)	0.00	23.37	106.84	267.11	320.53	240.40	100.17	20.03	0.00
BF (m³ s⁻¹)	7.26	7.26	7.26	7.26	7.26	7.26	7.26	7.26	7.26
Q (m³ s⁻¹)	7.26	30.63	114.10	274.37	327.79	247.66	107.43	27.29	7.26

3.4.2 Comparison of the short-cut method with the rational method

The rational method (variously attributed to Mulvaney, 1850; Kuichling, 1889; Lloyd-Davies, 1906) is sometimes still used for flood estimation on small catchments. In the metric version of the rational method, the flow peak *Q* in m³ s⁻¹ is given by:

$$Q = 0.28\ C\ i\ A \tag{3.5}$$

where C is a *runoff coefficient* typically varying between 0.1 and 0.5, i is a rainfall intensity (mm h^{-1}) and A is the catchment area in km^2. In practice, C represents not simply a runoff proportion, but also the effects of assumptions concerning rainfall frequency and storm profile.

The rational method is sometimes criticised for not being based on a formal approach of flood generation. However, §3.4.1 shows how, if certain fairly reasonable assumptions are made, the formal approach based on a rainfall-runoff model can be reduced to a rational-style formula. The short-cut method works purely because of the constant percentage runoff and the fixed shapes of the triangular unit hydrograph and the design rainfall hyetograph. The rational method can, therefore, be regarded as the outcome of applying a rectangular unit hydrograph to a uniform rainfall.

A second more serious criticism of the rational method is that it is uncalibrated: there remains no formal way to evaluate the C and i terms. The Bransby-Williams formula is often used to calculate a design rainfall duration for estimation of intensity (Beran, 1979), but successful application of the method depends largely on knowledge of the catchment and experience in applying the technique. In contrast, all the terms in Equation 3.3 are known or can be calculated. A comparison of peak flows obtained from the two methods concluded that, subject to an assumed use of identical runoff coefficients for small lowland catchments, the rational method yield flood peaks typically twice as large as those from the FSR rainfall-runoff method, but the two methods tend to a greater similarity for larger and steeper catchments (FSSR8: IH, 1978c).

The short-cut method is simple to apply, yet corresponds to the rigorous FSR rainfall-runoff method, provided that the runoff coefficient and design storm duration are estimated correctly, in accordance with the FSR design event method. Furthermore, for small catchment flood estimation, the rational method offers no particular advantage over the short-cut method (Hall, 1996).

Chapter 4 Probable maximum flood estimation

4.1 Introduction

The FSR rainfall-runoff method is used to estimate a probable maximum flood or PMF by applying a probable maximum precipitation or PMP to the unit hydrograph and losses model. A worst possible scenario is assumed, with extreme conditions combined to give a maximum flood. Conservative assumptions are made regarding catchment response and runoff potential, as well as the PMP event itself. Such assumptions are necessitated by the difficulties of analysing very large floods, which are rarely observed and almost never measured properly, in respect of both rainfall and runoff. The PMP event is specified by a set of rules for choosing rainfall duration, depth and profile, antecedent catchment wetness, and an optional snowmelt contribution. The procedure for estimating the PMF retains much of the structure of the FSR design event method for specifying the appropriate inputs for T-year flood estimation (Section 3.2). PMF estimates are necessary for the design of structures, notably reservoir spillways where the PMF is the inflow hydrograph to the reservoir. The topic of reservoir flood estimation is covered in Chapter 8.

This section considers the concepts of PMF and PMP. PMF estimation warrants changes to components of the unit hydrograph and losses model, and these are described in Section 4.2. In Section 4.3, the rules for choosing the PMP inputs of storm characteristics, catchment state and snowmelt contribution are considered in detail. Storm duration is calculated in the same way as for the *T*-year flood (see §4.3.1). However, there are differences to the derivation of storm depth and profile (see §4.3.2), and an allowance for snowmelt may be added (see §4.3.4). Catchment wetness index *CWI* is also determined in a different way to that for the *T*-year flood (see §4.3.3). Application of the PMP design storm to the unit hydrograph and losses model to estimate the PMF is described in Section 4.4. In Section 4.5, a nominal return period is assigned to the derived PMF so that it can be linked to the catchment flood frequency curve.

4.1.1 Concept of PMF

The concept of the probable maximum flood or PMF goes back at least to 1914 (Fuller, 1914). The US Corps of Engineers defines the PMF as "... the flood that may be expected from the most severe combination of critical meteorologic and hydrologic conditions that are reasonably possible in a region." (US Corps of Engineers, 1975). It can be regarded simply as the largest flood that might ever occur, caused principally by a PMP. Any storm event producing less rainfall (and snowmelt) than the PMP will result in a flood hydrograph somewhat smaller than the PMF. However, occurrence of a PMP does not necessarily mean that a PMF will ensue, as anything less than optimal runoff conditions will also result in a smaller flood hydrograph. Similarly, a PMP storm event shorter than the critical duration for the catchment will result in a reduced flood peak.

The FSR did not dwell on the semantics of definition, and concentrated on recommending, for practical purposes, a consistent procedure for estimating a likely maximum discharge. The FSR method provides realistic estimates of maximum rainfall which can be applied to the unit hydrograph and losses model for use in extreme flood estimation. The various aspects of the input data and the transforming model combine in the worst possible way, whilst remaining physically conceivable. The catchment is assumed to be saturated immediately before the maximum rainfall event occurs, and the rapid response runoff is assumed to be particularly rapid. Other options allow for snowmelt and for increased runoff from frozen ground in winter. It is important to realise that the derived likely maximum discharge is a flood estimate with a non-quantifiable error of estimation. Furthermore, the procedure implicitly provides more conservative maximum flood estimates in some parts of the UK than in others, e.g. through its incorporation of a fixed snowmelt rate (see §4.3.4).

The PMF is not the impossible flood, and the FSR method should not be taken to imply that calculated PMF values cannot be exceeded: they are estimates, and as such they are subject to error. There is a technique for assigning a nominal return period to the PMF, thus enabling it to be linked to a flood frequency curve (Lowing, 1995; Section 4.5).

4.1.2 Concept of PMP

In a comprehensive review of the various methods available for the estimation of PMP, the World Meteorological Organisation define the PMP as "theoretically the greatest depth of precipitation for a given duration that is physically possible over a given size storm area at a particular geographical location at a certain time of year [with no allowance made for long-term climatic trends]." (WMO, 1986).

In the FSR, the theoretical PMP for a catchment is based on an analysis of the storm efficiency of observed events combined with the theoretical maximum precipitable water in a vertical column above the catchment. Maps of estimated maximum precipitations or EMPs, for durations of 2 hours, 24 hours and 25 days were generated for the UK and Ireland, enabling extreme rainfalls to be estimated for any location and duration. The maps, known as EM-2h (Figure 4.1), EM-24h (Figure 4.2) and EM-25d (Figure 4.3), derive from maximum storm efficiency values for major 2-hour and 24-hour storms, and from maximised M5-25d rainfalls for 25-day events. Catchment-specific values of the specified durations are obtained by calculating the area-weighted average over the catchment. PMPs of durations not mapped are obtained by interpolation on a graph of PMP rainfall depth versus the logarithm of PMP duration, or from tables of values giving the PMP as a function of estimated maxima of known duration.

There are several choices of rainfall profile for maximum flood estimation. The FSR initially promoted the all-year PMP, which takes the maximum rainfalls of various durations and nests them centrally, out to the duration of the design storm, such that the estimated maximum occurs in every duration centred on the peak of the storm profile. For example the 1-hour PMP is embedded within the 3-hour PMP within the 5-hour PMP, and so on. Thus the total rainfall of the storm increases with duration, but with no compensating reduction of maximum intensity. However, the first edition of the ICE engineering guide to floods and reservoir safety (ICE, 1978) proposed that Summer (May to October) and Winter (November to April) PMPs should be considered separately, to see which gives the largest flood. This suggestion — which was based on the observation that it is over-pessimistic to nest a Summer thunderstorm rainfall in a Winter frontal rainfall and then add a snowmelt contribution and allow for the effect of frozen ground — has become recommended practice.

For practical purposes, it was recommended that the same duration formula be used as for estimation of the T-year flood, and that the antecedent catchment wetness be a function of maximum rainfalls preceding the event. Therefore, the maximum rainfalls of various durations are nested centrally, out to the duration of

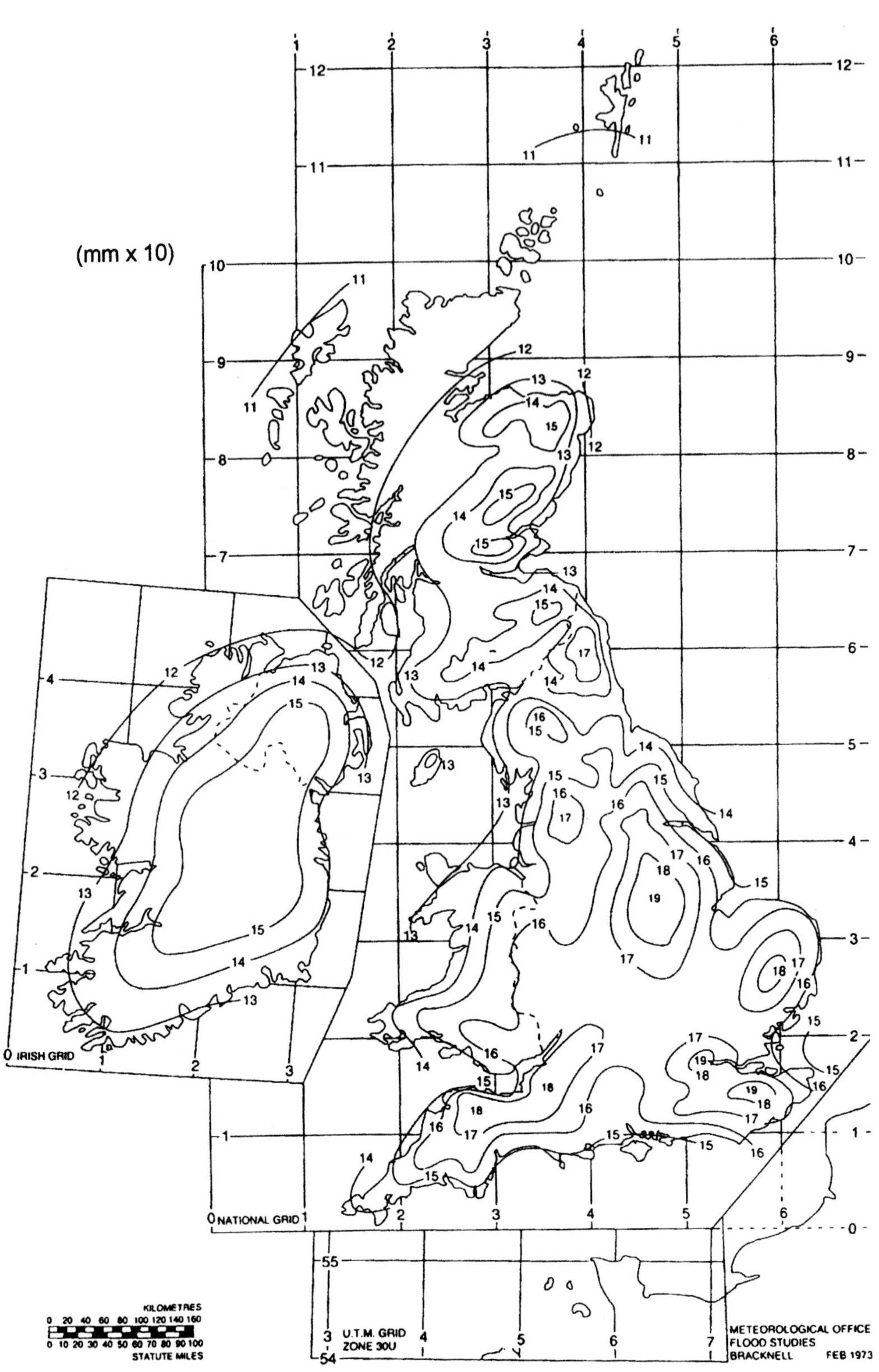

Figure 4.1 *Estimated maximum 2-hour rainfall EM-2h (NERC, 1975)*

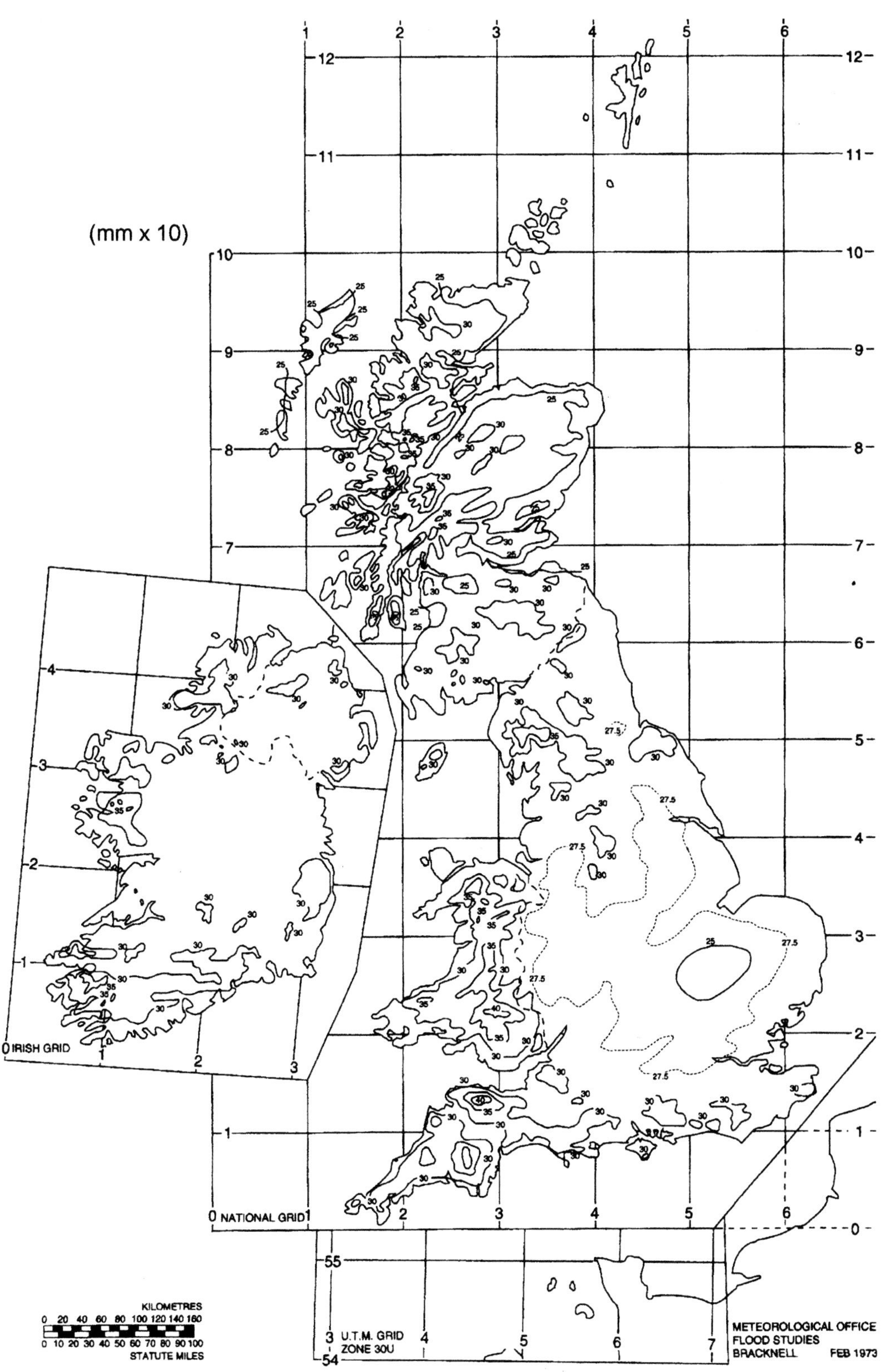

Figure 4.2 *Estimated maximum 24-hour rainfall EM-24h (NERC, 1975)*

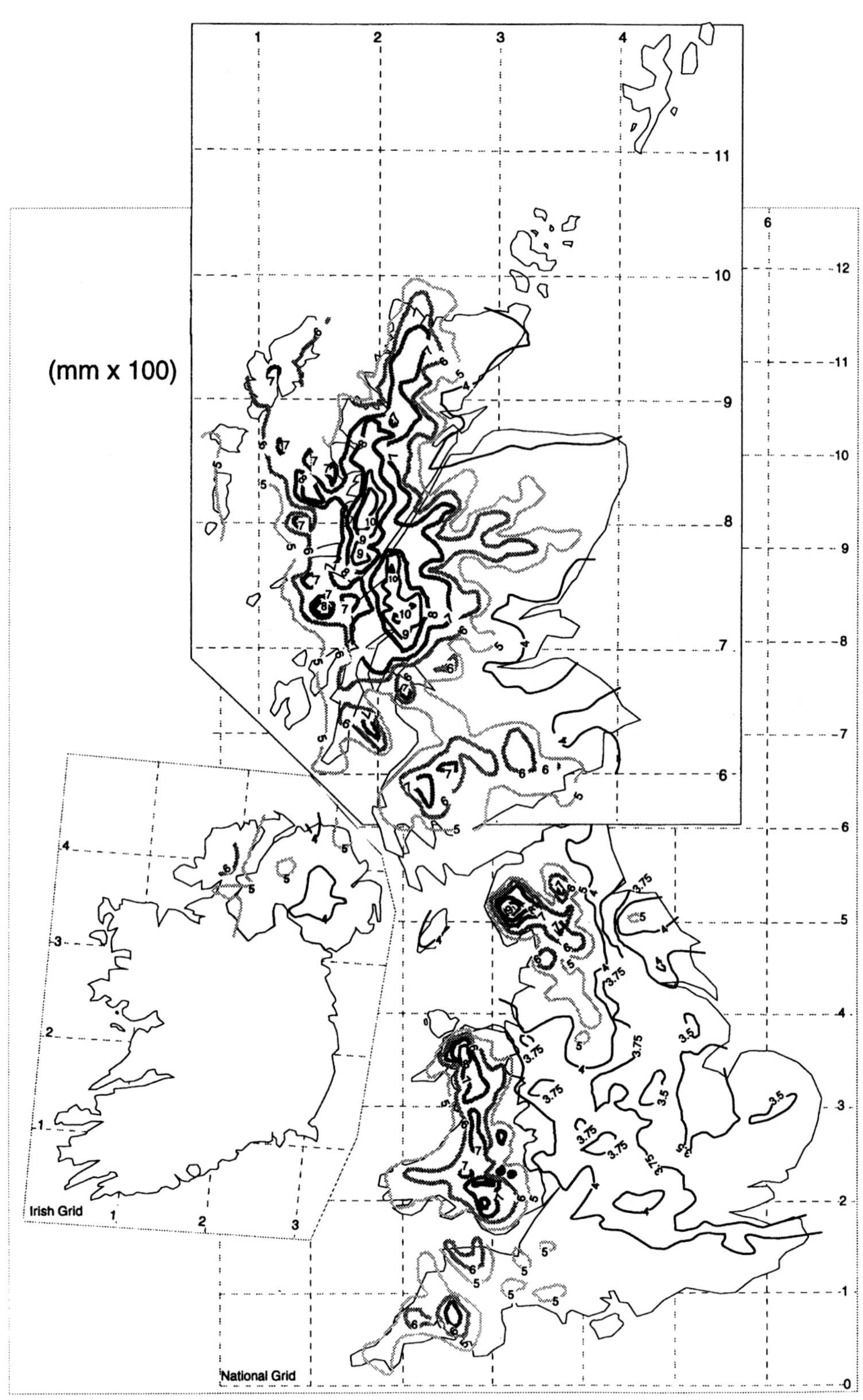

Figure 4.3 Estimated maximum 25-day rainfall EM-25d

the design storm, and then out to longer durations for the purpose of defining the antecedent condition (see §4.3.3). Options allow for snowmelt (see §4.3.4) and increased runoff from frozen ground (see §4.2.2).

4.1.3 Discussion

Historical flood events, recorded as flood marks on bridges and houses or reported in newspapers and journals, provide valuable information on the maximum size of floods which are likely to occur in the UK. However, flood marks must be converted to peak discharges which is problematic, even when the flood has been recorded at a gauging station, as the quality of such data is often poor. Six historical events where the reported peak discharge exceeds the FSR PMF have been reported (Acreman, 1989a). All but one of these events were on small catchments (< 10 km^2) and, although there may be some uncertainty over the estimated peak flows, the potential severe response from small catchments is clear. The chance of a maximum rainfall of small areal extent coinciding with a small catchment is much greater than that of a larger storm sitting squarely over a larger catchment, and so PMF may be approached more frequently on small catchments (Acreman and Lowing, 1989).

There have also been reports of exceedances of the FSR PMP. The intense storm rainfalls at Hewenden Reservoir in 1956 (Collinge *et al.*, 1992) and at Calderdale in 1989 (Acreman, 1989b; Acreman and Collinge, 1991) may both have exceeded the PMP. There are also some suggestions that heavy rainfall events over south-west England may be more common than has been hitherto believed (Clark, 1991; 1995; 1997).

The analysis upon which the FSR approach is based was carried out using data from raingauges to estimate storm rainfall. Since the late 1970s, data from weather radars have become increasingly available, and used to develop new approaches to estimating PMP (e.g. Cluckie and Pessoa, 1990). Collier and Hardaker (1995; 1996) used radar data for convective storms with a *storm model* in order to determine PMP over catchments in north-west England. Their results showed that the derived PMP values were similar to the FSR values for storm durations less than 11 hours, but increased PMP estimates relative to the FSR values were found for durations in excess of 12 hours. Storm durations greater than 12 hours seem to result from a class of meteorological system known as Mesoscale Convective Systems (MCSs), whereas shorter duration storms are multi-cell thunderstorms. Hence, the probability that an estimated maximum storm can be structured as a nested, symmetrical profile is more likely for storm durations of 12 hours or less than for longer durations. Further work to investigate the frequency of occurrence and climatology of MCSs, to help understand the differences for durations greater than 12 hours, was recommended by Austin *et al.* (1995). Furthermore, the storm model method needs to be generalised for application country-wide before it can be incorporated in common practice for PMF estimation.

4.2 Unit hydrograph and losses model

Chapter 2 describes the various methods for determining the three parameters of the unit hydrograph and losses model: unit hydrograph time-to-peak *Tp*, standard percentage runoff *SPR* and baseflow *BF*. In PMF estimation, the model parameters are initially estimated by one of these methods. However, there follows an important modification to the unit hydrograph and, in appropriate cases, changes are made to the way percentage runoff is calculated.

4.2.1 Unit hydrograph

The various methods for estimating time-to-peak of the instantaneous unit hydrograph $Tp(0)$ are presented in Section 2.2. Time-to-peak can be thought of as a characteristic catchment response time and the recommendation for PMF estimation is that the time-to-peak should be reduced by one-third, to represent the more rapid and intense response that is believed to occur in exceptional conditions. This adjustment matches the average ratio of minimum to mean observed time-to-peaks of 0.67, and takes account of tests on very large events, as well as allowing for the worst-case scenario of a storm moving downstream across a catchment (FSR I.6.6.3). The adjustment applies to the time-to-peak of the instantaneous unit hydrograph $Tp(0)$, *before* it is adjusted for an appropriate data interval:

$$Tp(0)_{PMF} = 0.67\ Tp(0) \qquad (4.1)$$

The subsequent effect of this modification is to increase all ordinates, including the unit hydrograph peak, by one-half, and to reduce the time base by one-third, in order to maintain unit volume, as illustrated in Figure 4.4. Once the adjusted time-to-peak of the instantaneous unit hydrograph has been derived, an adjustment for the appropriate data interval can be made in the usual way, and a triangular ΔT-hour unit hydrograph can be derived using Equations 2.6 and 2.7 (see Example 4.1a).

4.2.2 Percentage runoff

The percentage runoff model and the various methods for estimating the standard percentage runoff SPR component of percentage runoff are presented in Section 2.3. In PMF estimation, some adjustment to the model can be appropriate.

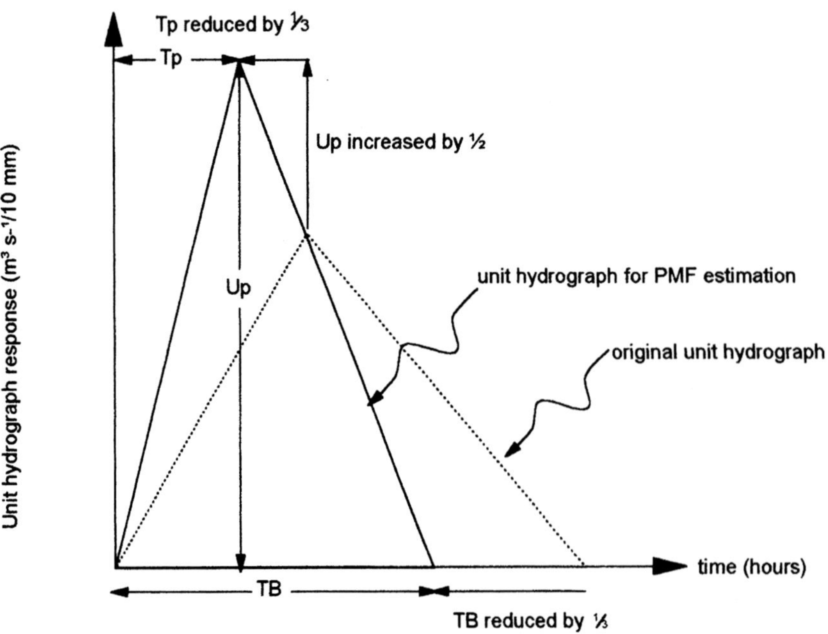

Figure 4.4 *Unit hydrograph for PMF estimation*

Example 4.1a
Adjustment of *Tp*(0) for PMF estimation

Catchment: West Lyn at Lynmouth (IHDTM grid ref. 272400 149450)
(Figure 4 of Appendix C)

Relevant catchment descriptors and other information:
Tp(0) = 4.63 hours (§2.2.5), *AREA* = 24.08 km²

The IUH time-to-peak *Tp*(0) is adjusted for PMF estimation using Equation 4.1:

$Tp(0)_{PMF} = 0.67\ Tp(0)$ $\quad$ $Tp(0)_{PMF} = 0.67\ (4.63) = 3.10$ hours

20% of 3.10 hours is 0.62 hours, so a 0.5-hour data interval is appropriate. *Tp*(0) is adjusted for the data interval ΔT using Equation 2.4: $\Delta T = 0.5$ hours

$Tp(\Delta T) = Tp(0) + \Delta T/2$ $\quad$ $Tp(0.5) = 3.10 + 0.5 / 2$
$= 3.35$ hours

$Tp(\Delta T)$ is hereafter referred to simply as *Tp*. The unit hydrograph peak *Up* and the time base *TB* are derived from *Tp* using Equations 2.6 and 2.7:

$Up = (2.2 / Tp)\ AREA$ $\quad$ $Up = (2.2 / 3.35)\ 24.08 = 15.80\ m^3 s^{-1}$

$TB = 2.52\ Tp$ $\quad$ $TB = 2.52 \times 3.35 = 8.45$ hours

The triangular unit hydrograph may be drawn, and ordinates u_t can be read off at ΔT-hourly intervals or calculated using Equation 2.8.

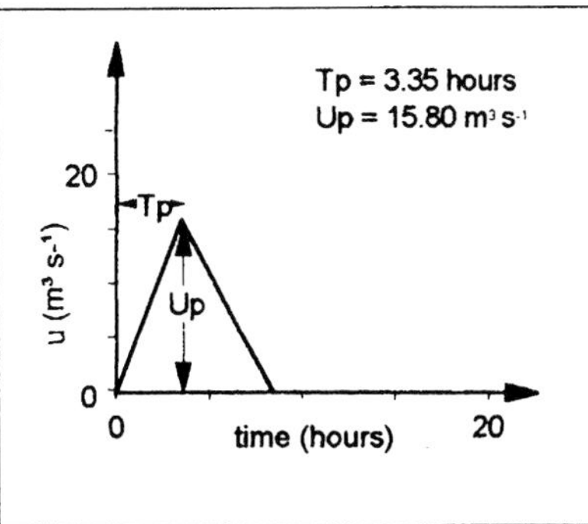

In the winter, frozen ground can affect catchment response by increasing runoff. The effect of frozen ground is most apparent for well-drained catchments on permeable soils. For example the March 1947 floods are believed to have been aggravated by the preceding long spell of cold weather, which froze the top layers of soil. When deriving a PMF from a winter PMP, frozen ground can be represented by assuming that the entire catchment acts as one of the more impermeable soil types, to a sensible limit. If the original *SPR* is less than 53%, then the frozen ground *SPR* is set to be 53%. However, if the original *SPR* is already greater than 53%, the frozen ground *SPR* is not reset, and remains the same as the original *SPR* (see Example 4.1b).

Example 4.1b
Adjustment of *SPR* for PMF estimation

Catchment: West Lyn at Lynmouth (IHDTM grid ref. 272400 149450)
(Figure 4 of Appendix C)

Relevant catchment descriptors and other information:
SPR = 24.8% (§2.3.5)

In PMF estimation using a winter PMP, the standard percentage runoff *SPR* can be adjusted for frozen ground. *SPR* < 53%, so *SPR* is increased to 53%:

$$SPR_{PMF} = 53\%$$

A frozen ground adjustment is not normally appropriate when deriving a PMF from a summer PMP, although it might be used as a device to meet concerns that a particular soil type could behave anomalously following a drought period, due to hardening and/or cracking of the upper soil layers. Whether the adjustment for frozen ground should be made remains a matter of judgement, since extreme quantities of rainfall are already being distributed in time with the worst profile, and possibly combined with extreme snowmelt.

4.3 PMP design inputs

The package for PMP design inputs provides a way of selecting a set of extreme conditions to synthesise the PMF. Figure 4.5 shows the influence of the design inputs with respect to the steps in the calculation of the PMF.

4.3.1 PMP design storm duration

As in the *T*-year case (see §3.2.1), the design storm duration *D* is calculated from unit hydrograph time-to-peak *Tp* and standard average annual rainfall *SAAR* (see Example 4.1c):

$$D = Tp\,(1 + \frac{SAAR}{1000}) \qquad (3.1)$$

Curves of flood magnitude against storm duration are generally relatively flat, so the choice of storm duration is not usually critical (Reed and Field, 1992). However, in reservoired applications, the design storm duration is extended by adding the reservoir response time to the catchment response time (see §8.2.1), and in other situations, it may be appropriate to consider a range of design storm durations (see §9.2.2).

It is necessary to have an odd number of rainfall blocks, for a reason explained in §4.3.2. Therefore, the computed value of storm duration is rounded, up or down, to the nearest odd integer multiple of the data interval ΔT (see Example 4.1c).

4.3.2 PMP design storm hyetograph (depth and profile)

The PMP design storm hyetograph for the appropriate design storm duration *D* is constructed directly. This approach differs from the *T*-year case, where the design

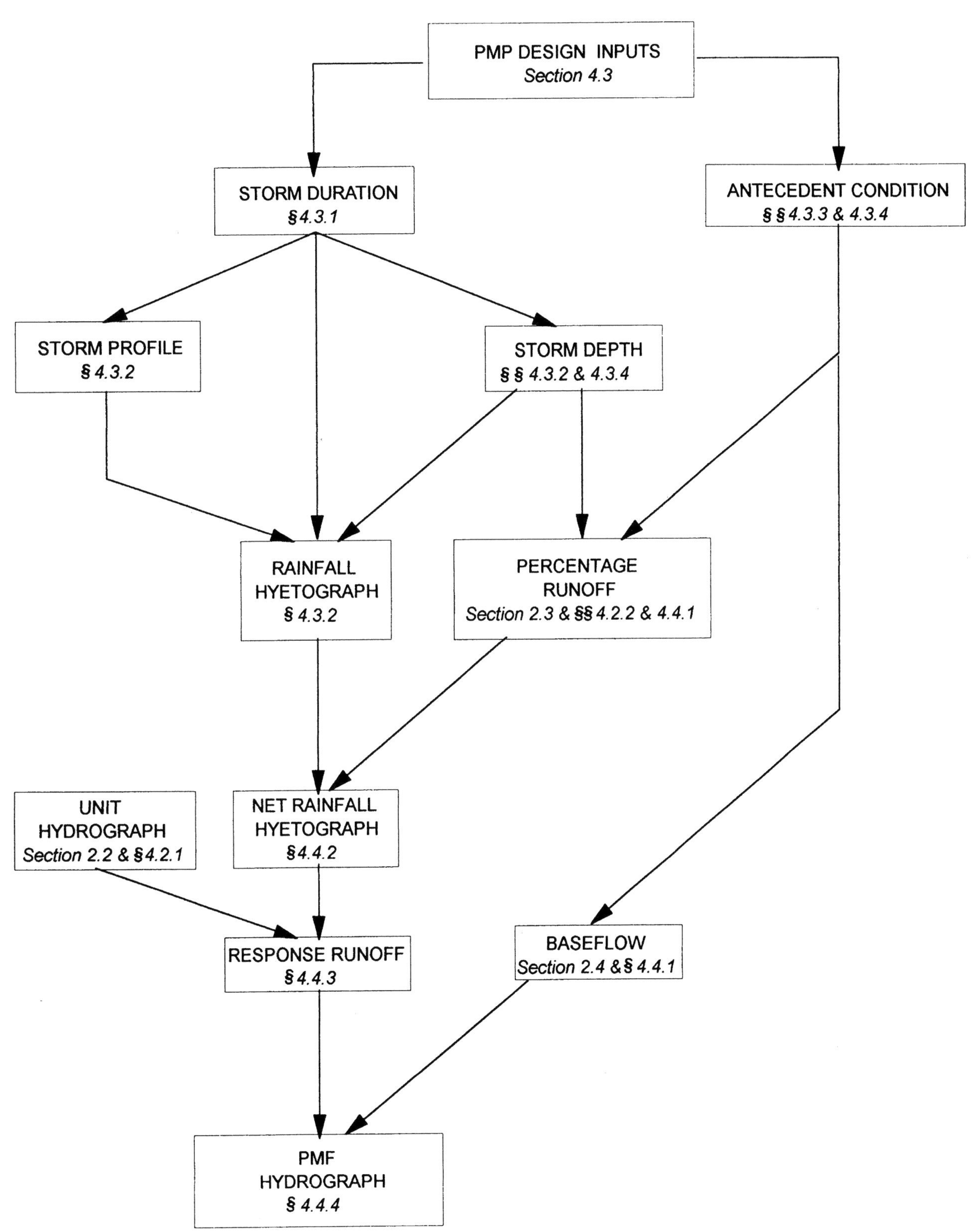

Figure 4.5 *Influence of PMP design inputs and the steps in the calculation of the PMF*

Example 4.1c
Calculation of PMP design storm duration D

Catchment: West Lyn at Lynmouth (IHDTM grid ref. 272400 149450)
(Figure 4 of Appendix C)

Relevant catchment descriptors and other information:
$SAAR$ = 1543 mm, ΔT = 0.5 hours (§4.2.1), $Tp(0.5)$ = 3.35 hours (§4.2.1)

The design storm duration D is calculated from Tp and $SAAR$ using Equation 3.1:

$D = Tp\,(1 + \text{SAAR} / 1000)$ $\qquad$ $D = 3.35\,(1 + 1543 / 1000)$
$= 8.5$ hours

In this instance, ΔT = 0.5 hours, so at 8.5 hours D is already an odd integer multiple of ΔT: $\qquad$ D = 8.5 hours

storm depth P is calculated first (see §3.2.2), and then distributed within the design storm duration D using the appropriate design storm profile (see §3.2.3).

The PMP design storm hyetograph for the appropriate design storm duration D is determined using various maps and tables. The maps (Figures 4.1 - 4.3) are of all-year point estimated maximum precipitations or EMPs of 2-hour, 24-hour and 25-day duration, known as EM-2h, EM-24h and EM-25d, respectively. EM-25d is used in estimating PMPs for very long durations. The tables relate EMPs of various durations to EM-2h, EM-24h and EM-25d (Table 4.1), and also relate seasonal EMPs to all-year EMPs (Table 4.2).

Table 4.2, relating seasonal EMPs to all-year EMPs, is based on FSR Tables II.2.11 and II.3.9, and includes a partial revision from IH Report 114 for durations of one to eight days (Reed and Field, 1992). For each duration, the all-year PMP is assigned to either summer or winter. The PMP for this nominated season is then 100% of the all-year PMP, and the PMP for the other season is scaled down from

Table 4.1 *Factors of EM rainfalls of various durations related to SAAR*

SAAR	Ratio of EM rainfall to 2-h value							Ratio of EM rainfall to 24-h value			Ratio of EM rainfall to 25-day value
mm	*1-min*	*2-min*	*5-min*	*10-min*	*15-min*	*30-min*	*60-min*	*48-h*	*72-h*	*96-h*	*192-h*
500-600	0.06	0.11	0.23	0.36	0.47	0.65	0.83	1.10	1.13	1.17	0.84
600-800	0.06	0.11	0.23	0.36	0.47	0.65	0.83	1.10	1.13	1.17	0.80
800-1000	0.06	0.11	0.23	0.36	0.47	0.65	0.83	1.10	1.14	1.18	0.76
1000-1400	0.06	0.11	0.23	0.36	0.47	0.65	0.83	1.11	1.16	1.20	0.71
1400-2000	0.06	0.11	0.22	0.34	0.45	0.62	0.79	1.12	1.18	1.24	0.68
2000-2800	0.06	0.11	0.22	0.34	0.45	0.62	0.79	1.14	1.23	1.32	0.65
2800-4000	0.06	0.10	0.21	0.32	0.43	0.59	0.75	1.20	1.31	1.42	0.62
>4000	0.06	0.10	0.21	0.32	0.43	0.59	0.75	1.23	1.35	1.48	0.60

Table 4.2 Seasonal variation in PMP

SAAR	Winter PMP as % of all-year 1-hour value					
mm	*1-min*	*2-min*	*5-min*	*10-min*	*15-min*	*30-min*
500-600	13	17	21	24	26	30
600-800	15	19	24	27	30	33
800-1000	19	24	30	35	38	42
1000-1400	26	32	40	47	50	57
1400-2000	30	38	47	55	59	67
>2000	33	42	53	61	66	74

SAAR	Seasonal PMP as % of all-year value					
	1-hour		*2-hour*		*6-hour*	
mm	*Summer*	*Winter*	*Summer*	*Winter*	*Summer*	*Winter*
500-600	100	33	100	38	100	45
600-800	100	37	100	42	100	51
800-1000	100	47	100	50	100	61
1000-1400	100	63	100	69	100	79
1400-2000	100	74	100	86	100	93
>2000	100	82	100	90	100	96

SAAR	Seasonal PMP as % of all-year value							
	1-day		*2-day*		*4-day*		*8-day*	
mm	*Summer*	*Winter*	*Summer*	*Winter*	*Summer*	*Winter*	*Summer*	*Winter*
500-600	100	55	100	63	100	64	100	67
600-800	100	62	100	69	100	73	100	80
800-1000	100	70	100	78	100	84	100	91
1000-1400	100	79	100	85	100	92	100	96
1400-2000	100	99	90	100	92	100	89	100
>2000	92	100	84	100	88	100	83	100

the all-year value by multiplying by the reduced percentage given. For example, for 2-hour extreme rainfalls for *SAAR*s between 600 and 800 mm, the summer PMP is the same as the all-year value, whilst the winter PMP is 42% of the all-year value. Similarly, for 2-day rainfalls for *SAAR*s between 1400 and 2000 mm, the winter PMP is the same as the all-year value, whilst the summer PMP is 90% of the all-year value. For durations less than 1 hour, summer PMPs are the same as the all-year values, and the winter PMP percentages are derived by extrapolation. Table 4.2 does not immediately identify the season providing the design flood because snowmelt must be added to winter events.

Equivalent tables from the third edition of the ICE guide (ICE, 1996) contain some errors: in the top section of the table, the fourth column should be headed '5 min' rather than '3 min', and in the middle section of the table, the value for winter 2-hour rainfall when *SAAR* is between 1400 mm and 2000 mm should be '86' rather than '84'. Furthermore, winter PMPs of durations less than 1 hour are presented as percentages of the all-year 1-hour value, derived from FSR Table

II.3.6, which are less extreme than the recommended factors in Table 4.2.

The PMP design storm hyetograph is determined by the following procedure:

i Calculate all-year point EMPs of durations between ΔT and $5D$;

ii Convert to seasonal point EMPs of durations between ΔT and $5D$;

iii Abstract seasonal point EMPs of durations ΔT, $3\Delta T$, $5\Delta T$, ..., D;

iv Convert to seasonal catchment EMPs of durations ΔT, $3\Delta T$, $5\Delta T$, ..., D;

v Nest the seasonal catchment EMPs to derive the PMP design storm hyetograph.

These steps are discussed below, together with relevant comment on related topics. The procedure is illustrated by Example 4.1d. If a winter PMP has been selected, there is an option to add snowmelt, covered in §4.3.4.

Calculation of all-year point EMPs of durations between ΔT and $5D$

In the majority of PMF cases, the data interval ΔT will be less than 2 hours and the duration $5D$ (i.e. five times the design storm duration D) will be greater than 24 hours. In these circumstances, it is necessary to calculate all-year point EMPs of durations between ΔT hours and 2 hours, and between 24 hours and at least 5D hours. EMPs of durations between 2 and 24 hours are obtained by interpolation. The factors relating the EMPs of various durations to EM-2h, EM-24h and EM-25d for stated ranges of standard average annual rainfall *SAAR* are given in Table 4.1. Multiply EM-2h, EM-24h or EM-25d, whichever is appropriate, by these factors to calculate the all-year point EMPs of durations between ΔT and $5D$ hours.

Conversion to seasonal point EMPs of durations between ΔT and $5D$

Where seasonal estimates are required, the all-year point EMPs are converted to equivalent summer or winter point EMPs. The factors relating seasonal EMPs of various durations to all-year EMPs are given in Table 4.2. For durations less than 1 hour, summer PMPs are the same as the all-year values. For durations between 1 min and 8 days not listed, interpolation is required. For durations greater than 8 days, extrapolation is required. Multiply the all-year EMPs by the appropriate factors to calculate the seasonal point EMPs of durations between ΔT and $5D$ hours.

Abstraction of seasonal point EMPs of durations ΔT, $3\Delta T$, $5\Delta T$, ..., D

Plot the seasonal point EMPs of durations between ΔT and $5D$ hours against duration on linear-log paper. Sketch in a smooth line through the points, as shown in Example 4.1d. Abstract the seasonal point EMPs of durations ΔT, $3\Delta T$, $5\Delta T$, etc., up to the design storm duration D.

Conversion to seasonal catchment EMPs of durations ΔT, $3\Delta T$, $5\Delta T$, ..., D

The seasonal point EMPs of durations ΔT, $3\Delta T$, $5\Delta T$ etc, up to the design storm duration D, must be converted to equivalent seasonal catchment EMPs. The areal reduction factors ARFs appropriate to each duration are read from Figure 3.4 which shows ARFs as percentages related to catchment area and duration. The concept of ARFs is discussed more in §3.2.2.

The seasonal catchment EMPs are the product of the seasonal point EMPs and the appropriate ARFs. The seasonal catchment EMP of duration D is the PMP design storm depth *P*. Note that if this is a winter PMP, there is an option to add a snowmelt contribution to the PMP design storm depth to give a total event precipitation, covered in §4.3.4.

Derivation of the PMP design storm hyetograph

The seasonal catchment EMPs of durations ΔT, $3\Delta T$, $5\Delta T$ etc, up to the design storm duration *D*, are nested into a symmetrical profile to form the PMP hyetograph. It will now become clear why it was convenient to select the storm duration as an odd integer multiple of the data interval.

For a *D*-hour storm, because the storm duration *D* is an odd integer multiple of the data interval ΔT, the storm is centred on the ΔT-hour rainfall occurring between $\{D/2 - \Delta T/2\}$ and $\{D/2 + \Delta T/2\}$ hours after storm commencement. Derivation of the PMP hyetograph entails nesting, from the storm centre, the ΔT-hour seasonal catchment EMP within the $3\Delta T$-hour seasonal catchment EMP within the $5\Delta T$-hour seasonal catchment EMP etc, up to the design storm duration *D*. The peak period in the centre of the storm contains the ΔT-hour rainfall depth. The central $3\Delta T$ period of the storm contains the $3\Delta T$-hour depth. Of this, the ΔT-hour depth occurs in the central ΔT block, so the remaining depth is divided equally between the two outer ΔT periods, placing half in each. The rest of the profile is constructed in similar fashion, as in the worked example. The procedure is broadly similar to derivation of the design storm profile for the *T*-year flood. However, the resulting PMP hyetograph, although symmetrical, is not of a fixed structure, so the short-cut to unit hydrograph convolution (Section 3.4) cannot be used.

4.3.3 PMP design antecedent catchment wetness

The state of the catchment prior to the storm is referred to as the antecedent catchment wetness, and is represented by the catchment wetness index *CWI*. Section 4.2 of Appendix A describes how *CWI* is defined in terms of pre-event soil moisture deficit *SMD* and a 5-day antecedent precipitation index *API5*:

$$CWI = 125 + API5 - SMD \qquad \text{(A.1)}$$

In PMF estimation, the catchment is assumed to *wet up* prior to the PMP storm event, over a period of duration $2D$. *CWI* is assumed to be 125 mm at the beginning of this antecedent period (i.e. *SMD* and *API5* are both zero). This *CWI* is then adjusted for the amount by which the catchment wets-up during the antecedent period to give *CWI* at the start of the PMP storm event. The amount by which the catchment wets-up is the estimated maximum antecedent rainfall EMa. For derivation of the PMP design storm hyetograph in §4.3.2, it is assumed that EMPs fall in all durations centred on the peak of the storm profile. The same assumption can be used to find EMa, by continuing the nesting of estimated maximum rainfalls out to a duration $5D$ (Figure 4.6). This approach differs considerably from the *T*-year case, where *CWI* was a simple function of *SAAR* (see §3.2.4). The PMP design antecedent catchment wetness is calculated by the following two steps:

i Derive EMa;

ii Calculate PMP *CWI*.

These steps are discussed below, and illustrated by Example 4.1e. If a Winter PMP has been selected, there is an option to add snowmelt (covered in §4.3.4).

Example 4.1d
Derivation of PMP design storm hyetograph (depth and profile)

Catchment: West Lyn at Lynmouth (IHDTM grid ref. 272400 149450, Figure 4, Appendix C)

Relevant catchment descriptors and other information: *SAAR* = 1543 mm, EM-2h = 160 mm, EM-24h = 300 mm, ΔT = 0.5 hours (§4.2.1), *D* = 8.5 hours (§4.3.1), *AREA* = 24.08 km^2

Calculating all-year point EMPs and Winter point EMPs of durations between ΔT and 5*D*:

Duration (hours)	0.5	1.0	2.0	24.0	48.0	
% EM-2	0.62	0.79	-	-	-	*from Table 4.1*
% EM-24h	-	-	-	-	1.12	*from Table 4.1*
All-year (mm)	99.2	126.4	160.0	300.0	336.0	*by calculation*
Winter %	0.67	0.74	0.86	0.99	1.00	*from Table 4.2*
Winter (mm)	66.5	93.5	137.6	297.0	336.0	*by calculation*

e.g. for EM-1h: *from Table 4.1*:
EM-60min / EM-2h = 0.79
EM-60min = 0.79 (EM-2h) = 0.79(160) = 126.4 mm
from Table 4.2:
Win EM-1h / Allyr EM-1h = 0.74
Win EM-1h = 0.74 (Allyr EM-1h)
= 0.74(126.4) = 93.5 mm.

Abstracting Winter point EMPs and converting to Winter catchment EMPs for durations ΔT, $3\Delta T$, $5\Delta T$ ..., *D*, and deriving the PMP design storm hyetograph:

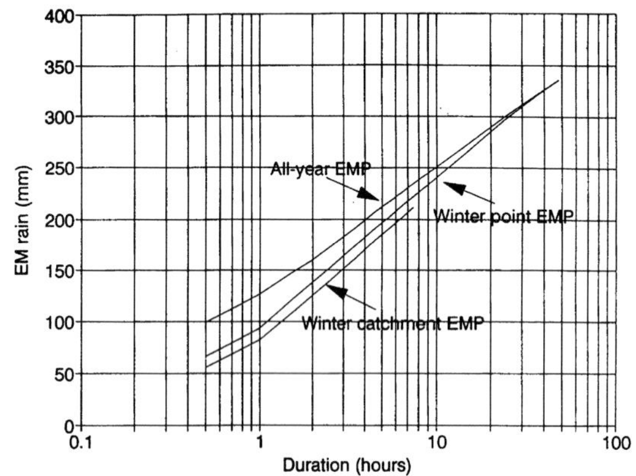

D = 8.5 h and ΔT = 0.5 h. Derivation of the PMP entails nesting the 0.5-h Winter EMP within the 1.5-h Winter EMP within the 3.5-h Winter EMP, etc., up to the duration 8.5 hours.

The peak period in the centre of the storm contains the 0.5-h rainfall depth 55.5 mm. The central 1.5-h period of the storm contains the 1.5-h rainfall depth 106.9 mm. Of this, 55 mm occurs in the central 0.5-h block, so the remaining 51.4 mm (106.9 – 55.5 mm) is divided between the two outer 0.5-h periods, with 25.7 mm in each. The rest of the profile is constructed in a similar way, as shown.

Duration (hours)	0.5	1.5	2.5	3.5	4.5	5.5	6.5	7.5	8.5
Point P (mm)	66.5	118.8	151.8	174.4	190.8	203.3	214.4	223.4	231.3
ARF (Fig 3.4)	0.848	0.900	0.918	0.925	0.933	0.940	0.943	0.948	0.951
Catch P (mm)	55.5	106.9	139.3	161.3	177.9	191.1	202.1	211.6	**220.0**
Diff (mm)	-	51.4	32.4	22.0	16.6	13.2	11.0	9.6	8.4

PMP design storm depth *P* = 8.5 h catchment rainfall = 220.0 mm

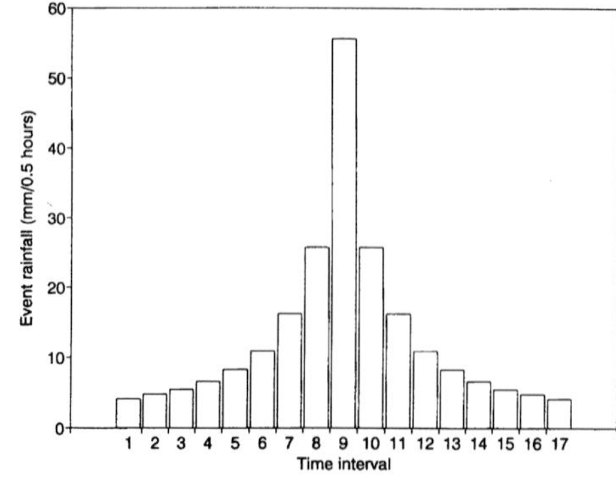

Interval	1	2	3	4	5	6	7	8	9	10	11	12	13	14	15	16	17
Rain (mm)	4.2	4.8	5.5	6.6	8.3	11.0	16.2	25.7	55.5	25.7	16.2	11.0	8.3	6.6	5.5	4.8	4.2

Derivation of EMa

EMa is the estimated maximum antecedent rainfall, assumed to be uniformly distributed over the $2D$ antecedent period. This antecedent rainfall EMa is a seasonal catchment EMP, and is derived using the plots of seasonal point EMPs of durations between ΔT and at least $5D$ hours against duration on linear-log graph paper constructed in §4.3.2. Indeed, parts of the procedure are similar to steps (iii), (iv) and (v) in the derivation of the PMP design storm hyetograph.

It is assumed that EMPs fall in all durations centred on the peak of the storm profile. To maintain the symmetrical storm profile and ensure a wetting-up period of $2D$, the PMP storm event of duration D is nested centrally within the seasonal catchment EMP of duration $5D$, as shown in Figure 4.6.

Seasonal point values of EM-*D*h and EM-5*D*h are abstracted from the plot of seasonal point EMPs of durations between ΔT and $5D$ hours against duration on linear-log graph paper constructed in §4.3.2. The seasonal point EMPs of durations D and $5D$ are converted to equivalent seasonal catchment EMPs using areal reduction factors *ARF*s for durations D and $5D$, read from Figure 3.4.

The PMP storm event in the centre of the $5D$ period has a duration D hours and contains the D-hour seasonal catchment EM-*D*h (or P). The complete $5D$ period contains the $5D$-hour seasonal catchment EM-5*D*h. Of this, the D-hour depth EM-*D*h occurs in the central D-hour block, so the remaining {(EM-5*D*h) – (EM-*D*h)} depth is divided equally between the two outer $2D$ periods, placing {(EM-5*D*h) – (EM-*D*h)} / 2 of the depth in each. Thus EMa is half the difference between the seasonal catchment EM-5*D*h and EM-*D*h rainfalls:

$$\text{EMa} = 0.5\,(ARF_{5D}\ \text{EM-}5D\text{h} - ARF_{D}\ \text{EM-}D\text{h}) \qquad (4.2)$$

Calculation of PMP *CWI*

Once EMa has been derived, calculation of *CWI* at the start of the PMP storm event is relatively straightforward. The procedure entails updating the *SMD* and *API*5 values at the beginning of the antecedent period to obtain equivalent values at the start of the PMP storm event. By substituting the appropriate *SMD* and *API*5 values into Equation A.1, the *CWI* can be calculated at the start of the event.

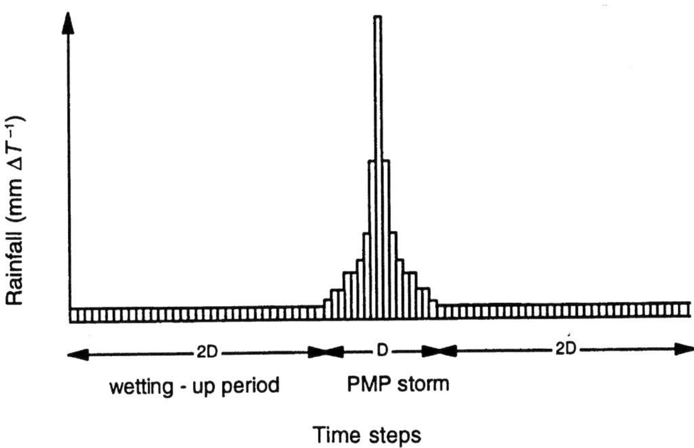

Figure 4.6 *'Wetting-up' period for PMF estimation*

SMD is reduced by the amount of antecedent rainfall that has fallen in the wetting-up period. However, because, in the PMF case, the catchment is assumed to be saturated at the beginning of the wetting-up period, *SMD* is already zero and cannot be reduced further. Therefore, *SMD* at the start of the PMP storm event will also be zero.

*API*5 is increased by the amount of antecedent rainfall that has fallen in the antecedent period, and is recalculated as:

$$API5 = \text{EMa}\ (0.5^{D/24}) \tag{4.3}$$

This equation assumes that the wetting-up effect of the antecedent rainfall is equivalent to the effect had the antecedent rainfall occurred instantaneously halfway through the 2*D* antecedent period. *API*5 and *SMD* at the start of the PMP storm event are combined to give *CWI* at the start of the event using Equation A.1, which simplifies to:

$$CWI = 125 + \text{EMa}\ (0.5^{D/24}) \tag{4.4}$$

If this is a winter PMP, there is an option to add a snowmelt contribution, covered in §4.3.4.

4.3.4 Snowmelt

Snowmelt in the UK is most frequently brought about by a sudden influx of warm moist air, and melt is often accompanied by rainfall. Combined rainfall and snowmelt provide large volumes of potential runoff, and occasionally lead to severe flooding e.g. the Tay floods of 1990 and 1993 (Anderson and Black, 1993). However,

Example 4.1e
Calculation of PMP design antecedent catchment wetness *CWI*

Catchment: West Lyn at Lynmouth (IHDTM grid ref. 272400 149450, Figure 4 of Appendix C)

Relevant information: D = 8.5 hours (§4.3.1)

Deriving EMa
The estimated maximum antecedent rainfall EMa is calculated using Equation 4.2, where the EM rainfalls are abstracted from the linear-log plot in §4.3.2 and the ARFs are abstracted from Figure 3.4:

$\text{EMa} = 0.5\ [\text{ARF}_{5D}\ \text{EM-5Dh} - \text{ARF}_{D}\ \text{EM-Dh}]$

$\text{EMa} = 0.5\ [0.974\ (329.0) - 0.951\ (231.3)]$
$= 50.2$ mm

Calculating *CWI*
The PMP design antecedent catchment wetness *CWI* is calculated using Equation 4.4:

$CWI = 125 + \text{EMa}\ (0.5^{D/24})$

$CWI = 125 + 50.2\ (0.5^{8.5/24})$
$= 164.3$ mm

snowmelt processes are not well understood, particularly when occurring in combination with extreme rainfall events, and quantifying the potential snowmelt contribution is difficult (Jackson, 1978). If the maximum rainfall for a certain catchment has a return period of T_R years (e.g. 10 000 years), the chances of the T_S-year snowmelt (e.g. 100-year) occurring in the same year are 1 in $T_R T_S$ (e.g. 1 000 000) assuming independence, and the chance of the rainfall and snowmelt events occurring on the same day is even smaller. Although the chance of a maximum rainstorm and a maximum snowmelt occurring together can be regarded as near zero, in some design situations it cannot be ignored. This partly reflects the concern that conditions for extreme rainfall and snowmelt events may not be fully independent.

For the FSR, the Met. Office carried out an assessment of maximum snow depths and potential snowmelt rates, whilst the University of Newcastle-upon-Tyne carried out an examination of snow cover and flood records to assess the relative importance of snowmelt in different regions and to review methods of estimating snowmelt runoff in British conditions. Based on these investigations, FSR I.6.8.3 recommended a melt rate of 1.75 mm h^{-1} (42 mm day^{-1}), irrespective of geographical location, sustained for as long as the 100-year snow depth water equivalent S_{100} will allow (normally two to three days). The return period of this melt rate was understood to be 100 years. It was believed that this combination of snow depth and snowmelt was a suitably rare occurrence for design purposes, particularly when combined with a maximum rainstorm.

Figure 4.7 shows the median (i.e. 2-year) annual maximum snow depth (FSR II.7.4.1). The map is derived from frequency analysis of daily snow depth records from about 100 stations for the period 1946-64. The 100-year maximum snow depth is about 7.5 times this 2-year depth. Using an average density of 0.13 g cm^{-3}, Figure 4.7 can be interpreted as an approximate guide to the 100-year snow depth water equivalent S_{100}. Daily changes of snow depth were compared with the corresponding daily maximum temperatures to give a relationship which led to a first approximation to snowmelt rates. From Figure 4.7, a melt of 1.75 mm h^{-1} could continue for 24 hours anywhere in the UK; in parts of Scotland and northern England, where the 100-year snow depth water equivalent exceeds 210 mm, it could last for more than five days. For catchments having long time-to-peaks, design storm durations can exceed 24 hours, and it is therefore necessary to check whether there is a sufficient snow depth to sustain the melt rate throughout the design event.

The FSR countrywide melt rate of 1.75 mm h^{-1} has provoked much controversy. Snowmelt is determined by various physical and climatic factors, such as altitude, temperature, vegetation, rainfall and wind conditions. Many of the stations on which the original analysis was based were at relatively low elevations, which introduced some bias. In the UK, an increase in altitude is almost always associated with a decrease in temperature and an increase in windspeed, rain and snowfall, which lead to an increased potential for snowmelt. Vegetation can affect snowmelt by providing shelter. In general, melt in a forest is less than in the open, often in the range 60-70%, though these numbers can vary widely depending upon the structure, density and maturity of the forest (Maidment, 1993). Work in northern England and Scotland proposes that a higher rate of 5 mm h^{-1} is more suitable in these regions (Archer, 1981; 1983; 1984). The findings are supported by Mawdsley *et al.* (1991), who consider extreme snowmelt rates from an energy budget point of view. However, in a reanalysis of some of Archer's events, Reed and Field (1992) suggest that the role of rainfall may have been underplayed. They do not

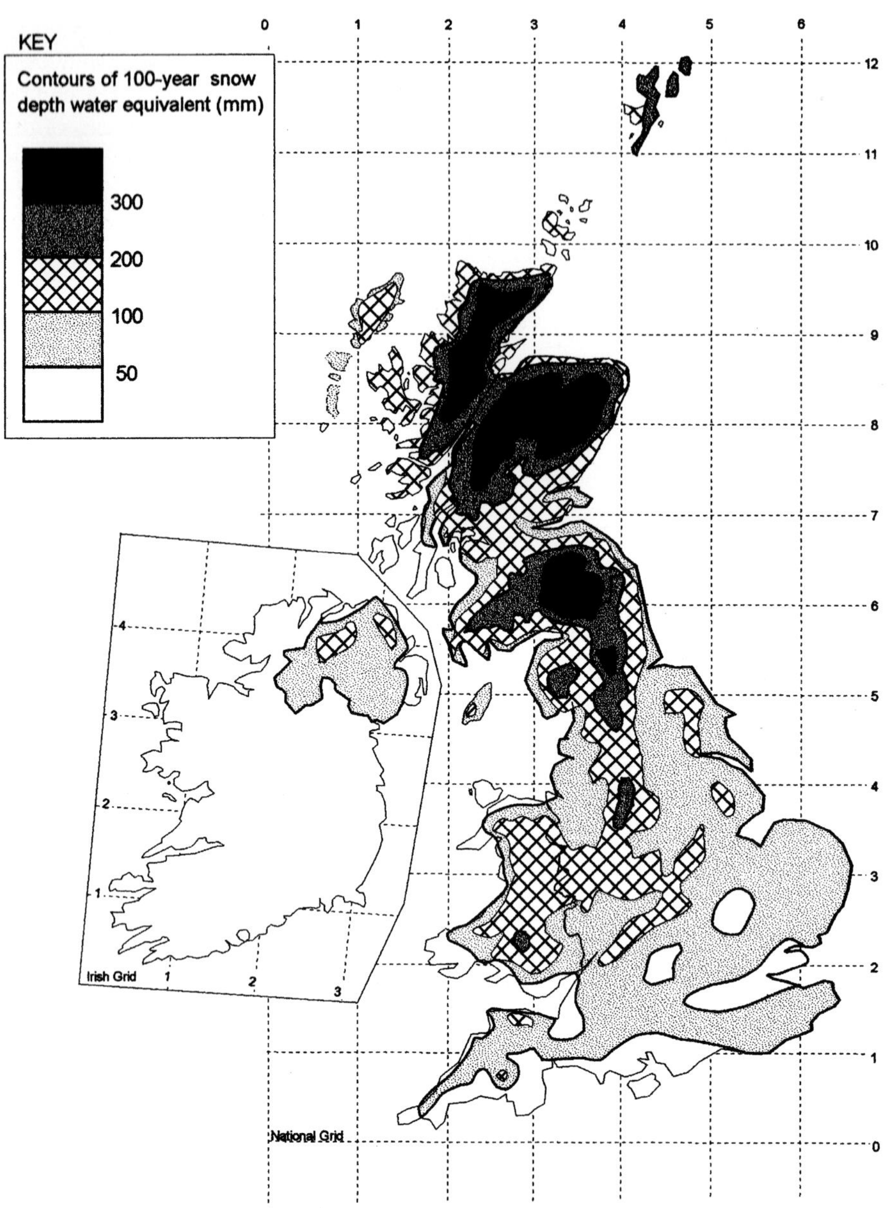

Figure 4.7 100-year snow depth water equivalent (after NERC, 1975)

dispute that such rates can occur, but query how common or sustainable they are, concluding that higher melt rates may be appropriate at some locations. Indeed, more recent work reiterates the high rates of melt and runoff that *can* occur in warm frontal events with associated high windspeeds (Archer and Stewart, 1995).

A recent Met. Office investigation of point snowmelt rates in the UK indicates that the FSR melt rate of 1.75 mm h^{-1} has a return period of less than 10 years at high altitude sites in northern England and Scotland, and of more than 1000 years at low altitude sites in England (Hough and Hollis, 1995; 1997). The results were used to derive Figure 4.8 which indicates areas where 5-year snowmelt rates higher than 1.75 mm h^{-1} might be expected (ICE, 1996).

In PMF estimation, there is an option to add a snowmelt contribution to a winter PMP. Snowmelt is added uniformly to the design storm depth P to give a total event precipitation P': this affects the value of storm depth used in calculation of percentage runoff. When snowmelt is assumed to occur with the storm event, it is sensible to assume that it could also occur through the period of antecedent rainfall. Therefore, snowmelt is added uniformly to the antecedent rainfall EMa to give a revised catchment wetness index CWI', based on the total antecedent precipitation. This affects the catchment wetness index value used in the percentage runoff and baseflow calculations. It is recommended that the snowmelt should be added to the storm and antecedent rainfall profiles at a uniform rate as it seems unreasonable to assume that the profile of the snowmelt (largely controlled by

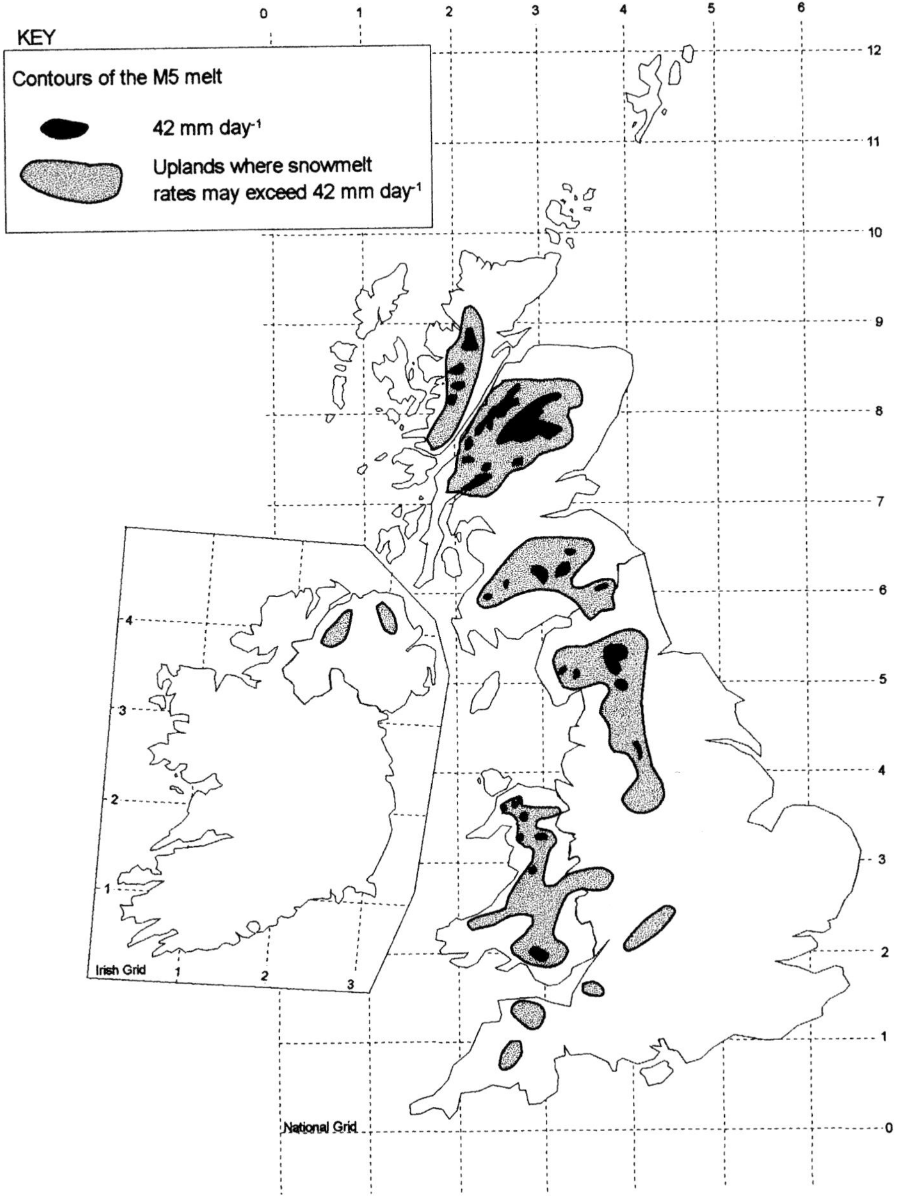

***Figure 4.8** Guide to 24-hour snowmelt rate (after ICE, 1996)*

temperature and windspeed) should mirror that of the storm rainfall (see Example 4.1f).

Snowmelt contribution to storm depth

The total snowmelt contribution to the storm depth SMp is given by:

$$SMp = D\,(\text{melt rate}) \tag{4.5}$$

It is necessary to check that the 100-year snow depth water equivalent S_{100} is large enough to support this snowmelt contribution. If the 100-year snow depth water equivalent S_{100} is not large enough to sustain the melt over the design storm duration D, it is necessary to calculate for how many hours the melt will last, and then add it at the appropriate melt rate to the winter PMP hyetograph from the centre outwards. In Equation 4.6, S'_{100} is what remains of S_{100} after the snowmelt contribution to storm depth:

$$S'_{100} = \begin{cases} S_{100} - SMp & [\text{for } S_{100} > SMp] \\ 0 & [\text{for } S_{100} \leq SMp : \text{i.e. } SMp = S_{100}] \end{cases} \tag{4.6}$$

The total event precipitation P' is the sum of the design storm depth P and the snowmelt contribution SMp:

$$P' = P + SMp \tag{4.7}$$

The winter PMP hyetograph is adjusted for snowmelt by simply adding melt at the appropriate melt rate to each block of the hyetograph.

Snowmelt contribution to antecedent rainfall

The total snowmelt contribution to the antecedent rainfall SMa is given by:

$$SMa = 2D\,(\text{melt rate}) \tag{4.8}$$

It is necessary to check that S'_{100} is large enough to support this snowmelt contribution. If S'_{100} is insufficient to sustain the melt throughout the antecedent period of duration $2D$, it is necessary to calculate the exact duration and amount. In Equation 4.9, S''_{100} is what remains of S'_{100} after the snowmelt contribution to antecedent rainfall:

$$S''_{100} = \begin{cases} S'_{100} - SMa & [\text{for } S'_{100} > SMa : \text{i.e. } \Delta SM = 2D] \\ 0 & [\text{for } S'_{100} \leq SMa : \text{i.e. } SMa = S'_{100} \text{ and } \Delta SM = S'_{100}/\text{melt rate}] \end{cases} \tag{4.9}$$

where ΔSM is the length of the antecedent period over which snowmelt occurs. The CWI calculated in §4.3.3 can then be adjusted for the snowmelt contribution:

$$CWI' = CWI + SMa\,(0.5^{\Delta SM/48}) \tag{4.10}$$

Example 4.1f
Snowmelt

Catchment: West Lyn at Lynmouth (IHDTM grid ref. 272400 149450, Figure 4 of Appendix C)

Relevant catchment descriptors and other information:
S_{100} = 75 mm, melt rate = 1.75 mm h^{-1}, ΔT = 0.5 hours (§4.2.1), D = 8.5 hours (§4.3.1), P = 220.0 mm (§4.3.2), CWI = 164.3 mm (§4.3.3)

Calculation of snowmelt contribution to storm depth

The snowmelt contribution to storm depth is calculated using Equation 4.5:

$SMp = D$ (melt rate) $\qquad SMp = 8.5\,(1.75) = 14.9$ mm

What remains of S_{100} after the snowmelt contribution to storm depth is given by Equation 4.6:

$S'_{100} = S_{100} - SMp$ [as $S_{100} > SMp$] $\qquad S'_{100} = 75.0 - 14.9 = 60.1$ mm

The total event precipitation is calculated using Equation 4.7 and the Winter PMP hyetograph is adjusted by adding the appropriate snowmelt to each block of the hyetograph:

Interval	1	2	3	4	5	6	7	8	9	10	11	12	13	14	15	16	17
Rain (mm)	4.2	4.8	5.5	6.6	8.3	11.0	16.2	25.7	55.5	25.7	16.2	11.0	8.3	6.6	5.5	4.8	4.2
Melt (mm)	0.8	0.8	0.8	0.8	0.8	0.8	0.8	0.8	0.8	0.8	0.8	0.8	0.8	0.8	0.8	0.8	0.8
Tot prec (mm)	5.0	5.6	6.4	7.5	9.1	11.9	17.0	26.6	56.4	26.6	17.0	11.9	9.1	7.5	6.4	5.6	5.0

$P' = P + SMp \qquad P' = 220.0 + 14.9 = 234.9$ mm

Calculation of snowmelt contribution to antecedent rainfall

The snowmelt contribution to antecedent rainfall SMa is calculated using Equation 4.8:

$SMa = 2D$ (melt rate) $\qquad SMa = 17.0\,(1.75) = 29.8$ mm

What remains of S'_{100} after the snowmelt contribution to antecedent rainfall is given by Equation 4.9:

$S''_{100} = S'_{100} - SMa$ [as $S'_{100} > SMa$] $\qquad S''_{100} = 60.1 - 29.8 = 30.3$ mm

As the length of the antecedent period over which snowmelt occurs is 2D, the CWI is adjusted for the snowmelt contribution using Equation 4.11:

$CWI' = CWI + SMa\,(0.5^{D/24}) \qquad CWI' = 164.3 + 29.8\,(0.5^{8.5/24}) = 187.6$ mm

If ΔSM is $2D$, then Equation 4.10 simplifies to:

$$CWI' = CWI + SMa\,(0.5^{D/24}) \qquad (4.11)$$

4.4 Derivation of PMF

The PMF is estimated from the PMP design storm and antecedent condition inputs by the following steps:

- i Calculate the percentage runoff and baseflow, to completely specify the unit hydrograph and losses model;
- ii Apply the percentage runoff to the total event hyetograph to derive the net event hyetograph;
- iii Convolve the unit hydrograph with the net event hyetograph to derive the rapid response runoff hydrograph;
- iv Add the baseflow to the rapid response runoff hydrograph to derive the total runoff hydrograph.

The steps which make up this procedure mirror those for estimation of the *T*-year flood in Section 3.3. If required, the derived PMF can be assigned a nominal return period, and thus linked to the catchment flood frequency curve, by a method outlined in Section 4.5.

4.4.1 Calculation of percentage runoff and baseflow

The values of catchment wetness index *CWI* and storm depth *P*, determined in §§4.3.3 (4.3.4 if snowmelt) and 4.3.2 (4.3.4 if snowmelt), respectively, can be substituted in Equations 2.14, 2.15 and 2.19 to calculate the percentage runoff and baseflow, as illustrated in Example 4.1g.

Percentage runoff

The percentage runoff from the natural part of the catchment PR_{RURAL} is estimated in two parts: a standard component *SPR* representing the normal capacity of the catchment to generate runoff, and a dynamic component *DPR* representing the variation in the response depending on the state of the catchment prior to the storm and the storm magnitude itself. *DPR* is, thus, made up of two components: DPR_{CWI} dependent on *CWI*, and DPR_{RAIN} dependent on *P*:

$$PR_{RURAL} = SPR + DPR_{CWI} + DPR_{RAIN} \qquad (2.13)$$

The various methods of estimating *SPR* are described in Section 2.3. The *DPR* equations are:

$$DPR_{CWI} = 0.25\,(CWI - 125) \qquad (2.14)$$

$$DPR_{RAIN} = \begin{cases} 0 & [\text{for } P \leq 40 \text{ mm}] \\ 0.45\,(P - 40)^{0.7} & [\text{for } P > 40 \text{ mm}] \end{cases} \qquad (2.15)$$

The PMP storm depth will, of course, be far greater than 40 mm in most instances. The total percentage runoff is usually estimated by adjusting PR_{RURAL} for the effects of catchment urbanisation. However, in PMF estimation, it is common for the estimated runoff from the natural catchment PR_{RURAL} to exceed the nominal 70% attributed to impermeable surfaces in urban areas. In such circumstances, the usual allowance for urbanisation would have the effect of reducing percentage runoff. Therefore, the adjustment should be omitted, and percentage runoff should be set equal to PR_{RURAL}:

$$PR = \begin{cases} PR_{RURAL}\,(1.0 - 0.615\ URBEXT) + 70\,(0.615\ URBEXT) & [\text{for } PR_{RURAL} \leq 70\%] \\ PR_{RURAL} & [\text{for } PR_{RURAL} > 70\%] \end{cases} \qquad (4.12)$$

Baseflow

The various methods for estimating baseflow are discussed in Section 2.4. In PMF estimation, baseflow should, in general, be estimated from catchment descriptors, and not be overidden by a local analysis of flood event data. The reason for this

Example 4.1g
Calculation of percentage runoff and baseflow

Catchment: West Lyn at Lynmouth (IHDTM grid ref. 272400 149450)
(Figure 4 of Appendix C)

Relevant catchment descriptors and other information:
SPR = 53.0% (§4.2.2), P = 234.9 mm (§§4.3.2 and 4.3.4), CWI = 187.6 mm (§§4.3.3 and 4.3.4), $URBEXT$ = 0.004, $AREA$ = 24.08 km^2, $SAAR$ = 1543 mm

Percentage runoff

The percentage runoff PR appropriate to the design event is calculated using Equations 2.12 to 2.15 and 4.12:

$DPR_{CWI} = 0.25\,(CWI - 125)$ $\qquad$ $DPR_{CWI} = 0.25\,(187.6 - 125) = 15.7\%$

$DPR_{RAIN} = 0.45\,(P - 40)^{0.7}$ [as $P > 40$ mm] $\qquad$ $DPR_{RAIN} = 0.45\,(234.9 - 40)^{0.7} = 18.0\%$

$PR_{RURAL} = SPR + DPR_{CWI} + DPR_{RAIN}$ $\qquad$ $PR_{RURAL} = 53.0 + 15.7 + 18.0 = 86.7\%$

$PR = PR_{RURAL} > 70\%$ [as $PR_{RURAL} > 70\%$] $\qquad$ $PR = 86.7\%$

Baseflow

The baseflow BF is calculated using Equation 2.19:

$BF = \{33\,(CWI - 125) + 3.0\ SAAR + 5.5\}\ 10^{-5}\ AREA$

$BF = \{33\,(187.6 - 125) + 3.0 \times 1543 + 5.5\}\ 10^{-5} \times 24.08 = 1.61\ \text{m}^3\,\text{s}^{-1}$

is that *CWI*, which is present in the catchment-descriptor equation, is driven by the PMP storm depth *P* (rather than *SAAR*):

$$BF = \{33\ (CWI - 125) + 3.0\ SAAR + 5.5\}\ 10^{-5}\ AREA \qquad (2.19)$$

4.4.2 Derivation of net event hyetograph

Percentage runoff is applied as a constant proportional loss to each hyetograph block through the PMP event. The net (or effective) event hyetograph is derived by multiplying each block of the total event hyetograph (from §4.3.2) by the percentage runoff (from §4.4.1), as shown in Example 4.1h.

Example 4.1h
Derivation of net event hyetograph

Catchment: West Lyn at Lynmouth (IHDTM grid ref. 272400 149450)
(Figure 4 of Appendix C)

Relevant information:
PR = 86.7% (§4.4.1)

The net rainfall hyetograph is derived by applying the percentage runoff *PR* to each block of the total rainfall hyetograph from §4.3.2:

Interval	1	2	3	4	5	6	7	8	9	10	11	12	13	14	15	16	17
Tot prec (mm)	5.0	5.6	6.4	7.5	9.1	11.9	17.0	26.6	56.4	26.6	17.0	11.9	9.1	7.5	6.4	5.6	5.0
Net prec (mm)	4.3	4.8	5.5	6.5	7.9	10.2	14.6	22.9	48.5	22.9	14.6	10.2	7.9	6.5	5.5	4.8	4.3

4.4.3 Derivation of rapid response runoff hydrograph

The rapid response runoff hydrograph is the product of convolving the unit hydrograph (from §4.2.1) with the net event hyetograph (from §4.4.2). The theory behind the convolution procedure is described in §2.2.1. A typical convolution table is laid out in Example 4.1i. The ΔT-hourly ordinates of the ΔT-hour unit hydrograph are set out in the header row across the top of the table. The net rainfall values in cm per time step are set out in the column down the left-hand side of the table. They have been converted from mm to cm because the synthesised unit hydrograph refers to 10 mm or 1cm input of net rainfall.

The convolution procedure starts by applying the first net rainfall value to each unit hydrograph ordinate in turn, the product being written directly beneath, thus forming the first row of the table. The process is repeated for the second net rainfall value forming the second row of the table, but the products entered are displaced one column to the right because the second rainfall value occurs one data interval after the first. The remaining net rainfalls are applied in the same way, and the columns are summed to give the rapid response runoff hydrograph, as illustrated.

Example 4.1i

Derivation of rapid response runoff hydrograph and total runoff hydrograph

Catchment: West Lyn at Lynmouth (IHDTM grid ref. 272400 149450) (Figure 4 of Appendix C)

Rapid response runoff hydrograph

The convolution of the 0.5-hour unit hydrograph from §4.2.1 and the net rainfall hyetograph from §4.4.2 may be set out as a table. The 0.5-hour ordinates of the unit hydrograph are set out in the header row across the top of the table. The net rainfall values in cm are set out in the column down the left-hand side of the table. The first net rainfall value is applied to each unit hydrograph ordinate in turn, and the product written directly beneath, forming the first row of the table. The second rainfall value is applied to each unit hydrograph ordinate in turn, but the product entered is displaced one column to the right. The rest of the table is constructed in a similar fashion, as illustrated. The column sums give the rapid response runoff hydrograph.

Total runoff hydrograph

The total runoff hydrograph is obtained by adding the baseflow *BF* from §4.4.1 to each ordinate of the rapid response runoff hydrograph. The PMF for the West Lyn at Lynmouth is estimated as 224.57 $m^3 s^{-1}$ and the complete hydrograph is also obtained.

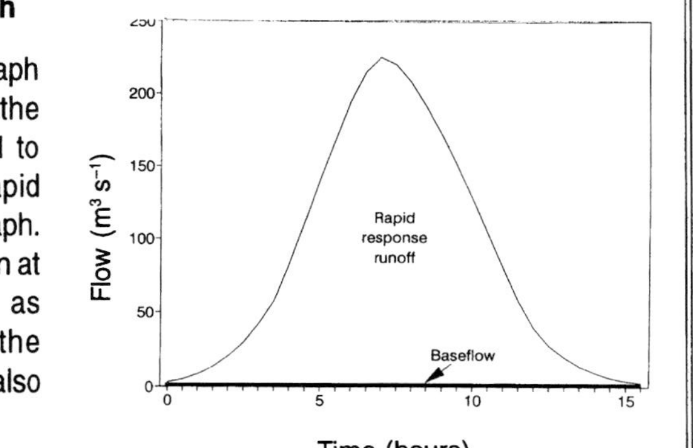

Net rain (cm)	Unit hydrograph response (cumecs)																													
	2.36	4.72	7.08	9.44	11.80	14.16	15.35	13.80	12.24	10.71	9.14	7.59	6.03	4.48	2.93	1.37														
0.43	1.01	2.03	3.04	4.06	5.07	6.09	6.60	5.93	5.26	4.61	3.93	3.26	2.59	1.93	1.26	0.59														
0.48		1.13	2.27	3.40	4.53	5.66	6.80	7.37	6.62	5.88	5.14	4.39	3.64	2.90	2.15	1.40	0.66													
0.55			1.30	2.60	3.89	5.19	6.49	7.79	8.44	7.59	6.73	5.89	5.02	4.17	3.32	2.46	1.61	0.75												
0.65				1.53	3.07	4.60	6.14	7.67	9.20	9.98	8.97	7.96	6.96	5.94	4.93	3.92	2.91	1.90	0.89											
0.79					1.86	3.73	5.59	7.46	9.32	11.19	12.13	10.90	9.67	8.46	7.22	5.99	4.77	3.54	2.31	1.08										
1.02						2.41	4.81	7.22	9.63	12.04	14.44	15.66	14.07	12.49	10.93	9.32	7.74	6.15	4.57	2.98	1.40									
1.46							3.45	6.89	10.34	13.78	17.23	20.68	22.41	20.14	17.87	15.64	13.34	11.07	8.81	6.54	4.27	2.00								
2.29								5.40	10.81	16.21	21.62	27.03	32.43	35.15	31.60	28.03	24.53	20.92	17.37	13.81	10.26	6.70	3.14							
4.85									11.45	22.89	34.34	45.79	57.24	68.68	74.44	66.92	59.38	51.96	44.31	36.79	29.26	21.72	14.19	6.66						
2.29										5.40	10.81	16.21	21.62	27.03	32.43	35.15	31.60	28.03	24.53	20.92	17.37	13.81	10.26	6.70	3.14					
1.46											3.45	6.89	10.34	13.78	17.23	20.68	22.41	20.14	17.87	15.64	13.34	11.07	8.81	6.54	4.27	2.00				
1.02												2.41	4.81	7.22	9.63	12.04	14.44	15.66	14.07	12.49	10.93	9.32	7.74	6.15	4.57	2.98	1.40			
0.79													1.86	3.73	5.59	7.46	9.32	11.19	12.13	10.90	9.67	8.46	7.22	5.99	4.77	3.54	2.31	1.08		
0.65														1.53	3.07	4.60	6.14	7.67	9.20	9.98	8.97	7.96	6.96	5.94	4.93	3.92	2.91	1.90	0.89	
0.55															1.30	2.60	3.89	5.19	6.49	7.79	8.44	7.59	6.73	5.89	5.02	4.17	3.32	2.46	1.61	0.75
0.48																1.13	2.27	3.40	4.53	5.66	6.80	7.37	6.62	5.88	5.14	4.39	3.64	2.90	2.15	1.40
0.43																	1.01	2.03	3.04	4.06	5.07	6.09	6.60	5.93	5.26	4.61	3.93	3.26	2.59	1.93
Rapid response (cumecs)	1.01	3.16	6.61	11.59	18.43	27.68	39.88	55.74	81.08	109.57	138.78	167.06	192.68	213.15	222.96	217.94	206.01	189.62	170.14	148.65	125.77	102.10	78.27	55.68	37.11	25.61	17.51	11.61	7.24	4.09
Baseflow (cumecs)	1.61	1.61	1.61	1.61	1.61	1.61	1.61	1.61	1.61	1.61	1.61	1.61	1.61	1.61	1.61	1.61	1.61	1.61	1.61	1.61	1.61	1.61	1.61	1.61	1.61	1.61	1.61	1.61	1.61	1.61
Total flow (cumecs)	2.62	4.77	8.22	13.20	20.04	29.29	41.49	57.35	82.69	111.18	140.39	168.67	194.29	214.76	224.57	219.55	207.62	191.23	171.75	150.26	127.38	103.71	79.88	57.29	38.72	27.22	19.12	13.22	8.85	5.70

4.4.4 Derivation of total runoff hydrograph

The total runoff hydrograph is obtained by simply adding the constant baseflow to each ordinate of the rapid response runoff hydrograph, as illustrated in Example 4.1i.

4.5 Linkage of flood frequency curve to PMF

In the past, *T*-year floods and the PMF could not be shown on the same graph except by drawing in the PMF as a horizontal upper limit line. However, it might be helpful to compute floods in the intermediate zone e.g. to provide a check on the 10,000-year flood, or to enable cost-benefit calculations to be completed across the full range of design discharges. Various arbitrary procedures for effecting a sensible-looking linkage such that a smooth single curve is obtained are reported by Rowbottom *et al.* (1986), and their preferred method is adopted in *Australian Rainfall and Runoff* (IEAust, 1987; 1999). A similar method, incorporating procedures for assigning a nominal return period to the PMF, and a generally applicable interpolation technique for producing a composite flood frequency curve defined up to the level of the PMF, was developed for the UK (Lowing, 1995; Lowing and Law, 1995). The linkage method provides a way of reconciling *T*-year and probable maximum flood estimates that some users may find valuable.

4.5.1 Associating a return period with the PMF

Two different approaches to estimation of T_{PMF}, the return period associated with the PMF, are used: methodology-based (Lowing, 1995) and geometry-based (Rowbottom *et al.*, 1986). The *lower* of the two return periods is adopted, as shown in Example 4.2a.

Methodology-based estimate of return period (Lowing, 1995)

The PMF is assigned a return period of 10^6 years. This value is increased by a factor of 10 (i.e. to 10^7) if any *two* of the following apply:

- PMP is being derived on a catchment larger than 100 km^2;
- FSR all-year PMP is being derived (i.e. summer PMP combined with snowmelt);
- Snowmelt rate is increased to 5 mm h^{-1}.

The value may be increased by a further factor of 10 if the catchment is between 100 and 500 km^2, and by a factor of 100 if the catchment exceeds 500 km^2.

Geometry-based estimate of return period (Rowbottom *et al.*, 1986)

The form of the linkage between the *T*-year flood frequency curve and the PMF is influenced by the relative magnitude of the flows concerned and the slope of the *T*-year curve. The FSR rainfall-runoff method is used to estimate the peak flows of the 100-year flood Q_{100}, the 1000-year flood Q_{1000} and the PMF Q_{PMF}. Table 4.3 shows the value of the nominal return period attributed to the PMF, depending on the value of the ratio defined in Equation 4.13.

4.5.2 Linking the flood frequency curve to the PMF

The linkage between the *T*-year flood frequency curve and the PMF is made by cubic spline interpolation. This objectively constructs a smooth curve between

Table 4.3 Geometry-based estimate of T_{PMF}

Ratio value	T_{PMF} (years)
<5	10^6
5-10	10^7
10-15	10^8
>15	10^9

$$\text{ratio} = \frac{\dfrac{Q_{PMF}}{Q_{1000}} - 1}{1 - \dfrac{Q_{100}}{Q_{1000}}} \tag{4.13}$$

two points where gradients are known. The arithmetic procedure is described in six steps and illustrated by Example 4.2b.

i Calculate the value of the Gumbel reduced variate y corresponding to the return period T_{PMF} computed in §4.5.1 using the following equation:

$$y_{PMF} = \ln(T_{PMF}) \tag{4.14}$$

ii Determine the slope S_{FFC} of the T-year flood frequency curve between T=100 years (y_{100}= 4.60) and T=1000 years (y_{1000}= 6.91), assuming linear scales for both the flow and the reduced variate:

$$S_{FFC} = \frac{1 - \dfrac{Q_{100}}{Q_{1000}}}{y_{1000} - y_{100}} \tag{4.15}$$

Example 4.2a
Associating a return period with the PMF

Catchment: West Lyn at Lynmouth (IHDTM grid ref. 272400 149450) (Figure 4 of Appendix C)

Relevant information: Q_{PMF} = 224.57 $m^3 s^{-1}$ (§4.4.4), Q_{1000} = 53.61 $m^3 s^{-1}$, Q_{100} = 30.53 $m^3 s^{-1}$

Methodology-based estimate of return period

The PMF is assigned a return period of 10^6 years. This may be increased to 10^7 if various conditions apply, but this is not appropriate for the West Lyn at Lynmouth: $T_{PMF(meth)} = 10^6$ years

Geometry-based estimate of return period

The value of the nominal return period depends on the value of the ratio in Equation 4.13:

ratio = $\{(Q_{PMF} / Q_{1000}) - 1\} / \{1 - (Q_{100} / Q_{1000})\} = \{(224.57 / 53.61) - 1\} / \{1 - (30.53 / 53.61)\} = 7.41$

The PMF return period corresponding to this ratio is read from Table 4.3: $T_{PMF(geo)} = 10^7$ years

Estimate of return period

The lower of the two return periods is adopted: $T_{PMF(meth)} = 10^6$ years iii Determine the slope S_{LINK} of the imaginary line joining the point (y_{1000},1.0) and the point ($y_{\text{PMF}}, Q_{\text{PMF}}/Q_{1000}$), again assuming linear scales for both the flow and the reduced variate:

$$S_{\text{LINK}} = \frac{\dfrac{Q_{100}}{Q_{1000}} - 1}{y_{\text{PMF}} - y_{1000}} \tag{4.16}$$

iv Compute coefficients for cubic-type expression:

$$\begin{aligned} a1 &= S_{\text{FFC}}\,(y_{\text{PMF}} - y_{1000}) \\ a2 &= (3\,S_{\text{LINK}} - 2\,S_{\text{FFC}})\,(y_{\text{PMF}} - y_{1000}) \\ a3 &= (S_{\text{FFC}} - 2\,S_{\text{LINK}})\,(y_{\text{PMF}} - y_{1000}) \end{aligned} \tag{4.17}$$

v Calculate the value of the Gumbel reduced variate y corresponding to several intermediate values of return period T' between 1000 years and T_{PMF}:

$$y_T = \ln(T') \tag{4.18}$$

Calculate the interpolation fraction yf corresponding to these reduced variates:

$$yf_T = \frac{y_T - y_{1000}}{y_{\text{PMF}} - y_{1000}} \tag{4.19}$$

vi Compute the flood peaks $Q_{T'}$ for the intermediate values of return period:

$$Q_{T'} = Q_{1000}\,\{1 + yf_{T'}\,\{a1 + [yf_{T'}\,[a2 + yf_{T'}\,(a3)\,]\,]\,\}\,\} \tag{4.20}$$

Plot the peaks against return period to produce the composite flood frequency curve.

Example 4.2b
Linking the flood frequency curve to the PMF

Catchment: West Lyn at Lynmouth (IHDTM grid ref. 272400 149450)
(Figure 4 of Appendix C)

Relevant information:
$Q_{PMF} = 224.57\ m^3 s^{-1}$ (§4.4.4), $T_{PMF} = 10^6$ years, $Q_{1000} = 53.61\ m^3 s^{-1}$, $y_{1000} = 6.91$,
$Q_{100} = 30.53\ m^3 s^{-1}$, $y_{100} = 4.60$

(i) $y_{PMF} = \ln(T_{PMF})$ $\qquad$ $y_{PMF} = \ln(10^6) = 13.82$

(ii) $S_{FFC} = [1 - (Q_{100} / Q_{1000})] / (y_{1000} - y_{100})$ $\qquad$ $S_{FFC} = [1 - (30.53/53.61)] / (6.91 - 4.60) = 0.1864$

(iii) $S_{LINK} = [(Q_{PMF} / Q_{1000}) - 1] / (y_{PMF} - y_{1000})$ $\qquad$ $S_{LINK} = [(224.57/53.61) - 1] / (13.82\ 6.91) = 0.4615$

(iv) $a1 = S_{FFC}(y_{PMF} - y_{1000})$ $\qquad$ $a1 = 0.1864\ (13.82 - 6.91) = 1.2880$

$a2 = (3\ S_{LINK} - 2\ S_{FFC})(y_{PMF} - y_{1000})$

$a2 = (3(0.4615) - 2(0.1864))\ (13.82 - 6.91) = 6.9908$

$a3 = (S_{FFC} - 2\ S_{LINK})(y_{PMF} - y_{1000})$

$a3 = (0.1864 - 2(0.4615))\ (13.82 - 6.91) = -5.0899$

(v) $y_T = \ln(T)$

$yf_T = (y_T - y_{1000}) / ((y_{PMF} - y_{1000})$

e.g. $y_{5000} = 8.52$, $yf_{5000} = 0.2330$
$y_{10000} = 9.21$, $yf_{10000} = 0.3329$
$y_{100000} = 11.51$, $yf_{100000} = 0.6643$

(vi) $Q_T = Q_{1000}\{1 + yf_T\{a1 + [yf_T\ [a2 + yf_T\ (a3)]]\}\}$

e.g. $Q_{5000} = 85.87\ m^3 s^{-1}$
$Q_{10000} = 108.06\ m^3 s^{-1}$
$Q_{100000} = 184.87\ m^3 s^{-1}$

Plot the peaks against return period to produce the composite flood frequency curve:

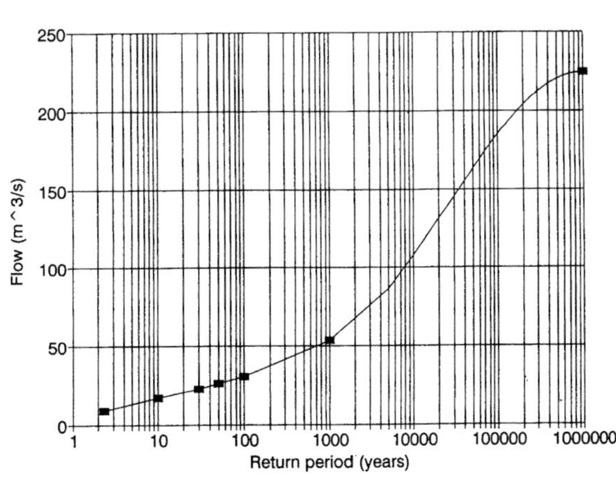

Chapter 5 Simulation of a notable event for return period assessment

5.1 Introduction

Many flood studies arise in the aftermath of a flooding incident, when it is necessary to ascertain just how rare the flood event was. Knowledge of its return period is important in assessing whether improvement works to defend against such a flood occurring again are likely to be economically viable. In some cases there will be a gauging station at or close to the subject site, and it will be possible to assign a return period to the event by statistical analysis of peak flow data (Volume 3). However, in many cases, there will be no relevant gauging station and an alternative method is required. FSSR12 (IH, 1983b) showed how the problem can be tackled using the FSR rainfall-runoff method.

Although intended for use in design flood estimation, the FSR rainfall-runoff method can also be used to simulate flood events. In simulation, observed hydrological inputs are converted to a flow hydrograph for a real event. This is distinct from design flood estimation where flood peaks are predicted for hypothetical events (Chapters 3 and 4). In simulation, the information passed through the model is concerned only with the magnitudes of the model inputs and output. In design, the model is also concerned with the return periods of these inputs and output.

Although originally intended for use on ungauged catchments, the simulation technique can also be a valuable tool on gauged catchments, where it can be used to reproduce observed hydrographs to ascertain how well the FSR rainfall-runoff method is performing. Accurate reconstruction of specific events is a necessary attribute of, for instance, flood forecasting.

The recommended procedure, outlined in the remainder of this section, encourages the user to seek out and use as much information as possible about the event. In §5.2 the observed rainfall and antecedent condition inputs are considered in detail. Application of the observed storm to the unit hydrograph and losses model to simulate the notable flood is described in §5.3. Section 5.4 describes the methods for estimating the return periods of the flood peak and the rainfall event.

5.1.1 Simulation — how big was that flood?

The essence of the problem is to accurately reconstruct the flood from whatever information can be gathered about the causal rainstorm (duration, depth and profile) and the state of the catchment before the storm. The unit hydrograph and losses model is applied to these observed inputs to simulate the event. The recommended approach avoids unnecessary assumptions, and allows a wide range of information to be incorporated when making the assessment.

The reliability of the simulation will be very much dependent on the quality of the rainfall and antecedent condition input information, and also on the quality of the unit hydrograph and losses model parameters. Section 2.1.4 discusses the various methods available for determining the unit hydrograph and losses model parameters. Simulation using catchment-descriptor estimates of the model parameters provides only a rough estimate of the peak flow for a notable event. An improved estimate of the peak flow will be obtained if the simulation uses model parameters derived from analysing local flood event data. On gauged catchments, the reliability of the simulated flood hydrograph can be judged immediately by reference to the observed flow data. However, on ungauged catchments, it is necessary that as much local information as possible has been used to ensure that the simulated flood hydrograph is reasonable. It may be necessary to utilise alternative methods for estimating a flow peak, such as wrack mark evidence (Dalrymple and Benson, 1967) and geomorphological evidence (Carling and Grodek, 1994).

5.1.2 Return period assessment — how rare was that flood?

Prior to publication of the FSR, the rarity aspect was usually tackled by estimating the return period of the storm rainfall and assuming that this was indicative of the return period of the resultant flood. However, making inferences about flood rarity from rainfall rarity is a proverbial minefield as catchment response depends on several contributory factors, as explained in §3.2.2. Therefore, such an approach can provide only a first approximation, and can give misleading results if, for example, the storm occurred on an exceptionally dry catchment, or if the duration of the storm was much different from that which is normally critical to flooding at the site in question. Other features of the rainstorm, such as its spatial distribution or its temporal profile, can also affect the severity of the resultant flood.

In the FSSR12 approach, the return period of a simulated flood event is estimated from the catchment flood frequency curve, without reference to flow data.

5.2 Observed rainfall and antecedent condition inputs

The inputs required to reconstruct an event are the appropriate observed storm variables (i.e. the duration, depth and profile) and antecedent conditions. This information includes many of the data items required for the analysis of observed flood events, described in Appendix A. Section A.3 discusses the data-gathering process, and lists the usual suppliers of the various data. Figure 5.1 shows the influence of these inputs with respect to the steps in the simulation of the flood.

Figure 5.2 shows the definition of an observed storm event that caused a notable flood on the River Bourne at Hadlow (40006). The data required to simulate the event are shown. The storm event starts at 01:00 on 15 September 1968 and finishes at 16:00 on the same day. A hydrological day typically runs from 09:00:00 on one day to 08:59:59 on the following day. Therefore, the storm event spans two hydrological days, starting on 14 September and finishing on 15 September. Recording raingauge and daily raingauge data are required for both days, 14 and 15 September, to specify the event rainfall and to identify any rain that falls between 09:00 on 14 September and the start of the event.

The state of the catchment prior to the storm is referred to as the antecedent catchment wetness, and is indexed by the catchment wetness index *CWI*. Section 4.2 of Appendix A describes how *CWI* is defined in terms of pre-event soil moisture deficit *SMD* and a 5-day antecedent precipitation index *API*5:

$$CWI = 125 + API5 - SMD \qquad \text{(A.1)}$$

A *CWI* value is required for the time when the storm event starts i.e. 01:00 on 15 September. *CWI* is first calculated at 09:00 on the first day of the event, i.e. 14 September. This *CWI* is then adjusted for the amount by which the catchment wets up or dries out between 09:00 and the start of the storm event, to give *CWI* at the start of the event. Daily raingauge data are required for the five days prior to the event, 9 to 13 September inclusive, to specify *API*5. *SMD* data on the first day of the event, 14 September, are also needed.

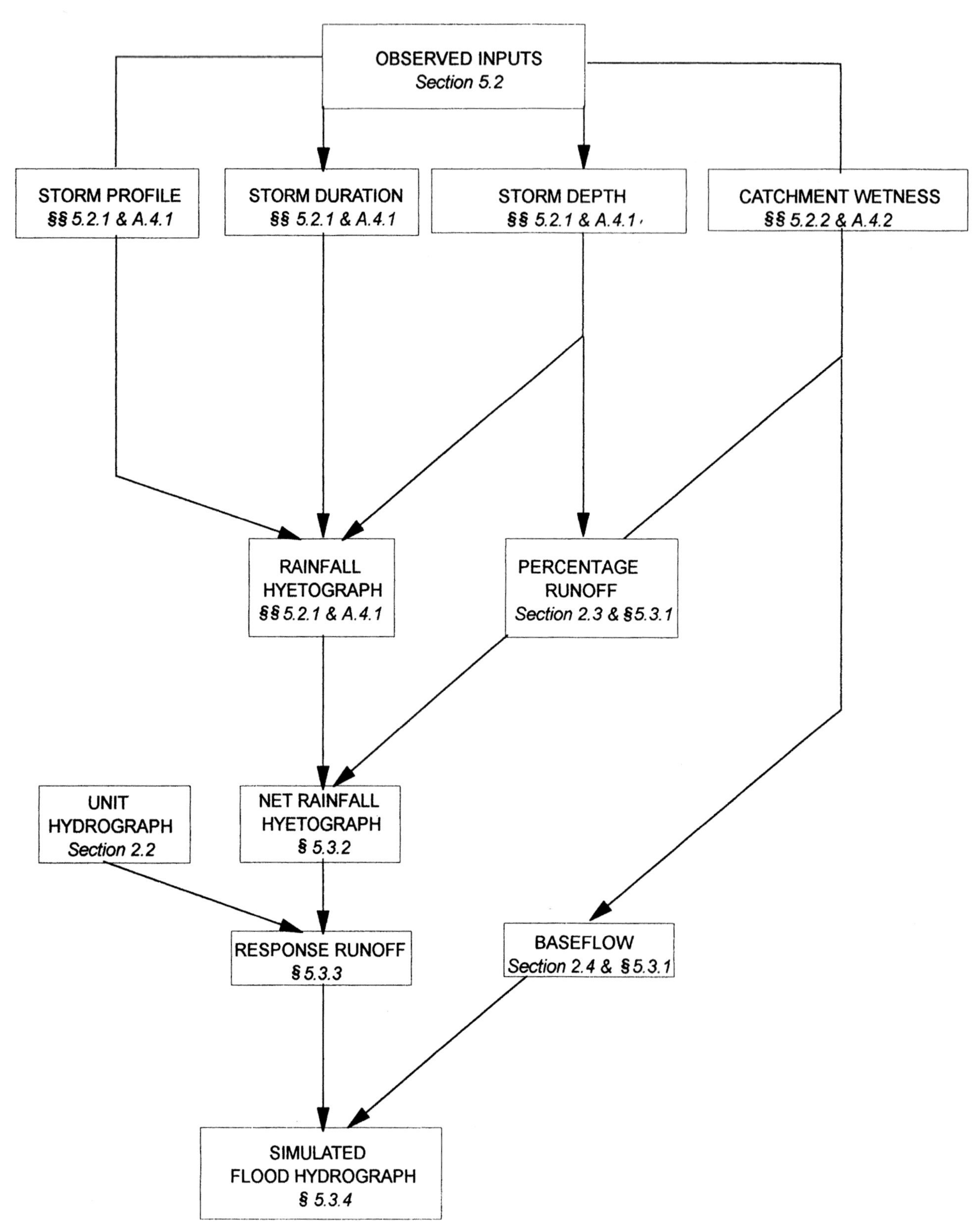

Figure 5.1 *Influence of observed inputs and the steps in the simulation of a notable event*

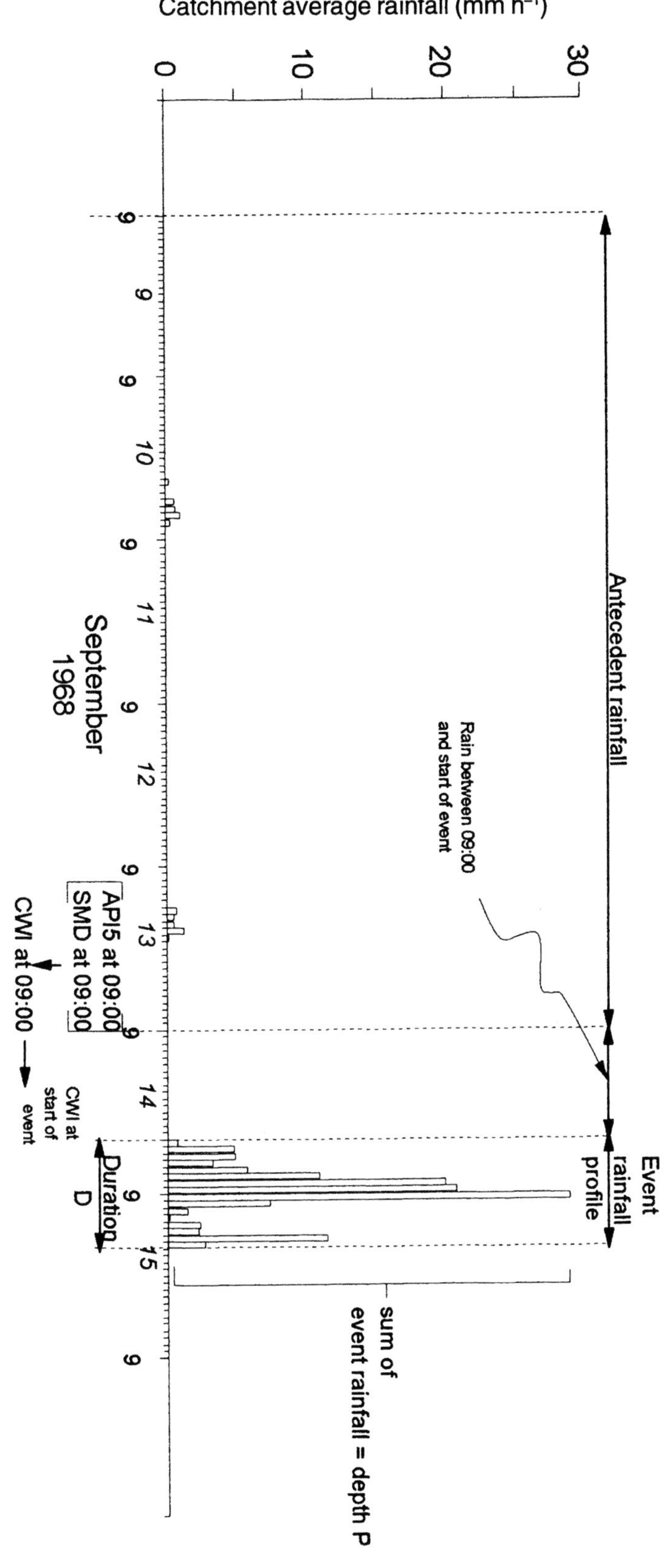

Figure 5.2 *Definition of event inputs: September 1968 event on the River Bourne at Hadlow*

5.2.1 Observed event and antecedent rainfall

Specification of the event rainfall and antecedent rainfall, and identification of any rain that falls between 09:00 of the first day of the event and the start of the event, are ideally accomplished by deriving the catchment average rainfall for the event. Distinguishing between event and antecedent rainfall and identifying the bursts of rainfall which were directly responsible for the flood can sometimes be difficult, and a certain amount of judgement may have to be used, for example in deciding whether to divide a multi-burst storm into antecedent rainfall (contributing to the initial catchment wetness) and event rainfall (contributing directly to the flood).

Traditional procedures for deriving catchment average rainfall, such as that used in the FSR, require at least one recording raingauge, ideally located toward the centre of the catchment, and several daily raingauges evenly distributed on, or close to, the catchment. Radar-derived rainfall data can provide a valuable additional source of information, when used in conjunction with measurements from at least one conventional raingauge. Guidance on deriving catchment average event and antecedent rainfalls is provided in Section 4.1 of Appendix A.

If only daily raingauge data are available, it is possible to obtain a good estimate of the event storm depth, but it may be necessary to rely on qualitative knowledge of the duration and profile of the storm, e.g. "The heaviest rain fell around tea-time, and after that there was fairly steady rain until about mid-evening." Local recollections, newspaper accounts and Met. Office daily weather reports are possible sources of information. These can also be useful in corroborating the areal extent of the storm, and putting a recent flood into long-term perspective.

Storm duration

The storm duration D is the duration of the event rainfall in hours (see Example 5.1a). In the design case, the storm duration has to be an odd number of rainfall blocks (see §3.2.1), but for simulation of an observed event it is immaterial whether there is an odd number or an even number of rainfall blocks. However, should it prove impossible to gain even a rough estimate of storm duration, a design value should be used.

Storm depth

The storm depth P is the total of the rainfall depths in each of the individual blocks making up the event rainfall (see Example 5.1a). The design storm depth required for estimation of the T-year flood (see §3.2.2) is determined from rainfall duration-magnitude-frequency relationships once the duration and return period of the design storm are known. The same rainfall statistics can be used to estimate the return period of an observed storm event, where the duration and depth of the storm event are known (discussed in §5.4.1).

Storm profile

The storm profile is the term given to the temporal distribution of the event rainfall (see Example 5.1a). An observed storm profile is likely to be rather different in shape to the symmetrical, bell-shaped profiles used for design flood estimation (e.g. §3.2.3). However, if little information can be found about the temporal distribution of the rainfall, it may be necessary to assume some standard storm profile, e.g. the 75% winter profile which is broadly typical of flood-producing winter storms, or the 50% summer profile to represent a known thunderstorm.

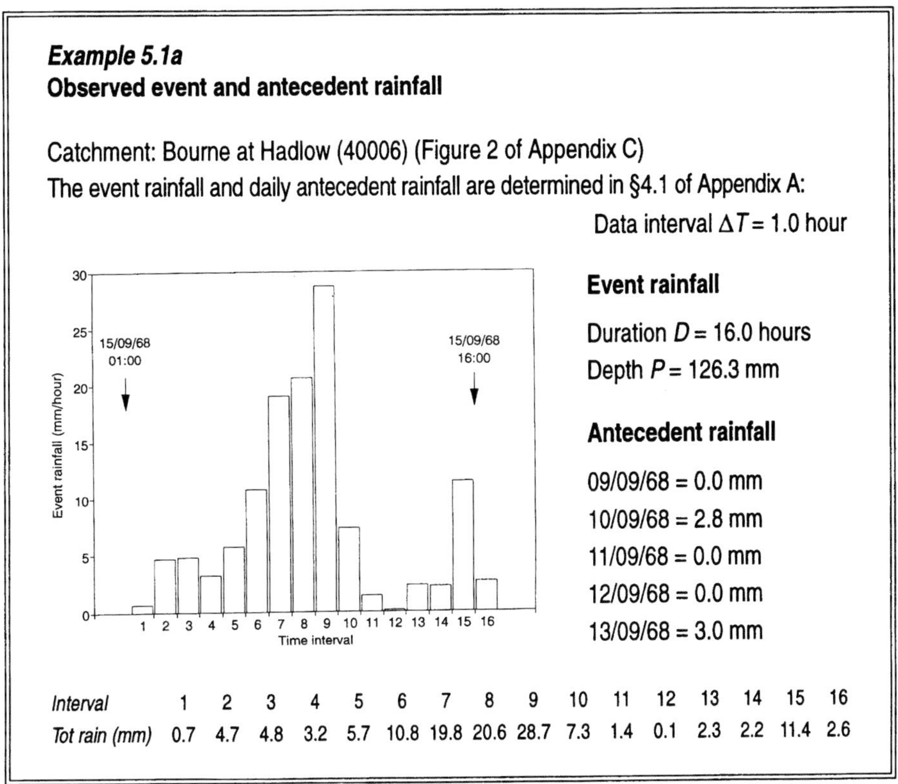

Example 5.1a
Observed event and antecedent rainfall

Catchment: Bourne at Hadlow (40006) (Figure 2 of Appendix C)
The event rainfall and daily antecedent rainfall are determined in §4.1 of Appendix A:

Data interval $\Delta T = 1.0$ hour

Event rainfall

Duration $D = 16.0$ hours
Depth $P = 126.3$ mm

Antecedent rainfall

09/09/68 = 0.0 mm
10/09/68 = 2.8 mm
11/09/68 = 0.0 mm
12/09/68 = 0.0 mm
13/09/68 = 3.0 mm

Interval	1	2	3	4	5	6	7	8	9	10	11	12	13	14	15	16
Tot rain (mm)	0.7	4.7	4.8	3.2	5.7	10.8	19.8	20.6	28.7	7.3	1.4	0.1	2.3	2.2	11.4	2.6

The input rainfall profile should be constructed to the same data interval as the unit hydrograph for the catchment, although if no better information is available it is permissible to assume that rain within the observing interval fell uniformly in time. For example, 10 mm in 1 hour might be assumed to have fallen as 5 mm in the first half-hour and 5 mm in the second.

5.2.2 Observed antecedent catchment wetness

Specification of the pre-event CWI is a two-stage process. *CWI* is first calculated at 09:00 on the first day of the event using 09:00 *SMD* and *API*5 values in Equation A.1:

$$CWI = 125 + API5 - SMD \tag{A.1}$$

The *SMD* term indicates the amount of water required to restore the soil to field capacity. In Winter months and in very wet conditions, *SMD* will usually be zero, which represents field capacity. The *API*5 term envelops the catchment average daily rainfall on the five days prior to the first day of the event, and allows for variations in catchment wetness above field capacity in Winter months when *SMD* is zero. The introduction of the constant of 125 is intended to ensure that *CWI* remains positive (because *SMD* rarely exceeds 125 mm).

This *CWI* value is then adjusted for the amount by which the catchment dries out or wets up between 09:00 and the start of the storm event. The adjustment is relatively straightforward. The *SMD* and *API*5 values at 09:00 are updated to give equivalent values at the start of each time interval until the event rainfall starts. By substituting the appropriate *SMD* and *API5* values into Equation A.1, the *CWI* can be recalculated at the start of each time interval until the event rainfall starts. Evaluation of *API5* and pre-event *CWI* is described in Section 4.2 of Appendix A (see Example 5.1b).

> ***Example 5.1b***
> **Observed antecedent catchment wetness**
>
> Catchment: Bourne at Hadlow (40006) (Figure 2 of Appendix C)
>
> The antecedent catchment wetness *CWI* is determined in Section 4.2 of Appendix A:
>
> *CWI* = 85.5 mm

5.3 Simulation of event

The notable flood is simulated from the observed rainfall and antecedent condition inputs by the following steps:

i Calculate the percentage runoff and baseflow, to completely specify the unit hydrograph and losses model;

ii Apply the percentage runoff to the total rainfall hyetograph to derive the net rainfall hyetograph;

iii Convolve the unit hydrograph with the net rainfall hyetograph to derive the rapid response runoff hydrograph;

iv Add the baseflow to the rapid response runoff hydrograph to derive the total runoff hydrograph.

The steps which make up this procedure mirror those for estimating the *T*-year flood in §3.3. The return period of the derived flood can be estimated by the method outlined in §5.4.

5.3.1 Calculation of percentage runoff and baseflow

The values of catchment wetness index *CWI* and storm depth *P*, determined in §5.2.2 and §5.2.1, respectively, can be substituted in Equations 2.14, 2.15 and 2.19 to calculate the percentage runoff and baseflow (if baseflow is being estimated from catchment descriptors), as shown in Example 5.1c.

Percentage runoff

The percentage runoff from the natural part of the catchment PR_{RURAL} is estimated in two parts: a standard component *SPR* representing the normal capacity of the catchment to generate runoff, and a dynamic component *DPR* representing the variation in the response depending on the state of the catchment prior to the storm and the storm magnitude itself. *DPR* is, thus, made up of two components: DPR_{CWI} dependent on *CWI*, and DPR_{RAIN} dependent on *P*:

$$PR_{RURAL} = SPR + DPR_{CWI} + DPR_{RAIN} \qquad (2.13)$$

Example 5.1c

Calculation of percentage runoff and baseflow

Catchment: Bourne at Hadlow (40006) (Figure 2 of Appendix C)

Relevant catchment descriptors and other information:
$SPR = 30.8\%$ (§2.3.3), $P = 126.3$ mm (§5.2.1), $CWI = 85.5$ mm (§5.2.2), $URBEXT = 0.024$, $AREA = 50.21$ km^2, $SAAR = 719$ mm

Percentage runoff

The percentage runoff *PR* appropriate to the design event is calculated using Equations 2.12 to 2.15:

$DPR_{CWI} = 0.25\ (CWI - 125)$

$$DPR_{CWI} = 0.25\ (85.5 - 125) = -9.9\%$$

$DPR_{RAIN} = 0.45\ (P - 40)^{0.7}$ [as $P > 40$ mm]

$$DPR_{RAIN} = 0.45\ (126.3 - 40)^{0.7} = -10.2\%$$

$PR_{RURAL} = SPR + DPR_{CWI} + DPR_{RAIN}$

$$PR_{RURAL} = 30.8 - 9.9 + 10.2 = 31.1\%$$

$PR = PR_{RURAL}\ (1.0 - 0.615\ URBEXT) + 70\ (0.615\ URBEXT)$

$$PR = 31.1\ (1.0 - 0.615 \times 0.024) + 70\ (0.615 \times 0.024) = 31.7\%$$

Baseflow

The baseflow *BF* is calculated using Equation 2.19:

$BF = \{33\ (CWI - 125) + 3.0\ SAAR + 5.5\}\ 10^{-5}\ AREA$

$$BF = \{33\ (85.5 - 125) + 3.0 \times 719 + 5.5\}\ 10^{-5} \times 50.21 = 0.43\ \text{m}^3\ \text{s}^{-1}$$

The various methods of estimating *SPR* are described in Section 2.3. The *DPR* equations are:

$$DPR_{CWI} = 0.25\ (CWI - 125) \qquad (2.14)$$

$$DPR_{RAIN} = \begin{cases} 0 & [\text{for } P \leq 40 \text{ mm}] \\ 0.45\ (P - 40)^{0.7} & [\text{for } P > 40 \text{ mm}] \end{cases} \qquad (2.15)$$

The total percentage runoff is estimated by adjusting PR_{RURAL} for the effects of catchment urbanisation:

$$PR = PR_{RURAL} (1.0 - 0.615\ URBEXT) + 70\ (0.615\ URBEXT) \qquad (2.12)$$

Baseflow

The various methods for estimating baseflow are discussed in Section 2.4. If baseflow is to be estimated from catchment descriptors, it is dependent on catchment area *AREA*, standard average annual rainfall *SAAR* and *CWI*:

$$BF = \{33\ (CWI - 125) + 3.0\ SAAR + 5.5\}\ 10^{-5}\ AREA \qquad (2.19)$$

5.3.2 Derivation of net rainfall hyetograph

Percentage runoff is applied as a constant proportional loss to each rainfall block through the storm event. The net (or effective) rainfall hyetograph is derived by multiplying each block of the total rainfall hyetograph (from §5.2.1) by the percentage runoff (from §5.3.1), as shown in Example 5.1d.

Example 5.1d
Derivation of net rainfall hyetograph

Catchment: Bourne at Hadlow (40006) (Figure 2 of Appendix C)

Relevant information:
PR = 31.7% (§5.3.1)

The net rainfall hyetograph is derived by applying the percentage runoff PR to each block of the total rainfall hyetograph from §5.2.1:

Interval	1	2	3	4	5	6	7	8	9	10	11	12	13	14	15	16
Tot rain (mm)	0.7	4.7	4.8	3.2	5.7	10.8	19.8	20.6	28.7	7.3	1.4	0.1	2.3	2.2	11.4	2.6
Net rain (mm)	0.2	1.5	1.5	1.0	1.8	3.4	6.3	6.5	9.1	2.3	0.4	0.0	0.7	0.7	3.6	0.8

The constant proportional loss model for percentage runoff is adequate for most applications, where the simulation is often being carried out for a notable flood event on an ungauged catchment. However, when simulating a flood event on a gauged catchment, where there are observed flow data through the event, an alternative decreasing proportional loss model for percentage runoff is available. In this approach, if the catchment is dry at the beginning of the storm, the loss-rate is initially high then reduces quickly as the catchment wets up; if it is wet at the beginning of the storm, the loss-rate is fairly constant through the event. Through the storm, percentage runoff is assumed to increase in proportion to *CWI*, whilst the loss-rate varies inversely with *CWI*. The decreasing proportional loss model is described in detail in Section 5.2 of Appendix A.

5.3.3 Derivation of rapid response runoff hydrograph

The rapid response runoff hydrograph is the product of convolving the unit hydrograph (from §2.2) with the net rainfall hyetograph (from §5.3.2). The theory behind the convolution procedure is described in §2.2.1. A typical convolution table is laid out in Example 5.1e. The ΔT-hourly ordinates of the ΔT-hour unit hydrograph are set out in the header row across the top of the table. The net rainfall values in cm per time step are set out in the column down the left-hand side of the table. They have been converted from mm to cm because the synthesised unit hydrograph refers to 10 mm or 1 cm input of net rainfall.

The convolution procedure starts by applying the first net rainfall value to each unit hydrograph ordinate in turn, the product being written directly beneath, thus forming the first row of the table. The process is repeated for the second net rainfall value forming the second row of the table, but the products entered are displaced one column to the right because the second rainfall value occurs one data interval after the first. The remaining net rainfalls are applied in the same way, and the columns are summed to give the rapid response runoff hydrograph, as illustrated.

5.3.4 Derivation of total runoff hydrograph

The total runoff hydrograph is obtained by simply adding the constant baseflow to each ordinate of the rapid response runoff hydrograph (Example 5.1e).

5.4 Assessment of return period

The return periods of a notable flood event and its causative storm are estimated by very similar procedures. In both instances, a frequency curve is constructed, and the return period of the notable event (the storm depth or the flood peak) simply read off.

5.4.1 Rainfall return period

The return period of the observed storm event is determined from the catchment rainfall frequency curve. The rainfall frequency curve is constructed from rainfall depth-duration-frequency statistics presented in Volume 2 and on the CD-ROM. The rainfall frequency curve is constructed by the following procedure:

i Abstract *T*-year *D*-hour point rainfalls *MT-Dh* for observed *D* and various *T*s using the CD-ROM (**2** 2);

ii Scale the *MT-Dh* point rainfalls to equivalent *MT-Dh* catchment rainfalls using the appropriate *ARF* in the procedure from §3.2.2;

ii Plot *MT-Dh* catchment rainfalls against return period.

The return period of the rainfall is then estimated from this rainfall frequency relationship, as shown in Figure 5.3 and Example 5.2.

5.4.2 Flood return period

The return period of the flood event is determined from the catchment flood frequency curve constructed by the design event method described in Chapter 3. The return period of the peak flow is then estimated from this flood frequency relationship, as shown in Figure 5.3 and Example 5.2.

Example 5.1e
Derivation of rapid response runoff hydrograph and total runoff hydrograph

Catchment: Bourne at Hadlow (40006) (Figure 2 of Appendix C)

Rapid response runoff hydrograph

The convolution of the 1-hour unit hydrograph from §2.2.3 and the net rainfall hyetograph from §5.3.2 may be set out as a table. The 1-hour ordinates of the unit hydrograph are set out in the header row across the top of the table. The net rainfall values in cm are set out in the column down the left-hand side of the table. The first net rainfall value is applied to each unit hydrograph ordinate in turn, and the product written directly beneath, forming the first row of the table. The second rainfall value is applied to each unit hydrograph ordinate in turn, but the product entered is displaced one column to the right. The rest of the table is constructed in a similar fashion, as illustrated. The column sums give the rapid response runoff hydrograph.

Total runoff hydrograph

The total runoff hydrograph is obtained by adding the baseflow *BF* from §5.3.1 to each ordinate of the rapid response runoff hydrograph. The simulated flood peak for the 15 September 1968 event on the Bourne at Hadlow is estimated as 44.57 $m^3 s^{-1}$ and the complete hydrograph is also obtained.

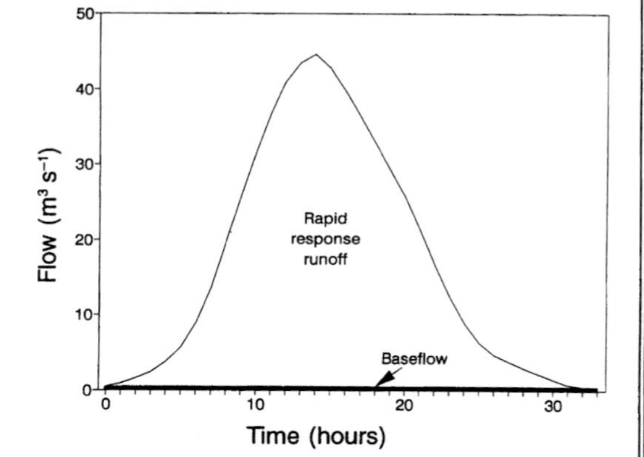

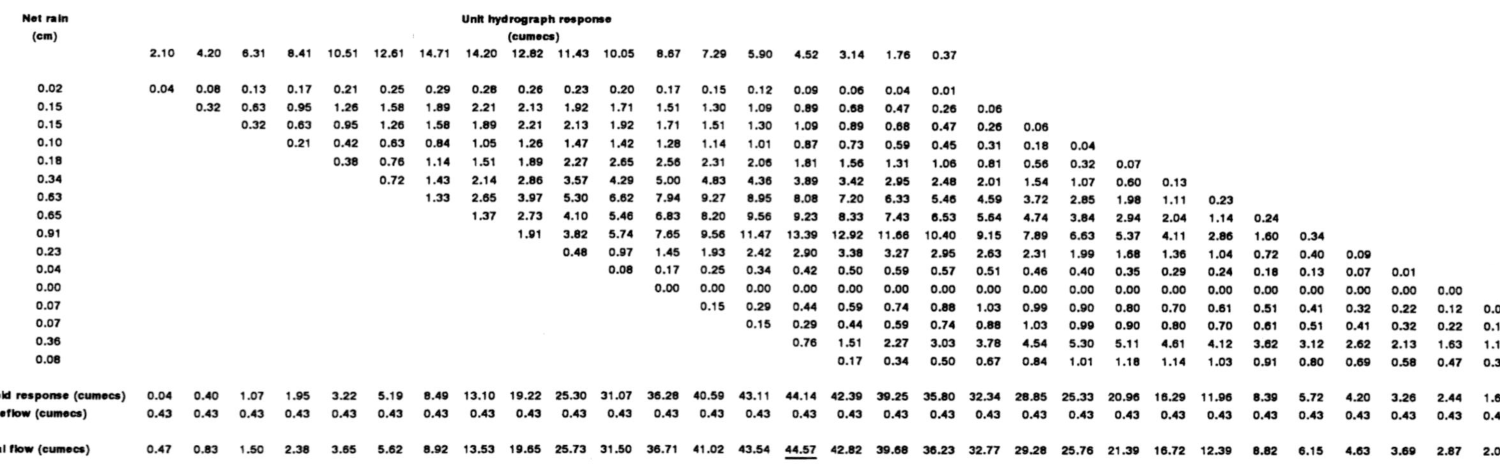

Net rain (cm)	Unit hydrograph response (cumecs)																														
	2.10	4.20	6.31	8.41	10.51	12.61	14.71	14.20	12.82	11.43	10.05	8.67	7.29	5.90	4.52	3.14	1.76	0.37													
0.02	0.04	0.08	0.13	0.17	0.21	0.25	0.29	0.28	0.26	0.23	0.20	0.17	0.15	0.12	0.09	0.06	0.04	0.01													
0.15		0.32	0.63	0.95	1.26	1.58	1.89	2.21	2.13	1.92	1.71	1.51	1.30	1.09	0.89	0.68	0.47	0.26	0.06												
0.15			0.32	0.63	0.95	1.26	1.58	1.89	2.21	2.13	1.92	1.71	1.51	1.30	1.09	0.89	0.68	0.47	0.26	0.06											
0.10				0.21	0.42	0.63	0.84	1.05	1.26	1.47	1.42	1.28	1.14	1.01	0.87	0.73	0.59	0.45	0.31	0.18	0.04										
0.18					0.38	0.76	1.14	1.51	1.89	2.27	2.65	2.56	2.31	2.06	1.81	1.56	1.31	1.06	0.81	0.56	0.32	0.07									
0.34						0.72	1.43	2.14	2.86	3.57	4.29	5.00	4.83	4.36	3.89	3.42	2.95	2.48	2.01	1.54	1.07	0.60	0.13								
0.63							1.33	2.65	3.97	5.30	6.62	7.94	9.27	8.95	8.08	7.20	6.33	5.46	4.59	3.72	2.85	1.98	1.11	0.23							
0.65								1.37	2.73	4.10	5.46	6.83	8.20	9.56	9.23	8.33	7.43	6.53	5.64	4.74	3.84	2.94	2.04	1.14	0.24						
0.91									1.91	3.82	5.74	7.65	9.56	11.47	13.39	12.92	11.66	10.40	9.15	7.89	6.63	5.37	4.11	2.86	1.60	0.34					
0.23										0.48	0.97	1.45	1.93	2.42	2.90	3.38	3.27	2.95	2.63	2.31	1.99	1.68	1.36	1.04	0.72	0.40	0.09				
0.04											0.08	0.17	0.25	0.34	0.42	0.50	0.59	0.57	0.51	0.46	0.40	0.35	0.29	0.24	0.18	0.13	0.07	0.01			
0.00												0.00	0.00	0.00	0.00	0.00	0.00	0.00	0.00	0.00	0.00	0.00	0.00	0.00	0.00	0.00	0.00	0.00	0.00		
0.07													0.15	0.29	0.44	0.59	0.74	0.88	1.03	0.99	0.90	0.80	0.70	0.61	0.51	0.41	0.32	0.22	0.12	0.03	
0.07														0.15	0.29	0.44	0.59	0.74	0.88	1.03	0.99	0.90	0.80	0.70	0.61	0.51	0.41	0.32	0.22	0.12	0.03
0.36															0.76	1.51	2.27	3.03	3.78	4.54	5.30	5.11	4.61	4.12	3.62	3.12	2.62	2.13	1.63	1.13	0.63
0.08																0.17	0.34	0.50	0.67	0.84	1.01	1.18	1.14	1.03	0.91	0.80	0.69	0.58	0.47	0.36	0.25
Rapid response (cumecs)	0.04	0.40	1.07	1.95	3.22	5.19	8.49	13.10	19.22	25.30	31.07	36.28	40.59	43.11	44.14	42.39	39.25	35.80	32.34	28.85	25.33	20.96	16.29	11.96	8.39	5.72	4.20	3.26	2.44	1.64	0.91
Baseflow (cumecs)	0.43	0.43	0.43	0.43	0.43	0.43	0.43	0.43	0.43	0.43	0.43	0.43	0.43	0.43	0.43	0.43	0.43	0.43	0.43	0.43	0.43	0.43	0.43	0.43	0.43	0.43	0.43	0.43	0.43	0.43	0.43
Total flow (cumecs)	0.47	0.83	1.50	2.38	3.65	5.62	8.92	13.53	19.65	25.73	31.50	36.71	41.02	43.54	44.57	42.82	39.68	36.23	32.77	29.28	25.76	21.39	16.72	12.39	8.82	6.15	4.63	3.69	2.87	2.07	1.34

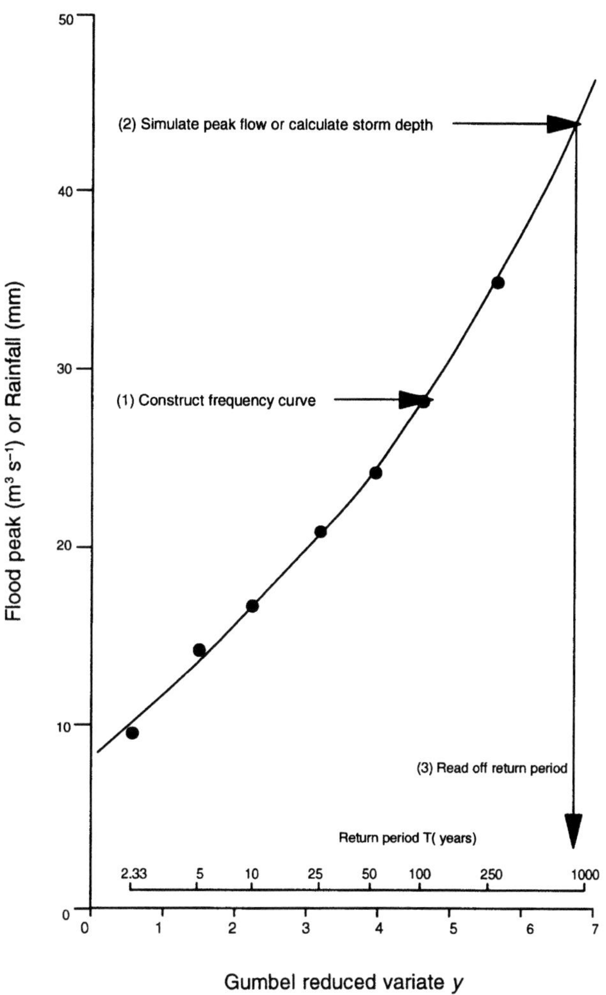

***Figure 5.3** Stages in assessment of flood or rainfall return period*

Assessment of flood return period by this method is less sensitive to imperfections in the unit hydrograph and losses model than might appear at first sight. This is because any slight bias of the unit hydrograph and losses model in constructing the flood frequency curve for the catchment is likely to be compensated by a similar bias in simulating the notable event. For example, if the SPR model parameter is in error, the consequent over- or underestimation in the design flood peaks making up the flood frequency curve will be mirrored by a similar over- or under-estimation in simulating the notable event, leaving the inferred return period much the same. If the approach has a particular weakness, it is that it accords much importance to conditions experienced in one (probably extreme) event, which may or may not be typical of other events on the catchment.

Example 5.2
Rainfall and flood return periods

Catchment: Bourne at Hadlow (40006) (Figure 2 of Appendix C)

Relevant catchment descriptors and other information:
AREA = 50.21 km^2, *P* = 126.3 mm (§5.2.1), *Q* = 44.57 m^3 s^{-1} (§5.3.4)

Rainfall return period

The rainfall frequency table for *D* = 16.0 hours (*ARF* = 0.940) is:

T (years)	2	10	20	50	100	500	1000	
Point P (mm)	34.0	54.7	65.7	83.1	99.1	148.9	177.4	
Catch P (mm)	32.0	51.4	61.8	78.1	93.2	140.0	166.8	T_R = 350 years

Flood return period

The flood frequency table from the design event method is:

T (years)	2.33	10	30	50	100	500	1000	
Q_T *(m³s⁻¹)*	10.16	20.29	28.58	33.28	39.62	59.76	75.05	T_F = 150 years

The return periods are different, in this case with $T_R > T_F$. There is no reason why the return periods should be the same, and for another event it might be that $T_F > T_R$. What is actually being compared is the return period of the output with the return period of one of the inputs.

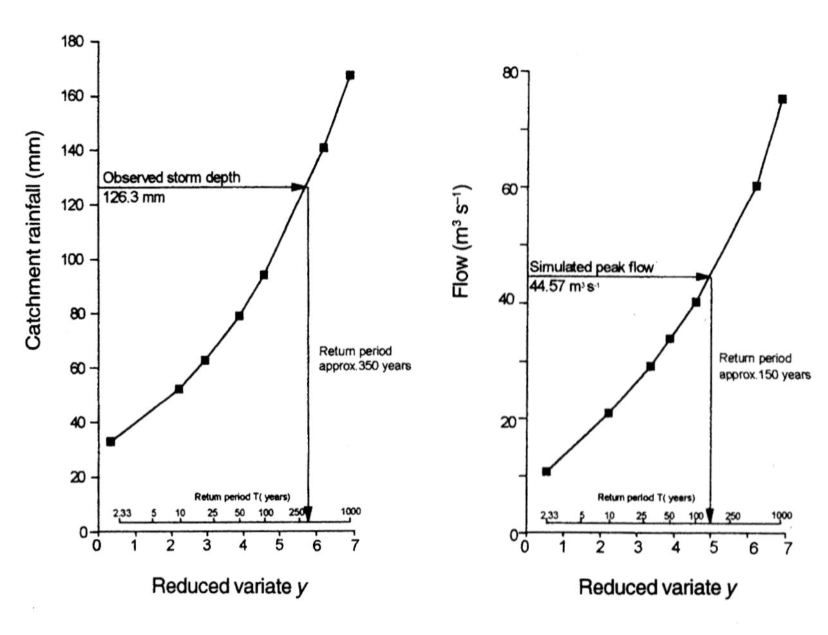

Chapter 6 Worked examples

6.1 Introduction

This chapter combines the procedures given in Chapters 2 to 5, through presention of three complete worked examples illustrating different applications of the FSR rainfall-runoff method. Sections 6.2 and 6.3 cover estimation of the *T*-year flood and the PMF, respectively. Section 6.4 illustrates simulation of a notable flood. In each example, the specific numerical values are given on the right-hand side of the page, alongside the description of the general procedure.

6.2 T-year flood estimation

Catchment: Ballysally Blagh at University of Ulster (203050) (Figure 5, Appendix C)

Relevant catchment descriptors:
AREA = 14.73 km^2, *URBEXT* (from $URBAN_{50K}$: see **5** 6.5, §§6.5.3 and 6.5.4) = 0.077, *SAAR* = 971 mm

1. **Estimation of *Tp*(0) and unit hydrograph**

The IUH time-to-peak *Tp*(0) is derived from the flood event analysis results in Table 3 of Appendix A:

The *Tp*(0) values range from 1.3 hours to 5.5 hours, with a geometric mean of 2.84 hours: *Tp*(0) = 2.84 hours

20% of 2.84 hours is 0.57 hours, so a 0.5-hour data interval is appropriate. *Tp*(0) is adjusted for the data interval ΔT using Equation 2.4: $\Delta T = 0.5$ hours

$Tp(\Delta T) = Tp(0) + \Delta T/2$ $\qquad$ $Tp(0.5) = 2.84 + 0.5/2 = 3.09$ hours

$Tp(\Delta T)$ is hereafter referred to simply as *Tp*. The unit hydrograph peak *Up* and the time base *TB* are derived from *Tp* using Equations 2.6 and 2.7:

$Up = (2.2 / Tp)\ AREA$ $\qquad$ $Up = (2.2 / 3.09)\ 14.73 = 10.49\ m^3 s^{-1}$

$TB = 2.52\ Tp$ $\qquad$ $TB = 2.52 \times 3.09 = 7.79$ hours

The triangular unit hydrograph may be drawn, and ordinates u_i can be read off at ΔT-hourly intervals or calculated using Equation 2.8.

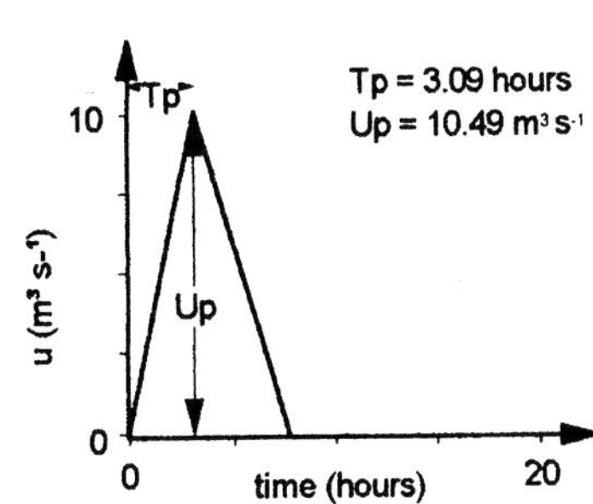

2. **Calculation of design storm duration *D***

The design storm duration *D* is calculated from *Tp* and *SAAR* using Equation 3.1:

$D = Tp\ (1 + SAAR / 1000)$ $\qquad$ $D = 3.09\ (1 + 971 / 1000) = 6.09$ hours

In this instance, $\Delta T = 0.5$ hours, so *D* is rounded up to 6.5 hours which is the nearest odd integer multiple of ΔT:
D = 6.5 hours

3. Calculation of design storm depth *P*

Determining appropriate rainfall return period T_R:

Decide upon flood return period T_F: T_F = 100 years

URBEXT < 0.125, so the appropriate rainfall return period T_R is obtained from Figure 3.2 / Table 3.1:

T_R = 140 years

Abstracting *T*-year *D*-hour point rainfall *MT-Dh*:

MT-Dh(point) is abstracted from the CD-ROM: M140-6.5h(point) = 60.0 mm

Calculating design storm depth *P*:

The design storm depth *P* is the *T*-year *D*-hour catchment rainfall, calculated by scaling *MT-Dh*(point) by an areal reduction factor *ARF*. The *ARF* appropriate to the catchment area and storm duration is obtained from Figure 3.4:

$ARF_{6.5}$ = 0.950

P is calculated using Equation 3.2:

$$P = MT\text{-}Dh(\text{catchment}) = ARF_D\, MT\text{-}Dh(\text{point})$$

P = 0.950 (60.0)
= 57.0 mm

4. Derivation of design storm profile

The design storm depth *P* is distributed within the design storm duration *D* using the appropriate design storm profile. *URBEXT* < 0.125, so the appropriate profile is the 75% winter profile from Figure 3.5b:

% D	7.7	23.1	38.5	53.9	69.2	84.6	100.0
% P	20.0	49.5	69.0	82.0	90.5	96.2	100.0
Diff (%)	20.0	29.5	19.5	13.0	8.5	5.7	3.8
Diff (mm)	11.4	16.8	11.2	7.4	4.8	3.2	2.2

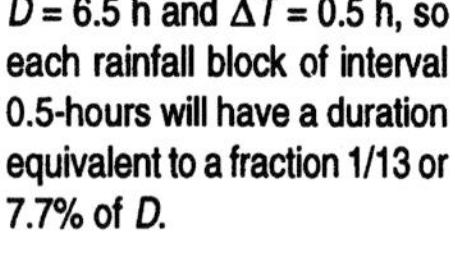
D = 6.5 h and ΔT = 0.5 h, so each rainfall block of interval 0.5-hours will have a duration equivalent to a fraction 1/13 or 7.7% of *D*.

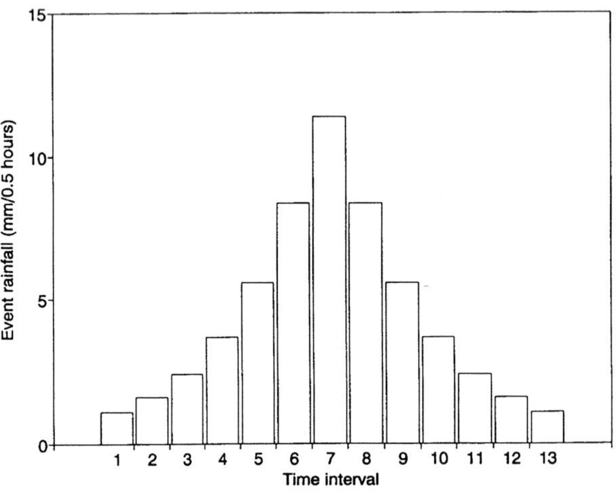

The storm is centred on the 0.5-hour period occurring between 3 and 3.5 h after storm commencement. This peak period represents 1/13 or 7.7% of *D* and the 75% winter profile specifies that thiscontains 20% of *P*.

The central 3 periods of the storm represent 3/13 or 23.1% of the storm duration. This contains 49.5% of *P*. Of this, 20% occurs in the central 0.5 hours; the remaining 29.5% of the depth (i.e. 49.5% – 20%) is divided between the two outer 0.5-hour periods, with 14.7% of *P* in each.

Interval	1	2	3	4	5	6	7	8	9	10	11	12	13
Tot rain (mm)	1.1	1.6	2.4	3.7	5.6	8.4	11.4	8.4	5.6	3.7	2.4	1.6	1.1

The rest of the profile is constructed in a similar way, as shown.

5. Derivation of design antecedent catchment wetness *CWI*

The design antecedent catchment wetness *CWI* is obtained for the appropriate value of *SAAR* from Figure 3.7:

CWI = 123.3 mm

6. **Calculation of percentage runoff**

The standard percentage runoff *SPR* is derived from catchment descriptors using Equation 2.17:

$SPR = SPRHOST = \Sigma_1^{29} SPR_i HOST_i$ $\qquad SPR = 29.9\%$

The percentage runoff *PR* appropriate to the design event is calculated using Equations 2.12 to 2.15:

$DPR_{CWI} = 0.25\ (CWI - 125)$ $\qquad DPR_{CWI} = 0.25\ (123.3 - 125) = -0.4\%$

$DPR_{RAIN} = 0.45\ (P - 40)^{0.7}$ [as $P > 40$ mm] $\qquad DPR_{RAIN} = 0.45\ (57.0 - 40)^{0.7} = 3.3\%$

$PR_{RURAL} = SPR + DPR_{CWI} + DPR_{RAIN}$ $\qquad PR_{RURAL} = 29.9 - 0.4 + 3.3 = 32.8\%$

$PR = PR_{RURAL}\ (1.0 - 0.615\ URBEXT) + 70\ (0.615\ URBEXT)$

$PR = 32.8\ (1.0 - 0.615 \times 0.038) + 70\ (0.615 \times 0.038) = 33.7\%$

7. **Derivation of net event hyetograph**

The net rainfall hyetograph is derived by applying the percentage runoff PR to each block of the total rainfall hyetograph from Step 4:

Interval	1	2	3	4	5	6	7	8	9	10	11	12	13
Tot rain (mm)	1.1	1.6	2.4	3.7	5.6	8.4	11.4	8.4	5.6	3.7	2.4	1.6	1.1
Net rain (mm)	0.4	0.5	0.8	1.2	1.9	2.8	3.8	2.8	1.9	1.2	0.8	0.5	0.4

8. **Derivation of rapid response runoff hydrograph**

The convolution of the 0.5-hour unit hydrograph from Step 1 and the net rainfall hyetograph from Step 7 may be set out as a table overleaf. The 0.5-h ordinates of the unit hydrograph are set out in the header row across the top of the table. The net rainfall values (in cm per 0.5 h) are set out in the column down the left-hand side of the table. The first net rainfall value is applied to each unit hydrograph ordinate in turn, and the product written directly beneath, forming the first row of the table. The second rainfall value is applied to each unit hydrograph ordinate in turn, but the product entered is displaced one column to the right. The rest of the table is constructed in a similar way, as shown. The column sums give the rapid response runoff hydrograph.

9. **Calculation of baseflow**

The baseflow *BF* is calculated using Equation 2.19:

$BF = \{33\ (CWI - 125) + 3.0\ SAAR + 5.5\}\ 10^{-5}\ AREA$

$BF = \{33\ (123.3 - 125) + 3.0 \times 971 + 5.5\}\ 10^{-5} \times 14.73 = 0.42\ m^3s^{-1}$

10. **Derivation of total runoff hydrograph**

The total runoff hydrograph is obtained by adding the baseflow *BF* from Step 9 to each ordinate of the rapid response runoff hydrograph. The 100-year flood for the Ballysally Blagh at University of Ulster is estimated as 15.21 $m^3\ s^{-1}$ and the complete hydrograph is also obtained.

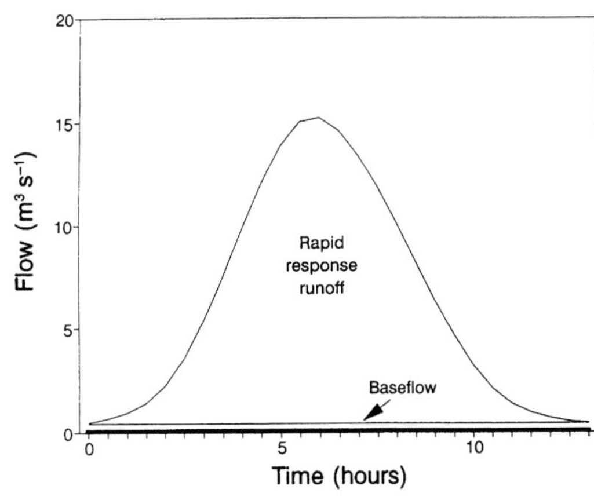

Net rain (cm)	Unit hydrograph response (cumecs)																							
	1.70	3.39	5.09	6.79	8.48	10.18	9.57	8.46	7.34	6.22	5.11	3.99	2.87	1.76	0.64									
0.04	0.07	0.14	0.20	0.27	0.34	0.41	0.38	0.34	0.29	0.25	0.20	0.16	0.11	0.07	0.03									
0.05		0.08	0.17	0.25	0.34	0.42	0.51	0.48	0.42	0.37	0.31	0.26	0.20	0.14	0.09	0.03								
0.08			0.14	0.27	0.41	0.54	0.68	0.81	0.77	0.68	0.59	0.50	0.41	0.32	0.23	0.14	0.05							
0.12				0.20	0.41	0.61	0.81	1.02	1.22	1.15	1.01	0.88	0.75	0.61	0.48	0.34	0.21	0.08						
0.19					0.32	0.64	0.97	1.29	1.61	1.93	1.82	1.61	1.39	1.18	0.97	0.76	0.55	0.33	0.12					
0.28						0.48	0.95	1.43	1.90	2.38	2.85	2.68	2.37	2.05	1.74	1.43	1.12	0.80	0.49	0.18				
0.38							0.64	1.29	1.93	2.58	3.22	3.87	3.64	3.21	2.79	2.36	1.94	1.52	1.09	0.67	0.24			
0.28								0.48	0.95	1.43	1.90	2.38	2.85	2.68	2.37	2.05	1.74	1.43	1.12	0.80	0.49	0.18		
0.19									0.32	0.64	0.97	1.29	1.61	1.93	1.82	1.61	1.39	1.18	0.97	0.76	0.55	0.33	0.12	
0.12										0.20	0.41	0.61	0.81	1.02	1.22	1.15	1.01	0.88	0.75	0.61	0.48	0.34	0.21	0.08
0.08											0.14	0.27	0.41	0.54	0.68	0.81	0.77	0.68	0.59	0.50	0.41	0.32	0.23	0.14
0.05												0.08	0.17	0.25	0.34	0.42	0.51	0.48	0.42	0.37	0.31	0.26	0.20	0.14
0.04													0.07	0.14	0.20	0.27	0.34	0.41	0.38	0.34	0.29	0.25	0.20	0.16
Rapid response (cumecs)	0.07	0.22	0.51	1.00	1.82	3.11	4.95	7.13	9.42	11.60	13.42	14.58	14.79	14.16	12.95	11.39	9.63	7.79	5.93	4.23	2.77	1.68	0.97	0.52
Baseflow (cumecs)	0.42	0.42	0.42	0.42	0.42	0.42	0.42	0.42	0.42	0.42	0.42	0.42	0.42	0.42	0.42	0.42	0.42	0.42	0.42	0.42	0.42	0.42	0.42	0.42
Total flow (cumecs)	0.49	0.64	0.93	1.42	2.24	3.53	5.37	7.55	9.84	12.02	13.84	15.00	15.21	14.58	13.37	11.81	10.05	8.21	6.35	4.65	3.19	2.10	1.39	0.94

6.3 Probable maximum flood estimation

Catchment: White Cart Water at Hawkhead (84012) (Figure 6 of Appendix C)

Relevant catchment descriptors:
AREA = 229.68 km^2, *URBEXT* = 0.127, *SAAR* = 1308 mm, EM-2h = 131 mm, EM-24h = 260 mm

1. **Estimation of *Tp*(0) and unit hydrograph**

The IUH time-to-peak *Tp*(0) is derived from the catchment lag results presented in Table 3 of Appendix A:

The LAG values range from 6.2 to 12.1 hours, with a geometric mean of 7.60 hours: LAG = 7.60 hours

Tp(0) is derived from LAG using Equation 2.9:

$Tp(0) = 0.879\ \mathrm{LAG}^{0.951}$ $\qquad$ $Tp(0) = 0.879\ (7.60)^{0.951}$
$= 6.05$ hours

Tp(0) is adjusted for PMF estimation using Equation 4.1:

$Tp(0)_{PMF} = 0.67\ Tp(0)$ $\qquad$ $Tp(0)_{PMF} = 0.67\ (6.05)$
$= 4.03$ hours

20% of 4.03 hours is 0.81 hours, so a 0.5-hour data interval is appropriate. *Tp*(0) is adjusted for the data interval ΔT using Equation 2.4: $\Delta T = 0.5$ hours

$Tp(\Delta T) = Tp(0) + \Delta T/2$ $\qquad$ $Tp(0.5) = 4.03 + 0.5 / 2$
$= 4.28$ hours

Tp(ΔT) is hereafter referred to simply as *Tp*. The unit hydrograph peak *Up* and the time base *TB* are derived from *Tp* using Equations 2.6 and 2.7:

$Up = (2.2 / Tp)\ AREA$ $\qquad$ $Up = (2.2 / 4.28)\ 229.28$
$= 117.85\ \mathrm{m^3\ s^{-1}}$

$TB = 2.52\ Tp$ $\qquad$ $TB = 2.52 \times 4.28$
$= 10.79$ hours

The triangular unit hydrograph may be drawn, and ordinates u_i can be read off at ΔT-hourly intervals or calculated using Equation 2.8.

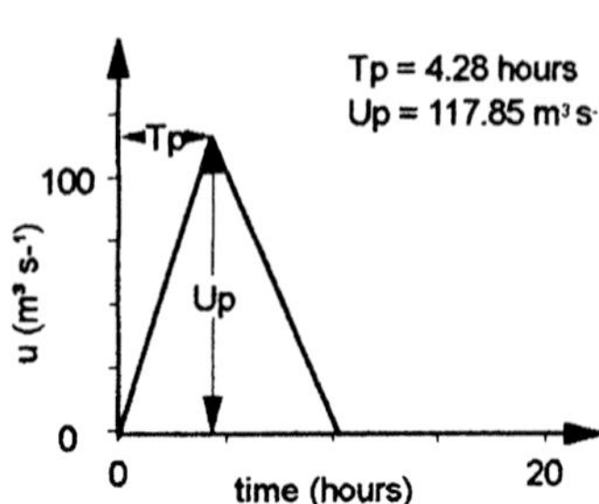

2. **Calculation of PMP design storm duration D**

The design storm duration *D* is calculated from *Tp* and *SAAR* using Equation 3.1:

$D = Tp\,(1 + SAAR / 1000)$ $D = 4.28\,(1 + 1308 / 1000)$
$= 9.88$ hours

In this instance, $\Delta T = 0.5$ hours so *D* is rounded down to 9.5 hours, which is the nearest odd integer multiple of ΔT:
$D = 9.5$ hours

3. **Derivation of PMP design storm hyetograph (depth and profile)**

Calculating all-year point EMPs and summer* point EMPs of durations between ΔT and 5*D*:

Duration (h)	0.5	1.0	2.0	24.0	48.0	
% EM-2h	0.65	0.83	-	-	-	from Table 4.1
% EM-24h	-	-	-	-	1.11	from Table 4.1
All-year (mm)	85.2	108.7	131.0	260.0	288.6	by calculation
Summer %	1.00	1.00	1.00	1.00	1.00	from Table 4.2
Summer (mm)	85.2	108.7	131.0	260.0	288.6	by calculation

e.g. for EM-0.5h:
from Table 4.1:
EM-30min / EM-2h = 0.65
EM-30min = 0.65 (EM-2h)
= 0.65 (131) = 85.2 mm

from Table 4.2:
SumEM-0.5h / AllyrEM-0.5h = 1.00
SumEM-0.5h = AllyrEM-0.5h
= 85.2 mm

* Alternative choice of winter PMP (§4.3.3)

Abstracting summer point EMPs and converting to summer catchment EMPs for durations ΔT, $3\Delta T$, $5\Delta T$, ..., *D*, and deriving the PMP design storm hyetograph:

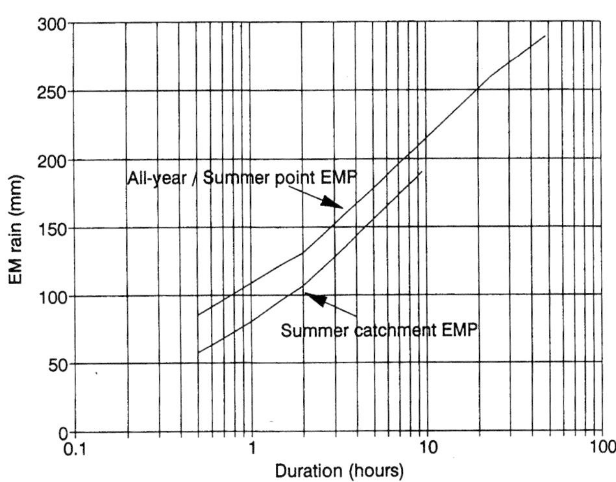

Duration (h)	0.5	1.5	2.5	3.5	4.5	5.5	6.5	7.5	8.5	9.5
Point P (mm)	85.2	121.7	142.6	160.1	173.1	183.5	192.2	199.6	206.1	211.9
ARF (Fig 3.4)	0.671	0.789	0.827	0.849	0.864	0.875	0.883	0.889	0.894	0.898
Catch P (mm)	57.2	96.0	118.0	136.0	149.6	160.6	169.8	177.5	184.2	**190.3**
Diff (mm)	-	38.8	22.0	18.0	13.6	11.0	9.2	7.7	6.7	6.1

$D = 9.5$ h and $\Delta T = 0.5$ h. Derivation of the PMP entails nesting the 0.5-hour Summer EMP within the 1.5-hour Summer EMP within the 3.5-h Summer EMP, etc., up to the duration 9.5 hours.

PMP design storm depth P = 9.5-hour catchment rainfall = 190.3 mm*

* Option to add snowmelt to catchment rainfall if Winter PMP (§4.3.3)

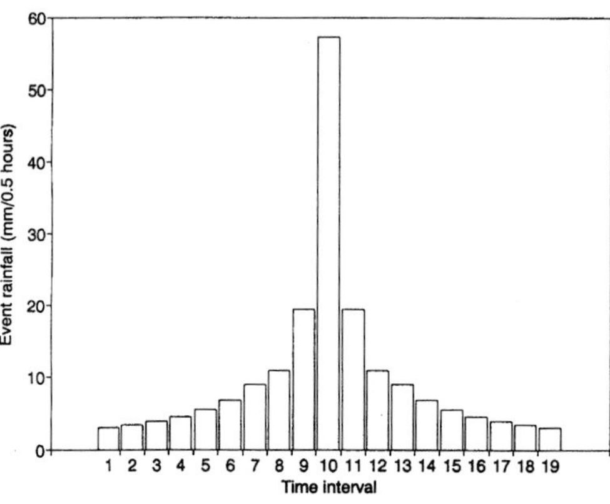

The peak period in the centre of the storm contains the 0.5-h rainfall depth 57.2 mm. The central 1.5-h period of the storm contains the 1.5-h rainfall depth 96.0 mm. Of this, 57.2 mm occurs in the central 0.5 h block, so the remaining 38.8 mm (96.0 – 57.2 mm) is divided between the two outer 0.5-h periods, with 19.4 mm in each. The rest of the profile is constructed in a similar way, as shown.

Interval	1	2	3	4	5	6	7	8	9	10	11	12	13	14	15	16	17	18	19
Rain mm	3.1	3.4	3.9	4.6	5.5	6.8	9.0	11.0	19.4	57.2	19.4	11.0	9.0	6.8	5.5	4.6	3.9	3.4	3.1

4. **Calculation of PMP design antecedent catchment wetness CWI**

The estimated maximum antecedent rainfall EMa is calculated using Equation 4.2, where the EM rainfalls are abstracted from the linear-log plot in Step 3 and the *ARFs* are abstracted from Figure 3.4:

$EMa = 0.5\ \{ARF_{5D}\ EM\text{-}5Dh - ARF_{D}\ EM\text{-}Dh\}$

$EMa = 0.5\ \{0.946\ (288.2) - 0.898\ (211.9)\}$
$= 41.2\ \text{mm}$

The PMP design antecedent catchment wetness *CWI* is calculated using Equation 4.4:

$CWI = 125 + EMa\ (0.5^{D/24})$

$CWI = 125 + 41.2\ (0.5^{9.5/24})$
$= 156.3\ \text{mm}^{*}$

* Option to add snowmelt to antecedent rainfall if Winter PMP (§4.3.4)

5. **Calculation of percentage runoff**

The standard percentage runoff *SPR* is derived from the flood event analysis results presented in Table 3, Appendix A:

The *SPR* values range from 47.7% to 72.7% with an arithmetic mean of 56.8%: SPR = 56.8%*

The percentage runoff *PR* appropriate to the design event is calculated using Equations 2.12 to 2.15:

$DPR_{CWI} = 0.25\ (CWI - 125)$

$DPR_{CWI} = 0.25\ (156.3 - 125)$
$= 7.8\%$

$DPR_{RAIN} = 0.45\ (P - 40)^{0.7}$ [as $P > 40$ mm]

$DPR_{RAIN} = 0.45\ (190.3 - 40)^{0.7}$
$= 15.0\%$

$PR_{RURAL} = SPR + DPR_{CWI} + DPR_{RAIN}$

$PR_{RURAL} = 56.8 + 7.8 + 15.0$
$= 79.6\%$

$PR = PR_{RURAL} > 70\%$ [as $PR_{RURAL} > 70\%$]

$PR = 79.6\%$

* *SPR* > 53% so frozen ground adjustment is not appropriate if Winter PMP (§4.2.2)

6. **Derivation of net event hyetograph**

The net rainfall hyetograph is derived by applying the percentage runoff *PR* to each block of the total rainfall hyetograph from Step 5:

Interval	1	2	3	4	5	6	7	8	9	10	11	12	13	14	15	16	17	18	19
Tot rain (mm)	3.1	3.4	3.9	4.6	5.5	6.8	9.0	11.0	19.4	57.2	19.4	11.0	9.0	6.8	5.5	4.6	3.9	3.4	3.1
Net rain (mm)	2.4	2.7	3.1	3.6	4.4	5.4	7.1	8.8	15.4	45.6	15.4	8.8	7.1	5.4	4.4	3.6	3.1	2.7	2.4

7. Derivation of rapid response runoff hydrograph

The convolution of the 0.5-hour unit hydrograph from Step 1 and the net rainfall hyetograph from Step 6 may be set out as a table. The 0.5-h ordinates of the unit hydrograph are set out in the header row across the top of the table. The net rainfall values (in cm per 0.5 h) are set out in the column down the left-hand side of the table. The first net rainfall value is applied to each unit hydrograph ordinate in turn, and the product written directly beneath, forming the first row of the table. The second rainfall value is applied to each unit hydrograph ordinate in turn, but the product entered is displaced one column to the right. The rest of the table is constructed in a similar way, as shown. The column sums give the rapid response runoff hydrograph.

8. Calculation of baseflow

The baseflow *BF* is calculated using Equation 2.19:

$$BF = \{33\,(CWI - 125) + 3.0\ SAAR + 5.5\}\ 10^{-5}\ AREA$$

$$BF = \{33\,(156.3 - 125) + 3.0 \times 1308 + 5.5\}\ 10^{-5} \times 229.68 = 11.40\ \text{m}^3\,\text{s}^{-1}$$

9. Derivation of total runoff hydrograph

The total runoff hydrograph is obtained by adding the baseflow *BF* from Step 8 to each ordinate of the rapid response runoff hydrograph. The PMF flood for the White Cart Water at Hawkhead is estimated as 1375.48 $\text{m}^3\,\text{s}^{-1}$ and the complete hydrograph is also obtained.

The PMF of 1375.48 $\text{m}^3\,\text{s}^{-1}$ derived from the Summer PMP compares with a PMF of 1233.27 $\text{m}^3\,\text{s}^{-1}$ derived from a Winter PMP with snowmelt. Hence, in this instance, the season providing the design flood is the Summer season.

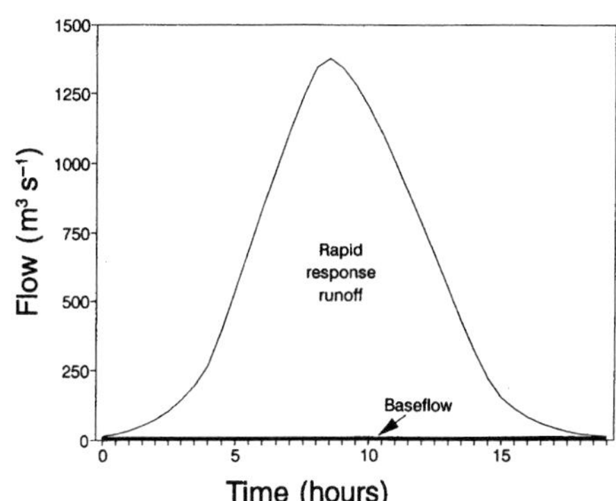

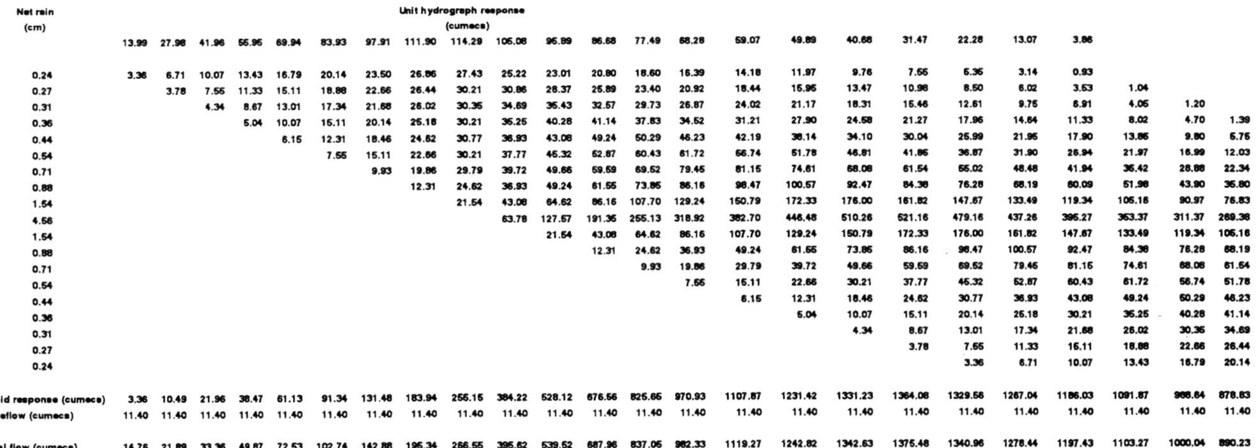

Net rain (cm)	Unit hydrograph response (cumecs)																							
	13.99	27.98	41.96	55.95	69.94	83.93	97.91	111.90	114.29	105.08	95.89	86.68	77.49	68.28	59.07	49.89	40.68	31.47	22.28	13.07	3.86			
0.24	3.36	6.71	10.07	13.43	16.79	20.14	23.50	26.86	27.43	25.22	23.01	20.80	18.60	16.39	14.18	11.97	9.76	7.55	5.35	3.14	0.93			
0.27		3.78	7.55	11.33	15.11	18.88	22.66	26.44	30.21	30.86	28.37	25.89	23.40	20.92	18.44	15.95	13.47	10.98	8.50	6.02	3.53	1.04		
0.31			4.34	8.67	13.01	17.34	21.68	26.02	30.35	34.69	35.43	32.57	29.73	26.87	24.02	21.17	18.31	15.46	12.61	9.75	6.91	4.05	1.20	
0.36				5.04	10.07	15.11	20.14	25.18	30.21	35.25	40.28	41.14	37.83	34.52	31.21	27.90	24.58	21.27	17.96	14.64	11.33	8.02	4.70	1.39
0.44					6.15	12.31	18.46	24.62	30.77	36.93	43.08	49.24	50.29	46.23	42.19	38.14	34.10	30.04	25.99	21.95	17.90	13.86	9.80	5.75
0.54						7.55	15.11	22.66	30.21	37.77	45.32	52.87	60.43	61.72	56.74	51.78	46.81	41.85	36.87	31.90	26.94	21.97	16.99	12.03
0.71							9.93	19.86	29.79	39.72	49.66	59.59	69.52	79.45	81.15	74.61	68.08	61.54	55.02	48.46	41.94	35.42	28.88	22.34
0.88								12.31	24.62	36.93	49.24	61.55	73.85	86.16	98.47	100.57	92.47	84.38	76.28	68.19	60.09	51.98	43.90	35.80
1.54									21.54	43.08	64.62	86.16	107.70	129.24	150.79	172.33	176.00	161.82	147.67	133.49	119.34	105.16	90.97	76.83
4.56										63.78	127.57	191.35	255.13	318.92	382.70	446.48	510.26	521.16	479.16	437.26	395.27	353.37	311.37	269.38
1.54											21.54	43.08	64.62	86.16	107.70	129.24	150.79	172.33	176.00	161.82	147.67	133.49	119.34	105.16
0.88												12.31	24.62	36.93	49.24	61.55	73.85	86.16	98.47	100.57	92.47	84.38	76.28	68.19
0.71													9.93	19.86	29.79	39.72	49.66	59.59	69.52	79.45	81.15	74.61	68.08	61.54
0.54														7.55	15.11	22.66	30.21	37.77	45.32	52.87	60.43	61.72	56.74	51.78
0.44															6.15	12.31	18.46	24.62	30.77	36.93	43.08	49.24	50.29	46.23
0.36																5.04	10.07	15.11	20.14	25.18	30.21	35.25	40.28	41.14
0.31																	4.34	8.67	13.01	17.34	21.68	26.02	30.35	34.69
0.27																		3.78	7.55	11.33	15.11	18.88	22.66	26.44
0.24																			3.36	6.71	10.07	13.43	16.79	20.14
Rapid response (cumecs)	3.36	10.49	21.96	38.47	61.13	91.34	131.48	183.94	255.15	384.22	528.12	676.56	825.65	970.93	1107.87	1231.42	1331.23	1364.08	1329.56	1267.04	1186.03	1091.87	988.64	878.83
Baseflow (cumecs)	11.40	11.40	11.40	11.40	11.40	11.40	11.40	11.40	11.40	11.40	11.40	11.40	11.40	11.40	11.40	11.40	11.40	11.40	11.40	11.40	11.40	11.40	11.40	11.40
Total flow (cumecs)	14.76	21.89	33.36	49.87	72.53	102.74	142.88	196.34	266.55	395.62	539.52	687.96	837.05	982.33	1119.27	1242.82	1342.63	1375.48	1340.96	1278.44	1197.43	1103.27	1000.04	890.23

6.4 Simulation of a notable event

Catchment: Kenwyn at Truro (48005) (Figure 7 of Appendix C) 11 October 1988 event

Relevant catchment descriptors:
AREA = 19.09 km^2, URBEXT = 0.031, SAAR = 1100 mm

1. Evaluation of catchment average event rainfall

The map shows the catchment boundary and centroid (+) and the location of daily raingauges (A, B) and one recording raingauge (*) with data over the period 05/10/88 to 11/10/88:

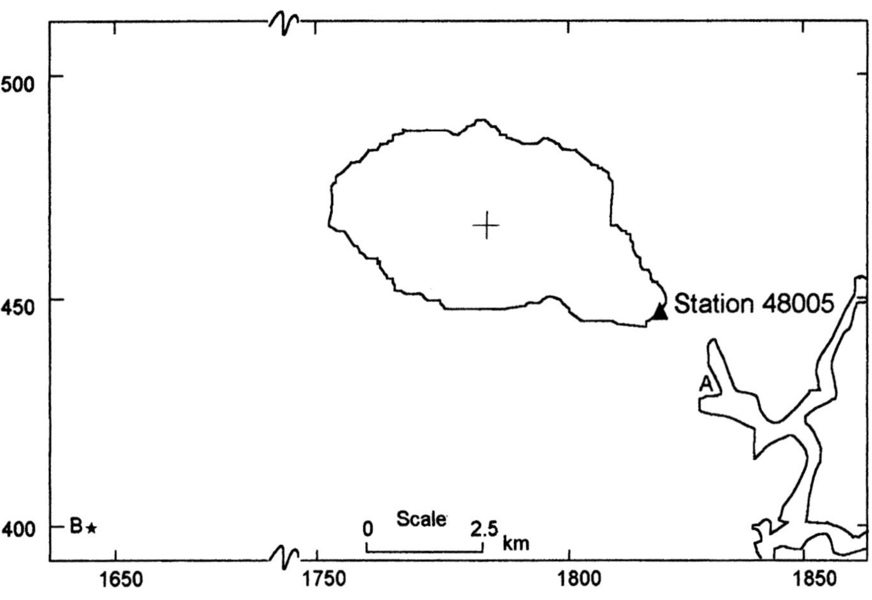

Event rainfall

Gauge	SAAR mm	Weight	10/10/88 mm	10/10/88 % SAAR	11/10/88 mm	11/10/88 % SAAR
A	1032	0.8655	11.4	1.1	32.4	3.1
B	1110	0.1345	22.7	2.0	18.5	1.7

10/10/88 weighted mean daily rainfall = 1.23% catch SAAR = 13.5 mm

11/10/88 weighted mean daily rainfall = 2.95% catch SAAR = 32.4 mm

Total = 45.9 mm

Hourly raingauge total = 39.1 mm between 04:00 11/10/88 and 14:00 11/10/88 plus 0.7 mm at 15:00 10/10/88, 0.7 mm 01:00 11/10/88 and 0.1 mm 19:00 11/10/88; 40.6 mm total

Interval	1	2	3	4	5	6	7	8	9	10	11
Gauge (mm)	1.0	3.8	7.9	5.4	2.8	4.8	3.2	2.3	3.3	3.3	1.3
Event (mm)	1.1	4.3	9.0	6.1	3.2	5.4	3.6	2.6	3.7	3.7	1.5

Scaling factor = 45.9 / 40.6 = 1.13

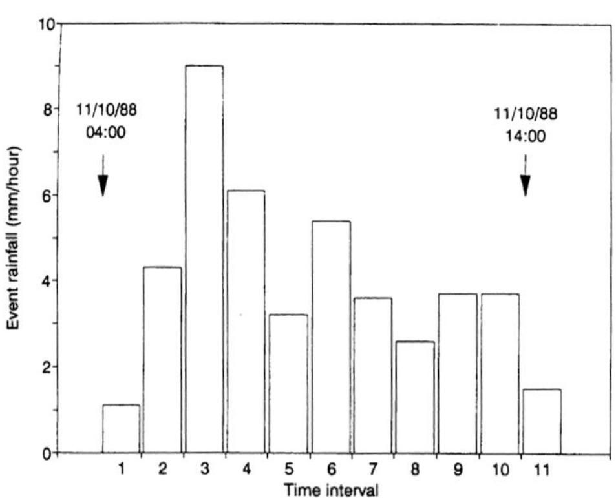

Event rainfall

Duration *D* = 11.0 hours

Depth *P* = 44.2 mm

plus 0.8 mm at 15:00 10/10/88 and 0.8 mm at 01:00 11/10/88 (see step 3)

2. Evaluation of catchment average antecedent rainfall

Gauge	*SAAR* mm	*Weight*	*05/10/88*	*06/10/88*	*07/10/88*	*08/10/88*	*09/10/88*
A	1032	0.8655	26.5	1.6	4.6	30.9	5.4
B	1110	0.1345	21.5	0.9	5.2	34.3	3.1

Antecedent rainfall

e.g. 05/10/88 weighted mean daily rainfall = 2.40% catch *SAAR* = 26.7 mm

Antecedent rainfall

05/10/88 = 26.7 mm
06/10/88 = 1.6 mm
07/10/88 = 5.0 mm
08/10/88 = 33.3 mm
09/10/88 = 5.4 mm

3. Evaluation of pre-event *CWI*

***CWI* at 09:00 on the first day of the event**

*API*5 at 09:00 on the first day of the event is calculated using Equation A.2:

$$API5 = (0.5)\,[P_{d-1} + (0.5)^2 P_{d-2} + (0.5)^3 P_{d-3} + (0.5)^4 P_{d-4} + (0.5)^5 P_{d-5}]$$

$$API5 = (0.5)\,[5.4 + (0.5)^2\,33.3 + (0.5)^3\,5.0 + (0.5)^4\,1.6 + (0.5)^5\,26.7] = 10.8\text{ mm}$$

SMD at 09:00 on the first day of the event is known:

SMD = 0.0 mm

CWI at 09:00 on the first day of the event is calculated using Equation A:1:

$$CWI = 125 + API5 - SMD$$

$$CWI = 125 + 10.8 - 0.0 = 135.8\text{ mm}$$

***CWI* at the start of the event**

As there is rainfall between 09:00 and the start of the event, *CWI* at the start of the event is calculated as in Table 1 of Appendix A:

Time at start of interval	*Total rain* mm	*SMD* mm	*API5 at start of interval (mm)*	*CWI* mm
09:00	0.0	0.0	10.8	135.8
10:00	0.0	0.0	10.5	135.5
11:00	0.0	0.0	10.2	135.2
12:00	0.0	0.0	9.9	134.9
13:00	0.0	0.0	9.6	134.6
14:00	0.0	0.0	9.3	134.3
15:00	0.8	0.0	9.1	134.1
16:00	0.0	0.0	8.8 + 0.8 = 9.6	134.6
17:00	0.0	0.0	9.3	134.3
18:00	0.0	0.0	9.0	134.0
19:00	0.0	0.0	8.8	133.8
20:00	0.0	0.0	8.5	133.5
21:00	0.0	0.0	8.3	133.3
22:00	0.0	0.0	8.1	133.1
23:00	0.0	0.0	7.8	132.8
00:00	0.0	0.0	7.6	132.6
01:00	0.8	0.0	7.4	132.4
02:00	0.0	0.0	7.2 + 0.8 = 8.0	133.0
03:00	0.0	0.0	7.7	132.7

$CWI_{04:00}$ = 132.7 mm

4. **Calculation of percentage runoff**

The standard percentage runoff *SPR* is derived from the flood event analysis results presented in Table 3 of Appendix A:

The *SPR* values range from 0.0% to 26.9% with an arithmetic mean of 12.9%: $SPR = 12.9\%$

The percentage runoff *PR* appropriate to the design event is calculated using Equations 2.12 to 2.15:

$DPR_{CWI} = 0.25\ (CWI - 125)$ — $DPR_{CWI} = 0.25\ (132.7 - 125) = 1.9\%$

$DPR_{RAIN} = 0.45\ (P - 40)^{0.7}$ [as $P > 40$ mm] — $DPR_{RAIN} = 0.45\ (44.3 - 40)^{0.7} = 1.3\%$

$PR_{RURAL} = SPR + DPR_{CWI} + DPR_{RAIN}$ — $PR_{RURAL} = 12.9 + 1.9 + 1.3 = 16.1\%$

$PR = PR_{RURAL}\ (1.0 - 0.615\ URBEXT) + 70\ (0.615\ URBEXT)$ — $PR = 16.1\ (1.0 - 0.615 \times 0.031) + 70\ (0.615 \times 0.031) = 17.1\%$

5. **Derivation of net event hyetograph**

The net rainfall hyetograph is derived by applying the percentage runoff PR to each block of the total rainfall hyetograph from Step 4:

Interval	1	2	3	4	5	6	7	8	9	10	11
Tot rain (mm)	1.1	4.3	9.0	6.1	3.2	5.4	3.6	2.6	3.7	3.7	1.5
Net rain (mm)	0.2	0.7	1.5	1.0	0.5	0.9	0.6	0.4	0.6	0.6	0.3

6. **Estimation of *Tp*(0) and unit hydrograph**

The IUH time-to-peak *Tp*(0) is derived from the flood event analysis results presented in Table 3 of Appendix A:

The *Tp*(0) values range from 2.5 to 7.6 hours, with a geometric mean of 3.67 hours: $Tp(0) = 3.67$ hours

20% of 3.67 hours is 0.73 hours so a 0.5-hour data interval is appropriate. *Tp*(0) is adjusted for the data interval ΔT using Equation 2.4:

$\Delta T = 0.5$ hours

$Tp(\Delta T) = Tp(0) + \Delta T/2$ — $Tp(0.5) = 3.67 + 0.5 / 2 = 3.92$ hours

$Tp(\Delta T)$ is hereafter referred to simply as *Tp*. The unit hydrograph peak *Up* and the time base *TB* are derived from *Tp* using Equations 2.6 and 2.7:

$Up = (2.2 / Tp)\ AREA$ — $Up = (2.2 / 3.92)\ 19.09 = 10.72\ m^3 s^{-1}$

$TB = 2.52\ Tp$ — $TB = 2.52 \times 3.92 = 9.88$ hours

The triangular unit hydrograph may be drawn, and ordinates u_i can be read off at ΔT-hourly intervals or calculated using Equation 2.8.

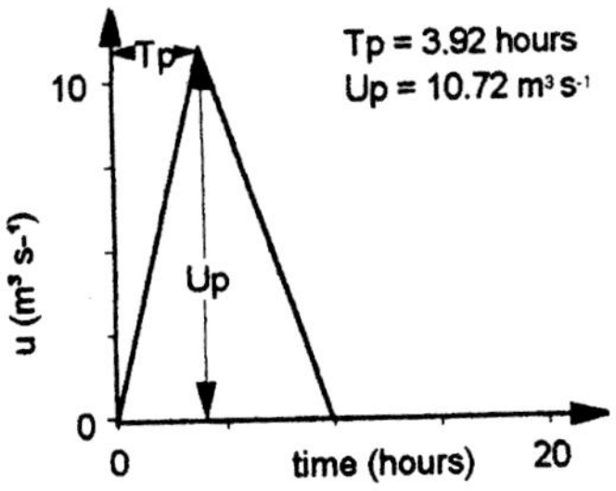

7. Derivation of rapid response runoff hydrograph

The unit hydrograph and rainfall profile should be constructed to the same data interval, but only hourly rainfall data are available, whereas the unit hydrograph is at a 0.5-hour data interval. Therefore, the rain is assumed to have fallen uniformly in time and each hourly net rainfall block is divided into two equal half-hourly blocks.

The convolution of the 0.5-hour unit hydrograph from Step 6 and the net rainfall hyetograph from Step 5 may be set out as a table. The 0.5-h ordinates of the unit hydrograph are set out in the header row across the top of the table. The net rainfall values in cm per 0.5 hours are set out in the column down the left-hand side of the table. The first net rainfall value is applied to each unit hydrograph ordinate in turn, and the product written directly beneath, forming the first row of the table. The second rainfall value is applied to each unit hydrograph ordinate in turn, but the product entered is displaced one column to the right. The rest of the table is constructed in a similar way, as shown. The column sums give the rapid response runoff hydrograph.

8. Calculation of baseflow

The baseflow *BF* is calculated using Equation 2.19:

$$BF = \{33\,(CWI - 125) + 3.0\ SAAR + 5.5\}\ 10^{-5}\ AREA$$

$$BF = \{33\,(132.7 - 125) + 3.0 \times 1100 + 5.5\}\ 10^{-5} \times 19.09 = 0.68\ \text{m}^3\,\text{s}^{-1}$$

9. Derivation of total runoff hydrograph

The total runoff hydrograph is obtained by adding the baseflow *BF* from Step 7 to each ordinate of the rapid response runoff hydrograph. The simulated flood peak for the 11 October 1988 event on the Kenwyn at Truro is estimated as 5.04 $\text{m}^3\,\text{s}^{-1}$ and the complete hydrograph is also obtained.

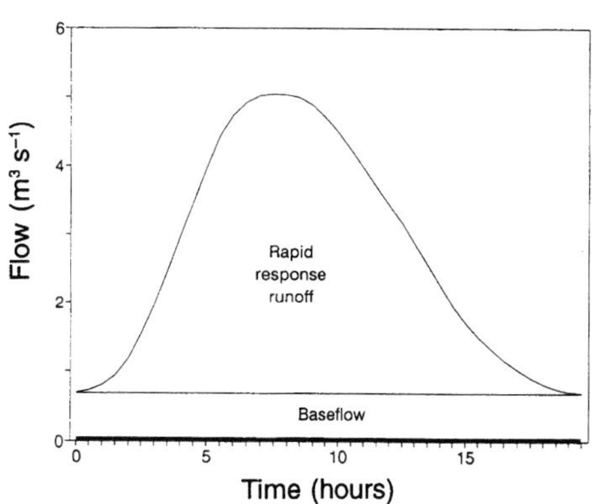

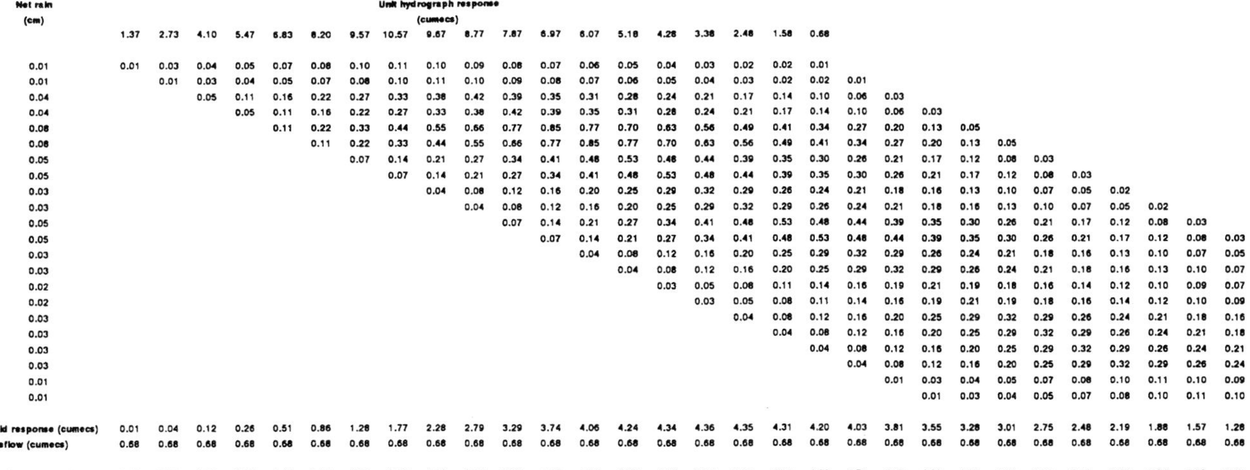

Net rain (cm)	Unit hydrograph response (cumecs)																													
	1.37	2.73	4.10	5.47	6.83	8.20	9.57	10.57	9.67	8.77	7.87	6.97	6.07	5.18	4.28	3.38	2.48	1.58	0.68											
0.01	0.01	0.03	0.04	0.05	0.07	0.08	0.10	0.11	0.10	0.09	0.08	0.07	0.06	0.05	0.04	0.03	0.02	0.02	0.01											
0.01		0.01	0.03	0.04	0.05	0.07	0.08	0.10	0.11	0.10	0.09	0.08	0.07	0.06	0.05	0.04	0.03	0.02	0.02	0.01										
0.04			0.05	0.11	0.16	0.22	0.27	0.33	0.38	0.42	0.39	0.35	0.31	0.28	0.24	0.21	0.17	0.14	0.10	0.06	0.03									
0.04				0.05	0.11	0.16	0.22	0.27	0.33	0.38	0.42	0.39	0.35	0.31	0.28	0.24	0.21	0.17	0.14	0.10	0.06	0.03								
0.08					0.11	0.22	0.33	0.44	0.55	0.66	0.77	0.85	0.77	0.70	0.63	0.56	0.49	0.41	0.34	0.27	0.20	0.13	0.05							
0.08						0.11	0.22	0.33	0.44	0.55	0.66	0.77	0.85	0.77	0.70	0.63	0.56	0.49	0.41	0.34	0.27	0.20	0.13	0.05						
0.05							0.07	0.14	0.21	0.27	0.34	0.41	0.48	0.53	0.48	0.44	0.39	0.35	0.30	0.26	0.21	0.17	0.12	0.08	0.03					
0.05								0.07	0.14	0.21	0.27	0.34	0.41	0.48	0.53	0.48	0.44	0.39	0.35	0.30	0.26	0.21	0.17	0.12	0.08	0.03				
0.03									0.04	0.08	0.12	0.16	0.20	0.25	0.29	0.32	0.29	0.26	0.24	0.21	0.18	0.16	0.13	0.10	0.07	0.05	0.02			
0.03										0.04	0.08	0.12	0.16	0.20	0.25	0.29	0.32	0.29	0.26	0.24	0.21	0.18	0.16	0.13	0.10	0.07	0.05	0.02		
0.05											0.07	0.14	0.21	0.27	0.34	0.41	0.48	0.53	0.48	0.44	0.39	0.35	0.30	0.26	0.21	0.17	0.12	0.08	0.03	
0.05												0.07	0.14	0.21	0.27	0.34	0.41	0.48	0.53	0.48	0.44	0.39	0.35	0.30	0.26	0.21	0.17	0.12	0.08	0.03
0.03													0.04	0.08	0.12	0.16	0.20	0.25	0.29	0.32	0.29	0.26	0.24	0.21	0.18	0.16	0.13	0.10	0.07	0.05
0.03														0.04	0.08	0.12	0.16	0.20	0.25	0.29	0.32	0.29	0.26	0.24	0.21	0.18	0.16	0.13	0.10	0.07
0.02															0.03	0.05	0.08	0.11	0.14	0.16	0.19	0.21	0.19	0.18	0.16	0.14	0.12	0.10	0.09	0.07
0.02																0.03	0.05	0.08	0.11	0.14	0.16	0.19	0.21	0.19	0.18	0.16	0.14	0.12	0.10	0.09
0.03																	0.04	0.08	0.12	0.16	0.20	0.25	0.29	0.32	0.29	0.26	0.24	0.21	0.18	0.16
0.03																		0.04	0.08	0.12	0.16	0.20	0.25	0.29	0.32	0.29	0.26	0.24	0.21	0.18
0.03																			0.04	0.08	0.12	0.16	0.20	0.25	0.29	0.32	0.29	0.26	0.24	0.21
0.03																				0.04	0.08	0.12	0.16	0.20	0.25	0.29	0.32	0.29	0.26	0.24
0.01																					0.01	0.03	0.04	0.05	0.07	0.08	0.10	0.11	0.10	0.09
0.01																						0.01	0.03	0.04	0.05	0.07	0.08	0.10	0.11	0.10
Rapid response (cumecs)	0.01	0.04	0.12	0.26	0.51	0.86	1.28	1.77	2.28	2.79	3.29	3.74	4.06	4.24	4.34	4.36	4.35	4.31	4.20	4.03	3.81	3.55	3.28	3.01	2.75	2.48	2.19	1.88	1.57	1.28
Baseflow (cumecs)	0.68	0.68	0.68	0.68	0.68	0.68	0.68	0.68	0.68	0.68	0.68	0.68	0.68	0.68	0.68	0.68	0.68	0.68	0.68	0.68	0.68	0.68	0.68	0.68	0.68	0.68	0.68	0.68	0.68	0.68
Total flow (cumecs)	0.69	0.72	0.80	0.94	1.19	1.54	1.96	2.45	2.96	3.47	3.97	4.42	4.74	4.92	5.02	5.04	5.03	4.99	4.88	4.71	4.49	4.23	3.96	3.69	3.43	3.16	2.87	2.56	2.25	1.96

This is an underestimate of the observed peak, which was around 30 $\text{m}^3\,\text{s}^{-1}$. There are several reasons for the underestimation: in particular, the observed flood events from which the unit hydrograph and losses model parameters were estimated were very small in comparison to the 11 October 1988 event; most significantly, a flood event analysis of the 1988 event revealed that *SPR* was a factor of four greater than the value used in the simulation. This example serves to illustrate the difficulties of using the FSR rainfall-runoff method on some particular types of catchment, in this instance small and permeable.

Chapter 7 Performance of the FSR rainfall-runoff method

7.1 Introduction

The problem facing the user is commonly: how to estimate the flood peak which has a specific probability of being equalled or exceeded? By far the greatest number of these estimates are for ungauged streams or streams with only short records, where there are few pieces of information to indicate the reliability of the estimates or whether the answers are *right* or *wrong*. It is unlikely that any method is completely reliable; indeed, absolute belief in any particular method is not justified (Linsley, 1987). It is generally necessary to assume that the methodology used (together with the inherent assumptions) gives the *correct* answer. However, there is now fairly wide recognition that the methods presently available for general use provide only relatively coarse estimates of flood frequency. That they should provide adequate estimates of extreme events (e.g. 10,000-year upwards events used in reservoir spillway design) is, more often than not, an act of faith (Reed and Field, 1992).

The FSR presented two complementary techniques for estimating flood magnitudes of given return period: a statistical approach and a rainfall-runoff approach. The statistical approach estimated only the peak flow up to a 1000-year return period, which was generally sufficient for the design of flood embankments, culverts and bridges. However, the peak flow alone was not adequate for the design of flood storages or reservoir spillways where the entire flow hydrograph, and possibly the maximum flood, are required for routing purposes. The rainfall-runoff approach had the distinction of allowing estimation of the complete flood hydrograph in addition to the peak flow, and also allowing estimation of the maximum flood.

Although the thinking behind statistical approaches in Volume 3 is somewhat different to that of the FSR, it remains the case that the method's primary output is the peak flow of the *T*-year flood. Therefore, a rainfall-runoff approach remains relevant where the shape and volume of a flood hydrograph are needed, or where an estimate of the maximum flood is required.

This chapter briefly reviews the performance of the FSR rainfall-runoff method. In Section 7.2, previous studies to assess the performance of the FSR rainfall-runoff model are reviewed, including a summary of the results of the comparison exercise presented in *IH Report 111* (Boorman *et al.*, 1990), which highlighted the value of utilising local data to refine flood estimates. Section 7.3 discusses the scope for further assessment of the FSR rainfall-runoff method, and also provides some guidance of the choice of estimation method, a topic presented in depth in Volume 1.

7.2 Performance evaluation

7.2.1 Background

Despite the widespread application of the FSR rainfall-runoff method, there have been few documented comparisons of its flood estimates with those obtained directly from the analysis of observed (annual maximum) flows. There have been many informal reports, particularly on a regional or local scale, and discussions at meetings and conferences, but this largely anecdotal evidence is not widely available to others and is difficult to summarise.

An early unpublished IH study (Lynn, 1978) showed the FSR rainfall-runoff method, using catchment characteristics estimates of the unit hydrograph and losses model parameters, to overestimate the mean annual flood by 13% and the 10-year flood by 56%. Moreover, it gave a marked regional pattern of errors, underpredicting in the south-west and south-east of England. However, the performance of the method when local data were used to refine the estimates of the model parameters was not assessed.

The somewhat disappointing performance of the FSR rainfall-runoff method in ungauged catchment applications was variously attributed to weaknesses in the design input package (Section 3.2) or to deficiencies of the unit hydrograph and losses model. With regard to the latter, the 5-class WRAP soil classification (at that time used to estimate *SPR*) was thought to be especially culpable: there were several reports that too-low a percentage runoff from WRAP class 5 soils was predicted in parts of northern England and upland Scotland, and too-high a percentage runoff from WRAP class 1 soils in southern and eastern England. There were also many concerns about the reliability of the method on small and/or urbanised catchments, neither of which was particularly well represented in the FSR data set.

Advice in the FSR, and later in FSSR13 (IH, 1983c), strongly recommended that values for the unit hydrograph and losses model parameters derived from data should always be used in preference to those derived from FSR catchment characteristics.

In 1985, the unit hydrograph and losses model parameter estimation equations were updated, and the revised equations were published in FSSR16 (IH, 1985). However, the FSSR16 equations were seen as more robust rather than more accurate and, therefore, unlikely to reduce the typical errors. For instance, the revised SPR estimation equation gave slightly higher runoff from impermeable soils, and lower runoff from permeable soils, than the original FSR equation, but still failed to perform well on very impermeable upland catchments and very permeable lowland catchments. Suggestions were made that substantial improvements would result only through refinement of the WRAP soil classification (Gurnell and Midgley, 1987).

The FSSR16 variant of the unit hydrograph and losses model, again using catchment characteristics estimates of the model parameters, was assessed for catchments in Northumberland (Archer and Kelway, 1987). The FSR rainfall-runoff method underpredicted the mean annual flood by 4.4%, but overpredicted the 30-year flood by 11.5%. A small-scale regional pattern of errors was identified but, again, the effects of including local data were not investigated. Similar findings were obtained in Northern Ireland, where the FSR rainfall-runoff method tended to overestimate floods (Bree *et al.*, 1989). There, catchment-characteristic estimates of time-to-peak were generally acceptable for well-drained catchments, but seriously underestimated for poorly-drained catchments, whilst catchment-characteristic estimates of SPR were underestimated, particularly in upland regions.

7.2.2 *IH Report 111* (Boorman *et al.*, 1990)

The objective of *IH Report 111* was to make a definitive assessment of flood estimates on predominantly rural catchments, thereby providing a quantitative insight into how the FSR rainfall-runoff method performed, and indicating some of its potential weaknesses. Comparisons were performed on a set of predominantly rural catchments ($URBAN_{FSR} < 10\%$) that had both 15 or more years of annual maximum flow data and rainfall-runoff data for five or more flood events. Out of more than 1200 gauged catchments in the UK, only 74 satisfied these requirements, and these were not particularly evenly distributed. There were no catchments north of the Highland Boundary Fault, in the Lake District, in the Southern Uplands of Scotland, or in Northern Ireland. Flood peaks up to the 25-year return period were examined, using the FSSR16 variant of the unit hydrograph and losses model, firstly with estimates of *Tp* and *SPR* from FSR catchment characteristics, and then with values of *Tp* and *SPR* from observed data, both individually and together.

The results showed that, with catchment-characteristic estimates of *Tp* and *SPR*, flood quantiles were, on average, overestimated by 22% for the mean annual flood to 41% for the 25-year flood. When observed *Tp* values were used, the overestimation was reduced slightly for all return periods; the effect was more pronounced when observed *SPR*s were used. When both observed *Tp* and *SPR* values were used, the mean error was 0% for the mean annual flood and 11% for the 25-year flood. The spatial distribution of the residuals for individual catchments showed general overestimation in the south-east of England and underestimation in south-west England and Wales; in other regions, residuals were mixed. The results resembled those reported in the FSR. Findings for particular subsets of catchments are summarised below.

Catchment size

With catchment-characteristic estimates of *Tp* and *SPR*, the FSR rainfall-runoff method performed generally better, in terms of both bias and variability, on catchments larger than 100 km^2. In contrast, with observed values of *Tp* and *SPR*, the method gave a consistent performance for both large and small catchments. From this it can be concluded that observed data are particularly beneficial on smaller catchments.

These results may partly reflect the problem of accurately abstracting the physiographic FSR catchment characteristics on small catchments, compared to larger catchments where errors tend to average out, and also illustrate some of the problems in transferring research results between catchments of different sizes (Pilgrim *et al.*, 1982; Pilgrim, 1983).

Permeable catchments

Inspection of the residuals for individual catchments suggested that, with catchment-characteristic estimates of *Tp* and *SPR*, the FSR rainfall-runoff method performed relatively badly on catchments with a high proportion of WRAP class 1 permeable soils, and that observed *Tp* and *SPR* values provided valuable information.

The results support the long-held view that conventional flood estimation techniques, developed for less permeable catchments, such as the FSR rainfall-runoff method, may not adequately represent permeable catchments. This is because the response from permeable catchments under extreme conditions, particularly the subsurface response, is often complex and uncertain, and rarely captured in available records.

Historical accounts show that severe floods can occur, albeit infrequently, in permeable catchments, but permeable catchment flooding remains one of the least understood areas of flood hydrology. Some aspects of practical application of the FSR rainfall-runoff method at ungauged sites, with permeable catchments featuring strongly, are discussed by Reed (1987), and in Section 9.2. More recent guidance on flood frequency estimation in permeable catchments, treating them as a distinct class (*SPRHOST* < 20%), is provided by Bradford and Faulkner (1997) and in Chapter 19 of Volume 3.

Dry catchments

Inspection of the residuals for individual catchments showed that estimates tended to be better on *wet* catchments than on *dry* ones. For catchments with *SAAR* greater than 800 mm, the average underestimation of the 2-year flood was 6%, whilst for catchments with *SAAR* less than 800 mm, the average overestimation was 1%. Relative overestimation in these drier catchments was also true of the 5-year and 10-year floods.

However, in this instance, *SAAR* is just providing a convenient way of splitting the catchments. The observed pattern of residuals is likely to be a combination of factors that will also include topography, soil type and, possibly, even design storm specification; there is a strong south-east to north-west rainfall gradient in the UK which is strongly related to both topography and soil type.

Urbanised catchments

Because catchments more than 10% urbanised were left out of the *IH Report 111* study, the performance of the FSR rainfall-runoff method on urbanised catchments could not be assessed. However, in terms of flood potential, urbanisation is probably the most significant land-use change that can be made to a catchment. The effects of urban development on catchment flood behaviour are reviewed in Section 9.3. Where the urbanisation is concentrated in a few locations in the catchment, a semi-distributed approach is recommended, as discussed by Packman (1980; 1986), and in Section 9.3.

7.3 Discussion

7.3.1 Scope for further assessment of the FSR rainfall-runoff method

In this chapter, general performance has been discussed by reference to the IH Report 111 findings. To date, this remains the most authoritative document giving an overview of average performance of the FSR rainfall-runoff method by comparison with flood peak data. It is to be expected that a nationally-calibrated method, such as the FSR rainfall-runoff method, will overestimate in some regions and underestimate in others. The most important step which can be taken to ensure optimum performance is to always make full use of available local information. It is both inevitable and desirable that guidance leaves some scope for experienced users to apply judgement.

There has yet to be a proper evaluation of the latest revision of the unit hydrograph and losses model within the FSR rainfall runoff method, against either observed data or the new statistical methods for flood estimation. However, some particular reservations have already been expressed about its performance in northern England (Archer, 1997; Spencer, *pers. comm.*). With the automation of flood frequency estimates made possible in the Handbook, it is anticipated that comprehensive national comparisons will be made.

7.3.2 Reconciling estimates from the FSR rainfall-runoff method and statistical approaches

Where there is a real choice between the FSR rainfall-runoff method and the statistical approach, the decision is a matter of judgement, and in many cases users will wish to consider both. Indeed, for practical application, it is often necessary to reconcile, over the return periods of interest, the flood frequency curve synthesised by the FSR rainfall-runoff method, preferably augmented by flood event analysis, with that observed or synthesised by statistical techniques.

There are several ways in which flood estimates from different methods can be harmonised. For example, an FSR rainfall-runoff model parameter such as SPR might be adjusted so that the flood frequency relationship tallied with a statistical analysis of peak flows (Reed, 1987). Alternatively, the ordinates of the rainfall-runoff method flood hydrograph could be rescaled by the ratio of the statistical and rainfall-runoff method flood peaks (Archer and Kelway, 1987; Archer, 1997). Similarly, it is possible to exploit the short-cut method to *flesh-out* a peak flow estimate to provide a design hydrograph (see §3.4.1 and **3** A.10). Chapter 5 of Volume 1 provides further guidance in tailoring the choice of estimation method to the particular problem and the available data.

Chapter 8 Reservoir flood estimation

8.1 Introduction

Reservoirs having a capacity of more than 25 000 m^3 are subject to the Reservoirs Act 1975, which supersedes the Reservoirs (Safety Provisions) Act 1930, and places various public safety obligations on their owners. In the UK, there are some 2400 large impounding reservoirs, many of them old and often sited above the communities which they serve. The accidental, uncontrolled escape of water from an impounding (or other) reservoir can threaten both life and property. The assessment of flood risk is a vital element in the safe design, maintenance and operation of such reservoirs.

For many years, the standard design method in general use in the UK was that published in the reports of the ICE committee on floods in relation to reservoir practice (ICE, 1933; 1960). The reports provided tables giving peak flood discharges from various sites (primarily upland catchments up to 100 km^2 in area), together with an enveloping *normal maximum curve* relating flood magnitude to catchment area. Larger *catastrophic* floods were expected to have peak discharges at least twice those of the normal maximum floods. No estimates of frequency were associated with these floods. The reservoir flood estimation procedures were reassessed when the FSR was published in 1975. The methods presented in the FSR became the standards for design flood estimation in the UK, and guidance was affirmed in the ICE engineering guide to floods and reservoir safety. The FSR has, of course, been superseded by the Flood Estimation Handbook. This volume, which restates the FSR rainfall-runoff method, is of particular relevance to reservoir flood estimation in light of the many and various revisions to the method.

The ICE guide categorises reservoirs in terms of the potential hazard, to life and property downstream, of a dam breach. To apply the standards it is necessary to route the appropriate design flood inflow through the reservoir using the appropriate initial reservoir condition, and to obtain the corresponding maximum still water level, to which an appropriate allowance for wave surcharge should be added. This traditional approach permits only the independent assessment of each factor and their combination to estimate maximum water levels, and makes only informal allowance for any dependence amongst hydrometeorological variables.

Regional flood and storm hazard investigations have demonstrated that the clustered siting of many UK reservoirs encourages a relatively long interval between design exceedances (Dales and Reed, 1989). However, a corollary is that, when such an event occurs, there may be multiple exceedances, affecting several reservoirs in a district. FSSR18 (IH, 1988) set out a procedure for assessing the collective risk of a design exceedance occurring at one of a network of sites which are sensitive to heavy rainfall, including an example of its application to a group of reservoirs.

This chapter focuses on estimation of the design flood inflow, and its subsequent routing through one or more reservoirs. The remainder of this section lists the relevant documentation and software and explains why a statistical approach is not recommended for this type of application. Particular aspects encountered in reservoir flood estimation are introduced in Section 8.2. The procedures for application of the FSR rainfall-runoff method to estimate spillway floods on single and multiple reservoir systems are presented, with worked examples, in Section 8.3. The reservoir routing problem and its solution are formulated in Appendix D.

Chapter 11 of Volume 1 discusses reservoir flood estimation in the context of public safety.

8.1.1 Documentation and software

The ICE guide is the primary reference. The Guide was originally drafted as a discussion paper on reservoir flood standards (ICE, 1975a). The paper was considered at both the Flood Studies Conference (ICE, 1975b) and the Newcastle Symposium of the British National Committee on Large Dams (Bass, 1975). The first edition of the Guide was published in 1978. An interim review after five years experience led to production of a second edition which was published in 1989. Following a more comprehensive review, a third edition was published in 1996.

Three other documents are of potential interest. Firstly, *IH Report 114* (Reed and Field, 1992) takes a wide-ranging look at reservoir flood estimation in a review primarily concerned with UK methods and experience. Although some of the methodology referred to has since been superseded, many of the topics discussed remain relevant. These include the sensitivity of reservoir flood estimates to the precise storm duration assumed, comparisons between Summer and Winter values of PMF, and snowmelt allowances in PMF estimation.

Secondly, the CIRIA guide to the design of flood storage reservoirs (Hall *et al.*, 1993) gives specific procedures for *T*-year flood estimation for the design of balancing ponds. The document is a revision to the now-withdrawn TN100 (Hall and Hockin, 1980). Many balancing ponds are small structures which do not fall under the Reservoirs Act 1975, but various complex factors (hydrological, hydraulic, legal, environmental) enter into their siting and sizing.

Finally, CIRIA Report 161 (Kennard *et al.*, 1996) provides a guide to the planning, design, construction and maintenance of embankment reservoirs for water supply and amenity use, which are too small to fall under the Reservoirs Act 1975. Design and construction of these reservoirs can be affected by many of the problems influencing larger reservoir construction, albeit on a reduced scale. The report presents a statistical method, rather than a rainfall-runoff approach, to assess the flood inflow into and through the reservoir.

Computer software is helpful in reservoir flood estimation, particularly in the routing of a design hydrograph through the reservoir, to take account of the delay and attenuation effects imposed by the temporary storage of water above the overflow level of the reservoir. Furthermore, multiple calculations may be required, particularly in complicated reservoir systems, where it is often necessary to consider a number of design storm durations; without some computational aid, repeated application of the FSR rainfall-runoff method becomes a time-consuming process. The mechanics of reservoir routing are discussed in standard texts, such as Shaw's *Hydrology in Practice* and Wilson's *Engineering Hydrology*. *IH Report 114* presents software for reservoir routing, the underlying concepts of which are reproduced in Appendix D. The software forms the basis of the reservoir routing module in the Micro-FSR (IH, 1991a; 1996) computer package.

8.1.2 Why a statistical approach is not recommended

The FSR and the ICE engineering guide to floods and reservoir safety state that reservoir flood estimation should be based on the FSR rainfall-runoff method, and statistical analysis presently plays a limited role in reservoir flood standards in the UK (Reed and Anderson, 1992). However, the reasons why reservoir flood estimation by statistical analysis of flood peaks is spurned are not stated prominently.

The obvious reason why a statistical approach is not recommended is that a design hydrograph, and possibly a maximum flood, are required, and that these call for use of a rainfall-runoff method. A second reason is that statistical method flood estimates extrapolated to the high return periods relevant to reservoir flood design may lead to gross under- or over-design, given the relatively short periods of gauged flood data typically available (Reed, 1992). Although this concern also applies to the use of local data in the rainfall-runoff method, the greater regional homogeneity in extreme rainfall and the longer record lengths available for analysis mean that the rainfall-runoff method is preferred. A further reason for favouring the rainfall-runoff method is that a rainfall-runoff approach is in some sense more supportable, since it is based on a structured model of flood formation rather than on statistics alone.

However, there are several ways in which flood estimates from different methods can be reconciled (see Chapter 7 and 15). For example, a rainfall-runoff model parameter such as SPR might be adjusted so that the flood frequency relationship tallied with a statistical analysis of peak flows (Reed, 1987).

8.2 Aspects of reservoir flood estimation

Design flood estimation using the FSR rainfall-runoff method involves applying an appropriate design storm and associated antecedent conditions to a unit hydrograph and losses model of the catchment, as described in Chapters 3 and 4. Reservoir flood estimation is, unfortunately, not simply a case of deriving a design inflow hydrograph by these methods, and routing it through the reservoir. The very presence of a reservoir can lead to some difficulties in methodology, and this section outlines these problems. Although the discussion refers to on-line reservoirs, it is relevant to other situations where storage effects can be appreciable, e.g. washlands.

8.2.1 Allowance for reservoir effects

The effect of a reservoir is to lag (i.e. delay) and attenuate (i.e. reduce the amplitude, whilst maintaining the volume) the flood hydrograph from the catchment. Reservoir lag time *RLAG* is defined as the time between the peak of the inflow and the peak of the outflow hydrographs. The attenuation ratio α is the ratio of the outflow peak to the inflow peak. Reservoir lag and attenuation are primarily governed by the storage-discharge characteristics of the reservoir; a measure of reservoir lag is given by the mean slope of the line relating reservoir storage S to outflow q. Flood magnitude also has some influence, as the lag and attenuation effects tend to be less pronounced in rarer events, as illustrated in Table 8.1. The exception to this is when a bellmouth spillway gorges, or the outflow drowns out in some other way.

The more that a reservoir attenuates flood inflows, the more sensitive it becomes to longer duration floods, and hence to longer duration storms. Subsections 3.2.1 and 4.3.1 describe how, in the unreservoired case, the design storm duration D is calculated from unit hydrograph time-to-peak Tp and standard average annual rainfall $SAAR$:

$$D = Tp\,(1 + \frac{SAAR}{1000}) \qquad (3.1)$$

In reservoired applications, the design storm duration is extended by adding the reservoir response time *RLAG* to the catchment response time Tp, so that:

Table 8.1 Examples of variation of reservoir lag and attenuation ratio with return period (after Reed and Field, 1992)

Name	Catchment area	Reservoir area	Reservoir lag *RLAG* (hours) return period (years)				Attenuation ratio α return period (years)			
	km^2	km^2	10	100	1000	10 000	10	100	1000	10 000
Colt Crag	18.05	0.850	3.70	3.38	3.06	2.60	0.77	0.80	0.84	0.86
Crafnant	6.20	0.216	3.01	1.79	1.23	0.86	0.44	0.61	0.76	0.86
Higher Naden	3.90	0.052	0.70	0.59	0.48	0.36	0.89	0.91	0.94	0.97
Leperstone	1.22	0.087	2.46	2.18	1.99	1.84	0.48	0.51	0.54	0.59
Little Denny	0.98	0.120	2.77	2.59	2.39	2.17	0.49	0.53	0.56	0.60
Loch Craisg	0.74	0.077	1.57	1.44	1.30	1.16	0.60	0.65	0.68	0.73
Loch Gleann	1.21	0.138	3.80	3.46	3.19	2.84	0.39	0.39	0.41	0.43
Loch Kirbister	20.73	1.015	2.17	2.07	2.04	2.05	0.83	0.84	0.84	0.84
Lower Carriston	3.94	0.097	1.68	1.46	1.30	1.11	0.84	0.86	0.89	0.92
Nanpantan	4.28	0.034	0.87	0.75	0.65	0.55	0.95	0.97	0.97	0.98
Parkhill House	1.21	0.029	3.15	3.09	3.67	4.45	0.51	0.51	0.42	0.34
Roadford	34.69	2.960	5.10	4.83	4.52	3.91	0.49	0.49	0.53	0.58
Staunton Harold	23.60	0.880	3.41	3.15	2.83	2.40	0.77	0.80	0.83	0.88
Upper Neuadd	5.74	0.230	1.19	1.08	0.97	0.86	0.74	0.77	0.80	0.84
Usk	13.50	1.174	3.97	3.54	3.07	2.77	0.47	0.50	0.55	0.59

$$D = (Tp + RLAG)\left(1 + \frac{SAAR}{1000}\right) \qquad (8.1)$$

It is still necessary to have an odd number of rainfall blocks. Therefore, the computed value of storm duration is rounded, up or down, to the nearest odd integer multiple of the data interval ΔT. For a cascade of reservoirs, the reservoir lag *RLAG* is substituted with a mean reservoir lag *MRLAG*, as described in §8.3.2.

Concern has been expressed that the recommended Equation 8.1 may fail to capture the storm duration to which the catchment-reservoir system is most sensitive. This may well be true in complex mixed rural-urban cases, where it is unclear whether the slow rural response or the fast urban response dominates. Curves of flood magnitude against storm duration are typically fairly flat, so the choice of storm duration is not usually critical (Reed and Field, 1992). However, in complicated problems, where portions of the catchment have widely differing response characteristics, it is often advisable to consider a range of storm durations, and adopt the one that yields the highest water level, i.e. the critical duration D_{CRIT}.

This guidance is reaffirmed by the CIRIA guide to the design of flood storage reservoirs, though the CIRIA guide specifies the critical storm duration as that giving rise to the maximum storage requirement, rather than the highest water level. However, since maximum storage corresponds to peak water level, and since the FSR equation for design storm duration was intended to give the duration which caused the greatest flood magnitude, the procedures are essentially equivalent and give similar results.

8.2.2 Allowance for rain falling on reservoir

It seems a rational assumption that the rain falling directly on the surface of the reservoir should not be subject to losses. However, if the surface area of the reservoir forms only a small fraction of the catchment, it may be reasonable to neglect the effect. If the reservoir is greater than about 5% of the catchment, the reservoir area should be excluded from the catchment area and the rain falling on the reservoir added directly to the inflow hydrograph: this is explicit treatment. However, if the reservoir occupies less than 5% of the catchment, the reservoir can be treated as part of the catchment, and the rain falling on the reservoir passed through the rainfall-runoff model: this is implicit treatment.

It is convenient to assume a fixed reservoir area for the purpose of modelling the rain falling directly onto the reservoir. The main reason for this is that it is highly inconvenient to have to calculate the inflow hydrograph to the reservoir for a variable land area. Should the rate of change of reservoir area with water level be significant in terms of the direct rainfall effect, it would be advisable to note the average reservoir area during passage of the flood and to repeat the calculations using this area as the fixed area for direct rainfall calculations.

8.2.3 Storm profile

The FSR design storm profiles recommended for application throughout the UK are unimodal and symmetrical. This presents particular problems when dealing with large multi-reservoired catchments, such as those in the Highlands of Scotland where critical durations can be as long as 7 to 10 days (Johnson *et al.*, 1981). Long critical durations reflect the sensitivity of large reservoired catchments to a succession of storms which can cause reservoir level to build-up over several days. In this case it is inappropriate to assume a single symmetrical design storm profile. However, the complexity of the reservoir system also makes it inappropriate to consider the alternative of a range of different observed profiles. The ICE guide recommends adopting the temporal pattern of the severest sequence of storms of the required duration that has been observed locally. The most critical case for a reservoir is generally the sequence with the most intense period at the end.

New long-duration profiles relevant to design flood estimation on large, multi-reservoired catchments have been developed for north-west Scotland (Stewart and Reynard, 1991). The approach uses the average variability method of Pilgrim *et al.* (1969), which successfully preserves the typically multi-peaked character of 3-day and longer accumulations.

8.2.4 Catchment descriptors

The presence of a reservoir, or cascade of reservoirs, can sometimes cause difficulties when determining some digital catchment descriptors. For instance, if the reservoir extends well up the catchment, abstracting the mean drainage path length and slope to the dam site may lead to a mean length that is too long and a mean slope that is too shallow, which may in turn lead to overestimation of the catchment response time. Similar problems in estimating catchment response time may occur for the direct subcatchment to a lower reservoir in a cascade. In each case the recommended guidance is to take appropriate catchment descriptors for the main tributary or a *typical* tributary to the perimeter of the reservoir, rather than to the dam site, for calculation of unit hydrograph time-to-peak (Appendix C, Section 2).

8.2.5 Use of local data

Chapter 2 states that estimation of the unit hydrograph and losses model parameters from flood event or hydrometeorological data are the best methods of parameter estimation. Even where the catchment is ungauged, estimates of the model parameters from catchment descriptors can often be refined using information from donor catchments. The importance of refining flood estimates by reference to local data is reaffirmed by the ICE guide. However, there appears to be some understandable reluctance to incorporate local data refinements even-handedly in flood calculations relating to reservoir safety assessment. Where local data support a higher flood estimate, they will be utilised, but where they suggest a lower estimate, they will be ignored. This practice has much to commend it, and the flexibility leaves scope for experienced users to apply judgement (**1** 5.5; **1** 11.1).

8.3 Flood estimation methodology

Flood estimation is complicated by the presence of one or more reservoirs in the catchment, as described in Section 8.2. The most common situations are single reservoirs or cascades where the reservoirs lie in series down a main valley (Figure 8.1a). However, reservoirs can be nested in other ways (Figure 8.1b). This section describes the procedures for flood estimation on single and multiple reservoir systems.

8.3.1 Single reservoirs

The presence of *RLAG* in Equation 8.1 means that the design storm duration is not known in the first instance: *RLAG* is only known *after* a flood inflow has been routed through a reservoir, whereas it needs to be known *before* in order to generate the design storm. Hence, an iterative procedure is required whereby the calculations to derive a design rainfall hyetograph, a net rainfall hyetograph, and subsequently an inflow flood hydrograph, which is then routed through the reservoir, are repeated until the value of the design storm duration has stabilised.

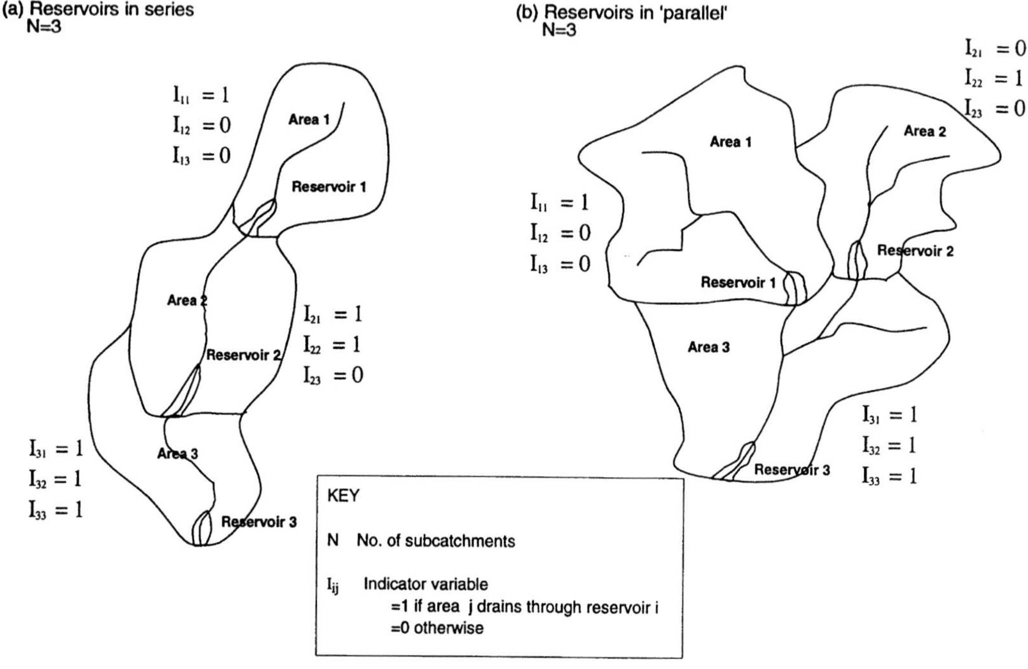

Figure 8.1 *Examples of multiple reservoir systems*

In PMF estimation, storm duration also influences *CWI*, which in turn has implications for the calculation of baseflow. The procedure has the following steps:

i Calculate the design storm duration from *Tp*, *SAAR* and *RLAG* by Equation 8.1, guessing a value of reservoir lag (a first choice of *RLAG* = 0.0 hours is adequate, although a considered estimate will speed convergence);

ii Derive the design event inputs for this duration, and use these to compute the design flood inflow to the reservoir;

iii Route the flood through the reservoir, noting the resultant value of *RLAG*;

iv Recalculate the design storm duration using the new value of *RLAG*, repeating from step (ii) if the duration has changed.

Three or four iterations usually suffice to determine the appropriate storm duration. Reservoir routing software enables this task to be performed both quickly and accurately. The iterative procedure for a single reservoir is shown in Example 8.1.

8.3.2 Multiple reservoir systems

Principles

FSSR10 (IH, 1983a), which was more of an extension to the ICE engineering guide than a supplement to the FSR, set out the particular procedure for calculating flood estimates for reservoirs in cascade. The following formulation is a generalisation of the FSSR10 procedure, and caters for all multi-reservoir systems rather than just those in cascade. The procedure involves the estimation of the direct inflow to each reservoir, its routing and superposition with the direct inflow to the reservoir below, taking care to preserve the timing of successive contributions. In carrying out such calculations, two underlying principles must be observed:

i Each reservoir should be checked by a tailored analysis (not as part of calculations undertaken to check another reservoir), using a design storm event appropriate to its *entire* catchment;

ii Floods from different subcatchments should only be combined when they have been derived from the *same* design storm (Farquharson *et al.*, 1975).

The single-reservoir case, summarised in §8.3.1, prescribes that the design storm duration is extended by adding the reservoir response time *RLAG* to the catchment response time *Tp*, so that:

$$D = (Tp + RLAG)\left(1 + \frac{SAAR}{1000}\right) \tag{8.1}$$

In multiple reservoir systems, the inflow to a reservoir is influenced by the collective routing effect of all reservoirs upstream. For example, in Figure 8.1, the inflow to reservoir 3 is influenced by the combined routing effect of reservoirs 1 and 2. The design storm duration must be extended accordingly, by replacing the *RLAG* term in Equation 8.1 by a mean reservoir lag *MRLAG*, so that:

$$D = (Tp + MRLAG)\left(1 + \frac{SAAR}{1000}\right) \tag{8.2}$$

MRLAG represents the mean lag imposed on runoff from the entire catchment to the reservoir being checked by the routing effects of the other reservoirs involved. The catchment to the reservoir being checked is subdivided into *N* subcatchments, according to the configuration of the reservoir system. The subcatchments and reservoirs are conveniently numbered in descending order of altitude. *MRLAG* is

Example 8.1
Single reservoir flood estimation

Reservoir: Upper Neuadd (IHDTM grid ref. 302950 218700) (Figure 8 of Appendix C) with 10 000-year design flood

Relevant descriptors and other information:
General descriptors: *AREA* = 5.73 km^2, *URBEXT* = 0.000, SAAR = 2243 mm, *SPR* from HOST = 36.5%
Tp(0) descriptors (to dam): *DPSBAR* = 253.72 m km^{-1}, *PROPWET* = 0.54, *DPLBAR* = 2.02 km, *URBEXT* = 0.000
Reservoir descriptors: water level *h* is defined above the spillway crest, $A = 0.23 + 0.008\,h$, $Q = 37.95\,h^{1.5}$, initial state = spilling baseflow

1. Calculation of design storm duration D
D is calculated from *Tp*, reservoir lag *RLAG* and *SAAR* using Equation 8.1;
a first guess of *RLAG* is 0.0 hours: *Tp*(0.25) = 1.60 hours
RLAG = 0.0 hours

$D = (Tp + RLAG)\,(1 + SAAR / 1000)$ $D = (1.60 + 0.0)(1 + 2243 / 1000)$
= 5.19 hours, rounded to 5.25 hours

2. Derivation of design event inputs and design flood inflow
Design storm depth *P* = 287.6 mm, distributed within the storm duration 5.25 hours using the 75% winter profile to derive the total rainfall hyetograph. Design antecedent catchment wetness *CWI* = 126.2 mm. *P* = 287.6 mm; *CWI* = 126.2 mm

SPR = 36.5%, DPR_{CWI} = 0.3%, DPR_{RAIN} = 21.3%, giving *PR* = 58.1%, which is applied to each block of the total rainfall hyetograph. *PR* = 58.1%

The unit hydrograph and net rainfall hyetograph are convolved to give the rapid response runoff hydrograph, to which *BF* is added to give the total runoff hydrograph which forms the design flood inflow.
BF = 0.39 m^3 s^{-1}
Inflow peak = 81.14 m^3 s^{-1}

3. Reservoir routing
The design flood inflow hydrograph is routed through the reservoir. The new *RLAG* is 0.93 hours, compared to the value used in this iteration of 0.0 hours.
Outflow peak = 64.78 m^3 s^{-1}
RLAG = 0.93 hours

4. Calculation of design storm duration *D*
D is calculated from *Tp*, reservoir lag *RLAG* and *SAAR* using Equation 8.1;
the new value of *RLAG* is 0.96 hours:
Tp(0.25) = 1.60 hours
RLAG = 0.93 hours

$D = (Tp + RLAG)\,(1 + SAAR / 1000)$ $D = (1.60 + 0.93)(1 + 2243 / 1000)$
= 8.20 hours, rounded to 8.25 hours

Example 8.1 (continued)

5. Derivation of design event inputs and design flood inflow

Design storm depth P = 329.2 mm, distributed within the storm duration 8.25 hours using the 75% winter profile to derive the total rainfall hyetograph. Design antecedent catchment wetness CWI = 126.2 mm. P = 329.2 mm; CWI = 126.2 mm

SPR = 36.5%, DPR_{CWI} = 0.3%, DPR_{RAIN} = 23.7%, giving PR = 60.6%, which is applied to each block of the total rainfall hyetograph. PR = 60.6%

The unit hydrograph and net rainfall hyetograph are convolved to give the rapid response runoff hydrograph, to which BF is added to give the total runoff hydrograph which forms the design flood inflow. BF = 0.39 $m^3 s^{-1}$

Inflow peak = 74.45 $m^3 s^{-1}$

6. Reservoir routing

The design flood inflow hydrograph is routed through the reservoir. The new $RLAG$ is 0.92 hours, which will give the same storm duration (8.25 hours) as the value used in this iteration of 0.93 hours. Outflow peak = 63.15 $m^3 s^{-1}$

$RLAG$ = 0.92 hours

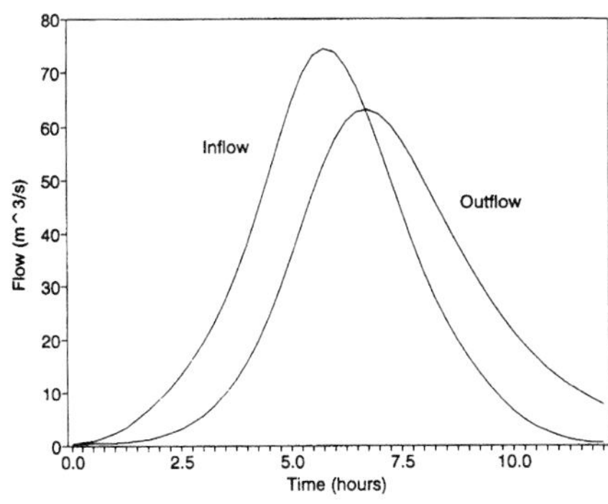

calculated as an areally-weighted average of reservoir lags, the summation of lags reflecting the topology of the reservoir network by:

$$MRLAG = \frac{\sum \sum RLAG_i \, AREA_j \, I_{ij}}{\sum AREA_j} \tag{8.3}$$

where $AREA_j$ is the area of the jth subcatchment and I_{ij} is an indicator variable which takes the value 1 if $AREA\ j$ drains through reservoir i, and 0 otherwise. Examples of indicator variables are shown in Figure 8.1, and the calculation is illustrated by Example 8.2a. $MRLAG$ is never less than the individual lag of the reservoir being checked.

In theory, there is no limit to the number of reservoirs in a multi-reservoir system which can be modelled in this way. However, there may become a point at which there are *too many* reservoirs to sensibly route the flow through each

Example 8.2a
Calculation of mean reservoir lag MRLAG

MRLAG is calculated using Equation 8.3:

$$MRLAG = \frac{\Sigma\Sigma\ RLAG_i AREA_j I_{ij}}{\Sigma\ AREA_j}$$

where $I_{ij} = 1$ if *AREA j* drains through reservoir *i*, and $I_{ij} = 0$ otherwise. For three reservoirs in parallel, as in Figure 8.1b, Equation 8.3 expands to:

$MRLAG = (RLAG_1 AREA_1 I_{11} + RLAG_1 AREA_2 I_{12} + RLAG_1 AREA_3 I_{13} + RLAG_2 AREA_1 I_{21} + RLAG_2 AREA_2 I_{22} + RLAG_2 AREA_3 I_{23} + RLAG_3 AREA_1 I_{31} + RLAG_3 AREA_2 I_{32} + RLAG_3 AREA_3 I_{33}) / (AREA_1 + AREA_2 + AREA_3)$

which, upon elimination of the zero terms, simplifies to:

$MRLAG = (RLAG_1 AREA_1 + RLAG_2 AREA_2 + RLAG_3 AREA_1 + RLAG_3 AREA_2 + RLAG_3 AREA_3) / (AREA_1 + AREA_2 + AREA_3) = ((RLAG_1 + RLAG_3) AREA_1 + (RLAG_2 + RLAG_3) AREA_2 + RLAG_3 AREA_3) / (AREA_1 + AREA_2 + AREA_3)$

For the following values for *AREA* and *RLAG*:

$AREA_1 = 4.34$ km^2, $RLAG_1 = 1.01$ hours
$AREA_2 = 21.06$ km^2, $RLAG_2 = 0.74$ hours
$AREA_3 = 10.41$ km^2, $RLAG_3 = 0.63$ hours

$MRLAG = ((1.01 + 0.63)\ 4.34 + (0.74 + 0.63)\ 21.06 + (0.63)\ 10.41)) / (4.34 + 21.06 + 10.41) = 1.19$ hours

one individually. It is not possible to give definitive guidance on taking account of reservoir effects in such circumstances, and each system must be evaluated on a case-by-case basis.

Solution

As in the single reservoir situation, the presence of *MRLAG* in Equation 8.2 means that the design storm duration is not known in the first instance, and an iterative procedure is invoked:

i Calculate the design storm duration from Equation 8.2, using *Tp* and *SAAR* values for the entire catchment to the reservoir being checked, and guessing a value of mean reservoir lag (or setting *MRLAG* = 0.0 hours initially);

ii Derive the design event inputs for the given storm duration;

iii Go to the first (i.e. highest) reservoir of the network and derive the flood inflow resulting from the design storm acting on the first subcatchment;

iv Route the flood through the first reservoir, noting the value of $RLAG_1$;

v Go to the second (i.e. next) reservoir of the network and derive the *direct* flood inflow to that reservoir by again applying the design storm, this time to the second subcatchment;

vi Route the flood, *together with the outflow from the first reservoir if this discharges upstream of the second reservoir,* through the second reservoir, noting the resultant value of $RLAG_2$;

vii Repeat steps (v) and (vi) for subsequent reservoirs until routing through the reservoir under scrutiny has been completed and $RLAG_N$ calculated;

viii Calculate MRLAG from Equation 8.3, and recalculate the design storm duration using Equation 8.2, repeating from step (ii) if this has changed.

Again, three or four iterations usually suffice to determine the appropriate storm duration. While software may not automate computation of *MRLAG*, design hyetographs and calculated hydrographs can usually be stored, for subsequent retrieval and strategic input into flood calculations for sites downstream (see similar procedure for disparate subcatchments in §9.2.2). In practice, it is also worth exploiting software to consider a range of design storm durations, to confirm that the procedure has correctly identified the case that gives the highest water level at the reservoir under study. The procedure for multi-reservoir cases is shown in Example 8.2b, for the lowest reservoir in a 3-reservoir system.

Other aspects

It is usually necessary to adopt a common data interval ΔT in the calculations. One approach is to choose a value which provides adequate definition of the unit hydrograph for the subcatchment with the fastest response time (i.e. the data interval is taken to be about one fifth of its time-to-peak, Tp). However, it is often adequate to adopt a data interval appropriate to the reservoir being checked.

If the distance between adjacent reservoirs in a cascade is such that the routed outflow from the upper reservoir is likely to take one or more time intervals to travel to the lower reservoir, then the routed outflow must be appropriately lagged before being added to the inflow hydrograph to the lower reservoir. In a few cases, the translation (time delay) from one reservoir to the next may be accompanied by significant attenuation of the hydrograph, in which case, river flow routing may be needed.

When the design storm is a PMP, it is possible for an upper reservoir, which was satisfactory when tested alone, to fail when subject to the longer duration PMP storm appropriate for a downstream reservoir. The reason is that the shorter storm on which the upper reservoir was previously successfully tested is now nested within a longer storm of greater overall depth. This anomaly concerns only PMF calculations for reservoirs in cascade, and can be ignored. It does not arise in T-year flood calculations.

For T-year events on catchments where there is significant spatial variation in rainfall characteristics, §9.2.2 describes how the stepwise procedure outlined above can be modified to reflect the catchment's typical rainfall pattern.

Example 8.2b
Multiple reservoir flood estimation

Reservoir cascade: Langsett (IHDTM grid ref. 421300 400400) — Midhope (IHDTM grid ref. 422250 399750)— Underbank (IHDTM grid ref. 425200 399000) (Figure 9 of Appendix C) with PMF for Underbank (from summer PMP)

Total catchment relevant descriptors and other information:
General descriptors: *AREA* = 35.81 km^2, *URBEXT* = 0.003, *SAAR* = 1212 mm, *EM-2h* = 160 mm, *EM-24h* = 299 mm
Tp(0) descriptors (to dam): *DPSBAR* = 63.76 m km^{-1}, *PROPWET* = 0.37, *DPLBAR* = 7.02 km, *URBEXT* = 0.003

Langsett subcatchment relevant descriptors and other information:
General descriptors: *AREA* = 21.06 km^2, *URBEXT* = 0.001, *SAAR* = 1317 mm, *SPR* from HOST = 51.6%
Tp(0) descriptors (tributary): *DPSBAR* = 128.21 m km^{-1}, *PROPWET* = 0.52, *DPLBAR* = 3.67 km, *URBEXT* = 0.000
Reservoir descriptors: water level *h* is defined above sea level, $A = 0.51 + 0.037\,(h - 246.89)$, $Q = 103.53\,(h - 246.89)^{1.5}$, initial state = spilling baseflow

Midhope subcatchment relevant descriptors and other information:
General descriptors: *AREA* = 4.34 km^2, *URBEXT* = 0.000, *SAAR* = 1156 mm, *SPR* from HOST = 50.2%
Tp(0) descriptors (tributary): *DPSBAR* = 125.29 m km^{-1}, *PROPWET* = 0.38, *DPLBAR* = 1.35 km, *URBEXT* = 0.000
Reservoir descriptors: water level *h* is defined above sea level, $A = 0.21 + 0.021\,(h - 243.84)$, $Q = 29.41\,(h - 243.84)^{1.5}$, initial state = spilling baseflow

Underbank direct subcatchment relevant descriptors and other information:
General descriptors: *AREA* = 10.41 km^2, *URBEXT* = 0.008, *SAAR* = 1023 mm, SPR from HOST = 30.9%
Tp(0) descriptors (tributary): *DPSBAR* = 134.16 m km^{-1}, *PROPWET* = 0.38, *DPLBAR* = 1.45 km, *URBEXT* = 0.000
Reservoir descriptors: water level *hours* is defined above sea level, $A = 0.42 + 0.074\,(h - 182.88)$, $Q = 114.30\,(h - 182.88)^{1.5}$, initial state = spilling baseflow

1. Calculation of design storm duration *D*
D is calculated from entire catchment *Tp*, mean reservoir lag *MRLAG* and *SAAR* using Equation 8.12; a first guess of *MRLAG* is 0.0 hours (i.e. individual *RLAG*s are 0.0 hours):

$Tp_{PMF}(0.25) = 4.27$ hours
MRLAG = 0.0 hours

$D = (Tp + MRLAG)(1 + SAAR/1000)$

$D = (4.27 + 0.0)(1 + 1212/1000)$
= 9.45 hours, rounded to 9.25 hours

2. Derivation of design event inputs (summer PMP)
PMP design storm depth *P* = 231.4 mm, distributed within the design storm duration 9.25 hours to derive the total rainfall hyetograph. PMP design antecedent catchment wetness *CWI* = 158.9 mm.

P = 231.4 mm; *CWI* = 158.9 mm

Example 8.2b (continued)

3. Langsett design flood inflow and reservoir routing

SPR = 51.6%, DPR_{CWI} = 8.5%, DPR_{RAIN} = 17.8%, giving PR = 77.9%, which is applied to each block of the catchment total rainfall hyetograph PR = 77.9%

The unit hydrograph and net rainfall hyetograph are convolved to give the rapid response runoff hydrograph, to which BF is added to give the total runoff hydrograph which forms the design flood inflow. $Tp_{PMF}(0.25)$ = 1.89 hours

BF = 1.04 $m^3 s^{-1}$

Inflow peak = 264.29 $m^3 s^{-1}$

The design flood inflow hydrograph is routed through the reservoir. The new $RLAG$ is 0.74 hours, compared to the value used in this iteration of 0.0 hours.

Outflow peak = 227.67 $m^3 s^{-1}$

$RLAG$ = 0.74 hours

4. Midhope design flood inflow and reservoir routing

SPR = 50.2%, DPR_{CWI} = 8.5%, DPR_{RAIN} = 17.8%, giving PR = 76.5%, which is applied to each block of the catchment total rainfall hyetograph PR = 76.5%

The unit hydrograph and net rainfall hyetograph are convolved to give the rapid response runoff hydrograph, to which BF is added to give the total runoff hydrograph which forms the design flood inflow. $Tp_{PMF}(0.25)$ = 1.47 hours

BF = 0.19 m^3s^{-1}

Inflow peak = 61.79 m^3s^{-1}

The design flood inflow hydrograph is routed through the reservoir. The new $RLAG$ is 1.01 hours, compared to the value used in this iteration of 0.0 hours.

Outflow peak = 43.82 $m^3 s^{-1}$

$RLAG$ = 1.01 hours

5. Underbank direct subcatchment design flood inflow and reservoir routing

SPR = 30.9%, DPR_{CWI} = 8.5%, DPR_{RAIN} = 17.8%, giving PR = 57.3%, which is applied to each block of the catchment total rainfall hyetograph PR = 57.3%

The unit hydrograph and net rainfall hyetograph are convolved to give the rapid response runoff hydrograph, to which BF is added to give the total runoff hydrograph.

$Tp_{PMF}(0.25)$ = 1.43 hours

BF = 0.42 $m^3 s^{-1}$

The total runoff hydrograph from Underbank direct subcatchment is routed, together with the outflow from Langsett (lagged by three time intervals) and Midhope (lagged by two time intervals) through the reservoir. The new $RLAG$ is 0.63 hours, compared to the value used in this iteration of 0.0 hours.

Inflow peak = 315.04 $m^3 s^{-1}$

Outflow peak = 295.83 $m^3 s^{-1}$

$RLAG$ = 0.63 hours

Example 8.2b (continued)

6. Calculation of MRLAG and design storm duration D

MRLAG is calculated using Equation 8.3:

$$MRLAG = \frac{\Sigma\Sigma\ RLAG_i AREA_j I_{ij}}{\Sigma\ AREA_j} \qquad MRLAG = 1.19 \text{ hours}$$

D is calculated from entire catchment *Tp*, mean reservoir lag *MRLAG* and *SAAR* using Equation 8.12: $Tp_{PMF}(0.25) = 3.92$ hours; $MRLAG = 1.19$ hours

$$D = (Tp + MRLAG)\,(1 + SAAR / 1000) \qquad D = (4.27 + 1.19)(1 + 1212/1000)$$

= 12.08 hours, rounded to 12.25 hours

7. Derivation of design event inputs (summer PMP)

PMP design storm depth $P = 247.8$ mm, distributed within the design storm duration 12.25 hours to derive the total rainfall hyetographs. PMP design antecedent catchment wetness $CWI = 154.4$ mm $P = 247.8$ mm; $CWI = 154.4$ mm

8. Langsett design flood inflow and reservoir routing

$SPR = 51.6\%$, $DPR_{CWI} = 7.4\%$, $DPR_{RAIN} = 18.9\%$, giving $PR = 77.8\%$, which is applied to each block of the catchment total rainfall hyetographs. $PR = 77.8\%$

The unit hydrograph and net rainfall hyetograph are convolved to give the rapid response runoff hydrograph, to which *BF* is added to give the total runoff hydrograph which forms the design flood inflow. $Tp_{PMF}(0.25) = 1.89$ hours

$BF = 1.01\ m^3 s^{-1}$

Inflow peak = $264.02\ m^3 s^{-1}$

The design flood inflow hydrograph is routed through the reservoir. The new *RLAG* is 0.74 hours, the same as the value used in this iteration.

Outflow peak = $227.87\ m^3 s^{-1}$

$RLAG = 0.74$ hours

9. Midhope design flood inflow and reservoir routing

$SPR = 50.2\%$, $DPR_{CWI} = 7.4\%$, $DPR_{RAIN} = 18.9\%$, giving $PR = 76.4\%$, which is applied to each block of the catchment total rainfall hyetograph $PR = 76.4\%$

The unit hydrograph and net rainfall hyetograph are convolved to give the rapid response runoff hydrograph, to which *BF* is added to give the total runoff hydrograph which forms the design flood inflow. $Tp_{PMF}(0.25) = 1.47$ hours

$BF = 0.18\ m^3 s^{-1}$

Inflow peak = $61.72\ m^3 s^{-1}$

The design flood inflow hydrograph is routed through the reservoir. The new *RLAG* is 0.99 hours, which is approximately the same as the value used in this iteration of 1.01 hours.

Outflow peak = $44.10\ m^3 s^{-1}$

$RLAG = 0.99$ hours

Example 8.2b (continued)

10. Underbank direct subcatchment design flood inflow and reservoir routing
SPR = 30.9%, DPR_{CWI} = 7.4%, DPR_{RAIN} = 18.9%, giving *PR* = 57.2%, which is applied to each block of the catchment total rainfall hyetograph *PR* = 57.2%

The unit hydrograph and net rainfall hyetograph are convolved to give the rapid response runoff hydrograph, to which *BF* is added to give the total runoff hydrograph.

$Tp_{PMF}(0.25)$ = 1.43 hours
BF = 0.40 $m^1 s^{-1}$

The total runoff hydrograph from Underbank direct subcatchment is routed, together with the outflow from Langsett (lagged by three time intervals) and Midhope (lagged by two time intervals) through the reservoir. The new *RLAG* is 0.62 hours, which is approximately the same as the value used in this iteration of 0.63 hours.

Inflow peak = 315.77 $m^3 s^{-1}$
Outflow peak = 297.04 $m^3 s^{-1}$
RLAG = 0.62 hours

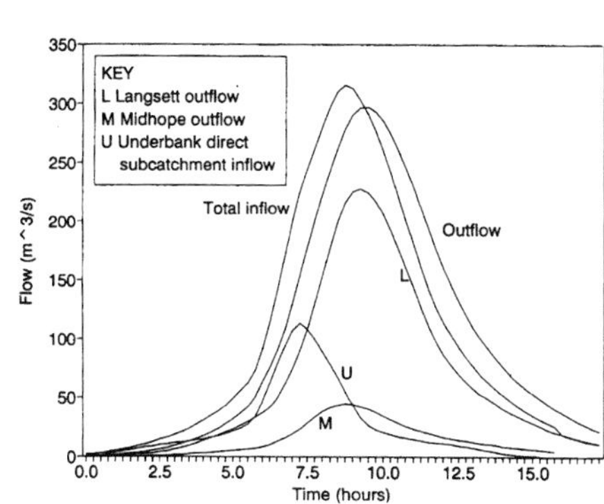

Chapter 9 Disparate subcatchments and land-use effects

9.1 Introduction

There can be little doubt that major land-use changes have an effect on flood frequency and that, in many cases, the effect is detrimental. Indeed, many flood investigations are stimulated by a previous or proposed land-use change. One land-use change has already been considered: Chapter 8 discussed application of the FSR rainfall-runoff method in the context of reservoir flood estimation. Other land-use changes include urban development, mining (both deep and opencast), and agricultural drainage and forestry.

One implication of land-use change is that past flood records may not be a good guide to the future; another is that different parts of the catchment may have different response characteristics, making it difficult to identify the storm duration that will yield the greatest flood peak. In such circumstances, it is usually advisable to separate the catchment into individual subcatchments and consider the consequences of a range of storm durations.

Hence, some of the techniques presented in Chapter 8 can be utilised in other flood estimation problems. This is not new guidance; semi-distributed application of the FSR rainfall-runoff method was suggested in the FSR and the FSSRs, in particular FSSR10 (IH, 1983a) and FSSR13 (IH, 1983c), and also by Price (1978), in IH Report 63 (Packman, 1980), by Packman (1986) and Reed (1987), and more recently by Hall *et al.* (1993). Indeed, this type of approach is becoming increasingly common as the FSR rainfall-runoff method is used to derive flow hydrographs as point inputs to hydrodynamic or flow routing models in river modelling.

This chapter first addresses disparate subcatchment problems, including river confluences, and their treatment (§9.2). It then considers the effects of particular land-use changes and the results of the latest research: this encompasses urbanisation (§9.3), opencast mining (§9.4), and agricultural drainage (§9.5), and afforestation and deforestation (§9.6). Again, access to software for computing design flood hydrographs is useful, since the solution of some problems may require a number of design storm durations to be considered.

9.2 Disparate subcatchment problems

9.2.1 Introduction

Contributions to a flood from different portions of a catchment depend on the drainage configuration and response characteristics, as well as on the spatial variability of the rainfall input and the catchment wetness. A river confluence is the most obvious example of a case where the complexity of the system makes a single-catchment approach to flood estimation unsuitable. A single-catchment approach may also be inappropriate in situations where rainfall patterns vary significantly over a large area, or where land-use or soil type on one part of the catchment differs markedly from the rest of the catchment.

Examples include predominantly rural catchments with urbanisation in one particular area, and chalk-clay catchments, which may be capable of generating significant floods of more than one type: from extreme rainfall alone, from rainfall/snowmelt when soils are frozen, or from rainfall when groundwater is exceptionally high. Another form of disparate subcatchment problem concerns catchwaters and other diversions to or from neighbouring catchments. Division of the catchment into subcatchments is also increasingly used in river modelling for flood defence.

Application of the FSR rainfall-runoff method to flood estimation in disparate subcatchment problems is described in §9.2.2. The procedure involves separating the catchment into subcatchments, and considering the consequences of a shorter or longer design storm.

Confluences

There are particular features of the river confluence problem which require consideration (Dwyer and Payne, 1995). Most importantly, differences in the response times of the upstream catchments may have a marked effect on the downstream flow e.g. the peak flow at the downstream site will be higher if the peaks in the tributaries typically coincide, than if one follows some time after the other. Therefore, it is necessary to consider the relative timings of the flow hydrographs for each tributary, and to allow for ungauged inflows joining between the upstream and downstream sites; solutions to this will vary according to the location and size of the inflows. Natural or artificial flood storage affects the magnitude and timing of flood peaks, and so will also need to be taken into account. An example of a confluence problem is at Monmouth which lies at the convergence of the rivers Monnow and Wye. James and Wright (1990) consider various combinations of floods on the Rivers Monnow and Wye for the hydrological and hydraulic modelling study behind the Monmouth flood alleviation scheme.

Approaches to solving river confluence problems tend to be statistical, focusing on the joint probabilities of rainfall and antecedent catchment conditions (e.g. Reed, 1992; Reed and Anderson, 1992; Acreman and Boorman, 1993; Dwyer and Payne, 1995). Another type of joint probability problem is the confluence of a river with the sea. Flooding problems exist in the upper reaches of estuaries and the lower portions of rivers, due to a combination of freshwater and marine causes. Flooding may also occur in creeks and tide-locked watercourses when freshwater is unable to discharge due to sustained high marine water levels. Mason *et al.* (1992) describe some of the factors which had to be taken into account in the flood control works for the Cardiff Bay Barrage which impounds the flow from the Rivers Taff and Ely. In a review of the hydrological aspects of combined effects of storm surges and heavy rainfall on river flow, WMO (1988) concluded that whilst the principles are clear, practical problems abound. Developing general solution methods to joint probability problems remains an important challenge (see **1** Appendix B for a wider discussion).

Variability in rainfall characteristics

Application of the FSR rainfall-runoff method is generally restricted to catchments where the assumptions supporting the method, such as uniform rainfall, may be reasonably valid: a nominal limit on catchment area of 500 km^2 was suggested in the FSR. However, there is sometimes a requirement for the subcatchment approach to be applied to very large catchments and catchments with significant spatial variation in rainfall characteristics. For example, in the 3000 km^2 Tyne catchment, *SAAR* varies from 600 mm near the coast to 2000 mm in the headwaters; applying the same *T*-year design depth to the coastal and headwater components will conceal the underlying rainfall pattern, with too much rain applied to the lowland subcatchments and too little to the upland ones.

Land-use and soil-type effects

One of the more complicated type of flood estimation problems concerns mixed geology catchments, such as a chalk and clay catchment where the interplay with urbanisation may also be important. An example of this type of catchment is the River Kennet at Theale, where the catchment consists of areas of great disparity (chalk and non-chalk portions), as well as having an urban area located at the downstream end of a chalk portion. Reed (1987) distinguishes the chalk and non-chalk parts of the catchment, and treats the problem as a confluence problem, deriving the overall catchment response in two parts (but never adding hydrographs that emanate from different design storms).

Conventional rainfall-runoff methods struggle to extend to highly permeable catchments, and permeable catchment flooding is one of the least understood areas of flood hydrology. A valuable source of information is the historical descriptive material collated by Potter and referred to in FSSR4 (IH, 1977b). There are two main types of permeable catchment flood: exceptional floods with only a limited groundwater component, and floods which include a major groundwater component (Bradford and Faulkner, 1997). In exceptional floods, a normally docile catchment can suddenly change into a rapidly-responding one. The most obvious agents are very high intensity rainfall and/or rapid snowmelt above frozen ground. Groundwater-dominated floods may be localised in fields, cellars, roads, valleys, etc., with impacts typically persisting for many weeks, or may be more dramatic, with the water table rising to such a level that changes in response occur, e.g. the River Lavant floods at Chichester in January 1994 (Midgley and Taylor, 1995).

Catchwaters

When catchwaters or diversions are present, even apparently simple tasks, like locating the catchment boundary and determining the area, can sometimes present difficulties and can only be resolved by site visits. In subsequent flood calculations, it may be necessary to adopt a subcatchment approach. Because the carrying capacity of catchwater systems is usually fairly small in comparison to the design flood coming from the natural catchment, in most cases it is reasonable to apply the design rainfall hyetograph, calculated for the natural catchment, to the diverted catchment as well. The hydrograph representing the contribution of the diverted catchment to or from the catchment of interest should be truncated to represent the limited carrying capacity of the catchwater or diversion.

9.2.2 Flood estimation methodology

Principles

The solution to confluence and other disparate subcatchment problems is rather similar to that for multiple reservoir systems (§8.3.2). In general, subcatchments should be as large as possible to meet the requirements of the study; very small areas may introduce needless complication and provide a spurious accuracy. Subcatchment division is generally appropriate at major confluences and at sites where local data exist. The procedure involves the estimation of the design flow hydrographs from each subcatchment and their summation, utilising local data wherever possible, taking care to preserve the translation lag of the individual contributions, and observing the fundamental rule that *floods from different subcatchments should only be combined when they have been derived from the same design storm* (Farquharson *et al.*, 1975). Combination of different storms on different subcatchments yields an overall design storm of unknown rarity, and cannot meet the objective of deriving a design flood hydrograph of a specified return period.

To illustrate this point, consider two subcatchments A and B making up a predominantly rural catchment AB. The recommended estimate of the 50-year flood peak at the confluence is the sum of the flood hydrographs from the confluent subcatchments; these being derived from application of the 81-year storm for the whole catchment AB to each of the subcatchments A and B individually. Application of the 81-year storm for subcatchment A to subcatchment A, and of the 81-year storm for subcatchment B to subcatchment B, will give the recommended estimates of the 50-year flood peaks for the subcatchments individually, but their combination will, in general, overestimate the 50-year flood peak at the confluence. In practical problems, there may also be floodplain storage and/or backwater effects to consider.

Solution

Since the duration which will give the largest combined peak is initially unknown, an iterative procedure is invoked whereby a range of durations is considered. Durations appropriate for the whole catchment and for the individual subcatchments provide useful lower and upper bounds in the search for a critical duration. The recommended procedure is:

i Calculate the design storm duration from Equation 3.1, using *Tp* and *SAAR* values for the entire catchment;

ii Derive the design event inputs for the given storm duration;

iii Go to the first subcatchment and derive the flood hydrograph resulting from the design storm and antecedent condition;

iv Go to the next subcatchment and derive the flood hydrograph resulting from the design storm and antecedent condition;

v Repeat step (iv) until flood hydrographs have been computed for all subcatchments;

vi Sum together the flood hydrographs from the individual subcatchments, allowing for any translation lag or river flow routing where appropriate;

vii Repeat steps (i) to (v) with a different duration, until the critical duration is found, i.e. the one that gives the highest peak flow (or water level in storage-sensitive problems).

Depending on the configuration of the catchment and the number of subcatchments, six or more iterations may be required to determine the critical storm duration. Software packages usually allow design hyetographs and calculated hydrographs to be stored, for subsequent retrieval and strategic input into flood calculations for sites downstream. The iterative procedure is shown in Example 9.1.

Variability in rainfall characteristics

In situations where there is significant variability in rainfall patterns, the stepwise procedure outlined above can be modified to reflect the catchment's rainfall pattern. The same *T*-year *D*-hour areal design storm is applied to each subcatchment, but the subcatchment point storm depth P and antecedent condition *CWI* reflect the subcatchment's particular rainfall and wetness characteristics. In step (ii), the storm duration, return period and profile, and the (total) catchment ARF, would be common to each subcatchment, but the storm depth and antecedent condition would be individually derived for each subcatchment. Application of the total catchment ARF to each subcatchment ensures that the average storm depth from

Example 9.1
Confluences and other disparate subcatchment problems

Confluence: Rhymney at Gilfach Bargoed (IHDTM grid ref. 315050 200250) (Figure 3 of Appendix C) with 30-year design flood

Total catchment relevant descriptors and other information:
General descriptors: *AREA* = 58.31 km^2, *SAAR* = 1507 mm
Tp(0) descriptors: *DPSBAR* = 101.40 m km^{-1}, *PROPWET* = 0.54, *DPLBAR* = 8.50 km, *URBEXT* = 0.026

East subcatchment relevant descriptors and other information:
General descriptors: *AREA* = 40.47 km^2, *SAAR* = 1524 mm, *SPR* from HOST = 42.8%
Tp(0) descriptors: *DPSBAR* = 76.29 m km^{-1}, *PROPWET* = 0.54, *DPLBAR* = 9.86 km, *URBEXT* = 0.033

West subcatchment relevant descriptors and other information:
General descriptors: *AREA* = 17.79 km^2, *SAAR* = 1469 mm, *SPR* from HOST = 30.6%
Tp(0) descriptors: *DPSBAR* = 161.36 m km^{-1}, *PROPWET* = 0.53, *DPLBAR* = 5.25 km, *URBEXT* = 0.011

1. Calculation of design storm duration *D*
D is calculated from entire catchment *Tp* and *SAAR* using Equation 3.1:

Tp(0.5) = 4.05 hours

D = *Tp* (1 + *SAAR* / 1000)

D = 4.05 (1 + 1507 /1000)
= 10.15 hours, rounded to 10.5 hours

2. Derivation of design event inputs
Design storm depth *P* = 85.5 mm, distributed within the design storm duration 10.5 hours using the 75% winter profile to derive the total rainfall hyetograph. Design antecedent catchment wetness *CWI* = 124.5 mm.

P = 85.5 mm
CWI = 124.5 mm

3. East subcatchment design flood inflow
SPR = 42.8%, DPR_{CWI} = -0.1%, DPR_{RAIN} = 6.5%, giving *PR* = 49.6%, which is applied to each block of the catchment total rainfall hyetograph

PR = 49.6%

The unit hydrograph and net rainfall hyetograph are convolved to give the rapid response runoff hydrograph, to which *BF* is added to give the total runoff hydrograph.

Tp(0.5) = 4.63 hours
BF = 1.85 m^{3}s^{-1}
Flood peak = 60.94 m^{3}s^{-1}

4. West subcatchment design flood inflow
SPR = 30.6%, DPR_{CWI} = -0.1%, DPR_{RAIN} = 6.5%, giving *PR* = 37.2%, which is applied to each block of the catchment total rainfall hyetograph

PR = 37.2%

Example 9.1 (continued)

The unit hydrograph and net rainfall hyetograph are convolved to give the rapid response runoff hydrograph, to which BF is added to give the total runoff hydrograph.

$Tp(0.5)$ = 3.00 hours
BF = 0.78 m^3 s^{-1}
Flood peak = 25.49 m^3 s^{-1}

5. Derivation of total catchment hydrograph
The total runoff hydrographs from the East and West subcatchments are added together to find the peak flow. Outflow peak = 82.90 m^3 s^{-1}

6. Derivation of highest peak flow
Repeat with different design storm durations until the critical duration is found, i.e. the one that gives the highest peak flow:

Total catchment			East subcatchment			West subcatchment			Total
D	*P*	*CWI*	*PR*	*BF*	*Q*	*PR*	*BF*	*Q*	Q_{TOTAL}
h	mm	mm	%	m^{3}s^{-1}	m^{3}s^{-1}	%	m^{3}s^{-1}	m^{3}s^{-1}	m^{3}s^{-1}
9.5	82.1	124.5	49.3	1.85	60.29	36.9	0.78	25.56	82.11
10.5	85.5	124.5	49.6	1.85	60.94	37.2	0.78	25.49	82.90
11.5	88.6	124.5	49.9	1.85	61.36	37.5	0.78	25.36	83.40
12.5	**91.5**	**124.5**	**50.2**	**1.85**	**61.50**	**37.8**	**0.78**	**25.16**	**83.53**
13.5	94.1	124.5	50.4	1.85	61.30	38.0	0.78	24.86	83.24

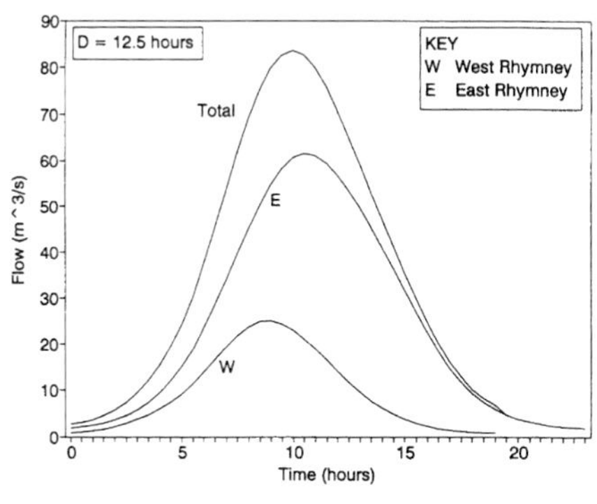

all the subcatchments is the same as the (total) catchment average storm depth, but preserves the variation in rainfall characteristics across the catchment.

This modification is only warranted when estimating *T*-year events on catchments of diverse rainfall characteristics. Its use on excessively small catchments introduces a spurious level of detail into the flood calculation, which can be supported only by extensive hydrometeorological data at the subcatchment level. In PMF estimation, subdivision of the catchment should be limited to that required to represent the features under study, e.g. a cascade (§8.3.2). Furthermore, the modification also extends the method, and some software packages, beyond their natural limits, and the solution may necessitate a combination of several forms of computation.

River modelling

Division of the catchment into subcatchments is also increasingly employed in river modelling for flood defence. Hydrodynamic or flow routing models typically require inflows from numerous subcatchments at different locations along a river, and the subcatchments may have different responses and/or rainfall characteristics. For instance, a model of a long length of major river might start in upland headwaters but finish in a downstream lowland, where the tributaries have quite different rainfall characteristics. Furthermore, the critical design storm duration will lengthen as the model is applied progressively downstream.

The situation is complicated by the fact that such hydraulic models are ultimately concerned with river levels or floodplain boundaries, rather than flows. Since a peak flow does not always translate into a peak level, there is the need to try a number of storm durations. Final design will necessarily involve a large number of model runs using flood hydrographs from a range of different storm durations. Some hydrological modules incorporated within river modelling packages are dedicated to this type of application.

Other aspects

It is usually necessary to adopt a common data interval ΔT in the calculations. One approach is to choose a value that provides adequate definition of the unit hydrograph for the subcatchment with the fastest response time (i.e. the data interval is taken to be about one-fifth of its time-to-peak). However, it is often adequate to adopt a data interval appropriate to the entire catchment.

Subcatchment division can sometimes cause difficulties when determining some digital catchment descriptors, particularly those required to estimate catchment response time (Appendix C, Section 2). Furthermore, it may sometimes be necessary to derive an inflow hydrograph for an area less than the 0.5 km^2 resolution of the gridded data sets. In this instance, the best approach is usually to scale the hydrograph derived for another subcatchment on the basis of size and/or *SAAR*.

9.3 Urbanisation

9.3.1 Introduction

In terms of flood potential, urbanisation is probably the most significant land-use change that can be made to a catchment, and the effects of urban development on catchment flood behaviour are reviewed in §9.3.2 (see **3** C9). Mixed land-use catchments are of particular concern as portions of the catchment have widely differing response characteristics. Flood estimation on very heavily urbanised catchments is more appropriately treated by sewer design methods, and these are recommended for catchments where *URBEXT* > 0.5.

The FSR rainfall-runoff method includes allowances for urbanisation in the unit hydrograph time-to-peak (see §2.2.4) and percentage runoff models (see §2.3.1), and in the variant to the design event method for urbanised catchments (Section 3.2). The presence of an urbanised area can, nevertheless, raise special considerations, as described in §9.3.3. Furthermore, in some instances, it may be required to store the increased runoff from an urban area temporarily in a balancing pond, which brings other factors into play (discussed in §9.3.4).

9.3.2 Effects of urbanisation

It is generally appreciated that urban development increases runoff because of the greater impermeability of urban surfaces. This effect is included in the following list, assembled from Hollis (1975), Packman (1980) and Hall (1984), together with other consequences of urbanisation that are not so widely recognised:

- **Increased runoff** Urban surfaces are typically less permeable than rural surfaces, so runoff volumes are greater (Figure 9.1);
- **Faster runoff** Urban development includes drainage works (e.g. gutters, pipes, sewers, channel improvements) to convey runoff away from the source; thus rainfall runs off more rapidly, and the response is faster to peak and faster to recede (Figure 9.1). The decreased response time means that the catchment becomes sensitive to shorter duration storms;
- **Antecedent catchment wetness less influential** Urban surfaces wet-up more readily than rural surfaces, so pre-storm catchment conditions are less influential;
- **Less recharge** Urban surfaces are less permeable than rural surfaces, so natural recharge to groundwater is reduced, and baseflows are correspondingly reduced. Whilst this is unlikely to be a major influence on flood behaviour, the reduction in groundwater abstractions associated with the decline in industrial activity within the boundaries of some major towns and cities in the UK has resulted in rising groundwater tables, which have contributed to increased baseflow. In some circumstances, baseflows may also be increased by effluent returns, particularly where water is imported to the catchment;
- **Interaction with soil type** Urban effects tend to be greater for naturally permeable catchments (which have a low percentage runoff and slow response) than for impermeable catchments (which already have a typically-urban high percentage runoff and fast response) (Figure 9.2);
- **Interaction with return period** Floods of all return periods are, in general, increased. However, urban effects tend to be more pronounced in the response to small, short return period storms (which otherwise yielded low

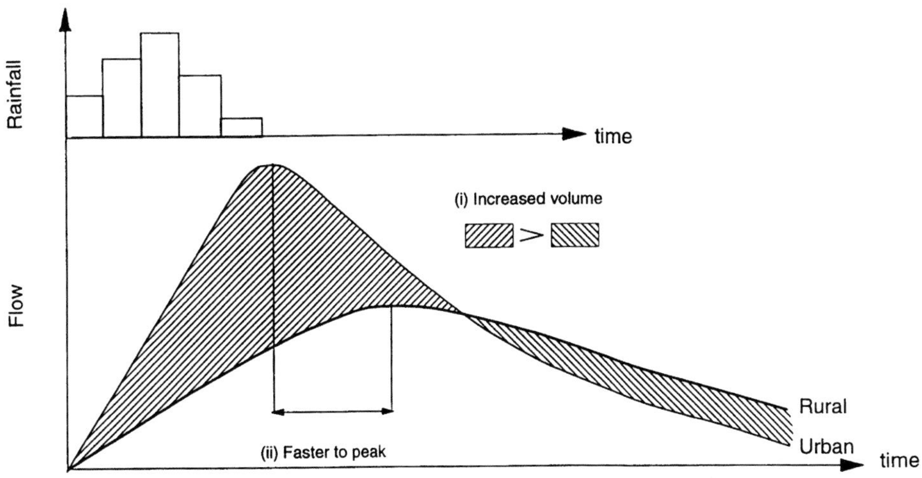

Figure 9.1 *Basic effect cf urbanisation*

percentage runoff and little overland flow), than in the response to severe, high return period storms (which already have a typically urban high percentage runoff and increased overland flow) (Figure 9.3);

- **Seasonality** Rural catchments tend to respond to longer duration rainfall events, more often associated with frontal rainfall; these are more prevalent in winter (November to April). Urbanised catchments tend to respond to short duration intense rainfall events, most commonly convective storms; these are more frequent in summer (May to October). Thus, the seasonality of flooding may move from winter to summer;

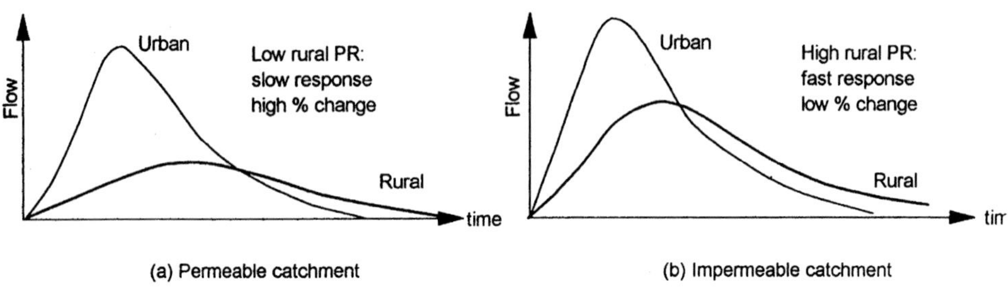

Figure 9.2 *Effects of urbanisation: interaction with soil type*

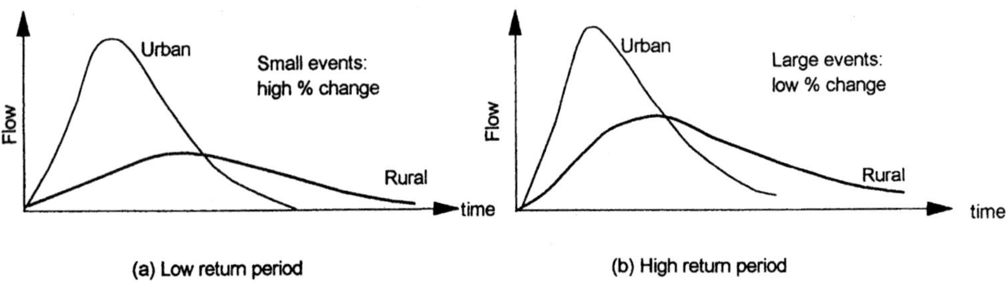

Figure 9.3 *Effects of urbanisation: interaction with return period*

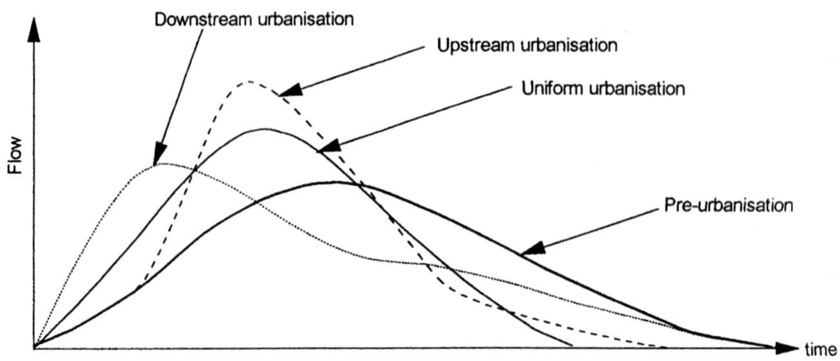

Figure 9.4 *Effects of urbanisation: location of urban area*

- **Possible separation effect** Where urban development is highly localised within the catchment, a separation effect can arise, particularly on naturally permeable catchments; the flood hydrograph then comprises two components: a short-term intense response from the urban area and a longer-term more attenuated response from the rural area (see Figure 9.4 opposite). On catchments where a two-part response typically occurs, it may be flood occurrence rates rather than flood magnitudes that increase through urbanisation;
- **Loss of floodplain storage** Where urban development encroaches on to the floodplain, possibly associated with levée construction, the available overbank storage is reduced, leading to increased flooding downstream.

Urban surfaces differ greatly in their permeability and porosity, so the effect of a given extent of urbanisation will not always be the same. Indeed, remedial works in heavily developed catchments, where drainage patterns and soil conditions have been altered considerably, can result in a reduction in peak flows. An approximate ranking of urban surfaces in terms of typical impermeability is: roofs (almost impermeable), highways, car parks, paved areas, waste ground, restored areas (though this is site-specific), and open spaces and gardens (which respond substantially as natural catchment).

9.3.3 Aspects of flood estimation on urbanised catchments

Location of urban area

The distribution of urbanisation within a catchment can be influential. The effect of a given amount of urbanisation is likely to be rather less if development is dispersed about the catchment, than if it is concentrated in a few key settlements. Location of such settlements with respect to the outfall can have various effects, downplaying or emphasising the separation referred to in §9.3.2 (at the top of this page). Urbanisation in upstream areas may result in a rapid urban response which coincides with and reinforces the slower rural response from downstream, so that the effect on flood frequency may be intensified. In contrast, urbanisation in downstream areas may cause the urban response to pass before the slow rural response from upstream arrives, so that the effect on flood frequency may be less extreme. However, observed storms can consist of two or more bursts and, in some instances, the urban response from the downstream areas may reinforce the upstream rural response to an earlier burst.

Critical storm duration

Identifying the storm duration that yields the highest water level i.e. the critical duration D_{CRIT}, is not straightforward when portions of the catchment have widely differing response characteristics. If the urbanisation is uniformly spread about the catchment, a standard procedure for flood estimation can normally be used. However, if there is a prominent separation effect, a semi-distributed application of the FSR rainfall-runoff method may be required. The flood estimation exercise becomes a disparate subcatchment problem, where it is necessary to consider a range of storm durations using the iterative procedure laid out in §9.2.2.

9.3.4 Balancing ponds

It is a typical requirement that the increased runoff from urban areas is temporarily stored in balancing ponds, also known as flood storage reservoirs. The rationale is to restrict flood peaks to their pre-urban (or some other target) level. Ponds are either on-line (i.e. on the river at, or upstream of, the subject site, with outlet-controlled storage and water level) or off-line (i.e. located off the river, with inlet-controlled storage and water level). Both types are reviewed in the CIRIA guide to the design of flood storage reservoirs (Hall *et al.*, 1993).

Routing flood hydrographs through on-line ponds follows the same principles as routing through reservoirs (Chapter 8), but may entail additional iterations. Balancing pond design is typically iterative on two or more levels, and may involve:

- Adjusting pond and outlet device dimensions such that maximum storage depth and discharge meet the specified target for a given pond inflow hydrograph;
- Checking pond design with different inflow hydrographs arising from storms of various durations (but the same return period) to identify the critical duration;
- Checking pond performance with inflow hydrographs due to storms of different return periods;
- Considering pond performance as a sediment and pollution trap; water pollution levels can rise appreciably following urban development, with increased amounts of sediment, nutrients, bacteria, oil and grease, toxic trace metals, vegetation and litter.

The first two iterations — to identify pond and outlet device dimensions and to identify the critical duration — may be separate or combined. It should be noted that the CIRIA guide to the design of flood storage reservoirs specifies iteration for the critical storm duration that gives the maximum reservoir storage, rather than the peak water level. Since maximum storage corresponds to peak water level, and since the FSR equation for design storm duration was intended to give the duration that caused the greatest flood magnitude, the procedures are broadly equivalent and give similar results. Various software packages are available to carry out these functions, though the iterative scheme used to find the required critical duration (see §9.2.2) is not as simple as the one used to calculate duration based on reservoir lag (see §8.3.1), and may take many more iterations to converge. Extending these recommendations to the design of off-line ponds requires particular care to take account of site-specific features (Hall *et al.*, 1993).

There are many factors to take into account when considering the option to build a balancing pond. It is important to establish whether the pond is intended to relieve a local problem or to alleviate more general flooding problems within the catchment. It is then necessary to identify the critical sites, where flooding will occur if balancing is not provided, and to ascertain whether the proposed storage will encourage the separation or reinforcement of the natural and urban components of the catchment response to the downstream site. The locations within the catchment of urbanisation and balancing ponds relative to the site of interest (which the pond is intended to protect) may be particularly important.

By their nature, balancing ponds are intended to hold back and attenuate floods rather more specifically than impounding reservoirs do. Hence it is necessary to size the control structures correctly to achieve the desired mitigation of flooding up to the design event, and to evaluate the effect (both at the pond and at the critical site) of an exceedance of the design event. Heavily throttled outlet devices are common, so it is to be expected that the design of balancing ponds will be rather sensitive to design storm duration. Finally, it is essential that the pond and any important channels are adequately maintained. The pond should not be sited on the floodplain as this presupposes that the urban and rural components of flood response are very unlikely to coincide. This assumption has some credibility where the development is concentrated close to the catchment outfall but (as discussed in §9.3.3) in the case of a severe storm with two or more bursts, the urban response to one burst may reinforce the rural response to an earlier burst.

9.4 Opencast mining

Opencast mining is more economical in its use of resources than deep mining, and has dominated coal production in the UK since the 1980s. When mining has ceased, the mine sites are reclaimed and managed. In most instances, the sites are covered by a low-density layer of topsoil. The soil might be the same as that in the surrounding area, preserved from the pre-mining environment, or more likely it is a fertiliser-rich imported mixture. Depths of applied topsoil range up to about 0.4 m. Nevertheless, the effects of opencast mining on flood flows are generally long-term and adverse.

Research on restored opencast sites has identified the principal hydrological problems of surface-mined land to be similar to those associated with urbanisation, namely faster response times, increased runoff volumes, decreased baseflows, and greater flow variability (Bragg *et al.*, 1984). In a number of cases in South Wales, there has been flooding and problems such as accelerated soil erosion and gullying (Haigh, 1992). Although most experiments have been at plot scale (e.g. 1 ha), the physical explanations proposed for these effects appear to be no less valid at small catchment scale (e.g. 1 km^2). The traditional reasons put forward are summarised in Reed (1987) and below:

- The passage of earthscrapers and other machinery over the area presents a very significant compaction. This leads to a reduction in soil pore space and, hence, in the capacity to store infiltrated water. Thus, a greater proportion of rainfall becomes rapid response runoff, travelling over or just beneath the land surface;
- The removal and replacement of topsoils disrupt their structure. Pronounced pores and cracks in the soil, whether induced by plants, animals or climate, are likely to be severed or destroyed, further reducing the capacity to receive infiltrated storm rainfall;
- The practice of replacing overburden soils in layers leads to pronounced lamination. This encourages lateral transmission of water, as opposed to vertical penetration;
- The restored landform is likely to be rather more uniform than before. Thus, fewer local depressions result in a reduction in the attenuating effect of surface ponding on flood runoff.

However, recent research on the hillslope hydrology of a reclaimed opencast site in South Wales has revealed the presence of soil pipes and fissures on the reclaimed land (Kilmartin, 1995). These results suggest that the hydrological system may be much more complicated than previously envisaged.

Specific treatments can be applied to counteract the agricultural degradation that the above effects would otherwise bring about (Carolan, 1985). Surface treatments such as tillage and stone removal can lessen the compaction and lamination effects, and sensitive contouring of land and drainage channels may also assist.

9.5 Agricultural drainage

Agricultural drainage is an important component of agricultural improvement schemes, and has been widely used in the east and south of the UK (Charnley, 1987). However, the impact of agricultural drainage on the influence of flooding downstream has been a source of controversy (Robinson, 1987; 1989). Drainage has been claimed to speed up the movement of water to stream channels and increase peak flows downstream, giving a more flashy pattern of behaviour with shorter response times and higher peak flows. It has also been reputed to lower soil-water tables in drained land, providing a buffer to absorb event rainfall, thus reducing peak flows and baseflows.

IH Report 113 (Robinson, 1990) assembles a nationwide set of data from published and unpublished field drainage experiments where flows were measured from both drained and undrained land. Flood event analyses on pre- and post-drainage flood events reveal that, in contrast to previously expressed opinions (e.g. Bailey and Bree, 1981), the drainage of heavy clay soils (prone to prolonged surface saturation in their undrained state) generally results in a reduction in flood peaks for large and medium events. This is because the natural response characteristics of these soils are flashy, with limited soil moisture storage available; when drained, surface saturation is largely eliminated, leading to a smaller peak flow for a given volume of runoff. On more permeable soils, less prone to surface saturation, the more usual effect of drainage is to intensify subsurface discharges, leading to higher peak flows. This is because drainage speeds up the routing of water to the catchment outlet, thereby increasing the peak flow for a given volume of runoff. This finding is at variance with earlier views which assumed that, due to their higher porosity, the storage buffer created by drainage of these soils would always act to attenuate maximum flows.

The difference in the effect of agricultural drainage between sites may explain the long-standing controversy regarding its implications: drainage may increase peak flows at some sites and reduce it at others. Since the purpose of agricultural drainage is to impose a required level of water table control, it is unsurprising that drainage results in a more uniform response between sites. The results emphasise the importance of the pre-drained response, and indicate that the likely effect of artificial drainage (to aggravate or alleviate flood risk) at the field scale may be assessed from measurable site characteristics. These include the soil water regime (if known) and the physical properties of the soil profile. Rainfall regime may also be significant, since drainage reduces the maximum discharge from higher rainfall areas. In contrast, baseflows tend to be higher from drained than undrained land, principally as a result of the greater depth of the extensive drainage network collecting water that would not have reached the former unimproved channels.

9.6 Afforestation and deforestation

The reputed hydrological effects of afforestation and deforestation are well known, and continue to provoke controversy. Deforestation has been associated with increased flows and considerable erosion, whilst afforestation has been linked with increased variability of flow, such as more rapid and higher spates in response to storm rainfall, and lower flows in dry weather.

There have been many national and international studies of the impacts of afforestation and deforestation on the range and pattern of flow behaviour, the majority of which have been carried out in the USA (Bosch and Hewlett, 1982;

McCulloch and Robinson, 1993). In the UK, studies have centred on three main upland sites: the IH research catchments at Plynlimon in mid-Wales and Balquhidder in the central Scottish Highlands, and the Coalburn research catchment in northern England, described in *IH Report 109* (Kirby *et al.*, 1991), *IH Report 116* (Johnson, 1995) and Robinson *et al.* (1998) respectively. Hudson and Blackie (1993), Hudson and Gilman (1993), Robinson (1986; 1989; 1993; 1998) and Robinson *et al.* (1991) provide further reading about these and other studies.

9.6.1 Deforestation

Deforestation can cause both the volume and timing of runoff to be modified substantially. One of the earliest catchment experiments studying the hydrological effects of deforestation was at Wagon Wheel Gap in Colorado, USA, where clear-felling of one catchment resulted in an increased streamflow of 30 mm year^{-1}, equivalent to approximately 6% of average annual rainfall (Bates and Henry, 1928). Hibbert (1967) provided an early review of such catchment experiments which indicated that most first-year streamflow increases were 300 mm or less and that, generally, the effect declined with time as revegetation occurred. More recently, Bosch and Hewlett (1982) summarised the results of 94 catchment experiments and demonstrated a consistent pattern of increased annual flow after deforestation, but a large variation between catchments. It is likely that a major source of the difference in response is due to different climatic conditions, especially annual precipitation regime.

In the short-term, the problems associated with deforestation are similar to those identified with urbanisation e.g. faster response times, increased runoff volumes, decreased baseflows and greater flow variability. The principal cause of these is soil disturbance, particularly compaction by logging machinery, which reduces the soil's capacity to store infiltrated water. Considerable erosion and soil loss are common, but are usually a consequence of the logging method used, rather than a direct effect of the deforestation. In the UK, it is unusual for a whole catchment to be clear-felled at one time. More likely, a patchwork-forest approach will be adopted, with different areas planted, and subsequently felled, at different times. This approach helps to reduce some of the hydrological problems that have been recognised as effects of deforestation. In the longer-term, the consequences of deforestation depend on what replaces the forest: new forest (§9.6.2), agriculture (Section 9.5) or development (Section 9.3).

9.6.2 Afforestation

In the upland areas where forestry is increasingly concentrated, land is usually poorly drained and peaty, so that the soils often require artificial drainage. Pre-afforestation land drainage generally involves the removal of surface water, the drying of the soil and the suppression of vegetation on the overturned turf ridges and in the excavated ditches. The drainage causes an immediate increase in both high and low flows: floods flows tend to be peakier, with shorter response times and higher peaks, whilst baseflows generally increase.

Flood event analysis on Coalburn data reveals that, in the first couple of years following drainage, lag times are about one-fifth to one-third shorter, and hydrograph peaks are 20% to 40% higher, than their pre-drainage values. An increase in baseflow as a proportion of total flow causes an increase in BFI values over the same period. These observations are explained by the observation that, in the early stages of afforestation, it is the ditches, rather than the young saplings, that exert the dominant hydrological influence.

In the 10-year period following drainage and planting, there is a tendency for the response times, peak flows and baseflows to begin to regress towards their pre-drainage values. Coalburn data show that response times become similar to their pre-drainage values, whilst peak flows remain about 10% higher. However, baseflow as a proportion of total flow, and hence BFI, is still much larger than its pre-drainage value. The progressive reduction in the effect of the ditches on flows can be attributed to their decay and partial infilling by vegetation, which reduces their hydraulic efficiency, together with the increasing consumptive water use of the growing tree crop.

The overall effect of mature forests on flows is still the subject of debate. The steady growth of trees on drained land appears to result in a steady reduction in peak flows, caused largely by a reduction in runoff volumes by up to 50%. However, there remains some uncertainty about the longer-term effects of forestry on baseflows. At Coalburn, baseflow as a proportion of total flow, and hence BFI, continues to reduce very slowly but, at other sites, tree growth has eventually reduced the total volume of recharge for a given volume of rain. The long-term extent of enhanced baseflows may, in part, be due to the depth of the original drains. The likelihood is that baseflows will eventually be reduced as the forest matures further.

In summary, the results indicate that the hydrological effects of tree growth and the associated pre-planting land drainage are often distinct, and may act in opposite directions. With the growth of the trees and deterioration of the ditch system, the balance between them will change over time.

Acknowledgements

Many of the fundamental ideas and concepts presented in this volume are based on the original contributions made by the Institute of Hydrology staff involved in the Flood Studies Report and subsequent updates, particularly Max Beran, David Boorman and Mike Lowing. Their substantial contribution to this area of flood hydrology is gratefully acknowledged.

Peter Spencer of the Environment Agency is thanked for his advice and comments on early drafts of the flood estimation procedures for disparate subcatchments (Section 9.2). The Department of Agriculture Northern Ireland and Cate Gardner, formerly of the University of Ulster, are thanked for supplying flood event analysis results for 17 catchments in Northern Ireland.

In addition to these individuals and organisations, several members of staff at the Institute of Hydrology are specifically thanked: Val Bronsdon produced the final versions of the majority of the diagrams, Helen Davies provided general assistance, Beate Gannon helped with HOST soil classification matters (Section C.3), John Packman gave advice on urban issues (Section 9.3) and Mark Robinson advised on agricutural drainage and forestry issues (Sections 9.5 and 9.6 respectively).

References

Acreman, M.C. 1989a. Extreme historical UK floods and maximum flood estimation. *J. IWEM* **3**, 404-12.

Acreman, M.C. 1989b. Extreme rainfall in Calderdale, 19 May 1989. *Weather* **44**, 438-446.

Acreman, M.C. and Boorman, D.B. 1993. Flood frequency analysis of the Cul de Sac River, St Lucia, using joint probabilities of rainfall and antecedent conditions. In: *Hydrology of Warm Humid Regions*, Yokohama, Japan *(IAHS Publ. No. 216)*. 353-364. International Association of Hydrological Sciences Press, Wallingford.

Acreman, M.C. and Collinge, V.K. 1991. The Calderdale storm revisited: An assessment of the evidence. In: *Proc. BHS Third National Hydrology Symposium, Southampton 1991*. 4.11-4.16. British Hydrological Society, Wallingford.

Acreman, M.C. and Lowing, M.J. 1989. Maximum flood estimation in the UK. In: *Proc. BHS Second National Hydrology Symposium, Sheffield 1989*. 3.15-3.24. British Hydrological Society, Wallingford.

Anderson, J.L. and Black, A.R. 1993. Tay flooding: act of God or climate change? *British Hydrological Society Newsletter, Circulation,* 38, 1-4.

Archer, D.R. 1981. Severe snowmelt runoff in north-east England and its implications. *Proc. Instn. Civ. Engrs. Part 2,* **71**, 1047-60.

Archer, D.R. 1983. Computer modelling of snowmelt flood runoff in north-east England. *Proc. Instn. Civ. Engrs. Part 2,* **75**, 155-73. *(Disc. ibid. 76 (Aug), 800-3).*

Archer, D.R. 1984. The estimation of seasonal Probable Maximum Flood. In: *British National Committee on Large Dams Conference*, Cardiff . 1-20. British National Committee on Large Dams, London.

Archer, D.R. 1997. The Flood Studies rainfall-runoff method – a fundamental flaw? *British Hydrological Society Newsletter, Circulation,* 56, 12-13.

Archer, D.R. and Kelway, P.S. 1987. A computer system for flood estimation and its use in evaluating the Flood Studies Report rainfall-runoff method. *Proc. Instn. Civ. Engrs. Part 2,* **83**, 601-12. *(Disc. ibid. 85 (Jun), 389-90).*

Archer, D.R. and Stewart, D. 1995. The installation and use of a snow pillow to monitor snow water equivalent. *J. CIWEM* **9**, 221-30.

Austin, B.N., Cluckie, I.D., Collier, C.G. and Hardaker, P.J. 1995. *Radar-based estimation of Probable Maximum Precipitation and Flood.* Meteorological Office, Bracknell.

Bailey, A.D. and Bree, T. 1981. Effect of improved land drainage on river flood flows. In: Institution of Civil Engineers (Ed.), *Flood Studies Report – Five Years On*, Manchester 1980. 95-106. Institution of Civil Engineers, London.

Bass, K.T. 1975. Selection of design flood: the engineer's dilemma. In: *Inspection, Operation and Improvement of Existing Dams, Newcastle 1975*. 4.1.1-4. British National Committee on Large Dams, London.

Bates, C.G. and Henry, A.J. 1928. Forest and streamflow experiment at Wagon Wheel Gap, Colorado. *Mon. Weath. Rev.* **30**, 1-79.

Bell, F.C. 1976. *The areal reduction factor in rainfall frequency estimation.* IH Report No. 35. Institute of Hydrology, Wallingford.

Beran, M.A. 1973. Estimation of design floods and the problem of equating the probability of rainfall and runoff. In: *Design of Water Resources Projects with Inadequate Data*, Madrid 1973 *(IAHS Publ. No. 108)*. 459-471. International Association of Hydrological Sciences Press, Wallingford.

Beran, M.A. 1979. The Bransby-Williams formula: An evaluation. *Proc. Instn. Civ. Engrs. Part 1,* **66**, 293-99. *(Disc. ibid. 68 (Feb), 145-47).*

Boorman, D.B. 1985. *A review of the Flood Studies Report rainfall-runoff model parameter estimation equations.* IH Report No. 94. Institute of Hydrology, Wallingford.

Boorman, D.B., Acreman, M.C. and Packman, J.C. 1990. *A review of design flood estimation using the FSR rainfall-runoff method.* IH Report No. 111. Institute of Hydrology, Wallingford.

Boorman, D.B., Hollis, J.M. and Lilly, A. 1995. *Hydrology of soil types: A hydrologically-based classification of the soils of the United Kingdom.* IH Report No. 126. Institute of Hydrology, Wallingford.

Boorman, D.B. and Reed, D.W. 1981. *Derivation of a catchment average unit hydrograph*. IH Report No. 71. Institute of Hydrology, Wallingford.

Bootman, A.P. and Willis, A. 1981. Discussion on papers 4-6. In: *Flood Studies Report – Five Years On*, Manchester 1980. 62-63. Institution of Civil Engineers, London.

Bosch, J.M. and Hewlett, J.A. 1982. A review of catchment experiments to determine the effects of vegetation changes on water yield and evapotranspiration. *J. Hydrol.* **55**, 3-23.

Bradford, R.B. and Faulkner, D.S. 1997. *Review of floods and flood frequency estimation in permeable catchments*. Report to MAFF. Institute of Hydrology, Wallingford.

Bragg, N.C., Griffiths, C., Jones, A. and Bell, S. 1984. A study of the problems and implications of land drainage on reinstated opencast coal sites. *Proc. North of England Soils Discussion Group* **19**, 37-59.

Bree, T., Curran, J. and Cunnane, C. 1989. Applications of regional flood frequency procedures in Ireland. In: Roald, L. *et al.* (Eds), *FRIENDS in Hydrology*, Bolkeskjø (Norway) 1989 *(IAHS Publ. No. 187)*. 189-196. International Association of Hydrological Sciences Press, Wallingford.

Bruen, M. and Dooge, J.C.I. 1992. Unit hydrograph estimation with multiple events and prior information: I. Theory and a computer program. *Hydrol. Sci. J.* **37**, 429-443.

Burn, D.H. and Boorman, D.B. 1992. *Catchment classification for hydrological parameter estimation*. IH Report No. 118. Institute of Hydrology, Wallingford.

Burn, D.H. and Boorman, D.B. 1993. Estimation of hydrological parameters at ungauged catchments. *J. Hydrol.* **143**, 429-54.

Calver, A. and Lamb, R. 1996. Flood frequency estimation using continuous rainfall-runoff modelling. *Phys. Chem. Earth* **20**, 479-483.

Calver, A., Lamb, R. and Morris, S.E. Generalised river flood frequency estimation by continuous simulation. *Proc. Instn. Civ. Engrs, Water, Maritime & Energy.* (in press).

Carling, P.A. and Grodek, T. 1994. Indirect estimation of ungauged peak discharges in a bedrock channel with reference to design discharge selection. *Hydrol. Proc.* **8**, 497-511.

Carolan, I. 1985. Ransomed, healed, restored, forgiven: the restoration of opencast sites. *Soil and Water* **13**, 8-12.

Charnley, P.R. 1987. Lowland Drainage. In: Brandon, T.W. (Ed.), *River Engineering Part 1: Design Principles*. 173-224. Water Practice Manuals **7**. Institution of Water and Environmental Management, London.

Clark, C. 1991. A four-parameter model for estimation of rainfall frequency in south-west England. *Met. Mag.* **120**, 21-31.

Clark, C. 1995. New estimates of Probable Maximum Precipitation in south-west England. *Meteorol. Appl.* **2**, 307-12.

Clark, C. 1997. How rare is that storm in south-west England? *Meteorol. Appl.* **5**, 139-48.

Cluckie, I.D. and Pessoa, M.L. 1990. Dam safety: An evaluation of some procedures for design flood estimation. *Hydrol. Sci. J.* **35**, 547-569. *(Disc. ibid. 36 (5), 487-490)*.

Collier, C.G. 1986a. Accuracy of rainfall estimates by radar, part I: Calibration by telemetering raingauges. *J. Hydrol.* **83**, 207-223.

Collier, C.G. 1986b. Accuracy of rainfall estimates by radar, part II: Comparison with raingauge network. *J. Hydrol.* **83**, 225-235.

Collier, C.G. 1992. Studies of short duration storm profiles using radar data. In: Verworn, H.R. (Ed.), *Proceedings of the 2nd International Symposium of Hydrological Applications of Weather Radar*, Hannover. University of Hannover, Germany.

Collier, C.G. and Hardaker, P.J. 1995. Estimating Probable Maximum Precipitation by combining radar with a storm model approach. In: *Proc. BHS Fifth National Hydrology Symposium, Edinburgh 1995*. 4.31-4.38. British Hydrological Society, Wallingford.

Collier, C.G. and Hardaker, P.J. 1996. Estimating Probable Maximum Precipitation using a storm model approach. *J. Hydrol.* **183**, 227-306.

Collinge, V.K., Thielen, J. and McIlveen, J.F.R. 1992. Extreme rainfall at Hewenden Reservoir 11 June 1956. *Met. Mag.* **121**, 166-171.

Cordery, I. 1970. Antecedent wetness for design flood estimation. *Trans. Instn. Eng. Aust. (Civ. Eng.),* CE**12**, 181-84.

Cordery, I., Pilgrim, D.H. and Rowbottom, I.A. 1984. Time patterns of rainfall for estimating floods on a frequency basis. *Water Sci. Tech.* **16**, 155-65.

Dales, M.Y. and Reed, D.W. 1989. *Regional flood and storm hazard assessment.* IH Report No. 102. Institute of Hydrology, Wallingford.

Dalrymple, T. and Benson, M.A. 1967. Measurement of peak discharges by the slope-area method. In: *Applications of hydraulics.* Techniques of water resource investigations of the US Geological Survey, Book 3. United States Geological Survey, Washington.

Diskin, M.H. and Boneh, A. 1975. Determination of an optimal IUH for linear, time-invariant systems from multi-storm records. *J. Hydrol.* **24**, 57-76.

Dwyer, I.J. and Payne, J. 1995. Flood estimation at river confluences: A review and case discussion. In: *Proc. BHS Fifth National Hydrology Symposium, Edinburgh 1995.* 3.21-3.26. British Hydrological Society.

Farquharson, F.A.K., Lowing, M.J. and Sutcliffe, J.V. 1975. Some aspects of design flood estimation. In: *Inspection, Operation and Improvement of Existing Dams, Newcastle 1975.* 4.7.1-9. British National Committee on Large Dams, London.

Faulkner, D.S. 1997. Characteristics of recent UK flood-producing rainfalls in relation to the Flood Studies Report design event method. *Meteorol. Appl.* **4**, 259-68.

French, R.H. 1986. *Open-Channel Hydraulics.* McGraw-Hill, Singapore.

Fuller, W.E. 1914. Flood flows. *Trans. Am. Soc. Civ. Engrs.* **77**, 564-617.

Gray, D.M. 1961. Synthetic unit hydrographs for small watersheds. *Proc. Am. Soc. Civ. Eng. J. Hydraul. Div.* **87** (HY4), 33-54.

Grindley, J. 1967. The estimation of soil moisture deficits. *Met. Mag.* **96**, 97-108.

Grindley, J. 1969. *The calculation of actual evaporation and soil moisture deficits over specified catchment areas.* Met. Office Hydrological Memorandum No. 38. The Meteorological Office, Bracknell.

Gurnell, A.M. and Midgley, P. 1987. Refining the estimation of percentage runoff in catchments with extreme hydrogeological conditions. In: *Proc. BHS First National Hydrology Symposium, Hull 1987.* 3.1-3.12. British Hydrological Society, Wallingford.

Gustard, A., Bullock, A. and Dixon, J.M. 1992. *Low flow estimation in the United Kingdom.* IH Report No. 108. Institute of Hydrology, Wallingford.

Gustard, A., Jones, P. and Sutcliffe, M.F. 1986. *Base Flow Index, Scotland.* Institute of Hydrology, Wallingford.

Haigh, M.J. 1992. Degradation of 'reclaimed' lands previously disturbed by coal-mining in Wales: causes and remedies. *Land Degradation and Rehabilitation* **3**, 169-80.

Hall, M.J. 1984. *Urban Hydrology.* Elsevier Applied Science, London.

Hall, M.J. 1996. Small catchment area flood estimation. *Proc. Instn. Civ. Engrs. Water, Maritime and Energy* **118**, 66-76.

Hall, M.J. and Hockin, D.L. 1980. *Guide to the design of storage ponds for flood control in partly urbanised catchment areas.* CIRIA Technical Note 100. Construction Industry Research and Information Association and Butterworth-Heinemann Ltd, London.

Hall, M.J., Hockin, D.L. and Ellis, J.B. 1993. *The Design of Flood Storage Reservoirs.* CIRIA Report No. RP393. Construction Industry Research and Information Association and Butterworth-Heinemann Ltd, London.

Hibbert, A.R. 1967. Forest treatment effects on water yield. In: Sopper, W.E. and Lull, H.W. (Eds), *Forest Hydrology,* 725-36. Pergamon, Oxford.

Hill, F.F., Browning, K.A. and Bader, M.J. 1981. Radar and raingauge observations of orographic rain over South Wales. *Quart. J. Roy. Met. Soc.* **107**, 643-70.

Hollis, G.E. 1975. The effect of urbanization on floods of different recurrence interval. *Wat. Resour. Res.* **11**, 431-35.

Hough, M.N. and Hollis, D. 1995. *Rare snowmelt estimation in the United Kingdom.* The Meteorological Office, Bracknell.

Hough, M.N. and Hollis, D. 1997. Rare snowmelt estimation in the United Kingdom. *Meteorol. Appl.* **5**, 127-38.

Hough, M.N. and Jones, R.J.A. 1997. The United Kingdom Meteorological Office rainfall and evaporation calculation system: MORECS version 2.0 – an overview. *Hydrol. Earth Sys. Sci.* **1**, 227-39.

Hough, M.N., Palmer, S.G., Weir, A., Lee, M.J. and Barrie, I.A. 1997. *The Meteorological Office Rainfall and Evaporation Calculation System MORECS version 2.0.* The Meteorological Office, Bracknell.

Houghton-Carr, H.A. and Boorman, D.B. 1991. A national archive of flood event data for the UK. In: *Proc. BHS Third National Hydrology Symposium, Southampton 1991.* 6.35-6.41. British Hydrological Society, Wallingford.

Hudson, J.A. and Blackie, J.R. 1993. The impact of forestry and forest practices on the quantity and quality of runoff in upland Britain. In: *Proc. BHS Fourth National Hydrology Symposium, Cardiff 1993.* 2.47-2.52. British Hydrological Society, Wallingford.

Hudson, J.A. and Gilman, K. 1993. Long-term variability in the water balances of the Plynlimon catchments. *J. Hydrol.* **143**, 355-80.

IH 1977a. *The Areal Reduction Factor in rainfall frequency estimation.* Flood Studies Supplementary Report No. 1. Institute of Hydrology, Wallingford.

IH 1977b. *Some results of a search for historical information on chalk catchments.* Flood Studies Supplementary Report No. 4. Institute of Hydrology, Wallingford.

IH 1978a. *Flood prediction for small catchments.* Flood Studies Supplementary Report No. 6. Institute of Hydrology, Wallingford.

IH 1978b. *A revised version of the Winter Rain Acceptance Potential (SOIL) Map.* Flood Studies Supplementary Report No. 7. Institute of Hydrology, Wallingford.

IH 1978c. *A comparison between the rational formula and the flood studies unit hydrograph procedure.* Flood Studies Supplementary Report No. 8. Institute of Hydrology, Wallingford.

IH 1979a. *Design flood estimation in catchments subject to urbanisation.* Flood Studies Supplementary Report No. 5. Institute of Hydrology, Wallingford.

IH 1979b. *Short cut to unit hydrograph convolution.* Flood Studies Supplementary Report No. 9. Institute of Hydrology, Wallingford.

IH 1980. *Low Flow Studies.* Institute of Hydrology, Wallingford.

IH 1983a. *A guide to spillway flood calculation for a cascade of reservoirs.* Flood Studies Supplementary Report No. 10. Institute of Hydrology, Wallingford.

IH 1983b. *Assessing the return period of a notable flood.* Flood Studies Supplementary Report No. 12. Institute of Hydrology, Wallingford.

IH 1983c. *Some suggestions for the use of local data in flood estimation.* Flood Studies Supplementary Report No. 13. Institute of Hydrology, Wallingford.

IH 1985. *The FSR rainfall-runoff model parameter estimation equations updated.* Flood Studies Supplementary Report No. 16. Institute of Hydrology, Wallingford.

IH 1988. *Collective risk assessment for sites sensitive to heavy rainfall.* Flood Studies Supplementary Report No. 18. Institute of Hydrology, Wallingford.

IH 1991a. *Micro-FSR v2.0 Operation Manual.* Institute of Hydrology, Wallingford.

IH 1991b. *Representative Basin Catalogue for Great Britain (5 vol.).* Institute of Hydrology, Wallingford.

IH 1996. *Micro-FSR v2.2 Release Notes.* Institute of Hydrology, Wallingford.

IH/BGS 1998. *Hydrological Data UK: Hydrometric Register and Statistics 1991-1995.* Institute of Hydrology / British Geological Survey, Wallingford.

ICE 1933. *Floods in relation to reservoir practice: Interim report.* Institution of Civil Engineers, Committee on Floods in Relation to Reservoir Practice, London.

ICE 1960. *Floods in relation to reservoir practice: Reprint with additional data on floods recorded in the British Isles between 1932 and 1957.* Institution of Civil Engineers, Committee on Floods in Relation to Reservoir Practice, London.

ICE 1975a. Reservoir flood standards: Discussion paper. In: *Flood Studies Conference.* Institution of Civil Engineers, London.

ICE 1975b. *Flood Studies Conference*, London. Institution of Civil Engineers, London.

ICE 1978. *Floods and Reservoir Safety: An Engineering Guide.* Institution of Civil Engineers, London.

ICE 1981. *Flood Studies Report – Five Years On*, Manchester 1980. Institution of Civil Engineers, London.

ICE 1989. *Floods and Reservoir Safety: An Engineering Guide.* (2nd ed.). Institution of Civil Engineers, London.

ICE 1996. *Floods and Reservoir Safety.* (3rd ed.). Institution of Civil Engineers. Thomas Telford, London.

Institution of Engineers, Aust. 1987. *Australian Rainfall and Runoff: A Guide to Flood Estimation (2 vol.).* Institution of Engineers, Australia, Barton.

Institution of Engineers, Aust. 1999. *Australian Rainfall and Runoff: A Guide to Flood Estimation (8 books).* Institution of Engineers, Australia, Barton.

Jackson, M.C. 1978. The influence of snowmelt on flood flows in rivers. *J. IWES* **32**, 495-508.

Jakeman, A.J., Littlewood, I.G. and Whitehead, P.G. 1990. Computation of the instantaneous unit hydrograph and identifiable component flows with application to two small upland catchments. *J. Hydrol.* **117**, 275-300. *(Disc. ibid. 129, 389-96).*

James, C.D. and Wright, D.J.C. 1990. The Monmouth flood alleviation scheme. *ADA Gazette* Spring 1990, 30-33.

Jefferies, C., Stevens, G.S.W. and Ashley, R.M. 1986. A Scottish burn. *J. IWES* **40**, 483-500.

Johnson, F.G., Jarvis, R.M. and Reynolds, G. 1981. Use made of the Flood Studies Report for reservoir operation in hydroelectric schemes. In: *Flood Studies Report – Five Years On,* Manchester 1980. 63-8. Institution of Civil Engineers, London.

Johnson, R.C. 1995. *Effects of upland afforestation on water resources: The Balquhidder experiment.* IH Report No. 116. Institute of Hydrology, Wallingford.

Jones, S.B. 1983. *The estimation of catchment average point rainfall profiles.* IH Report No. 87. Institute of Hydrology, Wallingford.

Keers, J.F. and Wescott, P. 1977. *A computer-based model for design rainfall in the United Kingdom.* Meteorological Office Scientific Paper No. 36. HMSO, London.

Kelway, P.S. 1977. Characteristics of rainfall conditions with particular reference to north-east England. *J. IWES* **31**, 251-84.

Kennard, M.F., Hoskins, C.G. and Fletcher, M. 1996. *Small embankment reservoirs.* CIRIA Report No. 161. Construction Industry Research and Information Association, London.

Kidd, C.H.R. and Packman, J.C. 1980. *Selection of design storm and antecedent condition for urban drainage design.* IH Report No. 61. Institute of Hydrology, Wallingford.

Kilmartin, M.P. 1995. Rainfall-runoff on reclaimed opencast coal-mined land. In: *Proc. BHS Fifth National Hydrology Symposium, Edinburgh 1995.* 4.25-4.30. British Hydrological Society, Wallingford.

Kirby, C., Newson, M.D. and Gilman, K. 1991. *Plynlimon research: The first two decades.* IH Report No. 109. Institute of Hydrology, Wallingford.

Koutsoyiannis, D. 1994. A stochastic disaggregation method for design storm and flood synthesis. *J. Hydrol.* **156**, 193-225.

Kuichling, E. 1889. The relation between the rainfall and the discharge of sewers in populous districts. *Trans. Am. Soc. Civ. Engrs.* **21**, 1-56.

Lamb, R. 1999. Calibration of a conceptual rainfall-runoff model for flood frequency estimation by continuous simulation. *Wat. Resour. Res.* **35**, 3103-3114.

Linsley, R.K. 1987. Flood estimates: How good are they? *Wat. Res. J. ESCAP* (Mar), 36-42.

Littlewood, I.G. and Post, D.A. 1995. Comparison of four loss models for time series analysis of rainfall-streamflow dynamics. *Env. Int.* **21**, 737-45.

Lloyd-Davies, D.E. 1906. The elimination of storm water from sewerage systems. *Proc. Instn. Civ. Engrs.* **164**, 41-67.

Lowing, M.J. 1995. *Linkage of flood frequency curve with maximum flood estimate.* Foundation for Water Research, Marlow.

Lowing, M.J. and Law, F.M. 1995. Reconciling flood frequency curves with the Probable Maximum Flood. In: *Proc. BHS Fifth National Hydrology Symposium, Edinburgh 1995.* 3.37-3.44. British Hydrological Society, Wallingford.

Lowing, M.J. and Mein, R.G. 1981. Flood event modelling: a study of two methods. *Wat. Res. Bull.* **17**, 599-606.

Lowing, M.J. and Newson, M.D. 1973. Flood event data collation. *Wat. Wat. Eng.* 77, 91-95.

Lynn, P.P. 1978. *A comparison of several methods of flood estimation*. Unpublished Applied Hydrology Informal Note 23. Institute of Hydrology, Wallingford.

Maidment, D.R. 1993. *Handbook of Hydrology*. McGraw-Hill, New York.

Marshall, D.C.W. The estimation of flood response times from digital catchment data. *J. CIWEM* (submitted).

Marshall, D.C.W. and Bayliss, A.C. 1994. *Flood estimation for small catchments*. IH Report No. 124. Institute of Hydrology, Wallingford.

Mason, P.J., Burgess, S.A. and Burt, T.N. 1992. The flood control works for the Cardiff Bay Barrage. In: Parr, N.M., Charles, J.A. and Walker, S. (Eds), *Water Resources and Reservoir Engineering*. 203-210. Proc. 7th Conference of the British Dam Society, Stirling. Thomas Telford, London.

Mawdsley, J.A., Dixon, A.K. and Adamson, A.C. 1991. Extreme snow melt in the UK. In: *Proc. BHS Third National Hydrology Symposium, Southampton 1991*. 5.17-5.22. British Hydrological Society, Wallingford.

Mawdsley, J.A. and Tagg, A.F. 1981. Identification of unit hydrographs from multi-event analysis. *J. Hydrol.* **49**, 315-327.

McCulloch, J.S.G. and Robinson, M. 1993. History of forest hydrology. *J. Hydrol.* **150**, 189-216.

Met. Office. 1992. *Snow Survey of Great Britain 1991/92*. The Meteorological Office, Bracknell.

Midgley, P. and Taylor, S.M. 1995. Chichester 1994: the impact of man on a groundwater flood. In: *Proc. BHS Fifth National Hydrology Symposium, Edinburgh 1995*. 3.27-3.35. British Hydrological Society, Wallingford.

Mulvaney, T.J. 1850. On the use of self-registering rain and flood gauges. *Trans. Instn. Civ. Eng. Ireland* **4**, 1-8.

Nash, J.E. 1960. A unit hydrograph study, with particular reference to British catchments. *Proc. Instn. Civ. Engrs.* **17**, 249-82.

NERC 1975. *Flood Studies Report (5 volumes)*. Natural Environment Research Council, London.

O'Donnell, T. 1966. Methods of computation in hydrological analysis and synthesis. In: Committee for Hydrological Research TNO (Ed.), *Recent Trends in Hydrological Synthesis, Proceedings of Technical Meeting 21*. 65-103. TNO, The Hague.

Onof, C., Faulkner, D.S. and Wheater, H.S. 1996. Design rainfall modelling in the Thames catchment. *Hydrol. Sci. J.* **41**, 715-29.

Packman, J.C. 1980. *The effects of urbanisation on flood magnitude and frequency*. IH Report No. 63. Institute of Hydrology, Wallingford.

Packman, J.C. 1986. Runoff estimation in urbanising and mixed urban / rural catchments. In: *Proc. Institution of Public Health Engineers Seminar on Sewers for Adoption, London 1986*. 2.1-2.15. Institution of Public Health Engineers, London.

Pilgrim, D.H. 1983. Some problems in transferring hydrological relationships between small and large drainage basins and between regions. *J. Hydrol.* **65**, 49-72.

Pilgrim, D.H. and Cordery, I. 1975. Rainfall temporal patterns for design flood estimation. *Proc. Am. Soc. Civ. Eng. J. Hydraul. Div.* **101** (HY1), 81-95.

Pilgrim, D.H., Cordery, I. and Baron, B.C. 1982. Effects of catchment size on runoff relationships. *J. Hydrol.* **58**, 205-21. *(Disc. ibid. 71, 191-95).*

Pilgrim, D.H., Cordery, I. and French, R. 1969. Temporal patterns of design rainfall for Sydney. *Trans. Instn. Eng. Aust. (Civ. Eng.)*, CE11 (1), 9-14.

Price, R.K. 1978. A river catchment flood model. *Proc. Instn. Civ. Engrs. Part 2*, **65**, 655-68.

Reed, D.W. 1976. *Deterministic modelling of catchment systems*. PhD thesis, University of Newcastle-upon-Tyne.

Reed, D.W. 1985. Extension of the S-curve method of unit hydrograph transformation. *Proc. Instn. Civ. Engrs. Part 2*, **79**, 193-201. *(Disc. ibid. 81 (Mar), 167-70).*

Reed, D.W. 1987. Engaged on the ungauged: Applications of the FSR rainfall-runoff method. In: *Proc. BHS First National Hydrology Symposium, Hull 1987*. 2.1-2.19. British Hydrological Society, Wallingford.

Reed, D.W. 1992. Triggers to severe floods: extreme rainfall and antecedent wetness. In: Parr, N.M., Charles, J.A. and Walker, S. (Eds), *Water Resources and Reservoir*

Engineering. 219-28. Proceedings of the 7th Conference of the British Dam Society, Stirling. Thomas Telford, London.

Reed, D.W. 1994a. Rainfall frequency analysis for flood design. In: Rossi, G., Harmancioglu, N. and Yevjevich, V. (Eds), *Coping with Floods*. 59-75. Proc. NATO Advanced Study Institute, Erice (Italy) 1992 (Series E: Applied Sciences Vol. 257). Kluwer Academic Publishers, Dordrecht.

Reed, D.W. 1994b. Some notes on generalised methods of flood estimation in the United Kingdom. In: Rossi, G., Harmancioglu, N. and Yevjevich, V. (Ed.), *Coping with Floods*. 185-91. Proc. NATO Advanced Study Institute, Erice (Italy) 1992 (Series E: Applied Sciences Vol. 257). Kluwer Academic Publishers, Dordrecht.

Reed, D.W. and Anderson, C.W. 1992. A statistical perspective on reservoir flood standards. In: Parr, N.M., Charles, J.A. and Walker, S. (Ed.), *Water Resources and Reservoir Engineering*. 229-39. Proc. 7th Conference of the British Dam Society, Stirling. Thomas Telford, London.

Reed, D.W. and Field, E.K. 1992. *Reservoir flood estimation: another look*. IH Report No. 114. Institute of Hydrology, Wallingford.

Reed, D.W. and Stewart, E.J. 1989. Focus on rainfall growth estimation. In: *Proc. BHS Second National Hydrology Symposium, Sheffield 1989*. 3.57-65. British Hydrological Society, Wallingford.

Reynard, N.S. and Stewart, E.J. 1993. The derivation of design rainfall profiles for upland areas of the United Kingdom. *Met. Mag.* **122**, 116-23.

Robinson, M. 1986. Changes in catchment runoff following drainage and afforestation. *J. Hydrol.* **86**, 71-84.

Robinson, M. 1987. Agricultural drainage can alter catchment flood frequency. In: *Proc. BHS First National Hydrology Symposium, Hull 1987*. 6.1-10. British Hydrological Society, Wallingford.

Robinson, M. 1989. Small catchment studies of man's impact on flood flows: Agricultural drainage and plantation forestry. In: Roald, L. *et al.* (Eds), *FRIENDS in Hydrology*, Bolkesjø (Norway) 1989 *(IAHS Publ. No. 187)*. 299-308. International Association of Hydrological Sciences Press, Wallingford.

Robinson, M. 1990. *Impact of improved land drainage on river flows*. IH Report No. 113. Institute of Hydrology, Wallingford.

Robinson, M. 1993. Impacts of plantation forestry on streamflow regimes: A case study. In: *Proc. BHS Fourth National Hydrology Symposium, Cardiff 1993*. 2.41-2.45. British Hydrological Society, Wallingford.

Robinson, M. 1998. 30 years of forest hydrology changes at Coalburn: water balance and extreme flows. *Hydrol. Earth Sys. Sci.* **2**, 233-38.

Robinson, M., Gannon, B. and Schuch, M. 1991. A comparison of the hydrology of moorland under natural conditions, agricultural use and forestry. *Hydrol. Sci. J.* **36**, 565-77.

Robinson, M., Moore, R.E. and Blackie, J.R. 1998. *From moorland to forest: The Coalburn catchment experiment*. IH Report No. 133. Institute of Hydrology, Wallingford.

Rowbottom, I.A., Pilgrim, D.H. and Wright, G.L. 1986. Estimation of rare floods (between the Probable Maximum Flood and the 1 in 100 flood). *Trans. Instn. Eng. Aust. (Civ. Eng.)*, CE28 (1), 92-105.

Shaw, E.M. 1994. *Hydrology in Practice*. (3rd ed.). Van Nostrand Reinhold (International), London.

Sherman, L.K. 1932. Streamflow from rainfall by unitgraph method. *Eng. News Record*, **108**, 501-5.

Snyder, F.F. 1938. Synthetic unitgraphs. *Trans. Am. Geophys. Union* **19**, 447-54.

Snyder, W.M. 1955. Hydrograph analysis by the method of least squares. *Proc. Am. Soc. Civ. Eng. (Separate)*, **81** (Paper 793), 1-25.

Spijkers, T.M.G., Houghton-Carr, H.A. and Naden, P.S. 1995. Continuous rainfall-runoff modelling at daily and sub-daily time intervals for flood frequency estimation. In: *Proc. BHS Fifth National Hydrology Symposium, Edinburgh 1995*. 4.39-4.46. British Hydrological Society, Wallingford.

Stewart, E.J. 1989. Areal reduction factors for design storm construction: Joint use of raingauge and radar data. In: *New Directions for Surface Water Modelling*,

Baltimore 1989 (IAHS Publ. No. 181). 31-40. International Association of Hydrological Sciences, Wallingford.

Stewart, E.J. and Reynard, N.S. 1991. Rainfall profiles for design events of long duration. In: *Proc. BHS Third National Hydrology Symposium, Southampton 1991*. 4.27-4.36. British Hydrological Society, Wallingford.

Sutcliffe, J.V. 1978. *Methods of flood estimation: A guide to the Flood Studies Report*. IH Report No. 49. Institute of Hydrology, Wallingford.

Thiessen, A.H. 1911. Precipitation for large areas. *Mon. Weath. Rev.* **39**, 1082-84.

Thompson, N., Barrie, I.A. and Ayles, M. 1981. *The Meteorological Office Rainfall and Evaporation Calculation System MORECS (July 1981)*. Meteorological Office Hydrological Memorandum No. 45. Meteorological Office, Bracknell.

US Department of Agriculture 1972. *National Engineering Handbook, Section 4 (Hydrology)*. US Department of Agriculture, Soil Conservation Service, Washington.

US Corps of Engineers 1975. *National Program of Inspection of Dams, Appendix D (Recommended guidelines for safety inspection of dams)*. US Corps of Engineers, Washington.

Watkins, L.H. 1962. *The design of urban sewer systems*. DSIR Road Research Technical Paper No . 55. Transport and Road Research Laboratory, Crowthorne.

Webster, P. 1998. *Rainfall boundary conditions for hydrological design*. PhD thesis, University of Birmingham.

Wheater, H.S., Jakeman, A.J. and Beven, K.J. 1993. Progress and directions in rainfall-runoff modelling. In: Jakeman, A.J., Beck, M.B. and McAleer, M.J. (Ed.), *Modelling change in environmental systems*. 101-32. John Wiley and Sons Ltd, Chichester.

Wilson, E.M. 1990. *Engineering Hydrology*. (4th edition). Macmillan, Basingstoke.

World Meteorological Organisation. 1986. *Manual for estimation of probable maximum precipitation*. World Meteorological Organisation Operational Hydrology Report No. 1 (WMO Report No. 332). World Meteorological Organisation, Geneva.

World Meteorological Organisation. 1988. *Hydrological aspects of combined effects of storm surges and heavy rainfall on river flow*. World Meteorological Organisation Operational Hydrology Report No. 30 (WMO Report No. 704). World Meteorological Organisation, Geneva.

Zhao, B., Tung, Y.K. and Yang, J.C. 1994. Determination of unit hydrographs by multiple storm analysis. *Stoch. Hydrol. Hydraul.* **8**, 269-80.

Appendix A Flood event analysis

A.1 Introduction

The FSR rainfall-runoff method is one of the principal methods used for estimating the magnitude of a flood of a given return period at any site in the UK, whether gauged or ungauged. This is achieved through a three-stage process: firstly, the estimation of losses to deduct from an appropriate total rainfall hyetograph, secondly, the estimation of a unit hydrograph with which to convert the net rainfall profile into a rapid response runoff hydrograph, and finally by the estimation of baseflow to add to the rapid response runoff hydrograph to give the total runoff hydrograph.

The method is based on results from the analysis of observed flood events. The analysis procedure entails separating the total flow hydrograph into rapid response runoff and baseflow, separating the total rainfall hyetograph into the net rainfall hyetograph and losses, and deriving the unit hydrograph from the net rainfall hyetograph and rapid response runoff hydrograph. The baseflow, losses and unit hydrograph components are related to physical and climatic descriptors of the catchments to develop estimation equations for use in the ungauged case. This appendix summarises the flood event analysis procedure.

Guidelines for selecting flood events for analysis, and the various data requirements and data sources, are given in Sections A.2 and A.3, respectively. Section A.4 is concerned with the preparatory data processing, including guidance on deriving the catchment average event rainfall and estimating the pre-event catchment wetness. Sections A.5 and A.6 describe the flood event analysis and parameter derivation procedures, respectively. Results from previous flood event analyses are listed in Section A.7. Where appropriate the techniques are illustrated with worked examples.

A.2 Event selection

Events can be selected from daily rainfall records, and from water level or flow records, by simply identifying days on which the rainfall, water level or flow were particularly high. Level charts are particularly useful at this stage because it is easier to identify and assimilate events from plots rather than from strings of numbers. Large rainfall events might not have caused noteworthy flows because of dry antecedent conditions; similarly, an unremarkable storm event on a saturated catchment might well have caused a significant flow. Suitable events can be single- or multi-peaked. A period of recession before and after the event aids analysis, in that isolated events tend to be easier to interpret. Some large events may be too complex to analyse, because responses to individual bursts of rainfall may be intrinsically different, yet inseparable e.g. from a mixed rural-urban catchment where the two types of response are distinct, but are combined in a composite hydrograph.

Flood event analysis can be attempted on catchments which produce a recognisable quick response to heavy rain. However, some types of catchment can create difficulties. For instance, clean-looking, isolated hydrographs may have arisen from small quantities of runoff originating from only part of the catchment. Catchments underlain by highly permeable rock can be problematic in this respect, with the observed response typically reflecting only the impermeable portion of the catchment. However, during an exceptional event when the groundwater levels are high, the catchment response to heavy rainfall may be of a different character. Other types of catchment which may pose particular problems are urbanised or steep ones with very short response times, where uncertainty in time-recording for rainfall and flow data can be debilitating, and catchments with substantial floodplain storage which becomes effective during large floods, so that the hydrographs tend to be longer and more attenuated than those from minor events.

At least five events should be analysed successfully for confidence in the results; the larger the number of events analysed, the greater the reliability of the derived unit hydrograph and losses model parameters (NERC, 1975; Mawdsley and Tagg, 1981). Since the drop-out rate for events once processing and analysis begin is typically around 50%, it is sensible to start with at least 10-12 of the larger events.

A.3 Data requirements and sources

The analysis of flood events requires data not commonly archived in a suitable way. The requirement is for different data types to be collated in a systematic and complete form, and for the data to be at a sufficiently fine time resolution to reveal the detailed structure of the event.

Figure A.1 shows the definition of an observed flood event on the River Bourne at Hadlow (40006). The data items required for analysis of the event are indicated. Flow data for the event are required, with reasonable periods of recession both before and after the peak. The storm event starts at 01:00 on 15 September 1968 and finishes at 16:00 on 15 September 1968. A hydrological day typically runs from 09:00:00 on one day to 08:59:59 on the following day. Therefore, the example storm event spans two hydrological days, starting on 14 September and finishing on 15 September. Recording raingauge and daily raingauge data are required for both 14 and 15 September, in order to specify the event rainfall and to identify any rain that falls between 09:00 on 14 September and the start of the event.

The state of the catchment prior to the storm is referred to as the antecedent catchment wetness, and is indexed by the catchment wetness index *CWI*. Section A.4.2 describes how *CWI* is defined in terms of pre-event soil moisture deficit *SMD* and a 5-day antecedent precipitation index *API*5:

$$CWI = 125 + API5 - SMD \tag{A.1}$$

A *CWI* value is required for the time when the storm event starts i.e. 01:00 on 15 September. *CWI* is first calculated at 09:00 on the first day of the event i.e. 14 September. This *CWI* is then adjusted for the amount by which the catchment wets-up or dries-out between 09:00 and the start of the storm event, to give *CWI* at the start of the event. Daily raingauge data are required for the five days prior to the event, i.e. 9 to 13 September inclusive, to specify *API*5. *SMD* data on the first day of the event, 14 September, are also needed.

Assembling the data from several data suppliers/holders, abstracting the particular periods of interest, assessing data quality and collating the data types is a time-consuming process. When collecting information, it is important to remember that most hydrometeorological variables are measured at 09:00, and to check that the total assigned to a particular day refers to the correct 24-hour period. Care is also needed to convert times from BST to GMT where appropriate.

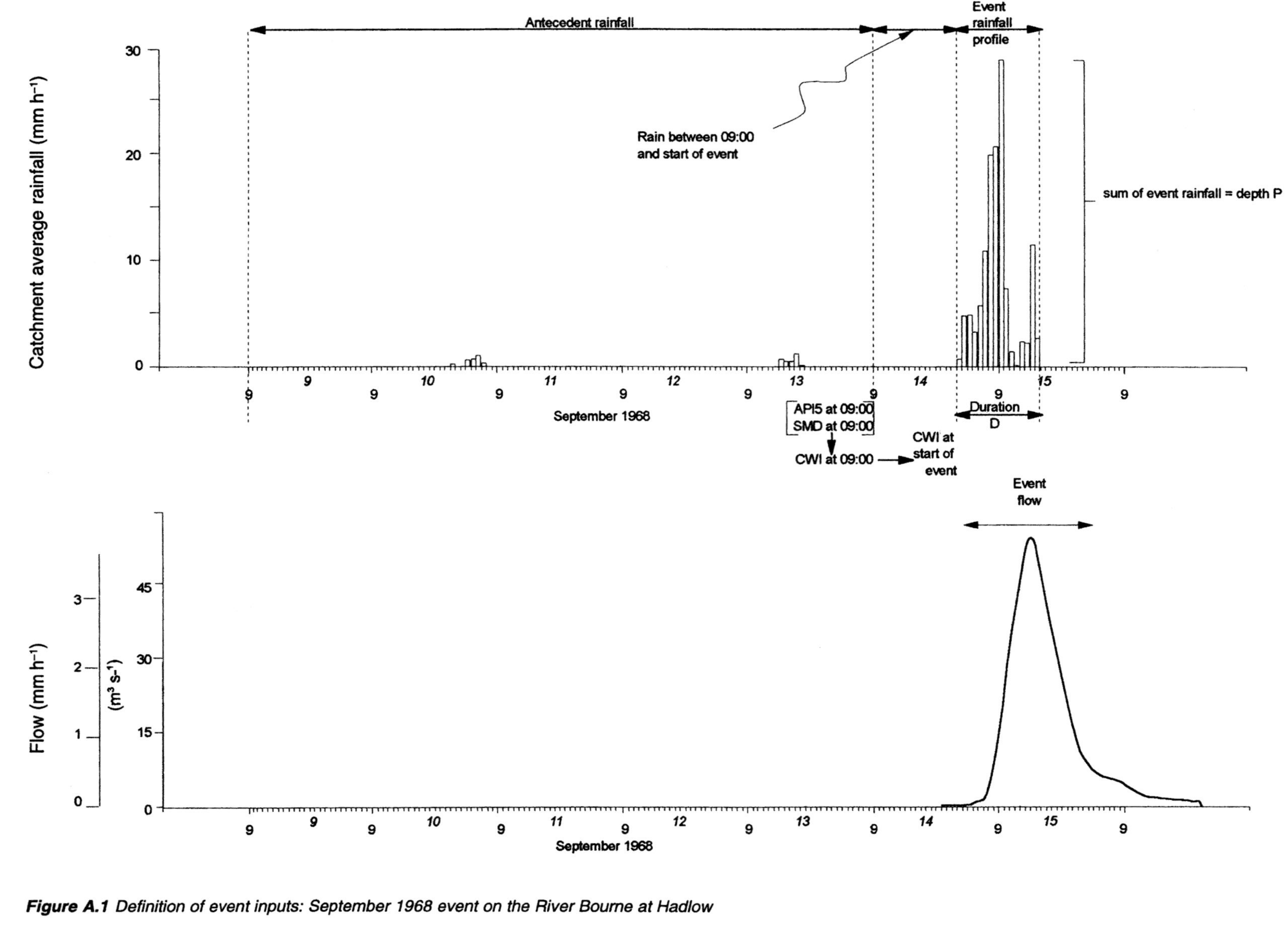

***Figure A.1** Definition of event inputs: September 1968 event on the River Bourne at Hadlow*

A.3.1 Flow data

Flow data at regular intervals are required through the event. The analysis data interval ΔT is usually selected according to the nature of the catchment response; it should have been chosen to give not less than five ordinates on the rising limb of a typical hydrograph. A suitable interval for a small, quickly-responding, part-urban catchment could be as short as 5 minutes, whilst data from a larger, rural catchment might be analysed using 0.5, 1 or even 3-hour intervals.

The National Water Archive register of yearbooks shows the locations of gauging stations within the UK (e.g. IH/BGS, 1998); the latest information about the range of data and dissemination services is available through the National Water Archive web site at http://www.nwl.ac.uk/~nrfadata/nwa/web/nwa.htm. Flow data are most usually obtained from the measuring authority in the form of stage data that must be converted to flows using a rating equation. In many cases, this requires stage charts to be digitised, but sometimes they can be obtained from stage levels on a computer archive (the data often being held in monthly blocks).

There may be doubts about the validity of the flow record, particularly for flood events. For example, the rating may be highly dubious above a certain water level, or the flow record may be artificially-influenced. It is important to confirm the accuracy of the rating curve and flow data through discussion with the measuring authority.

A.3.2 Rainfall data

Rainfall data are required from at least one recording raingauge for the days covering the event. Rainfall data are also required from one or more daily raingauges for the days covering the event, and for the five days preceding the event. While convenient and preferable, it is not essential that the recording raingauge data are available at the same time resolution as the flow data. The numbers of gauges from which data are required depends on the size of the catchment and the spatial distribution of raingauges. For a small catchment, one recording raingauge and one daily raingauge, both located in the catchment would be sufficient. However, since it is unlikely that there will be any gauges on a small catchment, gauges near the catchment would also be acceptable, e.g. two recording raingauges bracketing the catchment. Gauges on the other side of the watershed should be avoided where possible. For a larger catchment, more gauges are required in order to describe within-catchment rainfall variation.

Daily data can be obtained from the Met. Office archive of approved raingauges. Recording raingauge data are obtained from the relevant measuring authority as charts (to be digitised), tabulations showing hourly totals (often using software provided by the raingauge logger manufacturer) or as listings of bucket-tip times (to be converted to ΔT duration totals). An additional valuable source of semi-quantitative information is radar-derived rainfall data which can be used to improve the spatial and temporal definition of events. However, where such data are available, their images must be carefully interpreted and checked for errors (Collier, 1986a; 1986b).

A.3.3 *SMD* data

Relevant data concerning a flood event are not confined to rainfall and runoff. It is important to know something about the state of the catchment before the event. One of the pieces of information required to assess the catchment state is the pre-event soil moisture deficit *SMD*, estimated at 09:00 on the first day of the event.

SMD data are available in several forms for different periods. They can be obtained from the Met. Office as daily estimated SMDs at synoptic weather stations using a modified Penman model (Grindley, 1967; 1969). They can also be obtained as end-of-week or end-of-month areal averages over grass for 40 km × 40 km grid-squares from the Met. Office Rainfall and Evaporation Calculation System, MORECS (Thompson *et al.*, 1981; Hough *et al.*, 1997; Hough and Jones, 1997), which are usually adequate, unless the event is very localised (see **5** 5.6).

A.4 Data processing

Some appraisal and processing of the collected flood event data typically precedes any analysis. In addition to assessing data quality, it will usually be necessary to carry out preliminary processing to derive a catchment average event rainfall and a pre-event *CWI*. Furthermore, it is vital to make a visual inspection of the various data types plotted together, as this may identify problems which may cause the event to be rejected.

A.4.1 Evaluation of catchment average event and antecedent rainfall

Specification of the event rainfall and antecedent rainfall, and identification of any rain that falls between 09:00 on the first day of the event and the start of the event, are ideally accomplished by deriving the catchment average rainfall for the event. Distinguishing between event and antecedent rainfall is best achieved by plotting the rainfall and flow together, whereby it is usually possible to infer the bursts of rainfall which were directly responsible for the event. However, a certain amount of judgement may have to be applied e.g. in deciding whether to divide a multi-burst storm into antecedent rainfall (contributing to the initial catchment wetness) and event rainfall (contributing directly to the flood).

Traditional procedures for deriving catchment average rainfall, such as that used in the FSR/ FSSR16 (IH, 1985), require at least one recording raingauge, ideally located toward the centre of the catchment, and several daily raingauges evenly distributed on, or close to, the catchment. Radar-derived rainfall data can provide a valuable additional source of information, when used in conjunction with measurements from at least one conventional raingauge. There are many acceptable methods for deriving areal rainfall, ranging in sophistication. These are covered in standard texts, such as Shaw's *Hydrology in Practice* and Wilson's *Engineering Hydrology*. Therefore, the following description of the of the technique used for the FSR is given as an example of reasonable practice, rather than as a recommendation.

Event rainfall

The FSR/FSSR16 method for deriving a catchment average event rainfall is one of the simplest available. The technique requires both recording raingauge and daily raingauge data for the days of the event. The daily rainfall totals are averaged to give catchment average daily totals. This is distributed between the hours of the event, using an average profile calculated from the recording raingauge data, to give the catchment average event rainfall. Before averaging, recording and daily gauges can be weighted and daily gauge totals can be standardised.

There are many weighting methods available, reviewed in *IH Report 87* (Jones, 1983). One of the most widely-used techniques is Thiessen polygons (Thiessen, 1911), but this tends to be ill-suited to computer application. The FSR/

FSSR16 method uses the triangular method of spatial averaging (Jones, 1983), whereby each gauge is weighted by location, according to the reciprocal of its distance from the centre of the catchment i.e. the weighting factor is the ratio of the reciprocal of distance-to-centre for the gauge to the total of the reciprocals for all gauges.

In the FSR/FSSR16 method, daily raingauge totals are standardised by dividing the total event rainfall at each gauge by the standard average annual rainfall *SAAR* at that gauge. In general, during frontal storms, rainfall depths tend to exhibit a spatial distribution somewhat similar to that of *SAAR*, i.e. event depths are higher where *SAAR* is higher; in this situation, averaging the standardised rainfalls gives an improved catchment average. During convective storms, the rainfall depths tend to be more randomly distributed and bear little relation to the distribution of *SAAR*; therefore, estimates of the catchment average event rainfall may be better estimated by using (averaging) the original gauge totals. However, convective rainfalls tend only to cause significant flood events on small catchments so, on balance, using the standardised rainfalls is often to be preferred.

Each standardised daily raingauge total is multiplied by its weighting factor to yield a catchment average standardised event rainfall. This value is then rescaled by multiplying it by the catchment *SAAR*, to obtain the catchment average event total.

Where there is only one recording raingauge, its record is simply scaled to the required catchment average event total. Where there are two or more recording raingauges, it is necessary to check that there are no major differences in pattern. For the recording raingauges, weights can be derived by the same method as above.

For each recording raingauge, each interval's rainfall is expressed as a proportion of the total event rainfall at that gauge. For each hour in turn, the proportion at each gauge is then multiplied by the gauge weight, and these weighted proportions are summed across all the gauges to yield a catchment average event profile.

The time distribution of the rainfall event is obtained from distributing the catchment average event total over the catchment average event profile. Rain falling between 09:00 and the start of the storm is included even though it may have produced no response in streamflow, as it is involved in the calculation of *CWI* at the start of the event rainfall (see §A.4.2). The procedure is illustrated in Example A.1a.

Antecedent rainfall

Derivation of the antecedent rainfall requires only daily raingauge data for the five rainfall days prior to the event. The daily rainfall totals are averaged to give a catchment average daily totals. The method is as above for the daily gauges. Before averaging, the gauges can be weighted (e.g. by location) and the daily totals can be standardised by dividing the daily rainfall at each gauge by the standard average annual rainfall *SAAR* at that gauge. Each standardised daily rainfall is multiplied by its weighting factor to yield a catchment average standardised daily rainfall. These values are then rescaled by multiplying them by the catchment *SAAR*, to obtain the catchment average antecedent rainfall totals (see Example A.1b).

Example A.1a
Evaluation of catchment average event rainfall

Catchment: Bourne at Hadlow (40006) (Figure 2 of Appendix C)

Relevant catchment descriptors:
AREA = 50.21 km^2, *SAAR* = 719 mm

The map shows the catchment boundary and centroid (+) and the location of daily raingauges (A-H) and one recording raingauge (*) with data over the period 09/09/68 to 15/09/68.

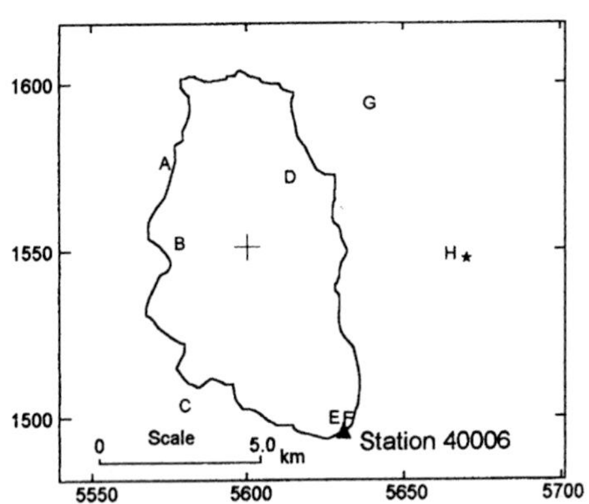

Event rainfall

Gauge	SAAR mm	Weight	14/09/68 mm	14/09/68 % SAAR	15/09/68 mm	15/09/68 % SAAR
A	754	0.1158	50.3	6.7	68.9	9.1
B	832	0.2222	67.8	8.1	83.9	10.1
C	715	0.0626	91.4	12.8	55.8	7.8
D	720	0.3214	76.1	10.6	45.3	6.3
E	675	0.2024	97.3	14.4	29.1	4.3
F	672	0.0148	98.4	14.6	43.7	6.5
G	720	0.0491	45.5	6.3	53.4	7.4
H	687	0.0116	71.7	10.4	41.8	6.1

14/09/68 weighted mean daily rainfall = 10.31% catch SAAR = 74.1 mm

15/09/68 weighted mean daily rainfall = 7.25% catch SAAR = 52.1 mm

Total = 126.3 mm

Hourly raingauge total = 131.7 mm between 01:00 15/09/68 and 16:00 15/09/68

Interval	1	2	3	4	5	6	7	8	9	10	11	12	13	14	15	16
Gauge (mm)	0.7	4.9	5.0	3.3	5.9	11.3	20.6	21.5	29.9	7.6	1.5	0.1	2.4	2.3	11.9	2.7
Event (mm)	0.7	4.7	4.8	3.2	5.7	10.8	19.8	20.6	28.7	7.3	1.4	0.1	2.3	2.2	11.4	2.6

Scaling factor = 126.3 / 131.7
= 0.96

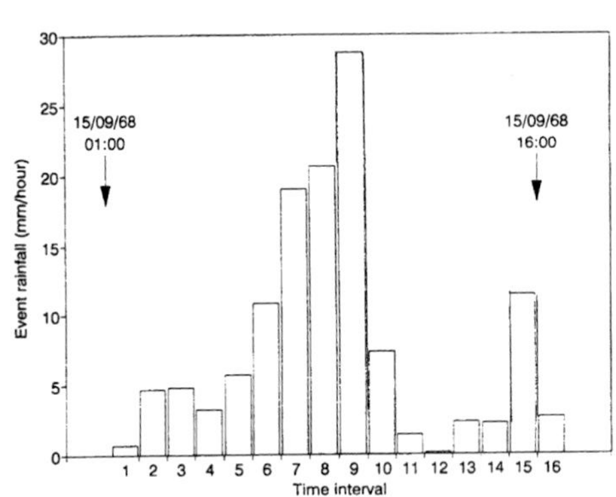

Event rainfall

Duration *D* = 16.0 hours
Depth *P* = 126.3 mm

Example A.1b:
Evaluation of catchment average antecedent rainfall

Catchment: Bourne at Hadlow (40006) (Figure 2 of Appendix C)

Antecedent rainfall

Gauge	*SAAR mm*	*Weight*	*09/09/68*	*10/09/68*	*11/09/68*	*12/09/68*	*13/09/68*
A	754	0.1158	0.0	3.0	0.0	0.0	0.3
B	832	0.2222	0.0	3.5	0.0	0.0	4.6
C	715	0.0626	0.0	4.2	0.0	0.0	0.9
D	720	0.3214	0.0	2.3	0.0	0.0	3.2
E	675	0.2024	0.0	2.3	0.0	0.0	4.1
F	672	0.0148	0.0	2.5	0.0	0.0	0.0
G	720	0.0491	0.0	5.8	0.0	0.0	3.0
H	687	0.0116	0.0	2.0	0.0	0.0	5.4

e.g. 10/09/68 weighted mean daily rainfall = 0.39% catch *SAAR* = 2.8 mm

Antecedent rainfall

09/09/68 = 0.0 mm
10/09/68 = 2.8 mm
11/09/68 = 0.0 mm
12/09/68 = 0.0 mm
13/09/68 = 3.0 mm

A.4.2 Evaluation of pre-event CWI

The state of the catchment prior to the storm is referred to as the antecedent catchment wetness, and is indexed by the catchment wetness index *CWI*. Specification of the pre-event *CWI* is a two-stage process. *CWI* is initially calculated at 09:00 on the first day of the event. This *CWI* value is then adjusted for the amount by which the catchment dries out or wets up between 09:00 and the start of the storm event. The procedure is illustrated in Example A.1c.

CWI at 09:00 on the first day of the event

CWI is initially calculated at 09:00 on the first day of the event using 09:00 *SMD* and *API*5 values in Equation A.1:

$$CWI = 125 + API5 - SMD \qquad \text{(A.1)}$$

SMD is the pre-event soil moisture deficit *SMD*. The *SMD* term indicates the amount of water required to restore the soil to field capacity. In winter months and in very wet conditions, *SMD* will usually be zero, which represents field capacity. The extent to which a catchment will produce rapid response runoff during this period will vary as a result of antecedent rainfall described below, which might have raised the soil moisture above field capacity.

*API*5 is the 5-day antecedent precipitation index. The *API*5 term allows for variations in catchment wetness above field capacity in winter months when *SMD* is zero. *API*5 envelops the catchment average daily rainfall (see §A.4.1) on the five days prior to the first day of the event, and is calculated by the equation:

$$API5 = (0.5)[P_{d-1} + (0.5)^2 P_{d-2} + (0.5)^3 P_{d-3} + (0.5)^4 P_{d-4} + (0.5)^5 P_{d-5}] \qquad \text{(A.2)}$$

Example A.1c
Evaluation of pre-event *CWI*

Catchment: Bourne at Hadlow (40006) (Figure 2 of Appendix C)

Relevant information:
Antecedent rainfall: 09/09/68 = 0.0 mm, 10/09/68 = 2.8 mm, 11/09/68 = 0.0 mm, 12/09/68 = 0.0 mm, 13/09/68 = 3.0 mm (§A.4.1), SMD at 09:00 on 14/09/68 = 41.0 mm, Rainfall between 09:00 on 14/09/68 and start of the event (01:00 on 15/09/68) = 0.0 mm

CWI at 09:00 on the first day of the event
API5 at 09:00 on the first day of the event is calculated using Equation A.2:

$$API5 = (0.5)[P_{d-1}+(0.5)^2P_{d-2}+(0.5)^3P_{d-3}+(0.5)^4P_{d-4}+(0.5)^5P_{d-5}]$$

$$API5 = (0.5)\,[3.0 + (0.5)^2\,0.0 + (0.5)^3\,0.0 + (0.5)^4\,2.8 + (0.5)^5\,0.0]$$
$$= 2.4 \text{ mm}$$

SMD at 09:00 on the first day of the event is known: SMD = 41.0 mm

CWI at 09:00 on the first day of the event is calculated using Equation A:1:

$$CWI = 125 + API5 - SMD$$

$$CWI = 125 + 2.4 - 41.0$$
$$= 86.4 \text{ mm}$$

***CWI* at the start of the event**
As there is no rainfall between 09:00 and the start of the event, *API5* at the start of the event is calculated using Equation A.4:

$$API5_t = API5_{09:00}\,(0.5)^{n\Delta T/24}$$

$$API5_{01:00} = 2.4\,(0.5)^{16\times1/24}$$
$$= 1.5 \text{ mm}$$

SMD at the start of the event is the same as at 09:00: $SMD_{01:00} = 41.0$ mm

CWI at the start of the event is calculated using Equation A.1:

$$CWI = 125 + API5 - SMD$$

$$CWI_{01:00} = 125 + 1.5 - 41.0$$
$$= 85.5 \text{ mm}$$

where P_{d-1} refers to the rainfall total one day ago (yesterday), P_{d-2} refers to the rainfall total two days ago (the day before yesterday), etc. The decay factor of 0.5 applied to each rainfall total means that the rainfall from one day ago has most influence on the index, and the rainfall from five days ago least influence. The constant of (0.5) outside the brackets ensures that the value of *API5* at the end of the day is consistent with the assumption that rainfall on the day before the event was centred half-way through the day.

The introduction of the constant 125 is intended to ensure that *CWI* remains positive (because SMD rarely exceeds 125 mm). There are several weaknesses to this index. Firstly, the choice of a 5-day *API* is arbitrary and ill-suited to representing antecedent catchment wetness effects on very permeable catchments, where wetness over many weeks may be more relevant. Secondly, it is unsatisfactory that when it rains the *CWI* model permits the same unit of rainfall *both* to neutralise the *SMD* by one unit and to contribute to the *API* by one unit, thus raising the *CWI* by two units.

CWI at the start of the event

When the event rainfall begins part-way through the rainfall day, it is necessary to adjust the *CWI* accordingly. In other words, between 09:00 and the start of the event rainfall, it is necessary to quantify by how much the catchment dries out if there is no rain before the event, or wets up if there is rain between 09:00 and the start of the event rainfall. The *SMD* and *API*5 values at 09:00 are updated to give equivalent values at the start of each time interval until the event rainfall starts. By substituting the appropriate *SMD* and *API*5 values into Equation A.1, the *CWI* can be recalculated at the start of each time interval until the event rainfall starts.

SMD and *API*5 are readjusted, by a continuous accounting procedure, from 09:00 to the start of the event rainfall. At the start of each time interval *SMD* is reduced by the amount of any rain that has fallen in the previous time interval. *API*5 is recalculated as:

$$API5_t = API5_{t-1}\,(0.5)^{\frac{\Delta T}{24}} + P_{t-1}\,(0.5)^{\frac{\Delta T}{48}} \qquad \text{(A.3)}$$

where $API5_t$ refers to the *API*5 at the start of the present time interval, $API5_{t-1}$ refers to the *API*5 at the start of the previous time interval, and P_{t-1} refers to the amount of any rain that has fallen in the previous time interval; ΔT is the data interval. This computation is consistent with the previous definition of *API*5, i.e. with uniform rainfall the same answer for *API*5 would be achieved after 24 individual hourly calculations as after a daily calculation.

Table A.1 *Example of CWI computation*

Time at start of interval	**Total rain** *mm*	***SMD*** *mm*	***API*5 at start of interval** *(mm)*	***CWI*** *mm*
09:00	5	25	0.0	100
10:00	18	20	0.0 + 4.9 = 4.9	110
11:00	9	2	4.8 + 17.7 = 22.5	146
12:00	23	0	21.8 + 8.9 = 30.7	156
13:00	17	0	29.8 + 22.6 = 52.4	177
14:00	34	0	50.7 + 16.7 = 67.4	192
15:00	6	0	65.4 + 33.4 = 98.8	224
16:00	0	0	96.0 + 5.9 = 101.9	227
17:00	0	0	98.8 + 0.0 = 98.8	224
18:00	0	0	96.0 + 0.0 = 96.0	221
19:00	5	0	93.1 + 0.0 = 93.1	218
20:00	11	0	90.4 + 4.9 = 95.3	220

Calculation of *CWI* is illustrated by a numerical example in Table A.1 where the *SMD* and *API*5 at 09:00 are 25.0 mm and 0.0 mm, respectively, and the data interval is 1 hour.

If there is no rainfall between 09:00 and the start of the event rainfall, the calculation is simplified, since no rain has fallen to reduce *SMD* or increase *API*5, neglecting evaporation during the period. *SMD* at the start of the event will then be the same as that at 09:00. *API*5 at the start of the event may be calculated from a simplified version of Equation A.3:

$$API5_t = API5_{09:00}\,(0.5)^{\frac{n\Delta T}{24}} \qquad \text{(A.4)}$$

where $API5_{09:00}$ refers to *API*5 at 09:00, and n is the number of hours between 09:00 and the start of the event.

A.4.3 Reasons for event rejection prior to analysis

There are various reasons why what appears to be a suitable event for analysis may be rejected at this preliminary stage, before the analysis has started. Some of these reasons may be apparent after data collection, but others only after some data processing. A visual inspection of the various data types plotted together may reveal further problems which are not apparent from the data collection or data processing phases.

- **Validity of flow record:** There may be serious doubts about the validity of the flow record. For example, the rating may be highly dubious above a certain water level, or the flow record may be artificially-influenced;
- **Position of recording raingauge(s):** The nearest recording raingauges may be poorly positioned in relation to the catchment, so that they are not representative of the rain falling on the catchment;
- **Instrument failure:** If the event was selected from water level records, it is possible that there is no corresponding rainfall data because the recording raingauge failed during the event, or vice versa;
- **No data:** The required data may simply be lost or inaccessible; the likelihood of coincident rainfall and runoff data of good quality reduces markedly before 1960;
- **Non-uniformity of rainfall:** The event rainfall may be highly irregularly-distributed across the catchment, making it unreasonable to expect the event to yield representative information about the typical catchment response to heavy rainfall. This aspect is discussed in more detail in §A.4.1;
- **Timing problems:** There may be timing problems between the event rainfall and flow e.g. the causative rain may appear to occur after the flood hydrograph has passed by;
- **Snowmelt:** The events may be affected by snowmelt. The possibility of a major snowmelt contribution can be judged from Met. Office snow reports (e.g. Met. Office, 1992) or from more local sources of information.

A.5 Flood event analysis

FSR flood event analysis is a three-stage process: an objective measure of catchment lag time is used as a basis for separating rapid response runoff from baseflow; a catchment wetness index CWI is used in the establishment of a net rainfall profile; finally, the unit hydrograph is derived from the rapid response runoff hydrograph and net rainfall hyetograph. The following sections present the analysis carried out for the FSR/FSSR16 as an example of reasonable practice.

A.5.1 Hydrograph separation

The first stage in flood event analysis is separation of the total flow hydrograph into its rapid response runoff and baseflow components. Many methods for hydrograph separation exist e.g. Lowing and Mein, 1981; Jakeman *et al.*, 1990; Littlewood and Post, 1995. If the baseflow proportion is relatively small (as for many flood events) then the difference between methods may not matter. If the baseflow proportion is large, different methods may give very different derived runoff volumes and unit hydrographs. After investigating several techniques, the FSR/FSSR16 used a hydrograph separation method based on Nash (1960).

The FSR defined the catchment lag *LAG* as the time from the centroid of total rainfall to the runoff peak (for a single-peaked event) or centroid of runoff peaks (for a multi-peaked event) of the total flow hydrograph, indicated by point B on Figure A.2. The rapid response runoff is separated from the baseflow by extending the preceding and succeeding recessions to point B. The preceding recession is extended from point A when the flow begins to increase. The succeeding recession is extended from point C when the time from the end of the rainfall is four times LAG. Points A, B and C can be joined with straight lines.

The model parameter baseflow *BF* represents the flow in the river before the event started (i.e. the non-response component), and to a lesser extent the start of the slow response runoff from the event itself. For each event, it is the average separated baseflow over the period A to C. Averaging abstracted baseflow values for several events provides a direct estimate of the baseflow parameter of the unit hydrograph and losses model for a particular catchment.

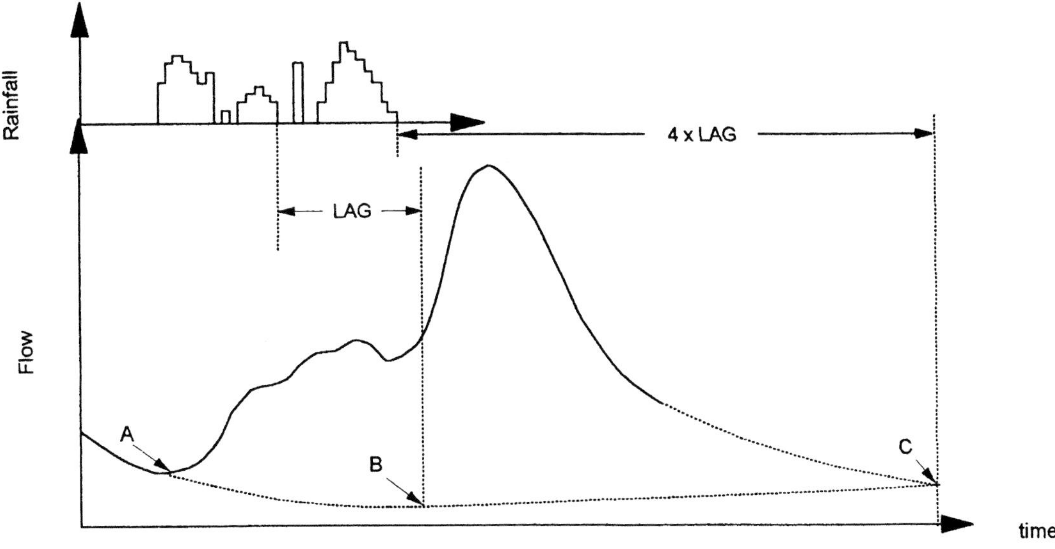

Figure A.2 *Definition of response runoff hydrograph*

A.5.2 Rainfall separation

The second stage in flood event analysis is separation of the total rainfall hyetograph into its net rainfall and loss components. The method used for the FSR/FSSR16 was based on the concept of a loss-rate curve: 100% of rainfall from at least 1% of the catchment was assumed to always contribute to rapid response runoff, whilst rainfall on the the remaining 99% of the catchment was then subject to infiltration losses according to the loss-rate curve, the actual value being determined by the changing *CWI*. For example, if the catchment is dry at the beginning of the storm, the loss rate is initially high then drops off quickly as the catchment wets up; if it is wet at the beginning, the loss rate is fairly constant through the event.

Later developments provided grounds for the belief that a percentage-based method of rainfall separation was more appropriate, as well as being easier to apply. A constant proportional loss model is recommended for design use, one in which the percentage runoff is constant through an event and is applied to each block of the total rainfall hyetograph. However, when simulating a flood event on a gauged catchment, where there are observed flow data through the event, the decreasing proportional loss model for percentage runoff, described here, provides a realistic alternative.

In the decreasing proportional loss model, percentage runoff increases in proportion to *CWI* through the storm, with the constraint that the volumes of net rainfall and rapid response runoff must be equal. Therefore, it is necessary to quantify the variation in *CWI* through the storm. *SMD* and *API*5 are readjusted by a continuous accounting procedure through the storm. At the start of each time interval *SMD* is reduced by the amount of any rain that has fallen in the previous time interval. *API*5 is recalculated as:

$$API5_t = API5_{t-1}\,(0.5)^{\frac{\Delta T}{24}} + P_{t-1}\,(0.5)^{\frac{\Delta T}{48}} \qquad \text{(A.3)}$$

where the variables are as explained above (p. 165). The procedure is as follows:

i Separate the rapid response runoff from the total runoff (see §A.5.1);

ii Calculate *CWI* from *API*5 and *SMD* at the end of every data interval (above and §A.4.2);

iii Multiply each rainfall block by the corresponding *CWI*; sum these products through the event and divide the rapid response runoff by this sum to obtain the factor *F*;

iv Multiply each *CWI* term by *F* to obtain percentage runoff, and then by rain to give the sequence of net rainfall increments.

This is illustrated in Table A.2 (an extension of Table A.1) where the *SMD* at 09:00 is 25.0 mm, *API*5 is 0.0 mm, rapid response runoff is 42 mm and the data interval is 1 hour. Net rainfall values from the constant proportional loss model (*PR* = 32.6%) are included for comparison.

The percentage runoff can be split to distinguish standard and dynamic components, *SPR* and *DPR*. Averaging *SPR* values thus derived for several observed events provides a direct estimate of the *SPR* parameter of the unit hydrograph and losses model for a particular catchment (see §A.6.1).

A.5.3 Unit hydrograph derivation

The final stage in flood event analysis is deconvolution of the rapid response runoff hydrograph and net rainfall hyetograph to give the unit hydrograph, from

Table A.2 Example of net rainfall computation

Time at start of interval	Total rain *mm*	SMD *mm*	API5 at start of interval *mm*	CWI *mm*	Rain x CWI *mm²*	Percent runoff *%*	Net rain DPL* *mm*	Net rain CPL* *mm*
09:00	5	25	0.0	100	500	19.3	1.0	1.6
10:00	18	20	0.0 + 4.9 = 4.9	110	1980	20.2	3.6	5.9
11:00	9	2	4.8 + 17.7 = 22.5	146	1314	27.2	2.5	2.9
12:00	23	0	21.8 + 8.9 = 30.7	156	3588	30.1	6.9	7.5
13:00	17	0	29.8 + 22.6 = 52.4	177	3009	34.2	5.8	5.6
14:00	34	0	50.7 + 16.7 = 67.4	192	6528	37.0	12.6	11.1
15:00	6	0	65.4 + 33.4 = 98.8	224	1344	43.2	2.6	2.0
16:00	0	0	96.0 + 5.9 = 101.9	227	0	43.8	0.0	0.0
17:00	0	0	98.8 + 0.0 = 98.8	224	0	43.2	0.0	0.0
18:00	0	0	96.0 + 0.0 = 96.0	221	0	42.6	0.0	0.0
19:00	5	0	93.1 + 0.0 = 93.1	218	1090	42.0	2.1	1.6
20:00	11	0	90.4 + 4.9 = 95.3	220	2420	42.5	4.7	3.6
Total	128				21773		41.8	41.8

* *DPL* is decreasing proportional loss model; *CPL* is constant proportional loss model
$F = 42/21773 = 0.193 \times 10^{-2}$

which the characteristic catchment response time can be abstracted. Unit hydrograph derivation can be carried out on individual events, which is the traditional approach, or collectively by superposition to derive a catchment average unit hydrograph (Boorman and Reed, 1981).

Derivation of event unit hydrograph

In §2.1.3, it was stated that if the unit hydrograph for a catchment can be found or estimated, the rapid response runoff hydrograph due to any effective rainfall input may be obtained using the principles of linearity, superposition and time-invariance (Figure 2.3), which may be expressed as the convolution equation:

$$q_j = \Sigma_{i=1}^{j} p_i \, u_{j-i+1} \qquad \text{for } j=1, 2, 3, \ldots \qquad (2.3)$$

where q_j denotes the *j*th ordinate of the rapid response runoff hydrograph, p_i the ith effective rainfall, and u_k the *k*th ordinate of the ΔT-hour unit hydrograph. For given values of *i* and *j*, the convolution equation can be expanded to a series of equations. Equation A.5 illustrates this for the simple case where there are three rainfall blocks (i = 1, 3) and six rapid response runoff ordinates (j = 1, 6), and therefore four unit hydrograph ordinates (k = 1, 4):

$$\begin{aligned}
p_1u_1 &= q_1 \\
p_2u_1 + p_1u_2 &= q_2 \\
p_3u_1 + p_2u_2 + p_1u_3 &= q_3 \\
p_3u_2 + p_2u_3 + p_1u_4 &= q_4 \\
p_3u_3 + p_2u_4 &= q_5 \\
p_3u_4 &= q_6
\end{aligned} \qquad (A.5)$$

The obvious way of deriving the unknown set of u values from known values of q and p appears to be to start in the first equation and work forwards, or start in the last one and work backwards. But this is unsatisfactory because data are imperfect and nature does not follow the unit hydrograph theory precisely. This kind of deconvolution problem is inherently ill-conditioned and oscillations of the u values soon start and magnify rapidly. More powerful techniques are required for large-scale application to the types of heavy rainfall event and resulting hydrograph which are generally observed in the UK.

Many different approaches to unit hydrograph derivation are possible, and there is an extensive published literature, partially reviewed in *IH Report 71* (Boorman and Reed, 1981). Most techniques are concerned with a search for the dominant signal (unit hydrograph) in the noise (imperfect but real data), and can take the form of trial and error or iterative solutions, direct analytical solutions, or solutions based on a prior assumption of a particular functional form for the signal. Direct analytical methods, with can be easily applied with computers, are generally preferred. Two of the better known of this type of method are the harmonic analysis technique (O'Donnell, 1966) and the matrix inversion (least-squares) technique (Snyder, 1955). The method adopted in the FSR/FSSR16 was matrix inversion with smoothing, which was found to give the most consistent results for a particular catchment.

In the matrix inversion technique, the sum of the squares of differences between ordinates of the observed and reconstituted unit hydrographs is minimised i.e. the u values form a series of numbers which, when recombined with the original p values, produce a rapid response runoff hydrograph with minimum sum of squares deviation from the original q values. However, the u values do not necessarily form themselves into the shape of a hydrograph as the values are often affected by oscillations. Therefore, some kind of smoothing scheme is needed to reduce the oscillations. A suitable form of smoothing is a simple moving average method. Each value is replaced by the average of itself and its two neighbours, and this is done twice in succession. The smoothed values are adjusted to be equivalent of unit depth of effective rainfall (10 mm) over the catchment area.

Time-to-peak values can be abstracted from the derived unit hydrographs. Averaging these time-to-peak values provides a direct estimate of the $Tp(0)$ parameter of the unit hydrograph and losses model for a particular catchment (see §A.6.2).

Derivation of catchment average unit hydrograph

As an alternative to the traditional approach, a number of procedures have been proposed by which several pre-separated events are analysed simultaneously to give a catchment average unit hydrograph directly (e.g. Diskin and Boneh, 1975; Mawdsley and Tagg, 1981; Boorman and Reed, 1981; Bruen and Dooge, 1992; Zhao *et al.*, 1994). The joint analysis of a number of events avoids the two-stage process of first deriving unit hydrographs and then averaging them.

One such joint analysis method is the event superposition technique (Boorman and Reed, 1981). The technique relies on the unit hydrograph assumptions of linearity and time-invariance. The superposition can be carried out by summing the event data in a simple way i.e. adding the first blocks of net rainfall together to form the first block of net rainfall in the superposed event, and so on. However, some systematic alignment of events prior to summation is advantageous, e.g aligning the peak elements of net rainfall. Figure A.3 illustrates the superposition, where the alignments prior to summation preserve the relative

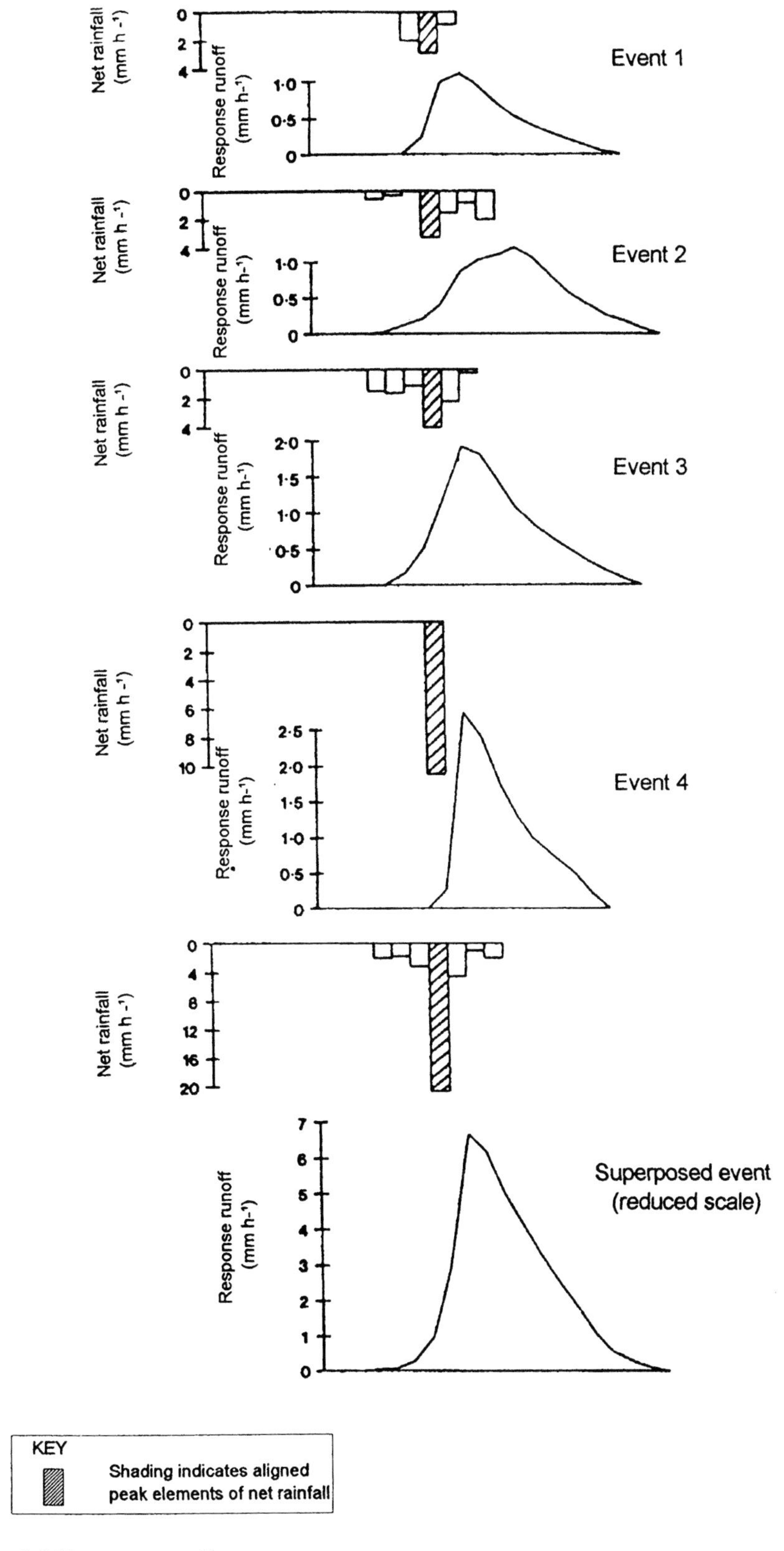

Figure A.3 *Event superposition*

timing of net rainfall and rapid response runoff for each event. The technique is coded up as the FORTRAN program *SUPER*.

The superposed event is then analysed by a suitable technique, such as the *restricted least-squares* method (Reed, 1976). This is based on a matrix transformation approach, related to the matrix inversion method, but incorporating numerical refinements. These include an option which allows constraints to operate so that a unimodal unit hydrograph results, incorporating a single point of inflection on each of the rising and falling limbs. The technique is coded up as the FORTRAN program *RLS*.

A.6 Unit hydrograph and losses model parameters

In the flood event analysis procedure described in §A.5, of the three parameters of the unit hydrograph and losses model, only the baseflow *BF* values are abstracted directly. The time-to-peak values need to be abstracted from the derived unit hydrographs and converted to $Tp(0)$ values, and the *SPR* values need to be calculated from the observed values of percentage runoff, rainfall depth and *CWI*.

A.6.1 Standard percentage runoff

SPR values are calculated from derived percentage runoff, rainfall depth and *CWI* by working the FSSR16 variant of the percentage runoff model backwards. The procedure entails a straightforward reversal of the FSSR16 percentage runoff calculations (see Example A.2a):

$$PR = PR_{RURAL}\,(1.0 - 0.615\ URBEXT) + 70\ (0.615\ URBEXT) \Rightarrow$$

$$\Rightarrow PR_{RURAL} = \frac{PR - 70\ (0.615\ URBEXT)}{1.0 - 0.615\ URBEXT} \qquad (2.12/A.6)$$

$$PR_{RURAL} = SPR + DPR_{CWI} + DPR_{RAIN} \Rightarrow \mathrm{SPR} = PR_{RURAL} - DPR_{CWI} - DPR_{RAIN} \qquad (2.13/A.7)$$

where $DPR_{CWI} = 0.25\ (CWI - 125)$ (2.14)

$$\text{and} \quad DPR_{RAIN} = \begin{cases} 0 & [\text{for P} \leq 40 \text{ mm}] \\ 0.45\ (\mathrm{P} - 40)^{0.7} & [\text{for P} > 40 \text{ mm}] \end{cases} \qquad (2.15)$$

A.6.2 Time-to-peak

Where flood event analysis has been carried out on events individually, rather than by joint analysis (e.g. superposition), it is necessary to abstract the $Tp(0)$ values for each event. Where joint analysis has been used to derive a catchment average unit hydrograph directly, this can be adjusted to another data interval using the *S*-curve technique, or transferred to another catchment using an extended *S*-curve technique (Reed, 1985).

Derivation of *Tp*(0) from event unit hydrograph

$Tp(\Delta T)$ values are abstracted from the derived unit hydrographs (see §A.5.3) and converted to $Tp(0)$ values. The derived unit hydrographs sometimes have smooth

Example A.2a
Derivation of standard percentage runoff

Catchment: Almond at Craigiehall (19001) (Figure 1 of Appendix C)

Relevant catchment descriptors and other information:
PR = 45.3%, $URBEXT$ = 0.034, CWI = 125.0 mm, P = 39.6 mm

The standard percentage runoff SPR for the observed event is calculated using Equations 2.14, 2.15, A.6 and A.7:

$PR_{RURAL} = \{PR - 70\ (0.615\ URBEXT)\}\ /\ (1.0 - 0.615\ URBEXT)$

$$PR_{RURAL} = \{45.3 - 70\ (0.615 \times 0.034)\}\ /\ (1.0 - 0.615 \times 0.034) = 44.8\%$$

$DPR_{CWI} = 0.25\ (CWI - 125)$

$$DPR_{CWI} = 0.25\ (125.0 - 125) = -0.0\%$$

$DPR_{RAIN} = 0$ [as $P \leq 40$ mm]

$$DPR_{RAIN} = 0.0\%$$

$SPR = PR_{RURAL} - DPR_{CWI} - DPR_{RAIN}$

$$SPR = 44.8 - 0.0 - 0.0 = 44.8\%$$

curved shapes, but often further manual smoothing must be done before an acceptable unit hydrograph can be determined. Straight line segments can be drawn by eye to fit the rising limb and upper half of the recession, mimicking the FSR technique, as shown in Figure A.4. Rules to guide this subjective approach require the volume of the rising limb and time-to-peak to be maintained. $Tp(0)$ values are then derived by converting the $Tp(\Delta T)$ values to $Tp(0)$ values using Equation A.8 (see Example A.2b):

$$Tp(0) = Tp(\Delta T) - \frac{\Delta T}{2} \qquad (A.8)$$

Application of extended *S*-curve to catchment average unit hydrograph

The derived catchment average unit hydrograph represents the response to a unit input of effective rainfall in a data interval ΔT. It is possible to derive the unit hydrograph for some other data interval, or to transfer the unit hydrograph to another catchment, using the *S*-curve method. This is a standard technique for transforming a unit hydrograph for one data interval to another, described in standard texts, such as Shaw's *Hydrology in Practice* and Wilson's *Engineering Hydrology*. The *S*-curve is a hypothetical hydrograph which describes the catchment

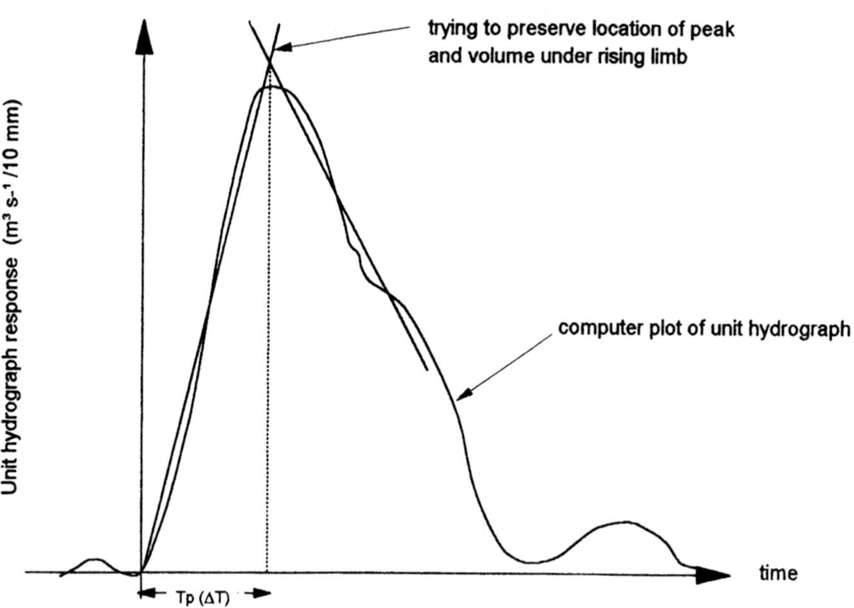

***Figure A.4** Fitting of unit hydrograph and losses model parameter Tp(ΔT)*

Example A.2b
Derivation of time-to-peak from event unit hydrograph

Catchment: Almond at Craigiehall (19001) (Figure 1 of Appendix C)

The unit hydrograph time-to-peak $Tp(\Delta T)$ is abstracted from the derived ΔT-hour unit hydrograph:

$\Delta T = 1.0$ hours

$Tp(1.0) = 6.00$ hours

$Up = 98.48\ \mathrm{m^3\,s^{-1}}$

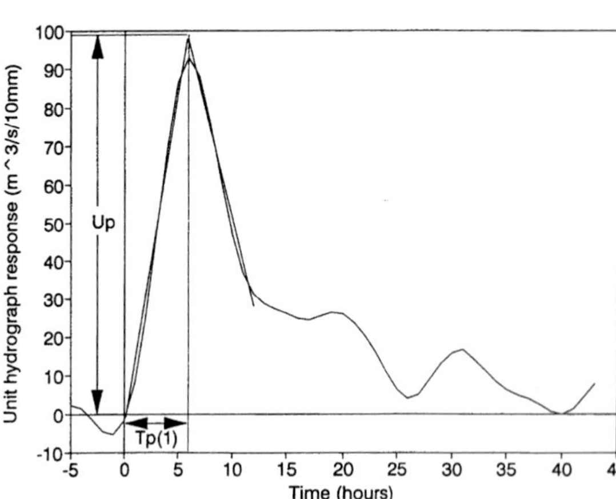

The IUH time-to-peak $Tp(0)$ is calculated from the abstracted value of $Tp(\Delta T)$ using Equation A.6:

$Tp(0) = Tp(\Delta T) - \Delta T / 2$

$Tp(0) = 6.00 - 1.0 / 2$
$= 5.50$ hours

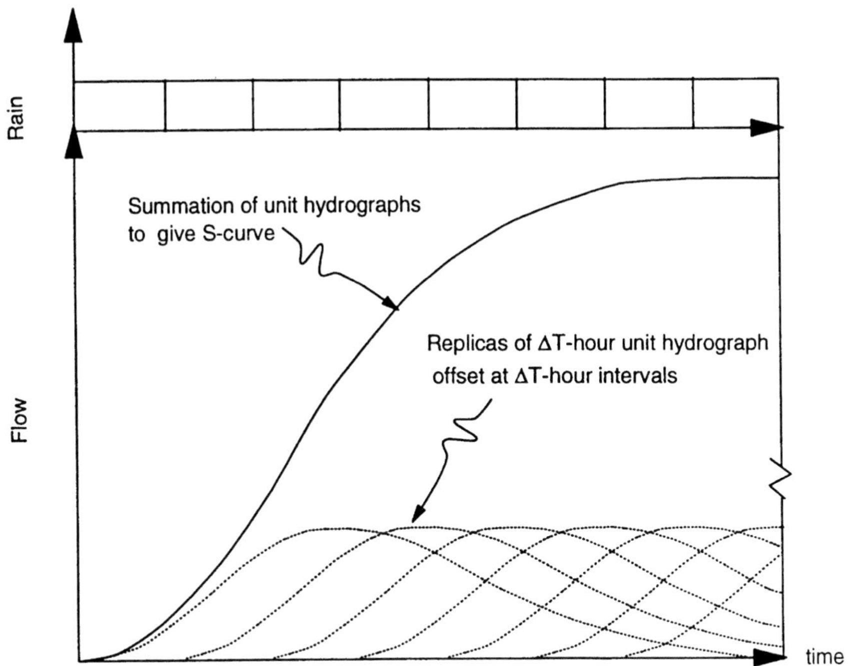

Figure A.5 *Unit hydrograph theory: the S-curve*

response from zero flow to steady state under constant intensity effective rainfall, and is obtained by superposing successive unit hydrographs (Figure A.5). By definition, the unit hydrograph of any data interval ΔT may be found by subtracting two *S*-curves a distance ΔT apart, and scaling the resulting hydrograph to unit volume.

A similar scheme can be used to transform a unit hydrograph derived at one site for use at another site (Reed, 1985). This technique assumes that the unit hydrograph derived at the gauged site can be applied at an analogous ungauged site provided only that an appropriate adjustment is made to the characteristic response time. When moving to an upstream site, the effect of the transformation is to squash the unit hydrograph to represent the faster and more intense response of the smaller area. In the extended *S*-curve method, the adjustment of characteristic response time is made in the *S*-curve domain, rather than the unit hydrograph domain. The method is:

i Construct the *S*-curve appropriate for the gauged site and adjust it for the data interval appropriate for the ungauged site;

ii Compact or stretch the time scale of the adjusted S-curve by a factor which is the ratio of the response times of the ungauged to gauged sites; the response times can be in the form of $Tp(0)$ values or catchment lag values (Figure A.6);

iii Derive the unit hydrograph for the ungauged site from the transferred *S*-curve.

The transformation will not be precise, but it is likely to provide a reasonable approximation if the sites are on the same river, or if the catchments are judged to

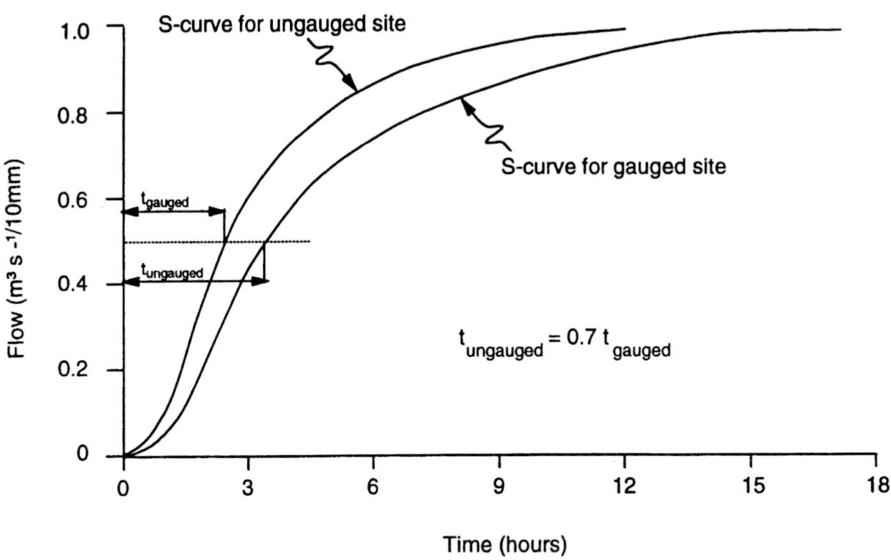

Figure A.6 *Example of S-curve compaction*

be hydrologically very similar in other ways. The technique is coded up as the FORTRAN program *SCURVE.*

A.7 Flood event analysis results

Table A.3 shows results for earlier flood event analyses from the UK Flood Event Archive (Houghton-Carr and Boorman, 1991). The first two columns show the catchment number and the date of the event. Next are three columns of figures based on observed data: the catchment average rainfall depth *P* (see §A.4.1), the storm duration *D* and the peak flow Q_P. Then there are two columns of derived values: the catchment lag *LAG* (§2.1.4) and the baseflow *BF* (§2.4.1). Next are three more columns of figures based on observed data: catchment wetness index CWI (§A.4.2), which is derived from soil moisture deficit *SMD* and antecedent precipitation index *API*5. Then there are three more columns of derived values: the storm runoff in millimetres (*R/O*), as a percentage (*PR*) and converted to standard percentage runoff *SPR* (see §2.3.1). The final column presents the IUH time-to-peak *Tp*(0) (see §2.2.1).

Table A.3 *Flood event analysis results*

The following table (described in Section A.7) summarises the characteristics and derived model parameters of flood events used in the derivation of the new estimation equations for unit hydrograph time-to-peak, marked with a # symbol (Marshall, 1999), and other events stored on the the UK Flood Event Archive (Houghton-Carr and Boorman, 1991). The catchment numbers enable cross-referencing with Table A5.3 in Volume 5, which details the catchment locations and descriptors. *a mean* refers to the arithmetic mean of the *SPR* values; *g mean* refers to the geometric mean of the *LAG*, *BF* and *Tp*(0) values.

Catch	Date	P	D	Q_p	LAG	BF	SMD	API5	CWI	R/O	PR	SPR	Tp(0)	
		mm	h	m^3s^{-1}	h	m^3s^{-1}	mm	mm	mm	mm	%	%	h	
3003	17 Sep 1984	33.3	55	133.46	9.7	6.83	12.2	3.2	116.0	27.8	83.4	85.7	—	
3003	27 Sep 1984	24.6	33	127.05	6.5	8.27	0.0	1.6	126.6	13.5	54.8	54.4	2.9	#
3003	17 Oct 1984	56.2	39	178.62	3.5	13.67	0.0	4.3	129.3	30.6	54.4	50.2	—	
3003	26 Nov 1984	40.9	53	87.96	6.7	9.60	0.0	5.4	130.4	22.2	54.3	52.5	—	
3003	6 Dec 1984	126.7	101	316.30	10.1	6.88	0.0	4.0	129.0	97.6	77.0	65.8	—	
3003	11 Jun 1985	21.1	42	63.27	8.0	2.96	13.5	2.5	114.0	7.3	34.4	37.2	3.6	#
3003	5 Jul 1985	27.4	23	75.46	6.8	5.22	13.2	3.8	115.6	12.1	44.3	46.6	4.5	#
3003	9 Jul 1985	24.3	26	56.47	5.9	9.38	5.8	4.6	123.8	13.4	55.0	55.3	—	
3003	1 Aug 1985	56.0	112	41.57	2.9	9.02	7.7	2.4	119.7	17.5	31.2	29.4	5.1	#
3003	15 Aug 1985	19.9	8	145.20	3.8	9.99	0.0	6.4	131.4	7.9	39.5	37.9	3.5	#
3003	14 Sep 1985	30.9	55	93.96	9.4	9.99	0.0	3.2	128.2	22.4	72.6	71.8	5.3	#
3003	18 Sep 1986	51.6	89	65.94	15.7	3.83	0.3	2.0	126.7	32.8	63.5	60.6	—	
3003	4 Nov 1986	28.8	50	103.34	8.5	10.90	0.0	5.1	130.1	16.4	56.9	55.6	4.5	#
3003	6 Nov 1986	71.0	94	195.72	8.2	12.12	0.0	7.9	132.9	42.2	59.4	52.4	3.5	#
3003	21 Nov 1986	78.8	112	172.20	15.1	7.80	0.0	11.3	136.3	63.0	79.9	71.2	4.3	#
3003	15 Mar 1987	54.9	40	179.48	4.6	10.56	0.0	7.5	132.5	30.9	56.3	51.4	5.0	#
3003	24 Mar 1987	56.0	93	90.26	13.9	6.33	0.8	3.9	128.1	32.5	58.1	54.2	—	
3003	9 Mar 1988	35.0	70	137.57	7.4	9.82	0.0	5.1	130.1	24.8	71.0	69.7	4.2	#
3003	3 Mar 1984	47.8	23	148.87	8.9	11.85	0.0	9.4	134.4	34.6	72.3	68.1	8.5	#
3003	27 Jul 1984	27.1	28	51.78	7.2	4.16	62.4	0.7	63.3	10.4	38.3	53.7	7.9	#
3003	29 Aug 1984	58.7	43	29.63	14.6	1.88	76.6	3.6	52.0	9.3	15.9	30.7	17.1	#
3003	16 Jul 1986	36.4	41	41.45	8.3	2.37	41.1	2.9	86.8	6.7	18.4	27.9	8.5	#
3003	24 Jul 1986	27.0	43	55.75	6.0	7.10	20.0	7.4	112.4	10.2	37.6	40.8	—	
3003	22 Jun 1987	34.2	31	69.88	11.3	2.58	13.4	4.0	115.6	8.4	24.5	26.9	8.0	#
3003	25 Oct 1986	22.4	27	98.73	4.1	18.85	0.0	12.2	137.2	9.0	40.1	37.0	5.5	#
3003	29 Oct 1986	45.6	42	211.26	2.9	18.55	0.0	11.0	136.0	25.3	55.5	51.2	3.4	#
3003	4 Dec 1986	43.1	48	76.84	6.3	19.53	0.0	11.7	136.7	13.9	32.3	28.4	4.7	#
3003	20 Aug 1985	18.9	22	92.58	6.1	8.88	4.0	4.1	125.1	10.2	54.2	54.2	5.5	#
3003	23 Aug 1985	41.5	67	153.49	7.1	8.57	1.3	10.3	134.0	37.3	89.9	87.1	4.4	#
3003	26 Aug 1985	22.9	26	155.28	5.2	14.05	3.5	9.8	131.3	15.2	66.2	64.6	5.5	#
3003	10 Sep 1987	36.3	55	240.31	3.0	8.11	0.7	6.1	130.4	32.3	88.9	87.6	3.6	#
3003	13 Sep 1987	32.6	36	186.45	5.0	9.89	0.0	10.1	135.1	25.1	77.1	74.6	3.5	#
3003	21 Oct 1984	29.8	20	143.81	1.6	22.52	0.6	15.8	140.2	14.2	47.8	44.0	4.5	#
3003	25 Jul 1985	16.9	6	45.57	4.7	5.92	2.3	2.3	125.0	3.5	20.9	20.9	5.4	#
3003	26 Jul 1985	10.1	11	33.24	5.6	7.52	4.2	8.9	129.7	3.0	29.5	28.3	5.6	#
3003	24 Mar 1984	59.1	22	99.59	15.3	2.33	1.8	0.5	123.7	20.7	35.1	31.9	—	
3003	2 Dec 1986	34.3	49	177.84	8.6	18.26	0.0	11.7	136.7	22.2	64.6	61.7	4.1	#
a mean												51.9		
g mean					6.7	7.91							5.0	
7001	15 Aug 1970	96.3	27	457.08	14.7	12.13	18.1	3.0	109.9	73.2	76.0	72.2	—	
7001	2 Jul 1978	70.4	47	155.59	9.7	4.48	77.0	2.2	50.2	23.5	33.4	47.2	8.4	#
7001	3 Oct 1979	32.8	42	92.60	9.7	4.38	36.2	0.6	89.4	9.7	29.5	38.4	5.9	#
7001	17 Nov 1979	48.6	47	97.48	12.5	3.70	7.9	0.9	118.0	25.6	52.7	52.4	—	
7001	24 Jul 1980	77.9	36	275.97	3.1	14.84	72.5	0.9	53.4	27.7	35.6	47.8	4.1	#
7001	26 Oct 1980	33.6	58	199.59	11.5	8.06	0.0	3.1	128.1	23.9	71.0	70.2	3.5	#
7001	23 Aug 1985	41.7	49	192.28	2.5	16.41	10.8	1.4	115.6	22.7	54.5	56.2	3.6	#
7001	9 Jan 1986	129.8	117	130.19	5.0	10.20	0.0	0.7	125.7	47.9	36.9	26.2	6.1	#
7001	19 Jan 1986	27.1	34	87.19	3.3	13.38	0.0	3.6	128.6	9.7	35.9	35.0	—	
7001	17 Jun 1986	29.5	18	102.32	9.2	6.38	20.0	0.2	105.2	8.5	28.7	33.6	—	
7001	30 Jul 1986	34.5	45	163.76	6.8	4.37	69.0	0.7	56.7	12.9	37.4	54.5	5.2	#
7001	28 Oct 1986	50.8	65	223.64	6.7	9.44	23.2	3.9	105.7	26.3	51.8	54.2	5.2	#
7001	2 Dec 1986	25.3	52	134.02	5.5	10.66	3.3	2.9	124.6	17.4	68.9	69.0	6.0	#
7001	9 Jul 1987	23.7	23	106.79	5.8	5.62	6.1	4.0	122.9	5.5	23.4	23.9	6.3	#
7001	14 Mar 1988	30.9	39	50.18	2.2	9.69	0.0	1.6	126.6	4.3	13.8	13.4	6.0	#
7001	22 Sep 1984	94.3	49	321.80	5.8	13.11	12.9	3.5	115.6	49.1	52.1	47.1	5.5	#
7001	7 Sep 1983	101.9	74	268.29	11.4	5.06	49.9	3.5	78.6	46.8	45.9	49.4	6.9	#
a mean												46.5		
g mean					6.4	8.03							5.4	
7003	16 Aug 1970	80.7	52	86.76	17.6	1.34	78.5	1.6	48.1	44.0	54.5	67.7	—	
a mean												67.7		
g mean					17.6	1.34							—	
7006	7 Jun 1987	32.2	21	6.81	7.4	1.16	18.7	11.3	117.6	16.7	51.8	53.6	7.7	#
7006	13 Nov 1987	34.4	20	6.02	8.5	0.40	0.0	1.8	126.8	13.4	39.0	38.5	7.9	#

Catch	Date	P mm	D h	Q_p m^3s^{-1}	LAG h	BF m^3s^{-1}	SMD mm	API5 mm	CWI mm	R/O mm	PR %	SPR %	Tp(0) h	
7006	18 Apr 1988	26.6	77	3.67	8.3	0.46	0.0	3.0	128.0	11.9	44.6	43.8	4.5	#
7006	6 Feb 1989	29.8	19	3.17	10.0	0.30	8.1	3.4	120.3	8.8	29.4	30.6	7.0	#
7006	28 Feb 1989	42.1	43	5.61	9.2	0.58	0.0	3.2	128.2	28.3	67.3	65.7	9.5	#
7006	22 Sep 1989	44.4	19	2.70	11.1	0.21	114.6	0.3	10.7	7.8	17.5	44.8	8.5	#
7006	15 Aug 1990	64.8	53	8.97	9.0	0.24	66.6	1.0	59.4	26.8	41.3	53.4	9.1	#
7006	5 Oct 1990	39.8	41	10.06	8.9	0.38	22.6	2.4	104.8	23.7	59.6	64.6	7.7	#
7006	28 Oct 1990	72.9	16	24.41	6.7	0.55	0.0	0.7	125.7	39.9	54.7	49.3	6.5	#
7006	1 Nov 1990	35.7	70	5.01	14.8	0.47	0.0	8.0	133.0	29.8	83.6	81.6	9.0	#
a mean												52.6		
g mean					9.2	0.42							7.6	
8009	15 Aug 1970	141.2	52	134.98	5.8	5.32	34.6	2.7	93.1	42.5	30.1	26.7	—	
a mean												26.7		
g mean					5.8	5.32							—	
19001	13 Aug 1966	41.6	20	149.40	9.4	6.34	1.5	4.9	128.4	23.5	56.5	54.7	7.3	#
19001	1 Nov 1967	39.6	32	106.29	6.5	7.79	0.0	0.0	125.0	17.9	45.3	44.8	5.5	#
19001	22 Dec 1967	18.3	21	113.86	6.6	8.33	0.0	4.4	129.4	10.0	54.8	53.4	6.6	#
19001	4 May 1968	55.2	34	130.35	6.3	11.61	3.6	6.7	128.1	28.5	51.7	47.5	5.1	#
19001	21 Nov 1969	57.5	29	169.77	14.8	4.22	16.0	2.9	111.9	33.8	58.7	58.6	8.4	#
a mean												51.8		
g mean					8.2	7.26							6.5	
19002	22 Jun 1966	40.0	26	13.57	8.8	1.36	21.2	9.9	113.7	28.7	71.8	74.7	—	
19002	13 Aug 1966	47.9	21	15.28	8.9	0.88	1.6	5.3	128.7	24.5	51.1	47.9	6.9	#
19002	5 Oct 1966	27.5	11	12.19	5.7	1.26	0.2	4.4	129.2	12.8	46.5	45.0	4.6	#
19002	11 Nov 1966	27.9	29	9.65	8.8	0.71	0.6	0.4	124.8	18.9	67.8	67.8	7.4	#
19002	18 Dec 1966	25.1	18	11.98	7.0	1.74	0.0	5.5	130.5	15.0	59.7	58.1	6.7	#
19002	6 Oct 1967	27.8	21	11.86	9.8	0.59	4.4	3.8	124.4	20.6	74.0	74.2	6.4	#
19002	8 Oct 1967	32.6	21	16.51	11.9	1.05	0.0	13.4	138.4	28.9	88.7	85.7	—	
19002	1 Nov 1967	38.8	32	11.32	9.5	0.70	0.0	0.1	125.1	22.5	57.9	57.6	5.3	#
19002	4 May 1968	50.8	34	17.71	8.8	2.00	3.6	5.6	127.0	32.3	63.5	60.5	5.7	#
19002	12 Sep 1968	31.6	16	10.43	7.3	1.08	60.8	5.4	69.6	15.3	48.4	61.8	9.1	#
19002	21 Nov 1969	64.3	27	18.62	12.3	0.74	0.0	3.7	128.7	39.2	61.0	55.7	—	
a mean												62.6		
g mean					8.8	1.02							6.4	
19005	13 Aug 1966	44.5	20	105.92	6.5	5.02	1.2	5.4	129.2	24.6	55.3	52.7	4.0	#
19005	5 Oct 1966	22.2	12	67.69	6.6	4.19	0.0	5.0	130.0	10.5	47.3	45.6	5.3	#
19005	19 Dec 1966	23.9	14	65.43	6.2	8.65	0.0	7.2	132.2	12.0	50.1	47.9	5.6	#
19005	8 Oct 1967	30.6	22	77.39	10.0	6.67	27.2	10.6	108.4	20.6	67.4	71.5	8.0	#
19005	1 Nov 1967	38.1	35	79.57	7.3	4.23	0.0	0.5	125.5	21.2	55.7	55.3	5.5	#
19005	22 Dec 1967	23.4	18	104.01	5.6	8.88	0.0	5.7	130.7	11.9	50.7	48.9	4.5	#
19005	4 May 1968	47.3	34	82.81	6.5	6.03	3.0	5.9	127.9	28.2	59.6	56.9	4.7	#
19005	12 Sep 1968	31.5	16	66.22	6.7	3.93	59.6	5.9	71.3	15.1	47.9	60.9	9.1	#
19005	21 Nov 1969	57.2	34	132.04	11.8	4.10	0.0	3.7	128.7	39.6	69.3	65.1	6.1	#
19005	28 Oct 1970	30.0	47	37.87	12.2	1.71	0.0	3.6	128.6	10.1	33.7	32.1	5.5	#
19005	2 Dec 1970	23.0	27	20.15	15.1	2.48	0.0	2.0	127.0	4.2	18.4	17.0	10.7	#
19005	4 Aug 1971	52.7	86	35.76	23.4	1.31	42.7	3.9	86.2	14.4	27.3	33.6	—	
19005	12 Aug 1971	27.9	33	24.45	15.3	1.20	29.3	0.3	96.0	7.1	25.5	31.9	10.1	#
19005	7 Nov 1974	20.0	48	28.68	8.5	2.72	18.0	1.5	108.5	7.2	36.2	39.7	7.5	#
19005	13 Nov 1974	22.2	35	37.32	9.1	4.34	0.0	6.6	131.6	11.5	51.8	49.8	5.4	#
19005	25 Dec 1974	36.0	70	39.56	9.6	3.91	0.9	15.7	139.8	17.6	48.8	44.7	5.3	#
19005	25 Jan 1977	21.2	13	55.12	8.1	7.21	0.0	1.1	126.1	11.6	54.7	54.1	7.9	#
19005	12 Jun 1977	16.8	17	26.26	7.6	2.02	24.6	8.5	108.9	5.8	34.8	38.2	8.7	#
19005	29 Sep 1977	29.0	46	34.99	10.1	4.16	28.2	16.8	113.6	11.8	40.8	43.1	8.1	#
19005	5 Oct 1977	39.9	49	63.86	17.0	2.66	18.3	3.4	110.1	22.5	56.5	60.0	4.7	#
19005	30 Oct 1977	70.6	32	165.58	3.3	9.05	4.5	1.7	122.2	29.4	41.7	37.0	3.7	#
19005	4 Nov 1977	20.2	30	32.37	9.9	5.61	0.0	7.2	132.2	9.3	45.9	43.7	6.5	#
19005	9 Nov 1977	20.0	29	46.99	5.3	7.29	0.0	8.4	133.4	10.3	51.5	49.1	6.0	#
19005	11 Dec 1977	20.0	41	26.31	12.5	2.70	0.0	1.4	126.4	7.4	37.2	36.3	9.5	#
19005	3 Jul 1978	32.9	48	12.75	14.1	0.95	75.6	13.9	63.3	4.2	12.7	27.1	14.2	#
19005	12 Sep 1978	17.3	26	20.79	12.9	1.94	29.4	7.1	102.7	7.3	42.3	47.4	17.1	#
19005	27 Sep 1978	31.7	44	46.69	10.4	2.56	24.4	4.6	105.2	13.9	43.8	48.3	4.6	#
19005	13 Oct 1979	29.9	25	64.65	4.4	4.81	48.7	3.3	79.6	10.8	36.1	46.8	3.7	#
19005	25 Nov 1979	26.9	27	53.72	10.7	5.19	0.4	4.6	129.2	16.4	60.9	59.7	—	

Catch	Date	P	D	Q_p	LAG	BF	SMD	API5	CWI	R/O	PR	SPR	Tp(0)	
		mm	h	m^3s^{-1}	h	m^3s^{-1}	mm	mm	mm	mm	%	%	h	
19005	6 Dec 1979	30.7	33	51.06	14.9	3.96	2.9	5.3	127.4	18.4	60.0	59.2	7.9	#
19005	26 Dec 1979	30.8	35	49.15	11.5	2.77	0.0	0.2	125.2	17.1	55.5	55.2	4.5	#
19005	9 Mar 1981	21.0	13	47.52	7.2	3.54	0.0	5.6	130.6	9.6	45.9	44.1	5.5	#
19005	31 Oct 1970	23.9	22	74.10	4.8	4.12	0.0	10.5	135.5	10.9	45.6	42.5	5.5	#
19005	10 Nov 1974	19.8	33	38.81	3.2	6.72	0.0	7.1	132.1	6.2	31.5	29.0	4.9	#
a mean												46.3		
g mean					8.8	3.73							6.4	
20001	14 Mar 1964	26.6	18	49.18	4.8	5.00	0.9	1.4	125.5	7.1	26.6	26.4	—	
20001	10 Oct 1964	46.1	24	36.51	12.2	1.16	61.9	2.3	65.4	8.5	18.4	31.6	7.8	#
20001	27 Jul 1965	37.0	40	44.83	15.5	1.94	50.6	5.1	79.5	10.9	29.4	40.7	7.5	#
20001	17 Sep 1965	29.2	15	63.55	12.9	4.55	0.8	0.5	124.7	10.7	36.7	36.7	—	
20001	3 Aug 1966	100.3	33	113.00	16.1	1.53	71.4	0.2	53.8	26.8	26.7	36.5	11.5	#
20001	13 Aug 1966	54.8	19	98.71	12.1	4.76	1.1	4.0	127.9	21.6	39.5	35.7	9.6	#
20001	6 Nov 1966	22.4	15	64.44	6.9	9.58	0.0	4.7	129.7	7.7	34.3	33.0	6.5	#
20001	4 May 1968	45.1	46	58.85	10.5	6.42	7.5	7.8	125.3	18.5	41.0	39.5	—	
20001	14 Jul 1968	51.5	53	69.05	9.7	2.90	59.0	4.2	70.2	16.1	31.2	42.3	8.0	#
20001	31 Oct 1968	47.3	37	52.68	13.6	2.51	30.0	2.0	97.0	18.8	39.8	44.9	—	
a mean												36.7		
g mean					10.8	3.33							8.3	
21018	12 Sep 1978	25.7	62	15.77	6.8	2.90	24.9	7.0	107.1	6.2	24.2	28.6	5.3	#
21018	7 Dec 1978	31.9	60	14.64	7.7	3.79	0.0	1.0	126.0	8.8	27.5	27.2	6.4	#
21018	13 Oct 1979	29.2	29	17.60	6.6	2.30	36.8	2.3	90.5	5.6	19.1	27.7	6.0	#
21018	24 Nov 1979	33.0	46	26.84	8.6	5.83	0.0	5.7	130.7	10.2	30.9	29.4	6.5	#
21018	13 Aug 1980	22.3	52	11.02	12.2	1.69	65.3	3.1	62.8	4.1	18.3	33.8	8.1	#
21018	29 Aug 1980	29.4	43	9.63	13.0	1.49	66.0	0.6	59.6	3.7	12.6	28.9	8.3	#
21018	13 Nov 1980	18.6	32	12.34	8.1	2.34	12.6	0.6	113.0	3.1	16.9	19.9	6.2	#
21018	23 Nov 1980	41.5	75	37.34	14.0	4.75	1.5	4.1	127.6	20.3	48.8	47.5	9.5	#
21018	29 Sep 1981	53.1	36	30.60	15.0	2.24	17.4	2.8	110.4	23.9	45.0	45.9	11.0	#
21018	9 Sep 1978	28.1	21	13.52	9.5	1.66	36.5	5.0	93.5	3.5	12.4	20.2	7.6	#
21018	16 Nov 1979	18.8	28	17.03	7.4	5.65	0.0	6.5	131.5	6.3	33.3	31.6	4.2	#
21018	7 Oct 1981	25.8	74	17.38	7.6	4.86	0.0	9.6	134.6	8.8	34.2	31.8	8.5	#
21018	25 Jul 1985	76.8	87	31.36	16.8	2.67	2.6	4.5	126.9	32.6	42.4	36.3	13.5	#
a mean												31.5		
g mean					9.8	2.92							7.4	
21028	8 Jan 1962	35.7	8	4.27	8.0	0.28	0.1	4.3	129.2	17.3	48.4	—	—	
21028	4 Aug 1962	49.0	44	5.43	26.7	0.28	72.5	1.1	53.6	29.8	60.9	—	—	
21028	29 Sep 1962	35.0	8	5.35	5.2	0.36	1.6	4.0	127.4	13.5	38.5	—	—	
21028	13 Aug 1966	62.7	19	4.49	10.9	0.10	3.8	5.1	126.3	22.6	36.0	—	—	
21028	4 Sep 1967	48.5	17	4.70	4.6	0.30	48.1	11.6	88.5	18.7	38.6	—	—	
21028	22 Jul 1969	46.9	15	3.10	2.3	0.16	63.2	0.7	62.5	9.0	19.2	—	—	
a mean												—		
g mean					7.1	0.23							—	
21030	18 Sep 1969	24.3	7	16.60	4.0	1.33	63.7	0.1	61.4	6.5	26.6	42.5	—	
21030	21 Nov 1969	58.1	23	29.64	8.5	2.52	11.1	4.1	118.0	27.1	46.6	44.9	—	
21030	17 Jun 1972	22.3	10	12.79	12.1	1.01	13.6	0.3	111.7	6.4	28.7	32.0	—	
21030	9 Nov 1972	41.5	9	26.63	5.6	1.14	85.6	0.6	40.0	13.3	32.1	52.8	—	
a mean												43.1		
g mean					6.9	1.40							—	
22009	13 Oct 1979	25.2	23	56.95	12.2	3.88	0.5	3.3	127.8	6.5	25.8	25.1	9.8	#
22009	6 Mar 1980	27.2	42	37.46	15.7	4.42	2.9	0.3	122.4	6.5	24.0	24.6	13.8	#
22009	17 Mar 1980	34.7	31	82.74	12.7	6.69	0.1	3.7	128.6	13.4	38.7	37.8	12.5	#
22009	10 Mar 1981	10.4	23	29.17	6.7	9.92	0.0	2.0	127.0	3.1	29.7	29.2	9.0	#
22009	21 Jul 1981	49.9	62	72.80	21.5	2.22	61.2	2.1	65.9	14.4	28.9	41.4	10.9	#
22009	25 Sep 1981	38.1	16	86.37	8.2	5.28	36.5	3.4	91.9	12.1	31.7	39.9	10.8	#
22009	19 Sep 1981	32.6	14	34.09	8.8	2.24	77.2	2.9	50.7	3.1	9.6	28.1	9.5	#
22009	6 Oct 1981	39.7	82	58.09	26.4	6.06	2.0	5.5	128.5	16.4	41.2	40.3	10.0	#
22009	1 Oct 1981	59.5	80	88.95	15.6	6.07	23.2	4.4	106.2	25.3	42.5	43.6	9.5	#
22009	30 Nov 1981	18.5	20	78.36	16.4	9.71	0.4	2.1	126.7	7.9	42.5	42.0	10.0	#
22009	22 Nov 1981	24.0	19	99.14	11.8	8.63	6.3	2.0	120.7	10.4	43.4	44.5	9.5	#
22009	2 Nov 1984	86.0	49	192.10	11.6	4.81	34.7	1.5	91.8	36.0	41.9	43.6	9.0	#
22009	17 Jan 1986	32.4	153	23.20	9.8	5.05	1.0	0.7	124.7	10.8	33.2	33.2	12.2	#

Catch	Date			P mm	D h	Q_p m^3s^{-1}	LAG h	BF m^3s^{-1}	SMD mm	API5 mm	CWI mm	R/O mm	PR %	SPR %	Tp(0) h	
22009	6	Nov	1986	10.6	26	19.20	11.3	3.41	11.6	0.4	113.8	2.5	23.6	26.4	10.1	#
22009	29	Oct	1986	17.2	76	15.77	12.9	2.97	13.7	4.3	115.6	3.3	19.0	21.3	9.5	#
22009	24	Oct	1986	11.6	24	11.31	13.2	1.76	23.1	2.4	104.3	1.4	12.4	17.5	10.5	#
22009	29	Dec	1986	35.5	73	76.90	12.4	7.54	0.0	0.8	125.8	15.0	42.2	42.0	9.5	#
22009	12	Dec	1986	12.5	10	68.55	8.8	9.61	0.0	4.6	129.6	6.5	52.2	51.0	8.5	#
22009	25	Aug	1987	30.9	16	102.56	12.0	4.98	4.6	1.8	122.2	15.1	49.0	49.7	14.5	#
22009	11	Nov	1987	24.4	33	36.04	9.1	6.63	0.0	6.4	131.4	7.0	28.6	27.0	9.5	#
22009	25	Dec	1987	17.9	44	107.68	13.1	6.89	0.7	0.5	124.8	10.7	59.9	59.9	9.5	#
22009	2	Feb	1989	19.0	41	32.13	9.7	3.43	31.8	0.4	93.6	4.8	25.3	33.1	12.5	#
a mean														36.4		
g mean							12.1	4.99							10.4	
23002	27	Jun	1963	45.8	44	25.88	14.3	1.10	48.3	4.8	81.5	12.9	28.1	37.4	—	
23002	23	Aug	1963	17.3	8	22.32	4.3	1.93	25.6	1.0	100.4	3.6	20.9	27.0	5.8	#
23002	10	Nov	1963	31.1	16	37.04	5.1	3.45	0.0	1.9	126.9	11.6	37.4	36.9	—	
23002	12	Nov	1963	22.7	18	39.24	5.0	5.58	0.0	10.2	135.2	10.4	45.9	43.3	—	
23002	21	Nov	1963	23.6	15	51.03	5.2	5.32	0.0	4.8	129.8	11.8	50.1	48.9	4.0	#
23002	24	Mar	1964	15.9	16	31.46	6.1	6.75	0.0	5.1	130.1	6.0	38.0	36.7	3.5	#
23002	6	Jun	1964	20.2	10	16.14	7.1	1.45	24.8	8.4	108.6	5.0	24.9	29.0	7.5	#
23002	18	Aug	1964	18.2	8	11.13	5.5	0.74	51.6	3.9	77.3	2.2	12.2	24.1	6.5	#
23002	8	Dec	1964	29.4	21	24.49	5.7	2.80	27.5	9.9	107.4	9.3	31.5	35.9	4.5	#
23002	16	Jan	1965	26.2	36	27.60	4.6	4.08	0.0	7.2	132.2	10.5	40.1	38.3	4.8	#
23002	6	Sep	1965	19.8	8	20.40	6.4	1.87	4.3	6.1	126.8	5.9	30.0	29.5	5.9	#
a mean														35.2		
g mean							5.9	2.58							5.2	
23005	16	Oct	1967	40.3	14	236.59	4.2	11.38	0.2	6.0	130.8	23.3	57.7	56.1	—	
23005	1	Nov	1967	28.2	9	130.92	6.3	5.00	1.0	0.4	124.4	13.3	47.0	47.2	—	
23005	12	Sep	1968	42.0	15	143.46	4.5	6.93	11.6	6.8	120.2	22.6	53.7	54.2	5.0	#
23005	17	Sep	1969	26.0	10	140.25	5.6	4.42	26.1	0.8	99.7	11.8	45.3	51.6	7.0	#
23005	30	Oct	1970	28.1	11	261.60	4.7	12.47	0.0	11.2	136.2	19.4	69.1	66.3	7.4	#
23005	9	Nov	1972	31.7	14	140.33	3.6	10.24	6.2	1.7	120.5	14.7	46.3	47.4	5.0	#
23005	25	Dec	1979	68.9	37	161.91	10.0	4.47	0.0	1.0	126.0	45.7	66.3	61.3	6.5	#
a mean														54.9		
g mean							5.3	7.19							6.1	
23006	18	Dec	1966	24.7	26	57.47	8.6	4.22	0.1	0.6	125.5	3.2	13.1	12.9	—	
23006	21	Feb	1967	39.0	24	36.36	0.0	4.33	0.0	7.2	132.2	2.6	6.7	4.9	—	
23006	5	Nov	1967	23.7	15	50.40	5.5	3.62	0.0	2.4	127.4	5.1	21.4	20.8	—	
23006	18	Apr	1968	22.6	14	148.15	1.0	13.56	7.5	1.8	119.3	7.1	31.5	32.9	—	
23006	12	Sep	1968	42.4	16	210.00	2.9	11.47	5.6	10.1	129.5	17.3	40.7	38.7	—	
23006	11	Sep	1969	28.2	13	139.45	6.3	9.48	36.7	8.5	96.8	11.5	40.9	47.9	—	
23006	29	Aug	1971	32.6	19	159.29	7.7	5.04	45.7	2.1	81.4	12.6	38.8	49.7	—	
23006	10	Sep	1976	90.0	42	174.26	7.9	3.08	105.2	8.8	28.6	27.1	30.1	47.2	—	
23006	22	Nov	1977	33.2	20	117.23	2.8	13.18	0.0	4.3	129.3	11.2	33.8	32.7	5.5	#
23006	14	Mar	1978	22.6	14	162.61	4.2	26.91	0.0	6.7	131.7	9.2	40.9	39.2	2.0	#
23006	19	Mar	1978	18.1	6	147.21	4.4	12.07	0.9	2.8	126.9	9.7	53.5	53.0	4.0	#
23006	12	Sep	1978	44.3	28	225.13	9.3	9.11	1.5	11.9	135.4	22.6	51.1	47.2	4.0	#
23006	11	Jun	1980	37.9	30	106.87	7.3	4.90	73.1	4.4	56.3	14.2	37.4	54.6	5.0	#
23006	16	Jun	1980	16.5	17	84.27	8.3	10.31	47.4	11.3	88.9	9.4	56.8	65.8	—	
23006	29	Jun	1980	18.6	19	67.75	5.8	7.30	13.9	2.4	113.5	6.9	37.0	39.9	6.0	#
23006	29	Jul	1980	25.4	7	94.35	5.1	5.92	5.5	2.7	122.2	6.2	24.4	25.1	4.5	#
23006	13	Sep	1980	28.4	16	128.96	2.8	12.69	2.1	9.4	132.3	9.7	34.3	32.5	—	
23006	6	Oct	1980	24.9	21	159.65	0.8	20.61	0.0	9.7	134.7	10.2	40.8	38.4	4.0	#
23006	26	Oct	1980	27.9	20	114.46	4.2	13.72	0.0	9.2	134.2	13.3	47.8	45.5	4.5	#
23006	13	Nov	1980	42.0	16	265.50	2.0	13.55	0.0	2.6	127.6	21.9	52.1	50.7	1.0	#
23006	16	Nov	1980	20.5	15	130.89	1.3	23.75	0.0	15.8	140.8	7.5	36.6	32.6	1.0	#
23006	20	Nov	1980	17.3	12	128.96	3.6	17.04	0.0	8.8	133.8	10.9	63.0	60.8	1.5	#
23006	10	Dec	1980	41.1	8	280.81	4.1	9.21	0.0	3.7	128.7	21.9	53.2	51.8	—	
23006	24	Dec	1980	14.9	15	95.88	8.9	13.39	0.0	7.8	132.8	9.1	60.9	58.9	—	
23006	2	Feb	1981	38.8	14	225.62	4.0	10.44	0.0	2.8	127.8	20.6	53.1	52.4	3.5	#
23006	19	Sep	1981	32.5	18	133.03	3.6	9.85	30.3	6.6	101.3	11.8	36.4	42.3	4.5	#
23006	23	Sep	1981	24.4	12	133.81	5.4	9.39	11.3	7.4	121.1	8.5	34.8	35.8	—	
23006	25	Sep	1981	27.5	18	223.92	6.3	11.70	0.0	10.0	135.0	16.3	59.2	56.7	3.0	#
23006	30	Sep	1981	62.7	37	238.45	9.0	10.72	0.0	7.5	132.5	46.9	74.8	68.9	4.0	#
23006	1	Nov	1981	21.9	17	128.76	6.7	8.75	0.0	5.0	130.0	12.0	54.6	53.3	3.5	#

Catch	Date	P mm	D h	Q_p m^3s^{-1}	LAG h	BF m^3s^{-1}	SMD mm	API5 mm	CWI mm	R/O mm	PR %	SPR %	Tp(0) h	
23006	23 Nov 1981	33.7	9	216.92	3.2	13.84	0.0	5.3	130.3	12.5	37.1	35.8	3.5	#
23006	26 Nov 1981	32.1	10	275.23	2.8	27.04	0.0	11.3	136.3	19.3	60.1	57.3	3.0	#
23006	25 Jan 1982	20.6	13	117.23	4.6	15.45	0.0	3.5	128.5	10.4	50.6	49.7	—	
23006	5 Oct 1982	38.3	22	231.01	3.6	9.66	0.0	3.4	128.4	20.0	52.3	51.4	—	
23006	19 Oct 1982	31.3	17	138.35	5.5	10.51	0.0	3.8	128.8	14.9	47.6	46.6	—	
23006	15 Nov 1982	20.4	13	137.16	3.9	11.61	0.0	5.8	130.8	10.9	53.5	52.0	4.5	#
23006	18 Dec 1982	29.9	14	217.88	4.6	15.83	0.0	5.8	130.8	17.1	57.1	55.6	4.5	#
23006	5 Jan 1983	24.4	19	205.54	4.6	19.26	0.0	10.5	135.5	22.4	91.8	89.2	4.0	#
23006	12 Jun 1984	42.0	15	155.04	4.3	5.44	60.1	1.2	66.1	13.4	31.8	45.8	—	
23006	6 Aug 1984	12.0	4	41.27	5.3	4.94	74.4	5.1	55.7	3.2	26.3	43.6	—	
23006	3 Sep 1984	27.2	16	91.83	3.5	5.26	82.4	5.8	48.4	6.2	22.9	42.0	—	
23006	16 Sep 1984	31.6	14	114.83	2.6	10.94	48.7	2.0	78.3	8.3	26.3	38.0	—	
23006	14 Aug 1985	16.4	8	82.98	1.1	16.89	3.8	6.3	127.5	3.8	23.1	22.5	—	
23006	27 Aug 1985	15.2	18	104.38	1.8	12.41	3.8	6.3	127.5	6.0	39.2	38.6	—	
23006	8 Nov 1985	30.1	13	152.75	5.2	12.01	0.0	5.4	130.4	11.6	38.5	37.1	4.0	#
23006	24 May 1986	27.1	12	107.94	5.9	6.19	7.1	3.8	121.7	9.2	33.9	34.7	5.0	#
23006	10 Jun 1986	28.2	17	121.34	5.3	5.86	13.6	1.6	113.0	9.9	35.1	38.1	7.5	#
23006	7 Nov 1986	16.7	15	104.38	7.1	11.42	0.0	5.2	130.2	8.5	50.8	49.5	—	
23006	3 Dec 1986	23.3	9	186.69	4.1	16.48	0.0	12.6	137.6	13.2	56.8	53.6	—	
23006	3 Jan 1987	18.3	10	196.71	4.7	12.40	0.0	7.9	132.9	15.7	85.7	83.7	—	
23006	27 Dec 1987	26.2	10	173.17	3.6	13.87	0.0	4.6	129.6	9.9	37.7	36.5	—	
23006	5 Jan 1988	29.3	11	195.10	2.5	19.84	0.0	6.8	131.8	10.7	36.6	34.9	—	
23006	25 May 1988	11.6	18	28.59	8.7	3.49	24.9	5.5	105.6	2.9	25.4	30.2	—	
23006	22 Dec 1988	44.8	23	252.33	4.0	13.10	0.0	5.3	130.3	28.8	64.3	61.6	—	
23006	13 Jan 1989	24.0	13	141.14	4.0	10.49	0.0	4.1	129.1	12.1	50.3	49.3	—	
23006	4 Feb 1989	33.6	15	205.77	0.4	31.87	0.0	11.8	136.8	13.1	39.1	36.1	—	
23006	23 Mar 1989	21.9	21	166.46	8.6	10.73	0.0	8.5	133.5	15.4	70.5	68.4	—	
23006	15 Aug 1985	18.2	9	150.07	1.1	23.85	0.0	14.0	139.0	7.3	40.2	36.7	—	
a mean												45.0		
g mean					4.0	10.57							3.5	
23008	25 Dec 1979	43.4	44	121.60	11.6	4.67	0.0	0.3	125.3	27.0	62.2	61.1	—	
23008	22 Nov 1981	28.7	19	136.64	13.1	5.94	1.8	2.6	125.8	19.1	66.5	66.3	10.0	#
23008	23 Dec 1983	21.5	16	125.96	7.1	11.39	0.0	10.7	135.7	11.1	51.8	49.1	8.0	#
23008	12 Jan 1984	20.3	10	100.54	8.5	9.06	0.0	4.7	129.7	10.8	53.3	52.1	9.5	#
23008	25 Mar 1984	27.1	21	99.93	7.4	9.88	0.0	12.5	137.5	17.3	63.7	60.6	6.5	#
23008	6 May 1986	24.8	14	96.71	6.4	7.32	4.3	6.5	127.2	10.6	42.8	42.2	7.5	#
23008	25 Aug 1986	80.7	46	190.07	8.9	3.51	7.4	0.6	118.2	39.9	49.5	45.2	—	
23008	18 Oct 1988	33.0	36	92.95	8.8	5.61	2.3	1.2	123.9	17.3	52.4	52.7	8.5	#
23008	29 Nov 1988	38.5	40	92.65	7.6	6.43	0.0	0.8	125.8	22.3	57.8	57.6	8.0	#
a mean												54.1		
g mean					8.6	6.67							8.2	
23010	17 Sep 1970	14.3	16	14.31	9.3	1.02	4.3	0.6	121.3	4.6	32.0	32.9	—	
23010	31 Oct 1970	21.1	11	56.96	2.8	3.15	0.0	6.5	131.5	8.8	41.6	40.0	—	
23010	16 Mar 1972	19.9	7	28.04	4.7	1.12	2.7	0.3	122.6	6.2	31.4	32.0	—	
23010	11 May 1972	17.3	19	24.52	9.4	1.19	2.4	2.4	125.0	9.3	53.5	53.5	—	
23010	3 May 1973	27.8	30	55.99	6.2	1.02	7.6	0.8	118.2	14.1	50.8	52.5	—	
23010	10 Nov 1974	21.4	13	60.75	4.4	3.46	0.0	5.4	130.4	11.5	53.7	52.3	—	
23010	2 Jan 1976	19.6	9	70.02	6.0	1.38	0.0	6.6	131.6	17.9	91.1	89.5	—	
23010	19 Jan 1976	18.1	20	40.99	9.2	2.09	0.6	1.5	125.9	12.9	71.1	70.9	—	
23010	23 Feb 1976	23.9	21	59.58	3.3	2.74	0.0	0.5	125.5	15.6	65.1	65.0	—	
23010	25 Dec 1979	48.3	41	41.29	8.3	1.19	0.0	0.5	125.5	30.2	62.5	60.4	—	
a mean												54.9		
g mean					5.8	1.64							—	
23011	25 Dec 1979	67.4	41	37.94	6.9	1.14	0.0	0.9	125.9	38.8	57.6	52.8	3.5	#
23011	13 Dec 1980	17.0	9	41.82	2.9	3.66	0.0	9.9	134.9	11.8	69.4	66.9	3.0	#
23011	22 Nov 1981	51.9	17	72.42	5.4	2.13	1.3	4.6	128.3	32.5	62.6	59.2	3.5	#
23011	23 Dec 1983	29.3	16	45.12	7.9	3.61	0.0	16.5	141.5	20.5	70.1	66.0	8.0	#
23011	12 Jan 1984	21.0	8	42.98	2.8	2.76	0.0	8.2	133.2	16.0	76.3	74.3	4.0	#
23011	6 May 1986	23.3	12	41.10	2.0	2.90	3.7	5.6	126.9	12.2	52.3	51.8	3.0	#
23011	25 Aug 1986	72.5	46	31.31	7.3	0.98	7.6	0.5	117.9	45.2	62.4	59.0	—	
a mean												61.4		
g mean					4.5	2.20							3.9	

Catch	Date	*P* mm	*D* h	Q_p m^3s^{-1}	*LAG* h	*BF* m^3s^{-1}	*SMD* mm	*API5* mm	*CWI* mm	*R/O* mm	*PR* %	*SPR* %	*Tp(0)* h	
23998	16 Nov 1990				—								3.4	#
23998	7 Dec 1990				—								2.8	#
23998	26 Dec 1990				—								1.6	#
23998	10 Nov 1990				—								3.3	#
23998	18 Nov 1991				—								1.9	#
23998	25 Oct 1992				—								4.0	#
g mean													2.69	
23999	16 Nov 1990				—								6.0	#
23999	7 Dec 1990				—								1.9	#
23999	26 Dec 1990				—								2.8	#
23999	1 Jan 1991				—								2.1	#
23999	27 Feb 1991				—								3.1	#
23999	4 Mar 1991				—								1.6	#
23999	20 Mar 1991				—								3.9	#
g mean													2.78	
24003	10 Nov 1963	26.9	16	70.89	4.2	4.80	0.0	3.3	128.3	13.9	51.8	51.0	—	
24003	17 Nov 1963	39.0	21	82.28	7.9	4.12	0.2	3.4	128.2	22.7	58.3	57.5	—	
24003	20 Nov 1963	36.1	15	143.90	4.1	6.63	0.0	6.8	131.8	19.6	54.2	52.5	—	
24003	30 Dec 1963	21.3	12	54.38	2.8	5.62	0.0	3.7	128.7	8.9	42.0	41.0	—	
24003	8 Dec 1964	45.4	19	138.98	5.4	7.13	0.0	25.4	150.4	26.2	57.6	49.8	—	
24003	16 Jan 1965	25.3	31	78.10	10.0	4.31	0.0	10.2	135.2	18.0	71.1	68.6	—	
24003	25 Sep 1965	42.9	15	72.81	7.6	2.06	1.7	1.0	124.3	18.1	42.2	41.4	—	
24003	17 Dec 1965	17.0	20	74.94	6.2	6.38	0.0	1.7	126.7	13.0	76.7	76.3	—	
24003	2 Oct 1966	48.4	34	121.03	5.6	1.85	3.7	3.3	124.6	20.7	42.8	40.9	—	
24003	17 Dec 1966	32.9	19	134.47	4.2	6.24	0.0	1.9	126.9	17.3	52.6	52.1	—	
24003	19 Dec 1966	27.3	16	69.16	3.8	6.32	0.0	13.0	138.0	13.3	48.6	45.3	—	
24003	27 Feb 1967	31.8	21	98.67	5.4	7.25	0.0	6.7	131.7	19.3	60.7	59.0	—	
24003	17 Aug 1967	40.1	28	114.87	2.3	3.93	3.5	3.9	125.4	16.1	40.1	39.9	—	
24003	4 Sep 1967	34.9	35	64.67	5.1	3.86	0.0	14.1	139.1	15.7	45.1	41.6	—	
24003	6 Oct 1967	25.5	18	76.80	6.2	3.30	0.6	4.1	128.5	15.5	60.6	59.7	—	
24003	16 Oct 1967	53.8	16	108.23	3.1	9.05	0.0	6.9	131.9	27.1	50.3	45.7	—	
24003	12 Sep 1968	26.0	16	60.23	3.2	3.72	0.0	7.5	132.5	9.7	37.3	35.4	—	
24003	4 Nov 1967	108.4	34	151.37	5.3	4.09	0.0	2.2	127.2	46.3	42.7	33.5	—	
a mean												49.5		
g mean						4.8	4.66						—	
24004	9 Feb 1977	25.8	38	13.77	7.2	2.59	0.0	4.3	129.3	11.2	43.4	42.3	4.7	#
24004	11 Nov 1977	23.8	19	12.95	6.1	1.45	30.0	6.3	101.3	7.1	30.0	35.9	3.5	#
24004	14 Jun 1980	26.3	9	21.52	2.9	1.90	75.7	7.2	56.5	5.5	21.0	38.1	2.9	#
24004	12 Dec 1980	25.9	55	11.86	11.0	1.25	0.0	2.8	127.8	10.5	40.5	39.8	4.5	#
24004	25 Sep 1981	35.1	26	10.98	10.6	0.43	72.1	3.2	56.1	7.1	20.2	37.4	6.1	#
24004	30 Sep 1981	75.1	76	37.26	7.0	1.32	44.2	6.0	86.8	31.5	42.0	46.1	3.4	#
24004	20 Nov 1982	55.4	100	13.32	7.6	1.69	0.0	3.5	128.5	23.2	41.9	38.0	3.2	#
24004	31 May 1983	23.7	17	17.85	3.5	1.62	14.3	1.5	112.2	6.2	26.0	29.2	4.9	#
24004	23 Dec 1983	19.0	21	27.96	4.5	3.99	0.0	9.1	134.1	10.3	54.3	52.0	3.0	#
24004	2 Nov 1984	37.4	45	9.11	11.1	0.83	52.7	0.5	72.8	10.0	26.8	39.8	7.2	#
24004	20 Jan 1986	17.1	28	15.86	3.3	2.68	0.0	7.5	132.5	6.8	39.9	38.0	2.9	#
24004	14 Apr 1986	40.9	23	33.81	8.8	2.71	0.0	3.7	128.7	24.3	59.4	58.1	7.5	#
24004	4 May 1986	45.9	62	17.61	16.2	0.98	17.8	0.1	107.3	12.2	26.6	29.4	4.1	#
a mean												40.3		
g mean						6.8	1.56						4.2	
24005	8 Dec 1954	33.6	11	34.99	8.0	4.24	3.2	0.3	122.1	9.8	29.2	29.2	7.0	#
24005	27 Aug 1956	27.7	10	31.02	10.0	1.87	0.8	1.8	126.0	7.3	26.4	25.4	9.3	#
24005	13 Mar 1964	36.5	31	27.30	3.5	2.82	0.0	3.4	128.4	8.0	21.9	20.2	4.5	#
24005	23 Mar 1964	30.1	30	44.48	9.1	4.73	0.6	1.6	126.0	11.0	36.6	35.8	7.0	#
24005	27 Sep 1965	14.9	8	18.80	8.6	1.80	25.3	3.3	103.0	3.3	21.9	26.6	8.0	#
24005	1 Oct 1965	14.9	12	20.64	8.3	4.56	0.0	10.5	135.5	3.4	22.8	19.4	8.5	#
24005	18 Nov 1965	43.0	46	48.39	6.5	11.43	0.0	10.0	135.0	15.8	36.7	32.7	—	
24005	9 Apr 1966	21.6	12	42.39	7.7	5.10	1.0	7.7	131.7	9.5	44.0	41.9	5.5	#
24005	13 Aug 1966	35.4	33	20.74	11.1	1.34	38.8	5.4	91.6	8.1	23.0	30.6	6.5	#
24005	3 Oct 1966	39.9	37	21.81	13.5	1.18	17.4	2.9	110.5	8.6	21.5	24.3	—	
24005	8 Aug 1967	42.8	21	28.38	10.1	0.96	62.0	1.5	64.5	5.7	13.4	26.7	4.2	#
24005	16 Oct 1967	42.5	16	40.67	8.1	1.84	0.6	1.7	126.1	11.8	27.7	25.9	—	

Catch	Date	P mm	D h	Q_p m^3s^{-1}	LAG h	BF m^3s^{-1}	SMD mm	API5 mm	CWI mm	R/O mm	PR %	SPR %	Tp(0) h	
24005	1 Nov 1967	16.0	9	19.10	9.5	1.99	1.2	0.7	124.5	3.8	23.9	23.3	8.0	#
24005	4 Nov 1967	56.2	22	58.48	9.0	4.29	0.0	2.5	127.5	23.1	41.1	36.8	6.5	#
24005	30 Oct 1968	71.9	63	33.06	9.6	1.56	0.0	3.0	128.0	29.6	41.2	34.9	—	
24005	11 Jan 1969	18.6	17	22.74	11.1	2.49	0.2	0.9	125.7	5.7	30.7	29.9	6.0	#
24005	2 May 1969	19.4	18	26.49	7.7	2.29	8.1	2.4	119.3	4.3	22.2	22.8	6.5	#
24005	6 May 1969	15.5	12	30.78	5.5	4.98	0.6	5.4	129.8	5.3	34.0	32.2	6.0	#
24005	5 May 1978	25.2	34	22.85	9.6	2.32	3.0	3.1	125.1	6.2	24.6	23.8	5.5	#
24005	25 Nov 1980	17.1	8	30.55	7.0	2.56	1.5	4.9	128.4	5.1	29.8	28.3	7.5	#
24005	7 Dec 1982	12.9	8	14.51	8.2	1.62	0.7	0.4	124.7	2.6	20.4	19.6	6.5	#
24005	27 May 1983	35.6	38	30.81	7.7	2.29	16.1	0.4	109.3	9.1	25.5	28.7	6.0	#
24005	1 Jun 1983	24.4	8	38.82	6.9	3.29	2.8	3.4	125.6	7.3	29.8	29.0	7.5	#
24005	8 Dec 1983	34.8	19	25.02	8.6	0.79	33.4	0.5	92.1	5.0	14.5	21.8	5.5	#
24005	24 Dec 1983	11.0	8	27.89	5.8	4.37	0.0	5.4	130.4	3.6	33.1	31.1	6.5	#
24005	2 Nov 1984	52.4	44	30.81	11.9	0.96	32.0	0.3	93.3	11.5	22.0	26.5	5.5	#
24005	15 Apr 1986	35.3	19	47.27	12.1	3.65	0.0	1.9	126.9	14.8	41.8	40.9	9.0	#
24005	6 May 1986	19.1	8	28.90	6.0	2.65	12.1	5.4	118.3	4.1	21.5	22.4	5.5	#
24005	10 Apr 1987	20.9	25	19.68	7.0	3.61	0.2	4.5	129.3	5.6	26.8	25.0	8.5	#
24005	20 Oct 1987	24.8	9	42.22	6.2	4.03	0.0	4.6	129.6	7.6	30.6	28.8	7.5	#
24005	6 Jan 1988	27.4	13	48.60	7.5	1.64	0.0	2.5	127.5	11.2	40.8	39.7	8.0	#
24005	23 Jan 1988	13.8	10	21.17	9.7	2.21	0.0	0.8	125.8	3.3	23.7	22.7	7.5	#
24005	16 Apr 1986	19.2	24	30.76	8.3	6.99	0.0	16.0	141.0	7.3	37.8	33.3	3.5	#
a mean												28.5		
g mean						8.2	2.59						6.5	
24007	30 Oct 1968	73.5	84	12.46	11.1	0.80	0.0	2.1	127.1	42.6	57.9	52.1	—	
24007	11 Jan 1969	18.0	17	8.03	7.3	1.25	0.2	1.0	125.8	7.9	44.0	43.8	5.2	#
24007	2 May 1969	16.2	17	8.27	6.7	0.71	5.8	2.2	121.4	4.2	26.2	27.1	4.3	#
24007	6 May 1969	15.0	22	8.47	6.4	1.48	4.3	9.2	129.9	5.9	39.5	38.2	4.1	#
24007	23 Jun 1969	21.6	21	8.86	6.7	0.49	11.8	3.5	116.7	5.7	26.3	28.3	3.5	#
24007	17 Sep 1969	20.2	11	8.36	5.0	0.67	42.0	2.0	85.0	5.1	25.3	35.3	4.4	#
24007	21 Jan 1971	16.7	12	7.24	6.8	0.70	2.7	1.3	123.6	5.7	33.9	34.2	6.8	#
24007	22 Apr 1971	51.9	33	13.66	12.0	0.66	21.3	0.0	103.7	18.8	36.2	38.9	7.7	#
24007	6 Aug 1972	13.9	6	3.12	3.6	0.16	69.3	0.8	56.5	0.9	6.7	23.8	—	
a mean												35.7		
g mean						6.9	0.67						5.0	
25003	20 Nov 1963	38.9	18	12.29	3.9	0.33	0.0	11.0	136.0	20.5	52.7	50.0	4.5	#
25003	8 Aug 1964	36.5	8	14.33	2.8	0.46	83.3	12.1	53.8	18.3	50.1	67.9	3.5	#
25003	14 Sep 1965	38.6	14	13.52	2.4	0.27	3.3	0.7	122.4	23.0	59.7	60.4	3.5	#
25003	3 Sep 1966	36.4	19	12.99	4.6	0.22	0.0	8.5	133.5	27.3	75.0	72.9	—	
25003	3 Jul 1968	29.7	8	24.11	2.5	0.92	0.0	11.6	136.6	21.9	73.6	70.7	3.5	#
25003	11 Sep 1968	44.5	14	15.93	3.1	0.47	8.8	5.0	121.2	31.5	70.7	70.4	—	
25003	20 Sep 1968	40.5	11	13.74	3.5	0.67	0.0	21.3	146.3	32.6	80.5	74.9	2.4	#
25003	22 Sep 1968	27.4	9	13.64	3.9	0.53	0.0	16.9	141.9	27.3	99.6	95.4	—	
a mean												70.3		
g mean						3.2	0.44						3.4	
25004	21 Jan 1959	28.5	32	26.85	4.1	10.28	0.0	9.3	134.3	4.8	17.0	12.6	—	
25004	14 Mar 1964	26.7	28	24.07	6.2	3.91	2.0	4.2	127.2	6.9	25.7	23.4	—	
25004	18 Feb 1966	23.6	54	23.54	30.7	2.00	0.8	0.2	124.4	18.5	78.6	79.1	—	
25004	9 Apr 1966	23.8	13	29.67	12.0	6.86	0.4	7.7	132.3	7.0	29.6	26.2	9.9	#
25004	16 Oct 1967	43.5	18	32.23	11.1	3.86	1.0	5.3	129.3	10.9	25.0	21.1	11.0	#
25004	4 Nov 1967	50.1	23	35.50	16.2	3.88	0.2	2.9	127.7	20.3	40.6	36.5	—	
25004	30 Oct 1968	69.8	60	29.14	10.2	4.61	0.0	4.0	129.0	18.5	26.5	19.0	—	
25004	17 Dec 1968	44.4	30	35.03	19.0	4.05	0.0	2.2	127.2	16.7	37.5	34.4	—	
25004	11 Aug 1971	78.9	41	33.11	15.7	3.52	36.6	10.2	98.6	18.1	23.0	21.9	—	
a mean												30.5		
g mean						12.0	4.34						10.4	
25005	5 Aug 1978	49.9	74	36.24	17.7	1.43	60.3	3.0	67.7	25.3	50.8	62.8	11.5	#
25005	7 Dec 1978	19.1	28	17.16	11.9	2.20	55.9	0.6	69.7	7.6	40.0	53.6	—	
25005	19 May 1979	35.3	32	43.83	9.8	2.84	22.2	3.7	106.5	14.6	41.4	45.8	6.5	#
25005	29 May 1979	28.3	7	57.52	5.6	7.13	3.0	4.5	126.5	11.9	42.1	41.6	5.0	#
25005	14 Nov 1979	41.9	28	32.01	12.3	1.84	42.2	2.2	85.0	13.9	33.2	42.3	12.5	#
25005	11 Mar 1980	13.3	13	17.49	12.8	2.54	0.0	1.9	126.9	5.3	39.8	39.1	13.5	#
25005	17 Mar 1980	16.8	35	19.73	15.7	2.64	0.7	1.1	125.4	8.9	53.1	52.9	—	

Catch	Date	P mm	D h	Q_p m^3s^{-1}	LAG h	BF m^3s^{-1}	SMD mm	$API5$ mm	CWI mm	R/O mm	PR %	SPR %	$Tp(0)$ h	
25005	29 Nov 1981	14.7	18	21.72	12.6	2.06	49.5	1.7	77.2	6.1	41.3	53.1	13.0	#
25005	26 Apr 1983	42.6	35	52.12	13.6	2.93	3.2	1.9	123.7	26.6	62.5	61.9	12.0	#
25005	8 Dec 1983	41.4	23	43.32	15.5	1.14	49.1	0.9	76.8	16.8	40.7	52.0	11.5	#
25005	5 Jan 1988	13.0	15	18.30	6.1	3.17	0.0	2.9	127.9	4.5	34.3	33.4	10.0	#
25005	3 Dec 1981	10.7	9	15.16	11.7	2.48	42.1	1.5	84.4	4.0	37.7	47.7	12.5	#
25005	20 Apr 1983	16.6	7	32.77	9.9	4.81	8.5	8.3	124.8	6.3	37.8	37.7	10.5	#
25005	1 Jun 1983	15.2	8	21.51	9.3	3.18	7.1	3.1	121.0	5.4	35.6	36.4	11.0	#
25005	3 Feb 1988	16.5	14	21.36	14.7	2.85	0.2	3.7	128.5	6.7	40.8	39.7	12.0	#
a mean												46.7		
g mean					11.4	2.62							10.5	
25006	23 Apr 1971	80.1	30	60.13	8.9	0.94	21.6	0.8	104.2	43.2	53.9	53.1	—	
25006	20 Nov 1971	24.3	9	29.11	5.4	1.63	0.1	1.9	126.8	9.8	40.3	39.8	—	
25006	19 Jan 1976	20.8	4	55.15	1.6	3.50	2.2	2.5	125.3	10.5	50.4	50.3	—	
25006	5 Jun 1980	46.4	9	30.10	5.4	0.65	77.4	13.1	60.7	9.0	19.5	33.9	7.5	#
25006	14 Jun 1980	27.9	9	33.41	4.1	2.37	73.7	7.3	58.6	8.7	31.1	47.7	4.5	#
25006	30 Jun 1980	33.4	16	51.05	6.9	1.51	55.3	2.7	72.4	15.8	47.4	60.5	8.7	#
25006	30 Jul 1980	27.7	7	15.01	4.9	0.58	78.8	3.1	49.3	4.0	14.4	33.3	5.6	#
25006	7 Aug 1980	36.7	20	36.14	5.7	1.46	63.8	2.2	63.4	14.7	40.1	55.5	6.3	#
25006	6 Oct 1980	33.8	36	25.96	6.2	1.07	77.5	2.0	49.5	11.4	33.8	52.7	9.5	#
25006	26 Oct 1980	44.6	58	28.17	9.9	1.79	31.2	6.7	100.5	32.9	73.8	78.6	11.5	#
25006	2 May 1982	34.2	14	30.28	4.3	0.95	65.6	4.1	63.5	8.6	25.2	40.6	4.3	#
25006	27 Apr 1983	36.1	45	28.76	0.5	2.67	3.7	6.7	128.0	23.0	63.6	62.8	3.9	#
25006	31 May 1983	36.3	17	44.68	5.9	1.72	8.7	1.7	118.0	15.9	43.8	45.5	4.5	#
25006	2 Nov 1984	40.4	23	45.49	11.9	1.35	71.9	2.5	55.6	26.0	64.4	81.5	13.5	#
25006	14 May 1985	45.3	26	46.89	4.2	1.67	32.6	1.8	94.2	16.8	37.1	43.3	3.1	#
25006	26 Jul 1985	32.7	16	30.96	2.0	1.07	43.9	2.1	83.2	6.2	19.0	29.4	3.6	#
25006	4 Aug 1985	58.7	29	63.18	3.2	2.34	8.5	9.7	126.2	27.3	46.5	42.7	4.9	#
25006	21 Sep 1985	29.4	28	31.64	2.7	2.10	0.0	3.1	128.1	16.4	55.9	55.1	7.5	#
25006	14 Apr 1986	65.1	24	70.10	6.7	3.62	0.0	4.0	129.0	36.0	55.3	50.0	2.7	#
25006	31 Oct 1986	37.2	17	43.03	4.5	2.93	74.5	8.9	59.4	17.5	47.0	63.4	2.7	#
25006	8 Feb 1987	26.2	27	25.16	6.9	2.09	3.2	3.6	125.4	16.0	61.1	61.0	6.0	#
25006	18 Jul 1987	47.8	26	31.27	4.7	1.08	44.5	0.8	81.3	19.3	40.3	49.3	6.3	#
25006	11 Nov 1987	55.3	43	37.61	2.5	2.06	2.1	5.2	128.1	26.6	48.1	44.3	3.3	#
25006	22 Nov 1987	25.8	34	21.45	5.2	2.03	0.0	3.7	128.7	14.6	56.5	55.6	4.9	#
25006	5 Jan 1988	21.4	16	37.88	2.8	3.82	0.0	11.7	136.7	11.8	55.2	52.3	4.5	#
a mean												51.3		
g mean					4.3	1.68							5.3	
25011	16 Mar 1972	35.4	5	15.16	1.5	0.66	1.1	0.2	124.1	16.6	46.8	47.0	—	
a mean												47.0		
g mean					1.5	0.66						—		
25012	16 Mar 1972	31.5	15	36.06	1.3	0.86	2.8	0.4	122.6	22.7	72.2	72.8	1.2	#
25012	17 Jun 1972	16.8	14	11.59	3.1	0.34	12.0	0.2	113.2	10.0	59.6	62.5	2.2	#
a mean												67.7		
g mean					2.0	0.54							1.6	
25019	24 Jan 1977	28.5	47	2.27	8.4	0.52	0.0	0.7	125.7	9.2	32.4	32.2	—	
25019	1 May 1977	47.1	47	2.74	13.1	0.17	23.7	1.5	102.8	10.4	22.1	25.8	3.5	#
25019	14 Dec 1978	28.8	59	0.92	11.3	0.22	15.2	2.1	111.9	6.4	22.3	25.5	—	
25019	20 May 1979	41.5	32	5.61	4.0	0.26	22.1	3.0	105.9	10.7	25.8	30.0	1.0	#
25019	7 Dec 1983	58.7	23	7.53	7.5	0.14	48.7	1.4	77.7	17.5	29.8	38.1	3.5	#
25019	1 Nov 1984	47.5	23	3.95	8.1	0.12	41.3	0.6	84.3	12.2	25.6	33.9	4.0	#
25019	10 Dec 1986	12.6	7	0.86	7.8	0.16	34.5	3.7	94.2	1.9	15.1	22.8	9.0	#
25019	21 Aug 1987	36.0	4	1.86	4.9	0.14	40.8	2.2	86.4	2.8	7.8	17.4	4.5	#
25019	25 Aug 1987	78.2	25	15.54	4.7	0.39	20.7	6.5	110.8	40.7	52.1	49.9	5.0	#
25019	18 Sep 1987	25.6	7	2.46	4.2	0.15	24.9	1.5	101.6	3.3	13.0	18.8	1.5	#
25019	9 Oct 1987	51.9	44	3.44	13.2	0.18	29.4	5.8	101.4	15.7	30.3	33.6	3.5	#
25019	15 Oct 1987	13.3	10	1.51	6.3	0.29	5.7	3.6	122.9	3.3	25.1	25.6	6.5	#
25019	19 Oct 1987	19.6	16	2.12	6.1	0.32	0.6	3.6	128.0	5.3	27.2	26.4	5.0	#
25019	30 Jan 1988	20.8	22	1.99	4.7	0.25	0.0	1.4	126.4	6.5	31.4	31.0	—	
25019	12 Dec 1986	21.8	5	2.64	5.9	0.26	26.9	7.8	105.9	5.7	26.3	31.1	4.5	#
25019	14 Dec 1986	13.8	6	1.99	6.3	0.34	24.0	6.4	107.4	5.1	36.9	41.3	6.5	#
a mean												30.2		
g mean					6.8	0.22							3.9	

Catch	Date	P mm	D h	Q_p m^3s^{-1}	LAG h	BF m^3s^{-1}	SMD mm	API5 mm	CWI mm	R/O mm	PR %	SPR %	Tp(0) h	
25809	13 Jul 1961	81.1	33	0.05	0.0	0.00	53.9	11.0	82.1	40.5	50.0	54.7	—	
25809	3 Aug 1961	58.9	19	0.06	3.3	0.00	50.4	0.7	75.3	30.2	51.2	60.1	—	
25809	16 Oct 1961	69.8	30	0.13	4.9	0.00	4.1	1.2	122.1	66.4	95.1	91.0	—	
25809	18 Aug 1961	28.5	30	0.02	8.3	0.00	50.7	1.1	75.4	13.8	48.3	60.7	—	
25809	21 Aug 1961	17.3	16	0.02	4.3	0.00	45.7	13.9	93.2	11.0	63.6	71.6	—	
a mean												67.6		
g mean					4.9	—							—	
25810	14 Jul 1961	81.2	33	0.05	2.0	0.00	53.9	11.0	82.1	34.9	43.0	47.6	—	
25810	3 Aug 1961	58.7	19	0.09	0.8	0.00	50.4	0.7	75.3	26.6	45.3	54.2	1.0	
25810	16 Oct 1961	69.9	30	0.09	3.5	0.00	4.1	1.2	122.1	45.6	65.2	61.1	2.0	
25810	17 Aug 1961	28.5	30	0.02	6.4	0.00	50.7	1.1	75.4	14.0	49.0	61.4	2.0	
25810	21 Aug 1961	17.3	16	0.03	2.8	0.00	45.7	13.9	93.2	10.8	62.3	70.3	1.8	
a mean												58.9		
g mean					2.5	—							1.6	
25811	18 Aug 1961	24.1	22	0.05	3.9	0.00	46.7	2.5	80.8	14.1	58.6	—	—	
25811	21 Aug 1961	17.3	16	0.05	3.3	0.00	45.7	13.9	93.2	10.4	60.1	—	—	
25811	19 Nov 1959	20.4	9	0.09	1.9	0.01	0.0	11.3	136.3	14.5	71.2	—	—	
a mean												—		
g mean					2.9	0.01							—	
27001	10 Nov 1963	29.9	15	76.62	8.5	11.99	36.8	3.9	92.1	6.5	21.7	29.2	—	
27001	21 Nov 1963	34.3	23	148.95	10.8	18.55	0.0	5.5	130.5	14.1	41.2	39.4	—	
27001	14 Mar 1964	42.0	24	84.21	8.9	8.46	0.0	4.1	129.1	12.2	29.1	26.7	9.7	#
27001	24 Mar 1964	29.8	26	89.63	12.4	15.54	0.8	1.9	126.1	13.3	44.5	43.8	9.5	#
27001	2 Dec 1965	28.8	35	96.32	21.9	11.34	0.0	4.1	129.1	20.4	70.7	69.7	—	
27001	8 Dec 1965	35.0	39	243.04	18.2	15.62	1.2	3.7	127.5	34.9	99.7	99.5	—	
27001	22 Feb 1967	23.7	12	98.14	8.1	13.87	0.0	4.9	129.9	7.7	32.4	30.6	7.7	#
27001	27 Feb 1967	35.9	26	138.50	14.9	14.87	0.0	3.6	128.6	14.9	41.6	40.3	—	
27001	18 Aug 1967	34.8	34	133.17	15.0	9.83	27.6	7.0	104.4	14.4	41.5	46.2	—	
27001	16 Oct 1967	51.3	29	274.18	15.5	19.82	1.4	6.7	130.3	32.9	64.1	60.2	—	
27001	2 Jul 1968	18.5	10	166.69	6.1	19.93	8.0	19.3	136.3	9.5	51.5	48.4	—	
27001	11 Sep 1968	66.8	31	303.85	13.8	10.74	51.6	7.4	80.8	34.7	51.9	58.2	—	
27001	31 Oct 1968	38.9	36	87.37	8.8	21.48	0.0	2.4	127.4	9.8	25.1	23.8	9.2	#
27001	1 Nov 1968	37.7	26	227.90	13.3	29.99	0.0	18.3	143.3	23.4	62.1	57.4	—	
a mean												48.1		
g mean					11.9	14.98							9.0	
27010	19 Sep 1968	60.1	42	9.84	7.9	0.26	88.0	0.4	37.4	20.6	34.2	52.4	—	
a mean											52.4			
g mean					7.9	0.26							—	
27026	25 Nov 1963	28.5	31	29.96	9.1	1.95	0.0	1.3	126.3	9.7	34.1	31.3	—	
27026	8 Sep 1965	30.0	13	34.73	5.6	1.87	0.2	11.1	135.9	8.8	29.4	23.8	—	
27026	8 Dec 1965	44.2	40	54.91	10.1	3.20	0.1	2.4	127.3	23.8	53.9	51.0	—	
27026	9 Apr 1966	21.1	12	42.04	4.9	3.70	0.0	2.7	127.7	9.1	42.9	40.3	—	
27026	8 Mar 1967	34.6	29	26.09	7.7	1.30	4.0	1.1	122.1	7.5	21.8	19.2	5.2	#
27026	14 May 1967	37.6	31	44.19	10.6	1.78	0.1	6.7	131.6	15.8	42.0	38.4	—	
27026	14 Jul 1968	38.2	17	35.28	10.4	0.62	17.8	5.1	112.3	10.4	27.1	27.3	13.0	#
27026	1 Nov 1968	33.3	18	31.08	5.4	2.05	0.0	3.1	128.1	10.6	31.8	28.4	—	
a mean												32.5		
g mean					7.6	1.83							8.2	
27027	7 Jan 1965	15.0	14	129.37	6.1	15.36	0.0	4.3	129.3	9.3	62.1	61.0	6.0	#
27027	9 Jan 1965	38.9	59	180.10	16.2	16.80	0.0	8.6	133.6	35.7	91.7	89.6	—	
27027	16 Apr 1965	12.4	15	71.28	3.4	15.85	0.0	2.4	127.4	4.2	33.9	33.3	—	
27027	1 Aug 1965	18.9	12	78.50	4.5	10.98	0.0	6.1	131.1	5.5	29.0	27.4	—	
27027	3 Aug 1965	17.6	14	87.25	4.7	12.97	3.5	15.4	136.9	6.1	34.4	31.4	6.5	#
27027	9 Sep 1965	11.7	9	79.22	6.1	10.94	0.0	5.5	130.5	4.8	41.4	40.0	—	
27027	24 Sep 1965	42.9	23	153.60	6.0	10.91	0.2	3.7	128.5	20.2	47.1	45.3	7.5	#
27027	29 Oct 1965	14.1	13	90.93	3.8	9.98	0.0	3.3	128.3	5.1	36.5	35.6	—	
27027	31 Oct 1965	45.8	45	195.90	9.6	13.01	0.0	10.0	135.0	37.1	81.0	77.0	—	
27027	16 Dec 1965	32.1	36	278.68	9.4	26.04	0.0	5.8	130.8	28.5	88.7	87.3	—	
27027	5 Feb 1966	18.6	15	163.88	8.1	24.43	0.0	3.1	128.1	16.9	91.0	90.2	—	
27027	7 Feb 1966	49.7	30	165.25	9.8	22.47	0.0	9.2	134.2	22.5	45.3	40.8	—	

Catch	Date	P mm	D h	Q_p $m^3 s^{-1}$	LAG h	BF $m^3 s^{-1}$	SMD mm	API5 mm	CWI mm	R/O mm	PR %	SPR %	Tp(0) h	
27027	26 Jun 1966	21.3	21	80.56	5.1	16.35	3.6	4.8	126.2	7.9	37.2	36.9	—	
27027	14 Nov 1966	26.7	37	144.45	5.5	21.59	0.0	9.1	134.1	13.1	49.0	46.7	—	
27027	17 Dec 1966	37.3	23	194.38	9.3	19.26	0.1	1.0	125.9	28.8	77.2	77.0	—	
27027	19 Dec 1966	29.9	20	173.58	9.4	30.26	0.0	18.0	143.0	16.1	53.7	49.2	7.1	#
27027	16 Oct 1967	61.9	23	310.91	10.5	31.19	0.0	13.0	138.0	35.3	57.0	49.8	7.0	#
27027	4 Nov 1967	38.5	20	123.33	5.7	20.45	0.0	3.1	128.1	14.5	37.6	36.8	6.5	#
27027	19 Mar 1968	47.1	33	224.37	10.6	22.36	0.0	8.4	133.4	39.4	83.6	79.7	9.7	#
27027	30 Oct 1968	49.8	37	206.50	7.3	34.68	0.0	8.4	133.4	25.0	50.2	45.9	8.3	#
27027	1 Nov 1968	34.6	22	171.18	8.0	51.01	0.0	23.8	148.8	14.3	41.3	35.3	6.5	#
27027	20 Jan 1969	36.9	25	158.65	7.3	12.87	0.0	1.2	126.2	20.8	56.4	56.1	—	
27027	31 Mar 1969	65.5	21	259.85	9.5	32.42	0.0	1.1	126.1	24.1	36.8	32.1	8.5	#
27027	21 Feb 1970	49.6	59	213.48	12.2	30.56	0.0	7.0	132.0	32.4	65.3	61.4	—	
27027	9 Nov 1972	32.4	16	222.59	9.1	11.83	0.0	1.3	126.3	17.9	55.1	54.8	7.8	#
27027	12 Feb 1971	47.5	54	214.67	8.6	12.66	0.0	0.0	125.0	32.8	69.0	67.2	—	
27027	20 Nov 1971	36.9	12	166.43	7.5	11.65	0.0	2.8	127.8	13.8	37.3	36.6	—	
a mean												52.7		
g mean					7.4	18.44							7.3	
27031	21 Jan 1975	31.3	18	124.09	7.3	11.45	0.8	8.2	132.4	18.7	59.6	57.2	4.5	#
27031	30 Apr 1975	35.1	14	76.43	3.7	4.59	8.3	3.3	120.0	9.0	25.5	24.5	4.4	#
a mean												40.9		
g mean					5.2	7.25							4.4	
27034	14 Aug 1967	21.7	14	140.97	7.6	13.23	0.4	5.6	130.2	11.1	51.3	50.0	7.2	#
27034	18 Aug 1967	46.9	23	208.41	8.7	17.01	3.6	4.1	125.5	24.5	52.3	50.4	7.2	#
27034	14 Oct 1967	43.6	42	202.45	11.6	20.54	0.0	3.3	128.3	29.1	66.7	64.8	—	
27034	16 Oct 1967	62.9	30	321.87	11.6	33.13	1.0	12.4	136.4	42.3	67.2	60.3	—	
27034	22 Dec 1967	41.7	31	212.04	11.1	15.53	0.0	1.0	126.0	27.1	64.9	64.0	—	
27034	19 Mar 1968	75.3	31	295.50	9.5	26.25	0.0	8.0	133.0	42.8	56.9	49.4	—	
27034	22 Mar 1968	88.5	43	379.28	11.5	22.83	0.0	8.4	133.4	66.5	75.1	66.2	—	
27034	11 Sep 1968	76.2	13	270.68	11.9	17.03	45.8	6.0	85.2	34.4	45.1	49.5	—	
27034	12 Feb 1971	53.0	25	206.51	17.3	9.81	3.7	0.3	121.6	33.8	63.7	61.8	—	
27034	12 Aug 1971	25.2	29	190.75	1.8	44.88	42.5	10.5	93.0	18.8	74.7	82.7	—	
a mean												59.9		
g mean					9.1	20.09							7.2	
27035	10 Nov 1969	31.8	21	58.59	6.2	13.37	27.1	12.6	110.5	11.5	36.1	39.5	6.5	#
27035	19 Feb 1970	12.5	9	47.65	7.6	10.97	0.0	2.7	127.7	6.4	51.4	50.6	7.7	#
27035	12 Apr 1970	31.5	17	53.40	8.9	4.61	2.1	1.3	124.2	10.4	33.1	33.1	5.3	#
27035	30 Oct 1970	25.9	8	58.93	5.5	16.44	96.9	11.0	39.1	7.6	29.5	50.8	—	
27035	12 Feb 1971	32.2	19	54.37	10.8	3.53	0.0	0.0	125.0	13.3	41.4	41.2	6.4	#
27035	18 Oct 1971	47.6	24	59.61	12.1	11.01	71.4	5.4	59.0	18.1	38.1	52.6	—	
27035	20 Nov 1971	24.5	11	52.99	7.5	6.19	0.0	1.5	126.5	9.0	36.9	36.3	7.7	#
27035	9 Nov 1972	33.0	16	45.64	8.1	1.60	86.1	1.4	40.3	7.7	23.3	44.2	5.2	#
27035	1 Dec 1972	22.1	11	57.58	6.8	13.80	0.0	5.1	130.1	8.0	36.3	34.8	6.0	#
27035	24 Nov 1974	23.9	19	54.05	11.4	9.44	0.1	4.4	129.3	10.0	41.7	40.5	7.0	#
27035	30 Apr 1975	25.9	26	32.72	9.8	1.85	12.7	1.8	114.1	6.4	24.9	27.4	6.8	#
a mean												41.0		
g mean					8.4	6.60							6.5	
27051	2 Oct 1974	21.9	20	0.53	11.3	0.03	25.6	0.2	99.6	3.5	15.9	22.2	—	
27051	13 Nov 1974	16.1	18	1.17	5.0	0.14	0.0	2.6	127.6	5.0	30.8	30.1	3.0	#
27051	24 Nov 1974	19.3	22	1.99	5.5	0.20	0.0	6.1	131.1	6.3	32.8	31.2	3.3	#
27051	10 Dec 1974	9.5	7	1.82	3.2	0.36	0.0	1.2	126.2	3.5	37.2	36.9	2.6	#
27051	23 Jan 1975	13.3	20	1.77	18.9	0.31	0.0	3.7	128.7	4.6	34.7	33.7	—	
27051	18 Apr 1975	11.9	12	0.80	3.2	0.13	0.0	3.7	128.7	2.4	19.8	18.8	—	
27051	2 Jan 1976	16.4	15	2.91	4.7	0.18	9.1	3.4	119.3	8.5	51.8	53.2	2.9	#
27051	8 Jan 1976	20.1	23	1.22	5.0	0.14	0.0	0.7	125.7	5.6	27.7	27.5	—	
27051	28 May 1976	30.0	27	1.61	0.0	0.11	17.4	4.8	112.4	8.8	29.4	32.5	—	
27051	1 Oct 1976	27.3	7	3.67	2.4	0.26	17.3	9.3	117.0	8.2	29.9	31.9	2.9	#
27051	1 Oct 1976	38.1	12	2.96	4.1	0.25	6.5	20.7	139.2	12.1	31.7	28.1	—	
a mean												31.5		
g mean					5.2	0.16							2.9	

Catch	Date			P mm	D h	Q_p m^3s^{-1}	LAG h	BF m^3s^{-1}	SMD mm	API5 mm	CWI mm	R/O mm	PR %	SPR %	Tp(0) h	
28016	1	Nov	1968	39.0	17	16.80	27.9	3.23	0.0	2.6	127.6	9.8	25.1	22.6	29.5	#
28016	12	Mar	1969	37.7	44	14.59	30.6	3.65	4.3	0.0	120.7	11.3	29.9	29.3	—	
28016	16	Mar	1969	27.8	45	15.01	28.1	5.03	0.0	3.0	128.0	9.6	34.5	32.3	—	
28016	16	Nov	1969	30.2	20	15.88	23.5	3.09	2.6	3.5	125.9	8.0	26.5	24.5	16.8	#
28016	12	Apr	1970	43.2	21	17.11	22.6	2.86	1.2	1.0	124.8	9.5	22.0	19.0	16.1	#
a mean														25.5		
g mean							26.4	3.50							20.0	
28023	8	Dec	1965	65.4	35	36.52	11.2	10.48	0.0	5.7	130.7	21.1	32.3	26.3	7.4	#
28023	22	Dec	1965	38.6	28	18.56	13.3	9.61	0.0	3.7	128.7	8.4	21.8	20.5	12.0	#
28023	29	Dec	1965	29.8	16	14.64	10.4	6.86	0.3	0.1	124.8	4.3	14.4	14.0	10.7	#
28023	19	Feb	1966	16.0	17	13.94	8.2	7.02	0.0	12.0	137.0	3.2	20.3	16.9	7.3	#
28023	27	Jun	1966	24.5	14	8.68	8.4	3.27	0.0	10.2	135.2	2.7	11.0	8.0	—	
28023	20	Aug	1966	39.1	15	9.81	7.1	3.64	14.4	0.0	110.6	2.2	5.6	8.7	—	
28023	14	Sep	1966	40.7	22	15.52	9.3	4.34	0.0	5.0	130.0	4.3	10.6	8.6	7.5	#
28023	9	Dec	1966	24.3	23	14.38	10.7	7.62	0.0	5.1	130.1	4.7	19.2	17.5	10.9	#
28023	3	Oct	1967	21.2	14	10.49	7.4	4.03	0.0	8.0	133.0	1.8	8.6	6.1	8.7	#
28023	16	Oct	1967	46.6	30	16.27	11.9	5.08	0.6	5.2	129.6	9.4	20.2	17.0	—	
28023	2	Jul	1968	24.8	24	13.81	4.1	3.08	8.1	1.9	118.8	2.5	10.1	11.2	—	
a mean														14.1		
g mean							8.9	5.43							9.0	
28026	4	Nov	1967	24.2	24	40.02	24.4	2.49	0.0	2.5	127.5	14.3	59.0	57.9	29.5	#
28026	10	Jul	1968	51.2	23	56.87	29.7	1.74	19.5	3.8	109.3	22.0	42.9	43.2	28.6	#
28026	1	Nov	1968	26.1	19	43.99	25.2	1.72	0.0	3.5	128.5	14.3	54.6	53.1	24.9	#
28026	12	Mar	1969	27.9	40	36.00	24.5	2.26	4.1	0.0	120.9	12.1	43.4	43.3	24.3	#
28026	5	May	1969	36.3	13	56.63	16.1	3.74	12.9	0.7	112.8	15.1	41.5	43.3	14.9	#
a mean														48.1		
g mean							23.5	2.29							23.8	
28033	26	Jun	1966	47.2	25	2.62	4.7	0.36	4.0	8.5	129.5	15.2	32.2	29.3	1.8	#
28033	28	Jul	1966	27.4	15	1.59	3.7	0.07	14.4	2.9	113.5	3.0	10.8	13.7	2.5	#
28033	14	Sep	1966	36.3	7	4.63	6.1	0.40	0.0	9.5	134.5	15.0	41.3	38.9	2.2	#
28033	4	Oct	1966	14.3	7	2.11	2.7	0.17	0.0	7.8	132.8	2.7	18.7	16.8	2.0	#
28033	14	May	1967	12.4	4	1.61	2.2	0.23	1.5	5.5	129.0	2.5	20.5	19.5	2.3	#
28033	14	May	1967	15.4	19	1.83	2.7	0.46	0.0	12.1	137.1	5.0	32.4	29.4	1.8	#
28033	29	Sep	1967	17.4	9	1.67	3.5	0.21	19.0	5.7	111.7	3.5	20.2	23.5	1.4	#
28033	3	Oct	1967	24.7	15	3.47	4.7	0.45	0.0	9.6	134.6	6.5	26.4	24.0	2.5	#
28033	20	Nov	1971	57.3	19	5.54	11.6	0.50	0.0	3.3	128.3	27.4	47.9	43.8	—	
a mean														26.5		
g mean							4.1	0.27							2.0	
28041	5	Aug	1973	46.4	16	41.37	6.1	0.55	3.2	7.0	128.8	20.6	44.5	41.8	—	
28041	19	Aug	1970	31.0	22	25.16	6.2	0.80	14.5	2.6	113.1	18.0	58.2	61.2	—	
28041	5	Apr	1970	15.5	13	7.92	2.2	0.96	0.8	2.1	126.3	4.5	29.1	28.7	—	
28041	7	Dec	1969	6.2	7	5.70	4.0	1.01	0.0	3.6	128.6	3.4	54.5	53.6	—	
28041	10	Nov	1969	20.5	15	19.60	1.4	1.04	0.0	12.4	137.4	8.0	38.8	35.6	—	
28041	10	Nov	1969	20.5	15	19.60	1.4	1.08	43.4	12.4	94.0	8.1	39.5	47.2	—	
28041	11	Nov	1969	17.2	6	16.11	1.4	3.77	0.0	20.3	145.3	5.4	31.6	26.4	—	
a mean														42.1		
g mean							2.7	1.09							—	
28070	2	Dec	1937	56.3	25	5.88	3.5	0.56	0.0	5.5	130.5	20.9	37.1	32.5	2.5	#
28070	1	Jul	1958	54.2	24	24.13	2.0	0.72	0.0	10.8	135.8	31.5	58.2	52.6	—	
28070	10	Oct	1961	27.9	13	3.22	3.0	0.22	70.7	3.7	58.0	7.2	25.9	42.7	1.4	#
28070	18	Jul	1964	49.8	10	7.19	3.2	0.21	39.1	2.5	88.4	18.0	36.1	43.0	2.0	#
28070	11	Dec	1964	57.0	44	6.14	7.7	0.19	24.4	2.6	103.2	44.1	77.4	79.6	3.0	#
28070	21	Jun	1965	31.2	9	2.43	3.8	0.19	26.8	1.7	99.9	6.5	20.9	27.2	3.2	#
28070	8	Sep	1965	41.9	12	5.45	3.1	0.35	1.3	7.6	131.3	13.7	32.6	30.3	2.0	#
28070	9	Apr	1966	26.1	11	3.69	5.6	0.40	0.0	3.9	128.9	11.6	44.3	43.3	—	
28070	21	Aug	1966	50.5	17	1.69	5.8	0.14	35.6	0.0	89.4	6.8	13.4	20.0	—	
28070	14	May	1967	45.9	15	2.81	5.2	0.26	2.0	6.3	129.3	9.4	20.5	17.9	—	
28070	16	Oct	1967	56.6	36	5.20	3.9	0.21	16.8	3.4	111.6	23.8	42.0	42.1	—	
28070	6	May	1969	26.6	12	4.20	2.3	0.28	6.4	0.6	119.2	13.1	49.3	50.8	2.0	#
a mean														40.2		
g mean							3.8	0.28							2.2	

Catch	Date	P mm	D h	Q_p m^3s^{-1}	LAG h	BF m^3s^{-1}	SMD mm	API5 mm	CWI mm	R/O mm	PR %	SPR %	Tp(0) h	
28997	5 Dec 1990				—								2.7	#
28997	8 Jan 1991				—								2.8	#
28997	11 Jan 1991				—								1.4	#
28997	2 Nov 1991				—								1.5	#
28997	17 Dec 1991				—								2.7	#
28997	2 Oct 1992				—								5.1	#
28997	25 Oct 1992				—								2.3	#
g mean													2.43	
28998	25 Oct 1990				—								2.2	#
28998	8 Jan 1991				—								2.0	#
28998	9 Jan 1991				—								2.0	#
28998	11 Jan 1991				—								2.3	#
28998	18 Jan 1991				—								3.8	#
28998	2 Oct 1992				—								6.2	#
28998	25 Oct 1992				—								4.0	#
g mean													2.94	
28999	5 Dec 1990				—								1.0	#
28999	8 Jan 1991				—								2.0	#
28999	11 Jan 1991				—								1.8	#
28999	18 Jan 1991				—								2.3	#
28999	2 Nov 1991				—								1.9	#
28999	2 Oct 1992				—								4.3	#
28999	25 Oct 1992				—								2.9	#
g mean													2.13	
29001	21 Apr 1962	16.0	11	1.25	7.9	0.34	2.0	1.6	124.6	0.4	2.7	2.6	5.1	#
29001	17 Aug 1963	44.4	27	1.47	12.0	0.23	57.7	2.0	69.3	1.1	2.5	15.0	11.1	#
29001	29 Nov 1965	32.6	14	2.51	7.8	0.56	0.0	3.7	128.7	1.1	3.3	2.2	5.2	#
29001	27 Oct 1966	19.7	18	0.81	6.8	0.21	11.6	1.6	115.0	0.3	1.7	4.0	4.6	#
29001	27 Feb 1967	17.8	19	1.13	5.7	0.42	1.2	1.6	125.4	0.4	2.4	2.1	11.5	#
29001	10 Jul 1968	60.4	24	1.09	8.3	0.17	71.2	1.8	55.6	0.6	1.0	14.4	—	
29001	1 Nov 1968	53.8	34	3.70	3.8	0.83	0.0	4.7	129.7	1.8	3.3	—	4.5	#
29001	15 Jul 1973	77.4	26	3.97	10.7	0.13	47.0	1.1	79.1	1.5	1.9	7.5	4.7	#
29001	6 Oct 1974	53.1	35	1.28	12.8	0.14	84.4	4.8	45.4	1.0	1.8	18.8	—	
29001	8 Mar 1975	15.1	30	2.48	25.7	0.36	0.2	3.5	128.3	1.9	12.4	11.4	—	
a mean												8.7		
g mean					8.9	0.29							6.1	
29002	26 Dec 1979	24.1	21	2.55	11.9	0.74	8.4	1.0	117.6	2.0	8.4	10.0	—	
29002	24 Feb 1980	28.0	22	4.13	11.3	1.47	0.0	2.5	127.5	2.9	10.2	9.4	6.0	#
29002	17 Dec 1980	8.7	8	2.33	7.1	1.12	10.0	4.7	119.7	0.9	10.8	11.9	7.2	#
29002	8 Feb 1981	35.0	34	3.88	11.0	0.98	0.3	0.5	125.2	3.3	9.5	9.2	6.8	#
29002	24 Apr 1981	84.9	56	8.80	19.8	1.42	11.1	2.3	116.2	13.1	15.4	11.0	—	
29002	15 Mar 1982	15.0	23	2.14	3.2	0.99	9.0	4.6	120.6	0.8	5.4	6.3	7.8	#
29002	26 Nov 1983	27.4	17	1.51	10.0	0.46	85.6	2.4	41.8	1.1	3.9	24.5	11.2	#
29002	1 Feb 1986	23.7	44	2.40	18.8	1.00	0.6	2.3	126.7	2.6	10.8	10.2	20.5	#
29002	29 Dec 1986	29.0	33	3.47	12.6	0.81	6.0	0.6	119.6	2.8	9.7	10.8	6.7	#
29002	31 Dec 1986	17.2	31	2.77	9.2	1.19	0.0	8.6	133.6	1.7	9.7	7.3	10.7	#
a mean												11.1		
g mean					10.4	0.97							8.9	
29004	1 Nov 1968	33.3	20	8.38	14.3	0.91	0.0	4.2	129.2	10.3	31.0	29.9	—	
29004	2 Jun 1969	26.9	16	5.38	7.5	0.68	9.4	2.2	117.8	4.6	17.1	18.8	5.3	#
29004	28 Jul 1969	50.8	11	7.60	9.7	0.06	94.0	1.1	32.1	5.9	11.7	32.4	7.5	#
29004	16 Nov 1969	31.6	11	8.62	9.9	0.69	42.2	2.1	84.9	8.2	25.8	35.7	8.8	#
29004	12 Apr 1970	33.1	17	7.43	11.2	0.65	0.7	0.4	124.7	8.9	26.9	26.9	9.7	#
29004	8 Mar 1972	11.2	12	6.05	8.7	1.74	0.0	8.9	133.9	4.1	36.6	34.3	—	
29004	15 Jul 1973	58.6	20	9.23	13.6	0.60	45.0	1.4	81.4	12.5	21.4	28.7	8.9	#
29004	6 Oct 1974	53.1	28	8.72	13.6	0.69	79.0	4.9	50.9	16.9	31.8	47.5	—	
29004	7 Dec 1973	17.3	21	1.91	12.8	0.14	1.3	0.0	123.7	3.0	17.3	17.5	—	
29004	18 Apr 1975	19.4	14	6.66	7.2	0.95	0.0	3.2	128.2	5.3	27.1	26.2	5.5	#
a mean												29.8		
g mean					10.6	0.53							7.4	

Catch	Date	*P* mm	*D* h	Q_p m^3s^{-1}	*LAG* h	*BF* m^3s^{-1}	*SMD* mm	*API5* mm	*CWI* mm	*R/O* mm	*PR* %	*SPR* %	*Tp*(0) h	
30001	29 Oct 1960	17.6	14	16.82	22.6	4.78	0.0	2.9	127.9	5.3	30.1	28.9	20.7	#
30001	3 Dec 1960	35.2	20	29.12	32.8	4.99	0.0	0.2	125.2	13.2	37.4	37.0	19.2	#
30001	18 Dec 1960	35.9	47	23.87	18.0	4.57	0.0	0.1	125.1	9.8	27.2	26.7	18.3	#
30001	28 Nov 1965	25.9	14	17.27	20.8	3.41	0.0	2.2	127.2	5.9	22.8	21.7	18.5	#
30001	9 Dec 1965	20.2	18	18.70	22.1	4.93	0.0	4.2	129.2	6.5	32.0	30.5	18.5	#
30001	18 Dec 1965	16.7	18	16.80	19.4	7.90	0.0	4.1	129.1	2.9	17.1	15.5	19.7	#
30001	14 May 1967	47.7	41	23.38	33.8	2.08	3.6	5.4	126.8	15.3	32.0	29.2	—	
30001	1 Nov 1968	36.5	19	26.35	26.8	2.90	0.0	5.5	130.5	11.8	32.2	30.4	20.0	#
30001	5 May 1969	27.7	10	19.29	22.4	2.26	15.0	0.8	110.8	6.0	21.8	24.8	20.5	#
30001	23 Jan 1971	24.0	23	13.90	17.5	2.57	29.0	1.8	97.8	4.6	19.1	25.3	23.5	#
30001	8 Mar 1975	35.8	18	33.34	19.2	3.28	0.0	2.0	127.0	11.1	30.9	29.9	15.5	#
a mean												27.3		
g mean					22.7	3.68							19.3	
30004	20 Dec 1962	15.5	10	3.09	9.8	0.52	0.0	0.6	125.6	2.3	14.7	14.2	7.7	#
30004	29 Nov 1965	36.9	16	11.05	10.9	0.98	0.0	3.1	128.1	10.1	27.4	26.3	11.0	#
30004	18 Dec 1965	18.9	19	5.45	13.4	1.25	0.0	8.4	133.4	5.1	27.2	24.8	—	
30004	5 Nov 1967	15.2	16	3.72	10.1	0.86	9.9	6.6	121.7	3.3	21.9	22.4	10.6	#
30004	10 Jul 1968	105.5	24	13.34	12.2	0.36	57.2	3.1	70.9	16.1	15.3	20.0	—	
30004	8 Aug 1968	33.8	7	5.09	5.7	0.67	32.3	2.3	95.0	2.9	8.6	15.7	5.5	#
30004	15 Sep 1968	30.1	29	6.58	6.9	0.74	2.8	1.9	124.1	6.6	22.0	21.9	9.5	#
30004	1 Nov 1968	48.7	26	10.17	10.9	0.92	0.0	6.4	131.4	12.2	25.0	21.0	10.2	#
30004	8 Feb 1974	11.9	8	4.33	9.0	0.92	0.0	5.2	130.2	2.4	20.1	18.5	9.5	#
30004	7 Oct 1974	27.7	8	7.88	10.7	0.90	50.4	5.4	80.0	6.7	24.3	35.2	11.1	#
30004	18 Apr 1975	22.0	10	8.64	6.5	1.19	0.0	6.3	131.3	4.9	22.4	20.5	4.5	#
30004	27 Dec 1979	16.7	12	5.32	7.3	0.85	4.8	4.5	124.7	4.3	25.8	25.6	5.6	#
30004	7 Aug 1980	35.6	18	1.75	6.5	0.32	91.0	4.7	38.7	1.4	3.8	24.9	9.0	#
30004	14 Aug 1980	32.6	22	7.06	11.8	0.38	83.2	0.9	42.7	6.6	20.3	40.5	5.6	#
30004	6 Mar 1982	21.4	22	4.73	9.4	0.69	18.9	1.9	108.0	4.0	18.9	22.8	7.8	#
30004	15 Mar 1982	16.0	23	4.14	4.6	0.88	8.8	5.0	121.2	3.1	19.5	20.1	5.6	#
30004	21 Jun 1982	65.3	41	5.37	12.5	0.27	90.2	4.0	38.8	6.7	10.3	27.1	7.7	#
30004	25 Jun 1982	23.2	7	5.86	6.5	0.69	46.8	10.9	89.1	3.5	15.0	23.6	4.6	#
30004	13 Nov 1982	26.7	43	4.32	8.7	0.74	5.3	1.5	121.2	5.8	21.8	22.4	6.7	#
30004	9 Dec 1982	18.3	10	6.39	7.1	0.94	0.0	3.7	128.7	3.8	20.9	19.6	5.5	#
30004	1 May 1983	21.2	37	5.02	11.4	0.90	4.1	5.8	126.7	5.1	23.9	23.2	10.8	#
30004	31 Jul 1983	36.0	18	1.74	6.8	0.25	101.9	0.1	23.2	0.9	2.5	27.5	6.2	#
30004	26 Nov 1983	29.7	33	3.09	7.0	0.38	85.5	2.8	42.3	2.9	9.7	30.0	8.2	#
30004	26 May 1984	38.0	40	3.65	12.9	0.36	50.1	4.8	79.7	4.3	11.2	22.1	4.8	#
30004	2 Aug 1984	53.0	18	5.19	5.0	0.24	101.3	9.1	32.8	2.3	4.4	24.3	4.9	#
30004	29 Jan 1985	18.9	10	8.32	7.7	1.16	0.0	4.4	129.4	5.7	30.0	28.6	8.6	#
30004	29 Dec 1986	29.5	17	7.61	13.9	0.75	4.9	1.1	121.2	7.9	26.7	27.4	14.9	#
30004	31 Mar 1987	24.2	36	4.94	9.1	0.90	1.9	1.5	124.6	6.5	26.9	26.7	4.0	#
30004	14 Oct 1987	30.3	34	7.25	11.0	0.79	5.2	2.9	122.7	8.6	28.4	28.7	5.7	#
30004	1 Jan 1988	17.0	9	6.85	6.8	0.90	0.0	1.6	126.6	4.3	25.1	24.4	7.3	#
30004	13 Dec 1979	27.6	34	8.41	6.9	1.07	9.5	7.1	122.6	6.8	24.5	24.8	6.8	#
a mean												24.4		
g mean					8.6	0.66							7.2	
30017	30 Jan 1980	10.3	8	2.47	8.1	0.38	1.5	2.1	125.6	1.8	17.5	17.1	9.0	#
30017	17 Mar 1980	26.9	24	4.02	14.1	0.45	0.0	4.2	129.2	5.5	20.6	19.3	7.9	#
30017	15 Oct 1980	31.1	12	3.99	10.0	0.12	112.6	0.8	13.2	3.9	12.6	40.3	7.8	#
30017	14 Nov 1980	16.6	30	2.40	18.4	0.22	51.9	1.9	75.0	2.9	17.7	30.0	9.8	#
30017	1 Jun 1981	20.1	3	3.24	8.0	0.22	16.0	2.1	111.1	2.3	11.2	14.4	7.1	#
30017	6 Mar 1982	22.7	24	3.74	9.3	0.28	37.4	1.6	89.2	3.9	17.4	26.1	8.5	#
30017	22 Jun 1982	40.4	31	3.46	18.0	0.11	92.9	5.6	37.7	4.6	11.3	32.6	9.4	#
30017	25 Jun 1982	33.6	6	11.49	7.7	0.69	73.4	11.2	62.8	7.9	23.4	38.8	7.3	#
30017	9 Dec 1982	16.3	10	4.41	8.7	0.41	24.5	4.3	104.8	3.6	22.1	27.0	8.3	#
30017	10 Apr 1983	22.7	28	2.97	14.1	0.19	1.7	2.1	125.4	5.0	22.2	21.9	11.5	#
30017	20 Apr 1983	10.4	11	3.44	7.1	0.41	0.8	5.0	129.2	2.2	21.6	20.4	6.7	#
30017	24 Apr 1983	13.0	5	2.69	7.3	0.34	0.0	2.2	127.2	1.5	11.8	11.0	6.5	#
30017	31 May 1983	24.6	14	5.31	8.1	0.28	14.6	1.1	111.5	4.5	18.1	21.3	8.4	#
30017	23 Nov 1984	14.5	14	3.24	10.1	0.41	53.5	5.7	77.2	2.8	19.3	31.0	8.9	#
30017	29 Jan 1986	16.6	27	2.63	11.7	0.31	6.5	0.9	119.4	2.8	17.0	18.2	8.0	#
30017	29 Dec 1986	30.5	73	3.11	12.6	0.25	49.3	0.3	76.0	6.2	20.2	32.2	6.9	#
30017	7 Apr 1987	17.3	10	6.13	5.3	0.65	0.0	4.1	129.1	4.1	23.8	22.6	4.7	#
30017	9 Oct 1987	26.5	42	1.18	12.8	0.06	109.0	4.7	20.7	2.0	7.4	33.2	13.6	#

Catch	Date	P mm	D h	Q_p m^3s^{-1}	LAG h	BF m^3s^{-1}	SMD mm	API5 mm	CWI mm	R/O mm	PR %	SPR %	Tp(0) h	
30017	15 Oct 1987	15.8	22	2.18	10.3	0.18	82.2	4.5	47.3	2.6	16.4	35.6	8.3	#
30017	20 Oct 1987	24.4	33	4.03	10.3	0.22	67.4	1.0	58.6	4.6	18.8	35.2	9.5	#
a mean												26.4		
g mean					10.1	0.27							8.2	
31005	27 Feb 1967	17.3	18	22.98	52.0	2.90	0.0	1.0	126.0	7.6	44.1	43.7	—	
31005	26 Nov 1968	16.5	22	20.33	49.3	2.28	0.0	0.8	125.8	9.3	56.5	56.2	—	
31005	12 Mar 1969	27.8	42	39.51	44.3	3.89	4.3	0.5	121.2	16.2	58.2	59.1	41.5	#
31005	9 Jan 1970	9.4	24	16.03	44.3	1.85	40.0	4.1	89.1	8.5	90.8	99.9	—	
31005	23 Jan 1971	26.3	22	33.46	37.9	4.47	24.1	2.1	103.0	11.2	42.4	47.8	—	
31005	6 Dec 1972	20.3	14	22.93	28.9	3.29	47.7	5.0	82.3	5.6	27.7	38.2	26.0	#
31005	20 Nov 1974	22.0	26	32.33	41.1	6.46	1.7	7.0	130.3	9.2	42.0	40.5	—	
31005	8 Mar 1975	39.7	28	106.44	26.3	4.64	0.0	3.4	128.4	29.8	75.0	74.2	—	
a mean												57.4		
g mean					39.5	3.47							32.8	
31006	13 May 1967	48.2	53	13.17	25.7	1.31	3.2	4.2	126.0	11.8	24.5	22.0	—	
31006	10 Jul 1968	68.2	47	18.37	29.3	0.72	67.9	3.1	60.2	11.1	16.3	27.5	—	
31006	1 Nov 1968	27.6	19	14.65	27.1	1.86	0.0	6.4	131.4	6.6	24.0	22.1	—	
31006	26 Nov 1968	15.7	18	9.54	18.1	1.62	0.0	1.9	126.9	3.7	23.6	22.8	—	
31006	12 Mar 1969	28.0	22	12.86	23.4	2.33	2.3	2.9	125.6	6.7	24.1	23.6	—	
31006	5 May 1969	42.8	19	22.89	19.0	1.28	30.0	0.3	95.3	9.2	21.4	27.6	—	
a mean												24.3		
g mean					23.4	1.43							—	
31010	10 Jul 1968	72.8	22	20.93	14.3	0.55	60.0	2.4	67.4	16.8	23.1	32.2	—	
31010	1 Nov 1968	26.0	15	12.39	15.7	1.07	0.0	5.7	130.7	10.6	40.9	39.4	—	
31010	5 May 1969	38.8	11	16.26	12.9	0.77	27.6	0.3	97.7	12.5	32.1	38.8	—	
31010	23 Jan 1971	25.5	28	8.35	21.1	0.99	24.1	2.5	103.4	12.1	47.6	52.9	—	
31010	6 Dec 1972	16.3	7	5.61	18.7	0.67	38.5	6.7	93.2	5.7	35.2	43.1	—	
31010	20 Nov 1974	19.9	24	7.60	17.3	1.13	2.6	4.6	127.0	8.8	44.3	43.7	13.6	#
31010	8 Mar 1975	32.8	23	15.63	12.6	0.79	0.0	3.0	128.0	14.1	43.1	42.3	—	
31010	18 Apr 1975	22.2	15	15.02	11.9	1.73	0.0	5.0	130.0	11.3	51.1	49.8	—	
a mean												42.8		
g mean					15.3	0.91							13.6	
31021	12 Apr 1970	12.6	10	25.90	16.6	6.08	0.5	1.2	125.7	6.8	54.1	53.8	—	
31021	23 Jan 1971	26.1	25	27.66	14.7	3.30	16.4	2.3	110.9	12.9	49.3	52.7	—	
31021	2 Dec 1972	27.0	21	18.20	16.0	1.01	59.8	3.1	68.3	6.1	22.6	36.5	—	
31021	6 Dec 1972	23.5	14	26.57	18.0	3.04	32.4	4.8	97.4	9.2	39.2	45.9	—	
31021	19 Jun 1973	52.0	21	13.88	13.2	0.49	86.8	0.0	38.2	3.6	7.0	25.8	—	
31021	27 Jun 1973	36.0	19	28.42	19.6	2.77	55.4	12.4	82.0	11.5	32.0	42.5	—	
a mean												42.9		
g mean					16.2	2.09							—	
31023	21 Jul 1973	20.3	14	1.17	3.5	0.06	35.9	4.8	93.9	5.1	25.2	33.0	3.8	#
31023	31 Mar 1972	11.7	16	0.31	7.8	0.03	4.1	2.3	123.2	2.9	24.5	24.9	—	
a mean												29.0		
g mean					5.2	0.04							3.8	
32801	13 Oct 1966	19.4	9	1.60	5.4	0.19	4.8	5.5	125.7	6.0	30.7	—	3.9	
32801	1 Dec 1966	9.2	10	1.14	2.6	0.28	0.0	4.8	129.8	3.9	42.9	—	4.9	
32801	9 Dec 1966	21.8	16	2.51	5.5	0.19	0.0	3.7	128.7	14.5	66.6	—	5.1	
32801	10 Jul 1968	71.9	26	2.92	9.3	0.08	28.8	1.2	97.4	19.3	26.8	—	5.8	
32801	1 Nov 1968	29.2	16	3.06	5.2	0.16	0.0	3.3	128.3	13.1	44.9	—	3.8	
32801	15 Jan 1969	9.7	7	1.21	2.1	0.24	0.0	1.9	126.9	3.2	32.8	—	2.2	
32801	12 Mar 1969	29.8	30	2.27	7.6	0.11	1.0	4.6	128.6	16.1	54.0	—	—	
32801	5 May 1969	30.4	13	1.25	5.0	0.09	33.7	0.1	91.4	4.9	16.0	—	3.3	
32801	30 May 1969	26.7	13	4.27	6.8	0.16	3.2	2.7	124.5	13.7	51.3	—	3.0	
a mean												—		
g mean					5.0	0.15							3.9	
32999	13 Feb 1990				4.9								5.5	#
32999	15 Feb 1990				8.7								9.5	#
32999	10 Jan 1991				8.7								11.8	#
32999	28 Feb 1991				8.8								10.1	#

Catch	Date	P	D	Q_p	LAG	BF	SMD	API5	CWI	R/O	PR	SPR	Tp(0)	
		mm	h	m^3s^{-1}	h	m^3s^{-1}	mm	mm	mm	mm	%	%	h	
32999	19 Nov 1991				11.0								5.5	#
32999	9 Jan 1992				7.6								5.3	#
32999	30 Mar 1992				9.2								8.3	#
32999	15 Apr 1992				12.5								9.8	#
32999	23 Sep 1992				6.1								5.6	#
g mean					8.3								7.58	
33014	27 Feb 1961	17.0	31	7.21	23.0	2.21	0.4	1.4	126.0	3.0	17.7	16.7	21.9	#
33014	21 Jan 1962	13.4	34	6.16	22.4	2.30	0.0	1.0	126.0	1.5	11.0	10.0	—	
33014	14 Mar 1964	35.5	33	7.45	38.9	0.90	4.9	0.5	120.6	3.5	9.9	10.2	—	
33014	8 Dec 1965	18.5	25	7.10	28.0	1.14	0.0	1.9	126.9	2.9	15.8	14.6	—	
33014	31 Dec 1966	11.8	11	6.05	24.4	2.24	0.0	3.6	128.6	1.3	11.2	9.5	—	
33014	5 Nov 1967	18.8	14	6.11	25.0	2.17	23.2	9.1	110.9	1.4	7.3	10.0	25.4	#
33014	4 Jan 1968	10.2	12	5.17	23.3	1.39	0.0	0.9	125.9	1.7	16.8	15.9	25.0	#
33014	14 Sep 1968	82.7	31	21.72	42.6	0.68	16.4	3.2	111.8	13.6	16.5	12.8	—	
33014	16 Dec 1968	14.8	12	6.78	22.8	1.15	0.0	1.8	126.8	2.5	16.6	15.4	—	
33014	22 Jan 1969	11.9	8	8.95	23.2	2.96	0.0	1.9	126.9	2.2	18.2	17.0	—	
33014	11 Mar 1969	23.3	39	11.22	28.1	1.94	12.3	3.0	115.7	5.3	22.9	24.6	—	
33014	5 May 1969	35.4	10	8.94	20.4	1.95	10.1	0.0	114.9	2.9	8.3	10.0	—	
a mean												13.9		
g mean					26.2	1.61							24.0	
33015	17 Nov 1963	46.9	53	16.16	20.8	1.03	46.7	0.6	78.9	11.4	24.3	33.0	23.0	#
33015	28 Nov 1963	18.6	21	12.14	17.8	1.96	9.2	0.9	116.7	5.8	31.1	32.3	13.7	#
33015	24 Sep 1965	41.0	43	11.24	30.6	0.65	48.2	0.3	77.1	7.5	18.4	28.7	32.7	#
33015	22 Dec 1965	15.9	18	14.42	16.6	3.15	0.0	1.1	126.1	6.0	37.8	36.8	—	
33015	18 Apr 1966	17.4	38	14.10	21.5	2.90	1.4	2.8	126.4	7.9	45.5	44.6	21.3	#
33015	1 Oct 1966	28.8	54	14.77	27.3	3.40	12.0	12.8	125.8	10.3	35.8	34.8	—	
33015	13 Oct 1966	27.6	29	14.57	19.3	2.34	0.1	1.1	126.0	8.7	31.7	30.6	17.5	#
33015	9 Dec 1966	15.4	9	16.16	21.9	2.96	0.0	1.7	126.7	6.8	44.3	43.3	15.3	#
33015	26 Feb 1967	16.0	17	14.67	19.0	2.42	0.0	2.5	127.5	6.4	40.0	38.7	14.5	#
33015	9 Jul 1968	53.5	27	23.30	22.6	0.69	62.1	2.8	65.7	9.8	18.3	29.2	—	
33015	13 Sep 1968	51.7	63	23.30	35.5	0.98	30.4	0.5	95.1	16.6	32.2	36.3	—	
33015	1 Nov 1968	15.3	11	16.38	16.6	2.59	0.0	1.8	126.8	5.5	36.0	34.8	12.5	#
a mean												35.3		
g mean					21.8	1.81							17.9	
33029	8 Dec 1965	25.7	39	3.53	10.2	0.97	0.2	2.4	127.2	2.6	10.2	9.4	6.0	#
33029	19 Feb 1966	19.6	16	3.79	10.9	1.76	0.0	6.6	131.6	2.2	11.1	9.2	9.7	#
33029	29 Aug 1966	51.6	29	1.90	18.9	0.07	65.3	0.8	60.5	1.6	3.1	16.4	14.3	#
33029	26 May 1967	23.7	10	2.81	8.4	0.65	14.8	2.3	112.5	1.8	7.4	10.2	—	
33029	5 Nov 1967	20.3	12	2.07	7.9	0.46	35.9	4.5	93.6	1.2	5.8	13.4	7.1	#
33029	13 Jul 1968	14.4	15	1.50	10.6	0.26	24.4	4.5	105.1	1.2	8.1	12.8	12.7	#
33029	15 Sep 1968	40.5	43	4.12	24.5	0.18	8.6	2.2	118.6	7.1	17.5	18.6	—	
33029	5 May 1969	20.9	9	2.04	9.0	0.60	15.6	0.0	109.4	1.1	5.1	8.7	—	
a mean												12.3		
g mean					11.6	0.42							9.4	
33045	16 Oct 1967	15.4	18	0.16	13.3	0.06	86.1	4.3	43.2	0.5	3.1	23.0	—	
33045	5 Nov 1967	14.9	13	0.84	18.6	0.33	22.8	7.2	109.4	1.9	12.9	16.4	18.9	#
33045	8 Aug 1968	24.2	8	0.46	20.0	0.10	37.2	7.7	95.5	1.9	7.8	14.7	16.9	#
33045	14 Sep 1968	83.6	34	3.57	21.3	0.52	16.7	2.8	111.1	23.8	28.5	25.3	15.3	#
33045	20 Dec 1968	15.9	35	0.97	17.8	0.39	0.0	2.4	127.4	4.5	28.1	27.2	14.7	#
33045	16 May 1969	13.1	23	0.94	11.8	0.30	1.6	8.3	131.7	3.5	26.4	24.4	—	
33045	26 Jan 1972	30.9	38	1.33	19.6	0.39	0.0	3.7	128.7	6.5	21.0	19.7	22.3	#
a mean												21.5		
g mean					17.1	0.24							7.4	
33809	13 May 1967	30.8	44	8.59	14.2	0.18	8.7	5.0	121.3	15.6	50.8	51.6	15.5	#
33809	9 Jul 1968	80.0	28	11.42	19.4	0.30	53.2	3.1	74.9	24.5	30.6	36.9	24.5	#
33809	13 Jul 1968	21.6	28	5.87	18.3	0.30	4.0	12.2	133.2	10.7	49.5	47.3	13.1	#
33809	7 Aug 1968	40.4	31	16.11	17.4	1.66	22.0	4.3	107.3	29.5	73.1	77.3	17.8	#
33809	15 Sep 1968	34.9	32	8.24	26.6	0.08	3.9	1.1	122.2	17.8	51.0	51.6	—	
33809	1 Nov 1968	22.1	21	6.35	16.6	0.19	0.3	2.9	127.6	9.9	44.6	43.8	18.5	#
33809	15 Jan 1969	22.3	12	10.95	17.2	0.58	0.0	3.2	128.2	14.9	66.9	66.1	14.6	#

Catch	Date	*P* mm	*D* h	Q_p m^3s^{-1}	*LAG* h	*BF* m^3s^{-1}	*SMD* mm	*API5* mm	*CWI* mm	*R/O* mm	*PR* %	*SPR* %	*Tp(0)* h	
33809	16 May 1969	21.8	32	7.23	14.7	0.56	2.4	5.5	128.1	9.6	44.1	43.1	26.3	#
33809	16 Jul 1968	14.5	15	7.46	15.0	0.49	1.6	5.8	129.2	11.9	82.1	81.1	14.9	#
a mean												55.4		
g mean					17.4	0.34							17.6	
33996	21 Jun 1990				2.1								1.6	#
33996	7 Jul 1990				1.3								0.9	#
33996	3 Oct 1990				1.1								1.9	#
33996	30 Oct 1990				1.8								1.6	#
33996	12 Nov 1990				2.1								1.6	#
a mean														
g mean					1.6								1.48	
33997	15 Jan 1990				0.8								1.1	#
33997	19 Apr 1990				0.9								0.7	#
33997	7 Jul 1990				0.7								0.7	#
33997	31 Dec 1990				0.8								0.7	#
33997	3 Jan 1991				0.6								0.8	#
g mean					0.8								0.79	
33998	15 Feb 1990				14.0								15.5	#
33998	28 Oct 1990				7.6								6.3	#
33998	10 Dec 1990				27.8								27.3	#
33998	16 Feb 1991				28.9								28.5	#
33998	28 Feb 1991				11.7								9.3	#
33998	19 Nov 1991				14.4								11.5	#
33998	9 Jan 1992				15.8								15.8	#
33998	23 Sep 1992				12.7								10.1	#
33998	20 Oct 1992				14.2								12.8	#
33998	25 Oct 1992				14.9								15.4	#
33998	11 Nov 1992				12.9								11.3	#
g mean					14.9								13.58	
33999	18 Dec 1989				5.4								2.5	
33999	2 Feb 1990				6.0								5.5	
33999	7 Feb 1990				10.9								11.5	
33999	11 Feb 1990				6.4								7.8	
33999	25 Dec 1990				2.5								2.5	
33999	3 Jul 1991				2.5								3.3	
33999	23 Aug 1991				2.3								2.3	
33999	19 Nov 1991				5.9								4.5	
33999	9 Jan 1992				5.8								1.5	
g mean					4.7								3.78	
34003	8 Dec 1965	34.4	32	8.86	24.2	1.70	0.0	3.1	128.1	5.8	16.9	15.7	—	
34003	18 Feb 1966	25.2	38	4.49	17.9	1.54	1.1	0.0	123.9	3.2	12.6	12.4	—	
34003	10 May 1967	17.9	19	6.54	6.5	1.16	16.6	0.2	108.6	1.5	8.4	12.0	—	
34003	14 Sep 1968	60.9	43	9.27	28.8	1.12	4.5	1.4	121.9	8.2	13.5	10.1	—	
34003	12 Mar 1969	22.9	38	4.55	19.0	1.61	4.1	0.0	120.9	2.2	9.5	10.1	13.1	#
34003	13 Apr 1969	21.3	27	4.59	16.5	1.39	1.6	3.6	127.0	2.0	9.4	8.4	—	
34003	17 May 1969	19.4	19	6.40	2.0	2.37	7.1	6.3	124.2	1.5	7.5	7.2	—	
34003	15 Dec 1969	11.1	20	4.69	10.6	2.44	0.0	4.0	129.0	1.1	10.1	8.7	—	
34003	12 Apr 1970	18.6	16	5.30	11.3	1.70	4.5	0.0	120.5	1.7	8.9	9.6	9.1	#
34003	13 Nov 1970	33.5	19	5.02	12.3	1.00	57.6	3.0	70.4	2.1	6.2	19.4	10.1	#
34003	23 Jan 1971	29.9	23	9.27	19.0	1.70	0.0	5.0	130.0	4.5	15.1	13.4	13.8	#
34003	26 Jan 1972	35.6	32	8.16	18.7	1.38	0.0	2.6	127.6	5.6	15.6	14.5	18.0	#
a mean												11.8		
g mean					13.1	1.54							12.4	
34005	8 Dec 1965	36.1	38	4.96	26.7	0.74	0.1	1.7	126.6	9.1	25.3	24.1	22.5	#
34005	7 Feb 1966	24.1	29	3.26	29.1	0.43	0.0	2.9	127.9	5.6	23.1	21.5	24.6	#
34005	19 Feb 1966	15.2	16	3.30	22.2	1.24	1.1	5.6	129.5	3.3	21.4	19.4	23.2	#
34005	13 Jan 1968	12.6	21	2.90	32.1	0.47	0.2	2.2	127.0	5.0	39.4	38.3	—	
34005	15 Sep 1968	62.1	42	3.95	37.0	0.27	4.1	1.7	122.6	11.6	18.6	14.3	—	
34005	1 Nov 1968	10.7	9	2.95	21.0	0.38	0.0	2.6	127.6	3.3	31.3	29.9	—	

Catch	Date	P	D	Q_p	LAG	BF	SMD	API5	CWI	R/O	PR	SPR	Tp(0)	
		mm	h	m^3s^{-1}	h	m^3s^{-1}	mm	mm	mm	mm	%	%	h	
34005	12 Mar 1969	22.7	21	2.92	24.2	0.60	2.9	1.7	123.8	4.9	21.5	20.9	22.1	#
34005	23 Jan 1971	30.5	21	4.02	26.4	0.54	0.0	5.9	130.9	7.4	24.3	22.0	24.6	#
34005	26 Jan 1972	33.0	33	3.53	31.3	0.28	0.0	3.7	128.7	7.0	21.2	19.3	—	
a mean												23.3		
g mean					27.4	0.49							23.4	
34007	9 Dec 1966	14.7	17	8.07	20.6	1.71	0.0	2.5	127.5	6.1	41.4	40.6	—	
34007	23 Dec 1966	11.6	22	4.58	12.7	1.09	0.0	0.4	125.4	3.1	27.1	26.7	—	
34007	14 Sep 1968	71.9	21	38.45	18.5	1.02	80.4	5.4	50.0	38.3	53.2	66.8	—	
34007	20 Dec 1968	21.3	44	7.42	19.9	1.10	5.6	1.6	121.0	9.1	42.9	43.7	—	
34007	12 Mar 1969	22.0	41	10.82	26.2	0.84	3.4	1.0	122.6	12.1	55.1	55.6	—	
34007	5 May 1969	27.2	17	10.32	18.2	0.65	22.8	0.3	102.5	8.3	30.6	36.0	—	
a mean												44.9		
g mean					18.9	1.02							—	
34011	16 Nov 1966	21.2	14	3.20	15.4	1.17	0.0	4.8	129.8	1.8	8.6	6.8	12.7	#
34011	27 Feb 1967	17.3	16	3.13	13.0	1.29	0.0	0.6	125.6	1.5	8.6	7.9	9.7	#
34011	27 May 1967	20.2	11	4.55	9.5	1.26	4.1	1.8	122.7	2.3	11.6	11.6	8.5	#
34011	30 May 1967	7.2	2	4.27	11.8	1.47	6.7	4.1	122.4	1.4	19.5	19.7	—	
34011	15 Sep 1968	48.9	43	4.54	46.0	0.61	4.1	3.5	124.4	8.4	17.1	14.7	—	
34011	22 Jan 1971	28.7	22	4.46	20.6	1.06	0.0	1.8	126.8	4.1	14.3	13.3	—	
a mean												12.4		
g mean					16.7	1.10							10.2	
35008	9 Dec 1966	15.3	19	11.68	13.2	1.52	0.0	2.4	127.4	6.7	44.1	43.2	—	
35008	30 Dec 1966	11.7	11	10.73	13.5	1.59	0.0	2.0	127.0	5.8	49.8	49.0	15.7	#
35008	5 Nov 1967	15.3	13	9.10	9.0	1.48	26.5	8.3	106.8	3.6	23.7	27.7	—	
35008	4 Jan 1968	11.7	20	7.42	12.4	1.17	0.0	1.0	126.0	4.3	36.4	35.7	12.3	#
35008	12 Jan 1968	10.0	15	10.44	21.1	0.67	0.8	0.1	124.3	8.8	88.2	88.6	—	
35008	14 Sep 1968	60.3	53	23.84	13.4	0.59	56.2	3.3	72.1	22.6	37.4	46.5	—	
35008	1 Nov 1968	12.3	7	11.02	8.1	1.57	22.0	3.4	106.4	4.5	36.3	40.5	6.5	#
35008	17 Dec 1968	12.2	9	7.10	10.0	1.14	10.4	3.2	117.8	3.2	25.9	27.1	—	
35008	22 Jan 1969	13.2	6	14.05	11.0	2.00	0.0	2.8	127.8	6.6	50.2	49.3	8.8	#
35008	11 Mar 1969	25.9	40	18.86	13.9	0.96	3.4	2.7	124.3	15.7	60.8	60.9	7.7	#
35008	5 May 1969	34.2	10	20.54	13.7	0.65	27.6	0.2	97.6	11.5	33.6	40.0	11.8	#
35008	25 Jan 1972	23.9	26	21.78	15.1	1.65	0.0	2.7	127.7	15.6	65.1	64.4	11.7	#
a mean												47.7		
g mean					12.5	1.16							10.2	
36008	20 Jan 1962	15.6	33	12.58	29.2	2.12	0.6	1.9	126.3	7.2	46.2	45.7	29.6	#
36008	4 Apr 1962	17.8	33	10.53	24.7	0.76	0.2	3.1	127.9	6.4	35.8	34.8	17.3	#
36008	1 May 1963	16.5	16	9.31	20.0	0.90	13.9	4.0	115.1	4.5	27.1	29.2	—	
36008	17 Nov 1963	40.8	50	20.79	32.9	0.43	49.6	0.2	75.6	18.4	45.0	56.7	30.5	#
36008	14 Mar 1964	38.9	45	22.04	32.5	0.47	9.6	1.2	116.6	18.9	48.5	50.4	—	
36008	8 Dec 1965	17.7	31	13.98	26.3	1.48	31.1	1.0	94.9	8.7	49.0	56.3	—	
36008	15 Dec 1965	21.1	49	14.56	15.2	4.00	16.8	0.6	108.8	9.8	46.5	50.3	23.1	#
36008	9 Dec 1966	16.1	20	12.54	25.9	1.59	8.6	2.3	118.7	7.0	43.3	44.6	26.5	#
36008	30 Dec 1966	11.0	10	11.18	17.8	2.48	0.0	2.2	127.2	5.0	45.2	44.4	17.6	#
36008	17 Dec 1968	14.2	14	13.06	20.8	1.15	7.3	1.9	119.6	6.8	47.7	48.8	19.5	#
36008	11 Mar 1969	28.5	42	23.72	26.7	0.86	0.0	3.1	128.1	17.1	59.9	59.0	28.7	#
36008	5 May 1969	27.4	11	13.26	15.3	0.86	42.0	0.0	83.0	6.0	21.9	31.9	12.1	#
a mean												46.0		
g mean					23.2	1.16							21.9	
37001	19 Sep 1960	22.5	32	21.13	20.2	0.96	38.1	4.5	91.4	9.4	41.7	49.2	—	
37001	3 Dec 1960	22.9	22	37.25	25.3	2.47	0.0	3.8	128.8	13.2	57.8	56.5	27.7	#
37001	27 Feb 1961	21.1	35	20.12	23.0	2.13	0.0	4.5	129.5	9.5	45.2	43.3	31.9	#
37001	20 Jan 1962	18.2	19	25.55	26.3	4.33	0.0	5.9	130.9	9.6	53.0	51.0	—	
37001	8 Mar 1963	11.6	22	13.46	32.3	2.64	7.5	1.4	118.9	4.7	40.8	41.4	34.5	#
37001	16 Nov 1963	41.1	43	27.50	25.1	1.38	20.4	1.3	105.9	20.2	49.2	52.8	—	
37001	27 Jan 1964	12.2	21	17.72	30.0	1.65	1.0	0.0	124.0	7.6	61.9	61.9	—	
37001	2 Sep 1965	37.8	27	8.21	18.7	0.28	84.4	0.9	41.5	4.1	10.9	29.9	36.8	#
37001	8 Dec 1965	21.9	29	24.49	23.8	2.78	0.2	1.3	126.1	10.0	45.6	44.6	33.0	#
37001	18 Apr 1966	27.8	66	23.12	25.8	2.64	3.1	3.6	125.5	13.5	48.4	47.6	38.5	#
37001	27 Feb 1967	15.6	25	20.33	24.4	2.91	0.0	3.6	128.6	9.0	57.4	56.1	26.0	#

Catch	Date	P mm	D h	Q_p m^3s^{-1}	LAG h	BF m^3s^{-1}	SMD mm	API5 mm	CWI mm	R/O mm	PR %	SPR %	Tp(0) h	
37001	16 Dec 1968	29.1	14	32.32	15.7	3.59	0.0	4.0	129.0	12.9	44.5	42.7	—	
37001	15 Sep 1968	45.7	47	15.43	21.9	0.65	85.1	8.5	48.4	13.1	28.7	45.0	—	
a mean												47.8		
g mean					23.6	1.78							32.3	
37003	13 Mar 1964	45.4	46	7.23	23.0	0.24	6.3	0.4	119.1	13.8	30.5	30.3	—	
37003	3 Sep 1965	54.5	25	3.10	20.0	0.06	75.2	0.5	50.3	4.4	8.0	23.5	—	
37003	8 Dec 1965	18.5	27	5.32	21.8	0.51	0.0	1.7	126.7	7.4	40.2	39.6	—	
37003	18 Apr 1966	21.8	40	5.01	24.0	0.43	3.2	3.0	124.8	8.3	38.2	38.1	—	
37003	11 Mar 1969	27.9	83	9.27	14.6	1.72	0.0	5.8	130.8	14.8	52.9	51.4	—	
a mean												36.6		
g mean					20.4	0.35							—	
37007	2 Sep 1965	59.3	25	7.90	20.0	0.05	100.0	0.4	25.4	5.9	10.0	29.6	16.5	#
37007	8 Dec 1965	21.4	28	16.48	17.5	1.34	0.0	1.6	126.6	10.0	46.7	45.6	10.3	#
37007	9 Feb 1966	13.0	26	11.32	14.8	1.93	0.0	2.3	127.3	6.3	48.4	47.2	12.0	#
37007	18 Apr 1966	31.5	45	16.92	16.3	1.95	2.9	3.3	125.4	15.9	50.4	49.7	—	
37007	28 Dec 1966	11.6	10	10.90	12.9	2.01	0.0	2.2	127.2	5.4	46.5	45.3	9.9	#
37007	27 Feb 1967	18.0	23	13.05	15.2	1.41	0.0	3.3	128.3	7.8	43.2	41.6	14.5	#
37007	15 Sep 1968	35.2	47	14.88	20.2	3.24	44.7	13.4	93.7	8.6	24.4	30.9	—	
37007	17 Dec 1968	21.8	13	29.55	14.1	1.08	0.0	3.1	128.1	15.4	70.7	69.9	—	
37007	19 Feb 1969	22.2	29	14.38	41.8	0.52	2.0	0.0	123.0	19.8	89.0	90.1	—	
37007	10 Mar 1969	18.8	10	12.31	13.2	0.73	6.3	0.0	118.7	6.4	34.3	34.8	14.1	#
a mean												48.5		
g mean					17.5	0.99							12.7	
37008	8 Dec 1965	19.1	27	13.62	27.4	1.58	0.0	1.5	126.5	6.3	32.9	32.0	—	
37008	15 Sep 1968	42.5	56	14.79	35.9	1.65	47.4	4.4	82.0	10.3	24.3	33.5	—	
37008	16 Dec 1968	22.4	35	19.77	32.8	1.94	0.0	4.8	129.8	12.2	54.3	52.9	—	
37008	12 Mar 1969	26.4	65	29.32	30.7	4.60	0.0	5.2	130.2	16.6	62.8	61.4	—	
a mean												44.9		
g mean					31.5	2.20							—	
37031	17 Apr 1966	39.2	57	17.03	9.8	0.57	3.1	3.4	125.3	24.1	61.5	60.6	—	
37031	22 Oct 1966	18.0	9	5.62	7.3	0.22	55.0	4.0	74.0	2.7	14.9	22.4	—	
37031	5 Dec 1966	10.5	14	4.61	5.9	0.32	4.2	0.6	121.4	2.2	21.1	17.3	—	
37031	9 Dec 1966	15.8	16	7.76	5.8	0.66	1.4	1.6	125.2	4.8	30.2	26.3	—	
37031	28 Dec 1966	11.1	9	7.27	5.1	0.93	0.0	2.3	127.3	3.7	33.1	29.0	—	
37031	20 Feb 1967	10.2	12	6.48	4.3	0.58	0.0	2.6	127.6	2.8	27.1	22.3	—	
37031	27 Feb 1967	12.5	17	8.16	5.8	0.61	0.0	3.4	128.4	4.1	33.0	28.6	—	
37031	10 Apr 1967	19.9	10	5.84	6.3	0.23	14.5	1.0	111.5	2.4	12.3	10.1	—	
37031	18 Dec 1967	18.4	13	7.45	7.1	0.29	9.6	0.3	115.7	4.4	23.9	21.8	—	
37031	8 Aug 1968	13.0	9	4.76	7.6	0.20	81.1	7.0	50.9	2.5	19.6	33.3	—	
37031	19 Feb 1969	20.5	27	10.93	19.1	0.51	2.0	0.0	123.0	17.4	85.1	87.1	—	
a mean												32.6		
g mean					7.0	0.41							—	
37999	1 May 1992				—								3.9	#
37999	13 Aug 1992				—								6.8	#
37999	3 Oct 1992				—								3.5	#
37999	20 Oct 1992				—								3.2	#
37999	25 Oct 1992				—								4.4	#
g mean													4.20	
38003	2 May 1961	8.4	6	1.64	4.3	0.98	4.7	1.3	121.6	0.1	1.4	0.4	—	
38003	12 Jun 1961	27.6	19	1.65	5.9	0.79	81.3	0.0	43.7	0.2	0.9	19.4	4.4	#
38003	6 Jul 1963	25.7	10	1.69	5.9	0.52	34.1	1.9	92.8	0.3	1.0	7.2	4.3	#
38003	21 Jul 1964	7.5	6	1.74	4.3	0.51	54.6	0.3	70.7	0.1	2.0	13.8	—	
38003	21 Aug 1966	27.0	17	3.22	0.5	0.59	55.7	0.0	69.3	0.5	2.0	14.1	—	
38003	25 Jun 1967	30.0	5	2.56	3.5	0.72	51.3	8.1	81.8	0.3	1.0	10.0	—	
38003	23 Jul 1967	25.3	9	2.18	4.1	0.63	88.4	0.7	37.3	0.2	0.9	21.0	—	
38003	15 Sep 1968	63.6	18	3.61	3.1	0.48	37.0	5.8	93.8	1.0	1.5	3.4	—	
a mean												11.1		
g mean					3.3	0.63							4.3	

Catch	Date	P	D	Q_p	LAG	BF	SMD	API5	CWI	R/O	PR	SPR	Tp(0)	
		mm	h	m^3s^{-1}	h	m^3s^{-1}	mm	mm	mm	mm	%	%	h	
38007	26 Jun 1958	39.1	24	10.27	5.5	0.32	14.2	5.6	116.4	18.7	47.7	47.2	3.0	#
38007	1 Jul 1958	36.1	30	14.04	5.6	0.26	6.3	2.0	120.7	20.5	56.7	56.2	3.0	#
38007	19 Sep 1960	21.4	15	8.57	3.0	0.25	44.4	4.4	85.0	11.7	54.8	63.0	3.9	#
38007	8 Oct 1960	18.6	11	6.88	4.4	0.50	9.6	4.3	119.7	10.2	54.9	54.4	4.4	#
38007	30 Oct 1960	14.2	6	7.61	3.7	0.76	0.0	10.3	135.3	7.5	52.5	47.8	3.0	#
38007	25 Nov 1960	15.9	8	7.17	4.1	0.67	0.0	5.2	130.2	10.5	66.2	64.4	5.2	#
38007	3 Dec 1960	13.6	9	10.82	4.2	1.04	0.0	5.3	130.3	12.9	94.7	96.3	—	
38007	14 Jul 1962	13.3	6	2.19	4.4	0.09	106.3	2.5	21.2	1.4	10.4	29.2	—	
38007	31 Aug 1963	15.1	9	2.68	1.8	0.04	62.9	1.4	63.5	1.3	8.6	16.6	1.8	#
38007	17 Nov 1963	13.3	7	2.60	5.5	0.21	0.0	1.0	126.0	3.4	25.3	19.7	4.8	#
38007	21 Jul 1964	39.4	4	8.46	3.3	0.27	66.8	1.3	59.5	7.0	17.7	27.8	—	
38007	20 Jul 1965	22.6	8	5.89	2.5	0.21	82.1	0.5	43.4	2.3	10.3	23.6	—	
38007	18 Nov 1965	11.3	7	3.84	3.0	0.37	23.4	3.4	105.0	2.9	25.9	25.6	2.7	#
38007	22 Jun 1966	33.5	6	8.08	2.4	0.34	75.5	0.5	50.0	4.5	13.3	25.3	2.2	#
38007	27 Feb 1967	14.4	12	4.34	4.8	0.46	0.0	3.7	128.7	8.0	55.3	52.6	2.8	#
38007	25 Jun 1967	25.6	5	4.37	1.7	0.20	58.5	2.3	68.8	2.7	10.4	17.3	1.8	#
38007	13 Jul 1968	25.8	7	7.60	2.1	0.31	68.4	1.8	58.4	4.8	18.7	29.2	3.0	#
38007	7 Oct 1968	21.1	22	6.27	5.0	0.19	7.9	0.1	117.2	7.7	36.4	34.3	2.8	#
38007	28 Oct 1968	15.1	8	4.85	2.5	0.35	15.9	0.7	109.8	3.2	20.9	18.8	3.0	#
a mean												39.5		
g mean					3.4	0.29							3.0	
39004	16 Jun 1965	12.8	9	1.53	1.6	0.01	71.4	1.2	54.8	0.1	0.8	11.7	1.2	#
39004	7 Jul 1965	10.1	11	1.88	1.1	0.04	88.9	0.1	36.2	0.1	1.0	16.5	—	
39004	23 Jul 1965	15.2	12	1.73	2.2	0.01	88.1	6.5	43.4	0.2	1.4	15.2	—	
39004	2 Sep 1965	18.0	10	2.37	1.9	0.07	95.5	1.7	31.2	0.2	1.0	17.8	2.8	#
39004	3 Sep 1965	58.4	14	3.72	2.3	0.08	82.7	14.2	56.5	0.8	1.3	8.3	1.4	#
39004	19 Nov 1965	19.9	13	2.02	2.2	0.01	4.9	2.7	122.8	0.2	1.1	—	1.2	#
39004	28 Nov 1965	27.3	18	2.47	3.8	0.01	0.0	1.7	126.7	0.4	1.4	—	2.0	#
39004	22 Jun 1966	29.1	6	3.07	1.8	0.13	82.7	0.7	43.0	0.3	1.1	14.9	—	
39004	25 Jun 1967	28.1	7	3.84	1.1	0.29	50.6	9.1	83.5	0.4	1.3	5.0	0.9	#
39004	22 Jul 1967	20.4	7	2.96	2.2	0.19	91.2	0.6	34.4	0.3	1.6	17.6	—	
39004	1 Nov 1967	20.7	7	2.84	1.7	0.17	0.8	9.1	133.3	0.4	1.7	—	1.0	#
39004	17 Apr 1968	9.3	2	3.06	0.8	0.25	8.0	2.4	119.4	0.1	1.1	—	—	
39004	4 May 1968	13.9	9	2.65	2.2	0.18	7.5	0.4	117.9	0.2	1.3	—	1.2	#
39004	18 May 1968	16.3	14	2.86	0.5	0.19	7.3	3.9	121.6	0.3	1.7	—	—	
39004	13 Jul 1968	17.6	6	3.52	2.3	0.15	35.3	2.2	91.9	0.2	1.3	2.9	1.5	#
39004	28 Aug 1968	16.4	4	3.94	1.3	0.23	56.4	2.2	70.8	0.2	1.1	8.0	1.5	#
39004	14 Sep 1968	121.9	32	5.75	2.1	0.29	38.8	2.4	88.6	2.1	1.7	—	—	
39004	6 Jul 1969	50.0	20	3.92	3.2	0.13	101.0	0.4	24.4	0.8	1.5	17.8	—	
39004	28 Jul 1969	39.6	15	3.92	1.5	0.15	108.2	0.1	16.9	0.5	1.2	21.6	0.8	#
39004	2 Aug 1969	27.4	9	4.53	1.7	0.14	81.2	4.3	48.1	0.3	1.1	13.7	—	
39004	6 Aug 1970	15.9	5	5.53	2.7	0.13	144.2	1.3	−17.9	0.4	2.5	31.7	—	
39004	13 Nov 1970	30.6	10	4.30	2.5	0.04	79.8	3.4	48.6	0.5	1.7	14.2	1.5	#
a mean												14.5		
g mean					1.8	0.09							1.3	
39005	26 Jul 1962	28.3	12	12.97	4.0	0.34	107.3	2.7	20.4	3.9	13.7	22.9	2.5	#
39005	30 Apr 1963	15.3	16	3.95	4.7	0.35	8.5	3.0	119.5	2.5	16.1	1.2	2.5	#
39005	5 Sep 1963	13.5	6	4.28	4.9	0.35	76.2	7.4	56.2	1.9	14.3	14.7	3.7	#
39005	20 Oct 1963	10.4	9	4.44	2.5	0.28	92.0	0.1	33.1	1.3	12.9	18.7	2.8	#
39005	17 Nov 1963	11.7	7	5.66	3.4	0.52	30.4	1.1	95.7	2.7	22.8	15.9	2.0	#
39005	16 Apr 1964	12.4	7	9.24	2.4	0.62	9.4	2.6	118.2	2.2	17.6	3.5	2.5	#
39005	20 Apr 1964	15.4	10	11.82	3.3	1.48	0.0	6.6	131.6	5.2	33.9	21.4	3.0	#
39005	1 Jun 1964	23.0	8	12.13	2.7	0.70	13.6	12.0	123.4	5.4	23.5	9.9	2.2	#
39005	14 Jun 1964	9.5	2	9.98	1.8	0.91	3.1	6.5	128.4	2.5	26.3	12.3	—	
39005	21 Jul 1964	23.2	2	14.83	4.1	0.50	97.2	0.2	28.0	4.1	17.6	26.1	—	
39005	22 Jun 1966	26.3	8	9.72	3.7	0.80	82.6	0.6	43.0	3.7	14.2	17.9	3.0	#
39005	19 Jul 1966	19.8	10	12.32	3.9	0.98	124.8	5.2	5.4	4.6	23.0	38.7	2.2	#
39005	29 Aug 1966	26.5	10	14.33	2.9	1.10	89.5	6.7	42.2	6.3	23.9	30.7	2.5	#
39005	25 Jun 1967	27.3	5	12.97	1.9	0.56	51.0	7.8	81.8	4.6	16.8	11.6	2.0	#
39005	19 Aug 1967	21.5	10	9.22	2.0	0.46	101.3	1.9	25.6	3.6	16.6	25.4	—	
39005	16 Dec 1968	36.4	9	14.37	4.5	1.46	0.0	3.9	128.9	12.3	33.9	22.0	—	
39005	6 Jul 1969	41.1	23	10.85	5.7	0.29	100.3	0.1	24.8	8.1	19.8	29.2	5.3	#
39005	28 Jul 1969	36.2	16	9.32	4.3	0.09	108.4	0.0	16.6	5.7	15.7	26.4	1.5	#
a mean												19.4		
g mean					3.3	0.54							2.6	

Catch	Date	P	D	Q_p	LAG	BF	SMD	API5	CWI	R/O	PR	SPR	Tp(0)	
		mm	h	m^3s^{-1}	h	m^3s^{-1}	mm	mm	mm	mm	%	%	h	
39007	23 Jan 1971	14.2	25	21.38	15.1	8.71	0.0	8.6	133.6	2.7	19.1	14.8	—	
39007	14 Mar 1971	18.2	13	13.95	11.9	3.04	4.7	0.4	120.7	2.4	13.0	11.6	10.3	#
39007	17 Mar 1971	23.5	23	20.33	12.6	3.96	0.6	3.8	128.2	5.3	22.6	19.8	9.7	#
39007	23 Apr 1971	31.4	31	21.85	21.2	3.00	27.1	0.2	98.1	5.7	18.0	22.5	13.0	#
39007	26 Apr 1971	16.2	13	20.13	13.5	5.44	8.5	9.6	126.1	3.6	22.3	20.0	—	
39007	10 Jun 1971	47.7	20	26.23	26.6	2.02	41.4	7.4	91.0	9.2	19.2	23.7	—	
39007	13 Jun 1971	31.4	29	23.83	22.7	4.26	13.8	8.2	119.4	7.4	23.6	23.0	—	
39007	18 Jun 1971	35.8	40	25.41	24.0	3.52	6.3	2.2	120.9	9.2	25.7	24.8	15.5	#
39007	13 Nov 1974	33.8	24	27.47	24.4	1.86	37.3	5.3	93.0	12.4	36.6	43.2	9.6	#
39007	21 Nov 1974	41.5	37	31.46	21.6	9.74	0.0	8.1	133.1	9.9	23.8	19.2	13.0	#
39007	18 Jan 1975	20.9	9	25.46	15.8	4.89	0.0	3.8	128.8	5.9	28.3	25.6	14.5	#
39007	20 Jan 1975	21.3	18	25.77	16.8	6.28	0.0	12.3	137.3	6.1	28.5	23.7	10.8	#
39007	18 Apr 1975	18.6	10	24.31	13.5	4.99	1.3	2.7	126.4	3.8	20.3	17.8	12.5	#
a mean												22.3		
g mean					17.8	4.24							11.9	
39012	7 Aug 1960	31.7	4	15.81	3.2	0.78	90.8	0.1	34.3	5.0	15.7	30.5	2.5	#
39012	20 Apr 1964	24.3	18	14.66	2.7	1.87	0.0	5.5	130.5	5.7	23.4	15.2	—	
39012	1 Jun 1964	23.4	9	11.31	3.1	1.25	12.8	6.9	119.1	3.4	14.7	8.1	3.7	#
39012	21 Jul 1964	24.6	4	10.13	3.0	1.10	57.3	0.1	67.8	2.1	8.7	14.1	—	
39012	3 Sep 1965	39.8	12	13.11	5.1	1.67	93.0	11.9	43.9	4.7	11.7	23.5	—	
39012	28 Nov 1965	25.9	19	12.23	4.8	0.93	0.0	1.1	126.1	6.3	24.2	17.3	3.5	#
39012	22 Jun 1966	28.9	9	11.18	4.6	1.15	70.6	2.3	56.7	2.8	9.7	18.0	3.4	#
39012	18 May 1968	24.3	23	14.07	6.3	1.13	6.8	0.7	118.9	5.2	21.5	16.0	—	
39012	14 Sep 1968	102.0	33	22.70	5.3	1.38	62.0	1.5	64.5	20.9	20.5	20.3	4.8	#
39012	29 Jul 1969	40.5	16	9.50	6.5	0.35	125.9	0.0	-0.9	4.0	9.8	32.2	4.0	#
39012	2 Aug 1969	31.5	10	11.98	3.4	0.86	81.2	3.1	46.9	3.9	12.3	23.4	—	
a mean												19.9		
g mean					4.2	1.05							3.6	
39017	18 Nov 1963	34.8	36	7.56	8.8	1.40	0.0	6.8	131.8	17.3	49.8	48.0	7.9	
39017	28 Nov 1963	15.9	23	3.47	7.2	0.18	0.1	0.6	125.5	9.1	57.0	56.8	8.5	
39017	23 Mar 1964	13.3	26	2.94	8.2	0.14	0.0	1.2	126.2	7.8	58.9	58.6	9.5	
39017	18 Apr 1964	12.4	27	1.80	15.5	0.12	10.0	4.1	119.1	5.2	41.9	43.3	8.5	
39017	21 Jul 1964	66.4	24	6.29	7.9	0.02	74.1	0.7	51.6	10.4	15.7	29.4	9.0	
39017	24 Sep 1965	37.2	48	2.64	12.4	0.04	86.8	0.0	38.2	9.4	25.4	46.9	—	
39017	22 Dec 1965	19.8	45	3.08	9.7	0.15	6.0	0.3	119.3	13.3	67.3	68.7	9.9	
39017	31 Dec 1965	9.8	18	2.28	11.6	0.27	0.0	3.7	128.7	6.9	70.4	69.5	9.9	
39017	19 Feb 1966	18.4	37	3.43	13.8	0.11	0.0	5.4	130.4	14.9	81.0	79.7	8.3	
39017	11 May 1966	22.5	32	5.31	9.7	0.07	4.9	1.3	121.4	11.6	51.6	52.4	8.8	
39017	12 Oct 1966	39.2	46	5.41	14.1	0.12	13.3	1.0	112.7	25.2	64.3	67.4	8.9	
39017	9 Dec 1966	18.6	15	5.62	8.4	0.24	0.0	2.0	127.0	12.1	64.8	64.3	9.6	
39017	17 Jan 1969	9.5	16	2.23	7.8	0.22	0.0	2.6	127.6	6.2	65.1	64.4	9.3	
39017	22 Jan 1969	11.1	5	3.36	9.0	0.26	0.0	2.3	127.3	6.7	60.3	59.7	8.4	
39017	12 Mar 1969	21.0	23	5.64	7.0	0.54	0.0	6.9	131.9	13.0	61.8	60.0	—	
39017	16 May 1969	27.6	15	7.11	11.6	0.07	32.3	3.5	96.2	13.6	49.2	56.3	8.5	
39017	24 Apr 1970	37.4	34	6.37	15.7	0.07	6.3	0.7	119.4	19.6	52.3	53.6	9.0	
39017	22 Jan 1971	18.2	29	3.04	9.4	0.34	4.1	5.1	126.0	11.3	61.9	61.6	8.5	
39017	29 Jan 1971	29.6	35	5.44	10.2	0.21	0.0	1.2	126.2	18.6	62.9	62.6	8.4	
39017	18 Dec 1967	18.7	14	3.80	10.0	0.09	0.2	0.6	125.4	9.8	52.2	52.0	9.0	
39017	9 Jul 1968	82.6	26	16.10	8.6	0.17	75.9	4.3	53.4	36.8	44.6	56.2	6.6	
39017	15 Sep 1968	28.6	28	2.86	17.6	0.05	41.0	8.0	92.0	15.2	53.0	61.2	—	
39017	1 Nov 1968	26.1	10	9.10	7.5	0.23	1.6	4.4	127.8	17.3	66.3	65.6	6.0	
39017	21 Dec 1968	9.5	6	3.83	9.4	0.41	0.0	0.0	125.0	6.1	63.7	63.7	10.5	
39017	17 Jul 1975	51.5	3	0.20	10.0	0.02	134.6	0.7	-8.9	0.2	0.3	31.0	10.8	
39017	9 Dec 1977	16.4	25	1.85	11.5	0.15	31.7	2.9	96.2	8.3	50.4	57.5	—	
39017	23 Jan 1978	11.3	17	2.01	7.3	0.18	0.0	1.9	126.9	5.8	51.4	50.9	—	
39017	27 Jan 1978	12.4	29	1.87	13.5	0.11	0.0	1.9	126.9	7.1	57.3	56.8	—	
39017	27 Mar 1979	13.5	17	2.49	3.8	0.51	0.4	5.5	130.1	5.8	43.0	41.6	—	
a mean												56.5		
g mean					9.8	0.15							8.7	
39018	22 Oct 1966	15.9	9	8.64	20.3	3.11	0.9	1.5	125.6	4.2	26.4	25.7	—	
39018	27 Feb 1967	22.2	27	10.62	37.7	2.99	0.0	2.6	127.6	7.1	32.0	30.9	—	
39018	18 Dec 1967	20.6	15	10.16	13.5	2.76	0.1	0.2	125.1	4.4	21.4	20.8	—	
39018	4 Feb 1968	20.9	27	9.99	25.5	2.17	0.4	0.4	125.0	6.5	30.9	30.4	—	

Catch	Date	P	D	Q_p	LAG	BF	SMD	API5	CWI	R/O	PR	SPR	Tp(0)	
		mm	h	m^3s^{-1}	h	m^3s^{-1}	mm	mm	mm	mm	%	%	h	
39018	14 Feb 1974	17.6	39	11.60	44.4	2.91	0.3	1.8	126.5	8.6	49.1	48.5	—	
39018	25 Dec 1974	23.7	64	7.85	28.5	1.36	0.0	1.1	126.1	6.4	27.1	26.3	—	
39018	8 Mar 1975	22.0	26	13.53	39.1	2.53	0.6	5.6	130.0	10.1	45.7	44.2	—	
a mean												32.4		
g mean					27.8	2.47							—	
39022	28 Nov 1965	31.5	19	17.50	23.8	2.40	3.3	1.9	123.6	10.7	34.1	33.4	25.3	#
39022	8 Dec 1965	18.7	26	13.41	19.4	2.98	0.1	1.1	126.0	6.6	35.3	34.1	16.5	#
39022	9 Feb 1966	25.2	39	18.07	21.4	3.37	0.0	4.3	129.3	10.1	40.0	38.1	19.5	#
39022	13 Apr 1966	23.3	44	13.88	33.6	2.18	0.2	1.9	126.7	9.3	39.9	38.6	—	
39022	28 Nov 1970	18.8	11	18.48	16.0	2.91	13.8	2.1	113.3	10.2	54.0	56.5	13.0	#
39022	17 Mar 1971	33.1	48	20.37	20.7	4.37	0.7	4.3	128.6	18.2	55.0	53.7	14.7	#
39022	26 Apr 1971	17.1	15	20.31	19.7	3.75	7.3	9.2	126.9	8.8	51.7	50.7	21.0	#
39022	10 Jun 1971	57.9	24	25.37	30.3	2.14	48.4	7.8	84.4	16.3	28.1	33.7	28.1	#
39022	14 Jun 1971	25.7	22	13.50	20.3	3.32	15.4	7.5	117.1	6.5	25.3	26.0	17.5	#
39022	18 Jun 1971	35.7	41	24.02	19.7	2.39	13.6	2.1	113.5	15.7	43.9	46.0	17.5	#
39022	13 Nov 1974	46.1	37	21.28	23.4	2.43	20.7	5.4	109.7	16.2	35.1	36.3	31.7	#
39022	17 Nov 1974	32.6	30	38.45	14.1	4.65	10.7	10.8	125.1	23.3	71.5	71.5	18.7	#
39022	18 Jan 1975	20.0	8	19.73	18.0	3.75	0.0	4.1	129.1	8.1	40.3	38.4	17.6	#
39022	20 Jan 1975	23.8	30	22.58	19.5	5.85	0.0	11.2	136.2	7.3	30.6	26.7	18.1	#
a mean												41.7		
g mean					20.9	3.17							19.3	
39025	15 Oct 1967	38.8	32	17.30	19.1	0.98	28.0	9.8	106.8	8.0	20.5	24.8	—	
39025	30 Oct 1967	14.8	21	11.12	7.3	1.89	19.2	6.1	111.9	3.4	23.2	26.2	—	
39025	18 Dec 1967	14.7	17	6.01	11.0	1.20	0.0	1.0	126.0	2.5	16.8	16.2	—	
39025	5 Feb 1968	17.2	29	9.04	14.5	2.11	0.0	6.9	131.9	3.7	21.3	19.3	—	
39025	13 Feb 1968	11.3	14	7.51	8.4	1.90	0.6	1.4	125.8	2.3	20.2	19.7	—	
39025	24 May 1968	21.4	13	5.65	10.0	0.87	13.2	0.0	111.8	1.7	7.9	10.8	—	
39025	26 Jun 1968	27.4	45	5.93	13.0	0.54	42.7	7.1	89.4	2.6	9.4	17.9	—	
39025	14 Sep 1968	85.6	73	26.20	19.1	0.84	44.4	0.8	81.4	27.6	32.3	36.5	—	
39025	27 Oct 1968	21.2	33	9.27	11.5	1.16	2.6	0.3	122.7	3.8	18.0	18.3	—	
39025	29 Nov 1968	18.2	56	5.91	10.1	1.58	0.0	2.2	127.2	4.2	23.0	22.2	—	
39025	17 Dec 1968	11.5	24	12.47	7.0	2.52	0.0	13.0	138.0	6.4	55.4	52.1	—	
39025	21 Dec 1968	17.3	5	18.73	15.6	3.62	0.0	6.3	131.3	6.9	39.6	37.8	—	
39025	24 Dec 1968	20.0	21	10.79	15.2	2.43	0.0	3.8	128.8	5.8	29.0	27.8	11.6	#
39025	17 Jan 1969	13.4	1	11.67	13.5	2.75	0.0	4.7	129.7	4.4	32.6	31.2	—	
39025	12 Mar 1969	23.2	26	21.45	16.1	2.17	0.0	16.0	141.0	11.7	50.4	46.3	17.4	#
39025	22 Jan 1971	23.6	30	23.28	16.6	4.51	1.4	7.2	130.8	9.3	39.3	37.7	14.5	#
a mean												27.8		
g mean					12.4	1.68							14.3	
39026	9 Dec 1966	19.6	24	17.54	26.9	2.82	0.0	2.6	127.6	7.9	40.5	39.6	28.1	#
39026	8 Mar 1967	24.1	49	9.34	14.6	1.52	0.0	1.5	126.5	5.8	23.9	23.1	—	
39026	14 May 1967	31.1	30	10.89	17.3	1.05	7.3	3.9	121.6	7.6	24.3	24.7	13.6	#
39026	27 May 1967	24.6	27	9.31	18.1	1.33	2.3	2.3	125.0	5.0	20.4	19.9	18.0	#
39026	21 Dec 1967	26.5	66	9.66	28.7	1.89	4.9	1.4	121.5	8.7	32.8	33.3	—	
39026	9 Jul 1968	70.7	26	27.09	28.8	0.56	45.9	3.1	82.2	15.7	22.2	27.5	25.5	#
39026	1 Nov 1968	16.0	17	17.93	26.3	2.14	0.0	6.4	131.4	8.1	50.4	48.6	—	
39026	21 Dec 1968	14.3	22	11.75	14.7	3.72	0.0	3.6	128.6	3.9	27.5	26.2	—	
39026	10 Jan 1969	13.1	32	11.59	23.4	2.76	0.0	1.2	126.2	6.0	45.6	45.1	14.0	#
39026	12 Mar 1969	25.0	33	25.37	25.0	0.70	1.2	6.8	130.6	15.2	60.6	59.1	—	
a mean												34.7		
g mean					21.7	1.58							19.0	
39036	18 Jun 1971	35.8	20	0.37	7.4	0.13	6.3	4.7	123.4	1.2	3.4	3.8	—	
a mean												3.8		
g mean					7.4	0.13							—	
39052	27 Feb 1967	14.9	17	4.83	4.9	0.91	0.0	4.4	129.4	4.9	32.8	28.8	5.5	#
39052	2 Nov 1967	18.3	18	6.82	3.1	2.18	0.0	8.0	133.0	4.2	22.8	17.1	3.4	#
39052	10 Jun 1971	52.4	29	10.66	8.5	0.45	49.0	7.8	83.8	13.2	25.2	29.4	5.7	#
39052	18 Jun 1971	37.2	15	10.73	8.2	0.57	20.0	3.2	108.2	12.2	32.8	34.1	8.1	#
39052	27 Aug 1973	15.3	3	4.55	2.7	0.22	112.6	0.0	12.4	1.0	6.5	29.7	—	
39052	18 Apr 1975	21.3	11	10.45	3.8	1.06	4.8	1.4	121.6	4.9	22.8	19.9	3.7	#

Catch	Date	*P* mm	*D* h	Q_p m^3s^{-1}	*LAG* h	*BF* m^3s^{-1}	*SMD* mm	*API5* mm	*CWI* mm	*R/O* mm	*PR* %	*SPR* %	*Tp(0)* h	
39052	13 Nov 1974	43.0	42	10.90	5.6	0.78	8.5	6.3	122.8	17.1	39.7	36.9	—	
39052	20 Nov 1974	39.2	31	12.13	5.1	2.46	0.0	8.4	133.4	14.5	37.1	32.4	3.8	#
a mean												28.5		
g mean					4.8	0.83							4.8	
39053	15 Sep 1968	127.9	21	63.36	11.7	1.45	0.0	2.3	127.3	54.1	42.3	29.7	13.0	#
39053	20 Feb 1969	23.3	27	21.00	13.4	1.29	1.1	0.3	124.2	15.0	64.3	64.2	—	
39053	13 Nov 1970	60.8	34	22.68	8.9	0.82	48.5	3.8	80.3	27.5	45.2	51.1	6.0	#
39053	18 Jun 1971	33.3	18	25.73	11.0	0.97	0.0	4.4	129.4	18.0	54.2	52.2	9.5	#
39053	10 Feb 1974	43.8	21	28.05	10.1	2.92	0.0	11.0	136.0	24.1	55.0	50.2	6.0	#
39053	14 Feb 1974	26.6	16	23.59	7.5	2.83	0.0	10.8	135.8	15.5	58.1	54.7	7.9	#
39053	20 Jan 1975	31.3	17	26.48	6.1	2.48	0.0	7.2	132.2	17.0	54.3	51.6	—	
a mean												50.5		
g mean					9.5	1.63							8.1	
39092	6 Aug 1956	38.9	13	14.82	4.5	0.47	77.9	5.0	52.1	15.9	41.0	53.9	—	
39092	23 Sep 1958	40.8	14	11.55	6.1	0.27	48.0	9.2	86.2	16.9	41.5	45.6	—	
39092	21 Jan 1962	22.0	20	7.88	4.4	0.76	0.0	6.8	131.8	11.7	53.1	48.3	—	
39092	7 Jun 1963	18.2	6	15.81	3.8	0.35	50.1	3.0	77.9	13.0	71.2	83.2	—	
39092	9 Dec 1966	16.6	14	5.84	6.7	0.29	0.1	2.1	127.0	8.4	50.8	46.8	5.5	#
39092	25 Jun 1967	19.7	8	5.62	3.1	0.24	58.1	4.0	70.9	5.4	27.2	32.9	—	
39092	15 Sep 1968	38.8	21	6.53	10.4	0.37	38.3	15.5	102.2	21.1	54.4	57.2	—	
39092	7 Oct 1968	22.1	22	5.07	5.1	0.19	4.9	0.0	120.1	7.2	32.7	27.1	—	
39092	1 Nov 1968	15.1	19	5.58	6.8	0.36	0.0	4.7	129.7	6.6	43.5	37.5	—	
39092	16 Dec 1968	33.8	17	6.35	6.5	0.34	0.0	2.8	127.8	14.0	41.4	35.4	6.6	#
a mean												46.8		
g mean					5.4	0.34							6.0	
39813	22 Jan 1960	41.1	44	3.48	7.9	0.65	0.0	5.1	130.1	21.5	52.3	49.1	—	
39813	2 Nov 1960	40.3	42	3.53	5.0	0.68	0.0	11.1	136.1	19.2	47.7	42.9	5.8	#
39813	2 Dec 1960	43.3	35	4.98	8.8	0.63	0.0	5.0	130.0	22.5	51.9	48.1	4.2	#
39813	29 Jan 1961	33.9	27	3.81	10.7	0.67	0.0	4.5	129.5	17.6	52.0	49.4	5.7	#
39813	4 May 1961	35.0	15	3.69	6.3	0.44	6.7	3.1	121.4	12.0	34.3	32.3	5.5	#
39813	1 Jun 1964	31.2	4	5.85	4.6	1.54	42.9	20.6	102.7	11.2	35.9	38.7	5.5	#
39813	24 Feb 1966	26.9	18	3.59	11.6	1.26	0.0	5.3	130.3	13.0	48.2	45.1	—	
39813	22 Oct 1966	37.6	19	3.55	7.3	0.39	39.7	3.9	89.2	18.4	48.9	56.1	6.5	#
39813	16 Dec 1968	29.1	27	2.52	7.3	0.59	0.0	8.2	133.2	12.5	43.1	38.9	8.0	#
39813	19 Feb 1969	21.6	21	2.65	12.8	0.29	2.1	0.3	123.2	14.2	65.6	65.7	—	
39813	14 Sep 1968	134.9	19	16.97	6.6	1.12	28.1	1.8	98.7	66.9	49.6	43.6	—	
a mean												46.4		
g mean					7.7	0.67							5.8	
39814	6 Aug 1960	7.9	2	2.89	0.6	0.03	108.6	1.3	17.7	2.5	32.1	—	—	
39814	14 Sep 1960	46.2	14	4.67	1.5	0.05	98.4	0.0	26.6	9.7	21.1	—	0.8	
39814	3 Dec 1960	32.8	13	6.24	2.4	0.21	0.0	10.8	135.8	19.0	57.9	—	0.9	
39814	3 Sep 1961	11.4	2	2.97	1.8	0.04	129.5	0.0	-4.5	2.7	24.0	—	1.8	
39814	12 Sep 1961	19.0	11	4.16	0.0	0.06	128.1	0.9	-2.2	10.4	54.5	—	—	
39814	1 Jun 1964	29.5	4	3.76	1.7	0.22	14.1	15.3	126.2	11.6	39.3	—	1.8	
39814	21 Jul 1964	17.3	2	9.50	1.1	0.28	62.1	5.3	68.2	11.8	68.0	—	1.6	
39814	22 Jun 1966	29.7	8	6.01	1.3	0.04	81.0	4.9	48.9	9.0	30.4	—	1.6	
39814	25 Jun 1967	21.3	5	3.71	1.8	0.06	50.6	11.3	85.7	7.1	33.1	—	1.2	
39814	17 Sep 1967	27.8	4	7.61	2.2	0.08	104.2	1.0	21.8	12.2	44.0	—	1.2	
39814	28 Oct 1968	30.0	23	6.42	2.0	0.02	6.1	0.2	119.1	8.3	27.8	—	1.2	
39814	31 Oct 1968	17.1	5	4.69	1.8	0.05	1.0	5.2	129.2	4.4	25.8	—	1.5	
39814	14 Dec 1969	19.8	9	5.36	2.6	0.12	20.2	1.1	105.9	11.4	57.4	—	1.8	
39814	19 Aug 1970	12.2	9	6.84	1.2	0.04	138.3	8.8	-4.5	5.4	44.2	—	1.0	
a mean												—		
g mean					1.6	0.07							1.3	
39830	6 Jul 1963	23.1	11	1.23	2.9	0.01	77.3	1.1	48.8	2.3	10.0	10.4	2.5	
39830	1 Jun 1964	25.4	8	2.03	2.0	0.10	24.5	16.8	117.3	4.4	17.3	2.9	2.5	
39830	18 Aug 1964	18.7	11	1.50	3.2	0.04	88.9	6.2	42.3	1.7	9.0	10.8	1.8	
39830	3 Sep 1965	55.4	14	2.56	4.1	0.24	104.0	7.3	28.3	8.6	15.6	19.9	—	
39830	22 Jun 1966	27.0	7	1.64	3.1	0.03	81.3	1.4	45.1	3.3	12.2	14.2	2.8	
39830	29 Aug 1966	31.5	16	1.28	2.8	0.07	101.7	0.0	23.3	2.7	8.7	15.1	—	
39830	3 Oct 1966	19.6	10	1.42	1.9	0.12	73.3	4.3	56.0	2.4	12.4	11.8	2.7	

Catch	Date	P mm	D h	Q_p m^3s^{-1}	LAG h	BF m^3s^{-1}	SMD mm	API5 mm	CWI mm	R/O mm	PR %	SPR %	Tp(0) h	
39830	30 May 1967	9.7	10	1.18	2.8	0.13	14.5	1.6	112.1	1.6	16.2	2.7	2.8	
39830	23 Jun 1967	26.2	8	1.62	2.4	0.05	60.5	0.0	64.5	3.4	13.0	10.4	2.3	
39830	10 Aug 1967	6.8	3	2.36	2.6	0.08	102.0	0.3	23.3	2.6	37.5	52.8	—	
39830	1 Nov 1967	19.9	9	1.95	3.1	0.19	22.0	5.8	108.8	3.9	19.6	8.0	3.5	
39830	16 Dec 1968	26.2	14	1.83	3.6	0.18	0.0	5.2	130.2	5.1	19.5	2.5	3.5	
39830	25 Jun 1967	26.9	5	2.21	2.5	0.11	51.4	8.7	82.3	4.0	15.0	8.6	2.8	
a mean												13.1		
g mean					2.8	0.08							2.7	
39831	6 Jul 1963	23.8	11	1.25	1.7	0.03	77.3	0.8	48.5	2.3	9.8	7.7	—	
39831	16 Apr 1964	11.5	9	1.45	1.1	0.04	8.5	4.2	120.7	1.4	12.2	—	1.1	
39831	1 Jun 1964	25.6	8	1.70	2.2	0.07	25.6	14.1	113.5	4.6	18.0	2.5	—	
39831	12 Jun 1964	14.5	8	1.28	1.4	0.02	18.0	0.2	107.2	1.3	9.1	—	0.7	
39831	7 Jul 1965	20.7	10	1.82	1.2	0.02	114.8	0.5	10.7	1.8	8.8	15.8	0.9	
39831	2 Sep 1965	15.3	5	1.65	1.4	0.03	120.0	1.9	6.9	1.5	9.5	17.7	1.1	
39831	3 Sep 1965	56.6	16	2.34	4.1	0.13	79.7	14.0	59.3	12.1	21.4	17.5	—	
39831	22 Jun 1966	26.4	7	2.23	1.0	0.04	81.3	2.2	45.9	3.2	12.1	11.4	—	
39831	21 Aug 1966	11.6	6	1.87	0.8	0.04	94.3	0.0	30.7	1.4	12.0	15.1	—	
39831	3 Oct 1966	19.7	10	2.06	1.2	0.07	73.2	3.8	55.6	2.8	14.4	12.1	—	
39831	18 Oct 1966	5.4	7	1.52	1.1	0.11	41.1	5.2	89.1	1.2	22.2	14.3	0.6	
39831	18 Oct 1966	10.3	4	2.18	1.5	0.21	35.6	6.7	96.1	2.3	22.2	12.6	0.9	
39831	30 May 1967	11.4	10	1.99	0.6	0.08	14.6	1.7	112.1	1.5	13.5	—	—	
39831	2 Jun 1967	3.5	3	2.06	0.7	0.08	15.2	2.2	112.0	1.3	37.2	28.9	—	
39831	25 Jun 1967	28.9	5	2.12	0.7	0.15	51.4	9.9	83.5	4.9	17.0	8.7	—	
39831	18 Sep 1967	16.4	5	1.89	1.9	0.03	104.2	0.8	21.6	1.9	11.6	16.8	1.1	
39831	1 Nov 1967	19.3	7	1.84	1.0	0.11	22.0	6.2	109.2	3.9	20.3	6.7	—	
39831	10 Jul 1968	14.4	4	1.87	1.0	0.08	90.0	6.1	41.1	1.4	9.9	9.7	—	
39831	13 Jul 1968	14.7	7	1.97	1.8	0.06	61.7	2.5	65.8	2.0	13.5	8.4	—	
39831	16 Dec 1968	29.1	17	2.02	3.3	0.12	0.0	5.2	130.2	7.9	27.3	10.9	—	
39831	6 Aug 1970	17.0	3	2.49	1.3	0.11	120.0	5.4	10.4	2.2	12.8	21.3	—	
39831	20 Aug 1971	16.0	3	2.67	1.6	0.10	78.2	5.9	52.7	2.5	15.8	14.7	1.4	
39831	23 Jun 1967	26.2	8	1.69	1.0	0.06	60.9	0.0	64.1	2.8	10.6	4.9	—	
a mean												12.9		
g mean					1.3	0.06							0.9	
39990	12 Jan 1990				1.3								0.2	
39990	14 Apr 1990				0.5								0.4	
39990	3 Oct 1990				0.4								0.6	
39990	30 Oct 1990				0.3								0.4	
39990	25 Jun 1991				0.4								0.7	
39990	22 Sep 1991				0.6								0.9	
39990	26 Sep 1991				0.5								0.6	
39990	30 Oct 1991				0.4								0.4	
g mean					0.5								0.48	
39991	13 Mar 1990				0.48								0.7	
39991	19 Apr 1990				0.33								0.4	
39991	14 May 1990				0.18								0.4	
39991	30 Jun 1990				0.13								0.3	
39991	4 Apr 1991				0.40								0.4	
g mean					0.27								0.42	
39992	12 Dec 1989				1.1								1.3	#
39992	23 Dec 1989				0.7								0.8	#
39992	8 Jan 1990				1.2								1.3	#
39992	13 Apr 1990				1.0								1.3	#
39992	4 May 1991				1.3								1.3	#
g mean					1.0								1.18	
39993	6 Jan 1990				4.6								3.9	#
39993	31 Jan 1990				4.5								2.5	#
39993	2 Feb 1990				5.0								5.3	#
39993	10 Jan 1991				6.6								9.8	#
39993	7 Mar 1991				5.3								3.5	#
39993	19 Nov 1991				7.4								2.4	#
39993	15 Apr 1992				8.4								14.3	#

Catch	Date	*P* mm	*D* h	Q_p m^3s^{-1}	*LAG* h	*BF* m^3s^{-1}	*SMD* mm	*API5* mm	*CWI* mm	*R/O* mm	*PR* %	*SPR* %	*Tp(0)* h	
39993	29 May 1992				3.3								4.1	#
39993	1 Jun 1992				4.4								4.3	#
g mean					5.3								4.68	
39994	15 Feb 1990				6.1								7.5	
39994	26 Nov 1990				4.1								7.0	
39994	1 Jan 1991				4.9								3.5	
39994	23 Feb 1991				10.8								7.5	
39994	17 Mar 1991				13.3								15.0	
g mean					7.1								7.30	
39995	23 Dec 1989				0.8								0.5	
39995	13 Apr 1990				1.1								1.3	
39995	21 Jun 1990				1.5								1.1	
39995	30 Jul 1990				1.5								2.3	
39995	17 Sep 1990				1.5								2.1	
g mean					1.2								1.28	
39996	4 Jul 1990				4.5								4.8	#
39996	3 Oct 1990				3.7								4.1	#
39996	26 Oct 1990				3.2								2.5	#
39996	24 Nov 1990				4.0								5.5	#
39996	26 Nov 1990				3.8								3.4	#
39996	27 Sep 1991				3.9								3.4	#
39996	29 Sep 1991				3.2								3.4	#
g mean					3.7								3.76	
39997	19 Oct 1989				1.1								0.9	
39997	23 Dec 1989				0.7								0.9	
39997	7 Jul 1990				1.1								1.1	
39997	30 Oct 1990				1.1								0.9	
39997	3 Jan 1991				0.6								0.9	
g mean					0.9								0.94	
39998	11 Feb 1990				2.3								1.8	#
39998	25 Feb 1990				1.7								1.4	#
39998	1 Jan 1991				4.0								1.8	#
39998	6 Jan 1991				2.9								1.8	#
39998	8 Jan 1991				5.5								7.8	#
g mean					3.0								2.30	
39999	21 Dec 1989				9.7								7.5	
39999	7 Jan 1990				7.5								6.4	
39999	23 Jan 1990				8.1								5.8	
39999	3 Feb 1990				8.8								8.6	
39999	19 Mar 1990				4.5								2.6	
39999	28 Feb 1991				6.6								3.4	
39999	3 Jul 1991				8.0								8.3	
39999	25 Jul 1991				15.0								15.5	
39999	19 Nov 1991				6.9								5.0	
39999	9 Jan 1992				4.7								3.0	
g mean					7.5								5.77	
40004	11 Mar 1969	36.3	36	38.63	15.1	3.12	4.0	6.2	127.2	23.2	63.9	63.3	18.6	#
40004	6 Jan 1971	7.7	29	18.35	2.1	3.56	1.2	0.1	123.9	5.8	75.2	75.5	—	
40004	23 Jan 1971	30.6	12	48.00	20.7	3.80	0.0	5.2	130.2	20.9	68.4	67.1	18.7	#
a mean												68.6		
g mean					8.7	3.48							18.6	
40006	8 Sep 1965	24.2	8	2.23	7.0	0.25	30.4	2.8	97.4	1.7	7.2	13.2	5.9	#
40006	8 Dec 1965	29.2	25	5.24	14.3	0.35	0.2	1.0	125.8	6.7	23.0	22.1	7.9	#
40006	24 Feb 1966	20.0	22	5.07	11.6	0.66	0.0	3.2	128.2	5.3	26.5	25.0	—	
40006	17 Apr 1966	16.4	17	3.91	7.0	0.54	0.8	4.2	128.4	2.9	17.8	16.2	6.4	#
40006	29 Nov 1966	15.6	8	3.80	8.1	0.50	0.0	3.1	128.1	3.0	19.0	17.5	6.3	#
40006	9 Dec 1966	16.7	21	4.09	11.1	0.60	0.0	2.5	127.5	3.7	22.0	20.7	8.1	#

Catch	Date	*P*	*D*	Q_p	*LAG*	*BF*	*SMD*	*API5*	*CWI*	*R/O*	*PR*	*SPR*	*Tp*(0)	
		mm	*h*	m^3s^{-1}	*h*	m^3s^{-1}	*mm*	*mm*	*mm*	*mm*	*%*	*%*	*h*	
40006	25 Jan 1967	12.8	7	4.63	7.2	0.84	0.0	4.0	129.0	3.2	25.2	23.5	6.4	#
40006	20 Feb 1967	14.7	15	3.51	7.3	0.53	0.0	6.6	131.6	3.4	23.1	20.7	7.3	#
40006	27 Feb 1967	17.3	17	4.17	10.3	0.51	0.0	2.2	127.2	4.0	22.9	21.6	6.5	#
40006	9 Apr 1967	22.4	14	4.39	6.1	0.49	3.5	1.0	122.5	3.8	17.0	16.8	6.0	#
40006	25 Jun 1967	33.6	5	4.90	7.0	0.46	64.2	8.6	69.4	2.9	8.5	21.5	6.5	#
40006	3 Nov 1967	35.0	20	7.93	13.4	0.57	16.0	6.3	115.3	10.5	30.1	31.9	—	
40006	18 Dec 1967	19.3	13	3.60	6.9	0.42	9.6	0.2	115.6	3.4	17.5	19.1	7.0	#
40006	21 Dec 1968	9.7	8	4.17	6.5	0.90	0.0	6.1	131.1	3.0	30.5	28.4	6.9	#
40006	**19 Feb 1969*	19.0	36	4.08	24.9	0.45	1.4	0.1	123.7	8.4	44.3	44.2	—	
40006	11 Mar 1969	31.3	44	6.52	10.8	0.73	0.0	8.6	133.6	10.0	31.8	29.1	5.9	#
40006	14 Sep 1968	126.3	16	54.86	7.2	0.72	41.0	1.5	85.5	46.4	36.7	35.9	6.5	#
a mean												24.0		
g mean					9.1	0.54							6.7	

* Note that the event of *19 Feb 1969* was not used in deriving the unit hydrograph and losses model parameters for worked examples involving this catchment.

Catch	Date	*P*	*D*	Q_p	*LAG*	*BF*	*SMD*	*API5*	*CWI*	*R/O*	*PR*	*SPR*	*Tp*(0)	
40007	8 Oct 1960	32.0	26	31.99	14.0	3.24	4.3	3.5	124.2	12.2	38.1	37.9	—	
40007	25 Oct 1960	30.8	17	62.08	14.5	4.23	0.0	2.5	127.5	16.4	53.4	52.6	—	
40007	28 Oct 1960	26.4	20	47.08	19.2	7.70	0.0	11.6	136.6	12.4	47.0	43.8	—	
40007	31 Oct 1960	27.8	28	48.63	12.2	12.53	0.0	18.0	143.0	13.0	46.9	42.1	—	
40007	25 Nov 1960	23.4	14	42.97	14.4	7.84	0.0	6.6	131.6	14.6	62.5	60.8	—	
40007	2 Dec 1960	52.1	31	100.80	9.3	7.81	0.0	2.6	127.6	25.7	49.4	45.9	—	
40007	1 Jan 1961	30.9	31	40.42	18.7	4.85	0.2	4.2	129.0	19.4	62.8	61.7	—	
40007	29 Jan 1961	32.9	24	68.24	15.9	8.90	0.0	8.6	133.6	17.6	53.6	51.2	—	
40007	27 Feb 1961	19.3	10	38.40	11.8	5.98	0.0	6.6	131.6	8.3	43.1	41.1	—	
40007	9 Jan 1962	20.6	14	40.81	13.9	4.72	0.0	7.3	132.3	9.8	47.6	45.5	—	
40007	20 Jan 1962	20.9	19	33.09	10.8	10.69	0.0	6.9	131.9	6.8	32.7	30.5	—	
40007	11 Mar 1963	23.2	24	35.14	12.0	5.04	0.0	7.5	132.5	9.2	39.8	37.5	—	
40007	11 Nov 1963	22.6	13	41.25	12.0	4.99	0.0	4.0	129.0	8.3	36.7	35.3	—	
40007	17 Nov 1963	80.6	53	57.01	14.1	6.11	0.0	4.6	129.6	42.0	52.1	44.7	—	
40007	24 Nov 1963	22.3	30	28.95	14.9	4.80	0.0	1.7	126.7	9.3	41.7	40.9	—	
40007	9 Feb 1966	26.8	31	41.44	22.8	13.65	0.0	3.4	128.4	7.0	26.1	24.7	—	
40007	17 Jun 1964	42.0	22	43.84	17.6	2.47	8.4	1.7	118.3	12.1	28.8	29.2	—	
40007	27 Nov 1965	28.4	20	43.04	11.9	3.11	0.0	3.2	128.2	10.8	38.0	36.8	—	
40007	21 Oct 1966	35.1	21	43.94	15.4	3.47	7.2	3.6	121.4	13.0	37.1	37.6	—	
40007	27 Feb 1967	28.8	17	45.40	15.3	4.28	0.0	2.1	127.1	13.4	46.6	45.8	—	
a mean												42.3		
g mean					14.2	5.68							—	
40008	11 Mar 1963	18.8	12	16.32	16.0	3.65	0.0	8.1	133.1	4.8	25.6	22.7	—	
40008	3 Apr 1964	27.1	35	15.88	24.1	2.03	6.7	0.2	118.5	7.9	29.0	29.8	—	
40008	9 Dec 1965	20.3	12	18.04	18.1	2.42	0.0	2.0	127.0	7.4	36.4	35.3	—	
40008	9 Feb 1966	25.3	30	20.23	10.9	4.43	0.0	2.9	127.9	9.2	36.4	35.0	—	
40008	24 Feb 1966	21.1	30	19.35	18.6	3.87	0.0	3.0	128.0	7.0	33.2	31.7	—	
40008	22 Oct 1966	25.5	23	19.30	24.1	3.36	0.0	7.1	132.1	11.1	43.5	41.2	—	
40008	27 Oct 1966	44.0	41	27.78	26.1	3.02	1.0	4.4	128.4	24.2	55.0	52.7	—	
40008	9 Dec 1966	19.6	18	20.51	22.3	4.81	0.0	3.6	128.6	7.9	40.4	38.9	—	
40008	27 Feb 1967	18.6	24	17.51	10.9	3.40	0.0	2.2	127.2	5.6	30.0	28.7	—	
40008	19 Feb 1969	21.8	41	24.54	31.0	2.38	1.2	0.5	124.3	19.3	88.7	89.2	—	
40008	17 Nov 1963	42.0	51	22.47	20.3	5.30	0.0	10.5	135.5	15.0	35.6	31.6	—	
a mean												39.7		
g mean					19.3	3.37							—	
40009	9 Jan 1962	28.3	43	27.94	7.3	1.68	0.0	0.1	125.1	20.8	73.4	73.4	—	
40009	20 Apr 1963	17.8	12	22.64	7.2	2.84	2.8	2.1	124.3	6.9	38.6	38.7	7.0	#
40009	18 Jun 1964	40.6	38	37.23	7.3	1.48	8.5	3.0	119.5	16.4	40.5	41.5	—	
40009	3 Sep 1965	68.8	26	29.77	9.0	0.45	78.8	0.3	46.5	10.3	14.9	29.6	8.5	#
40009	28 Nov 1965	23.5	16	26.34	7.4	1.54	0.0	2.4	127.4	9.5	40.5	39.8	8.5	#
40009	8 Dec 1965	41.3	38	41.74	15.8	1.82	0.2	1.1	125.9	24.8	60.0	59.2	13.7	#
40009	9 Feb 1966	18.9	17	30.86	7.2	6.39	0.0	9.4	134.4	10.7	56.8	54.4	4.6	#
40009	20 Oct 1966	20.5	13	27.63	9.3	6.72	0.6	11.3	135.7	5.2	25.6	22.8	8.5	#
40009	27 Feb 1967	26.8	18	34.13	6.9	2.88	0.0	4.9	129.9	13.7	51.3	50.0	7.8	#
40009	9 Apr 1967	28.7	29	25.13	19.7	0.90	3.2	0.7	122.5	9.8	34.1	34.6	—	
40009	19 Feb 1969	25.4	36	24.76	21.4	1.31	1.4	0.1	123.7	16.2	63.9	64.2	—	
40009	17 Nov 1963	71.3	53	39.73	5.5	5.22	0.0	8.4	133.4	40.6	56.9	49.7	—	

Catch	Date	P mm	D h	Q_p m^3s^{-1}	LAG h	BF m^3s^{-1}	SMD mm	API5 mm	CWI mm	R/O mm	PR %	SPR %	Tp(0) h	
40009	23 Jan 1971	24.2	24	32.02	8.4	3.46	4.3	5.1	125.8	14.8	61.0	60.8	7.9	#
40009	18 Nov 1970	25.8	22	24.01	7.5	1.86	22.9	10.1	112.2	8.6	33.5	36.6	8.9	#
40009	18 Jun 1971	23.2	15	23.05	9.2	1.63	12.1	4.2	117.1	8.0	34.5	36.4	7.3	#
a mean												46.1		
g mean					9.1	2.11							8.0	
40010	3 Dec 1961	23.2	47	14.91	18.9	1.00	11.1	1.9	115.8	8.5	36.8	38.8	17.0	#
40010	12 Dec 1961	18.5	13	16.36	19.3	2.80	0.0	1.7	126.7	8.0	43.1	42.4	15.1	#
40010	15 Mar 1963	10.0	6	14.03	14.0	4.75	0.0	3.5	128.5	3.1	30.5	29.2	15.2	#
40010	10 Nov 1963	12.5	13	15.38	16.9	1.28	0.0	3.0	128.0	7.0	56.2	55.3	15.3	#
40010	17 Nov 1963	57.4	53	31.00	20.5	2.93	0.0	2.1	127.1	30.7	53.5	49.5	17.5	#
40010	24 Nov 1963	19.2	31	16.42	16.3	2.82	0.0	1.5	126.5	7.5	39.2	38.5	16.3	#
40010	13 Mar 1964	47.3	47	29.65	18.0	1.16	0.4	4.0	128.6	24.8	52.4	49.5	—	
40010	19 Mar 1964	15.9	25	19.07	23.4	3.27	1.4	4.2	127.8	7.8	48.9	48.0	14.2	#
40010	20 Apr 1964	23.6	41	15.27	17.7	1.73	1.0	4.3	128.3	10.7	45.5	44.4	15.0	#
40010	31 May 1964	40.2	29	14.83	18.1	0.50	31.3	0.0	93.7	8.0	19.9	27.1	13.0	#
40010	18 Jun 1964	28.3	38	19.31	15.8	1.22	8.9	2.4	118.5	10.4	36.9	38.2	11.1	#
40010	13 Jan 1965	15.6	9	15.82	13.7	2.59	2.9	1.8	123.9	6.3	40.1	40.1	13.2	#
40010	20 Nov 1965	22.7	10	18.38	28.0	2.26	0.0	4.3	129.3	7.7	33.9	32.5	—	
40010	28 Nov 1965	24.2	20	24.91	24.6	1.33	0.0	2.0	127.0	15.1	62.5	61.9	20.1	#
40010	4 Dec 1965	12.0	23	13.70	17.6	2.43	0.0	2.2	127.2	4.7	39.4	38.5	14.1	#
40010	8 Dec 1965	25.6	26	24.75	24.7	1.50	0.2	1.1	125.9	13.2	51.4	51.0	22.4	#
40010	17 Dec 1965	18.0	26	20.34	20.9	7.20	0.0	6.3	131.3	6.7	37.1	35.2	16.5	#
40010	9 Feb 1966	21.6	26	25.44	24.8	2.77	0.0	2.7	127.7	15.3	70.9	70.2	21.1	#
40010	18 Feb 1966	30.1	67	21.67	26.9	1.22	2.4	0.0	122.6	18.2	60.6	61.1	12.9	#
40010	24 Feb 1966	26.5	54	29.91	13.0	3.96	0.0	4.4	129.4	15.2	57.4	56.2	—	
40010	18 Apr 1966	32.0	62	24.00	24.1	2.66	0.8	4.3	128.5	16.9	52.7	51.7	20.5	#
40010	22 Oct 1966	30.6	19	29.30	22.7	1.35	7.2	2.0	119.8	18.5	60.5	61.7	17.9	#
40010	9 Dec 1966	17.8	21	21.63	16.1	2.92	0.0	2.0	127.0	9.0	50.3	49.6	13.7	#
40010	25 Jan 1967	16.1	8	23.25	16.2	4.91	0.0	4.4	129.4	8.8	54.6	53.3	11.4	#
40010	27 Feb 1967	20.3	26	22.11	19.3	1.47	0.0	1.8	126.8	10.9	53.9	53.3	—	
40010	3 Nov 1967	32.4	55	38.13	12.0	5.00	1.4	7.1	130.7	16.2	50.1	48.5	—	
40010	18 Dec 1967	23.8	14	21.67	20.7	0.53	0.1	0.3	125.2	11.6	48.7	48.4	21.5	#
40010	19 Feb 1969	22.6	36	23.25	26.7	2.51	1.4	0.1	123.7	16.0	70.7	71.0	—	
a mean												48.0		
g mean					19.2	2.08							15.8	
41005	19 Feb 1966	31.2	36	23.97	19.3	3.02	0.0	3.9	128.9	15.9	51.0	49.8	16.1	#
41005	25 Feb 1966	27.3	20	37.69	17.5	5.99	0.0	5.3	130.3	16.3	59.8	58.3	13.6	#
41005	16 Apr 1966	36.0	65	23.06	18.5	3.23	0.8	3.8	128.0	18.8	52.3	51.3	17.5	#
41005	6 Aug 1966	27.7	22	18.83	22.0	2.19	54.1	4.2	75.1	10.1	36.5	48.5	—	
41005	21 Oct 1966	32.7	18	33.24	20.2	1.96	5.1	4.8	124.7	18.7	57.3	57.2	20.5	#
41005	9 Dec 1966	13.2	21	12.21	16.3	2.60	0.0	2.3	127.3	6.2	46.7	45.8	—	
41005	28 Dec 1966	18.1	22	18.08	20.8	2.43	0.0	2.8	127.8	8.4	46.6	45.6	17.0	#
41005	25 Jan 1967	14.4	7	24.80	20.6	7.06	0.0	7.7	132.7	7.3	50.5	48.3	20.9	#
41005	27 Feb 1967	26.1	18	28.01	18.7	2.33	0.0	1.6	126.6	12.8	49.0	48.3	19.1	#
41005	8 Mar 1967	17.8	25	14.68	16.1	3.79	1.3	1.0	124.7	7.1	40.0	39.7	15.7	#
41005	9 Apr 1967	24.4	12	16.70	14.5	1.58	0.7	0.6	124.9	6.4	26.1	25.5	13.7	#
41005	3 Nov 1967	45.0	26	84.96	13.6	5.30	1.4	8.8	132.4	25.6	56.9	53.5	—	
41005	6 Feb 1968	18.2	22	22.32	15.4	5.37	0.0	8.9	133.9	7.8	43.0	40.4	17.3	#
41005	15 Sep 1968	66.0	17	48.88	19.8	1.07	53.4	3.6	75.2	19.0	28.8	36.3	—	
41005	25 Sep 1968	23.3	17	20.03	20.6	2.34	0.9	2.6	126.7	9.1	38.9	38.0	17.4	#
41005	1 Nov 1968	12.7	11	17.71	14.9	4.53	0.0	12.6	137.6	5.1	40.5	36.9	15.3	#
41005	20 Dec 1968	20.8	24	21.83	19.9	2.99	0.0	3.6	128.6	9.3	44.9	43.7	—	
41005	21 Dec 1968	19.6	20	22.59	13.6	5.88	0.0	11.1	136.1	8.5	43.6	40.5	15.5	#
41005	15 Jan 1969	13.1	13	17.25	15.5	4.15	0.0	5.1	130.1	5.6	42.4	40.7	16.7	#
41005	17 Jan 1969	14.0	12	21.43	15.2	3.87	0.0	4.7	129.7	9.0	64.6	63.3	16.0	#
41005	27 Jan 1969	17.6	17	17.79	15.2	4.17	0.0	1.4	126.4	6.2	35.2	34.4	16.5	#
41005	19 Feb 1969	28.5	46	19.46	23.8	2.85	1.4	0.3	123.9	13.1	45.9	45.8	—	
41005	12 Mar 1969	26.7	33	30.18	13.3	5.51	0.0	11.7	136.7	13.5	50.4	47.2	17.1	#
a mean												45.2		
g mean					17.4	3.31							16.7	
41006	3 Nov 1967	45.4	26	42.23	11.9	1.48	1.4	9.7	133.3	33.1	72.9	69.4	12.3	#
41006	6 Feb 1968	22.2	22	24.91	13.3	3.32	0.0	7.6	132.6	13.5	60.8	58.8	15.0	#
41006	14 Sep 1968	31.0	14	9.63	10.1	0.39	55.2	5.4	75.2	4.7	15.2	26.8	12.4	#

Catch	Date	P	D	Q_p	LAG	BF	SMD	API5	CWI	R/O	PR	SPR	Tp(0)	
		mm	h	m^3s^{-1}	h	m^3s^{-1}	mm	mm	mm	mm	%	%	h	
41006	21 Dec 1968	12.3	6	18.84	11.5	1.64	0.0	8.3	133.3	8.9	72.6	70.6	11.5	#
41006	19 Feb 1969	20.8	16	20.99	19.1	0.78	1.4	0.0	123.6	11.1	53.6	53.7	—	
41006	12 Mar 1969	23.8	31	31.68	8.6	2.58	0.0	11.1	136.1	15.8	66.5	63.7	10.6	#
41006	18 Jun 1971	31.0	19	37.84	15.6	0.43	2.0	7.1	130.1	18.9	61.1	59.7	—	
41006	16 Nov 1969	32.4	23	34.23	12.3	1.53	45.7	12.1	91.4	14.1	43.5	51.5	13.0	#
41006	18 Nov 1970	23.3	23	21.52	11.1	2.17	22.0	8.3	111.3	10.7	46.0	49.1	14.0	#
41006	23 Jan 1971	24.5	20	26.65	14.4	1.53	0.0	4.9	129.9	19.4	79.0	77.9	16.0	#
41006	14 Jun 1971	43.3	22	24.55	11.6	0.29	38.4	18.6	105.2	18.7	43.1	46.6	—	
41006	18 Jun 1971	30.6	13	36.97	14.8	0.40	14.4	6.8	117.4	18.6	60.9	62.7	—	
41006	8 Dec 1972	22.6	15	22.76	13.2	2.85	23.4	14.1	115.7	10.3	45.6	47.6	11.5	#
41006	10 Feb 1974	39.5	19	46.60	12.7	1.53	0.0	5.5	130.5	32.0	80.9	79.7	10.9	#
41006	14 Feb 1974	27.9	18	39.95	11.1	2.62	0.0	11.9	136.9	21.1	75.5	72.6	10.0	#
41006	17 Nov 1974	21.4	16	43.79	10.0	3.88	0.0	10.3	135.3	19.4	90.6	88.3	—	
41006	20 Jan 1975	32.0	25	42.54	3.9	2.64	0.0	8.9	133.9	22.6	70.6	68.4	—	
41006	1 Dec 1975	26.2	18	32.78	12.1	1.13	13.4	4.1	115.7	17.4	66.3	68.6	11.0	#
a mean												62.0		
g mean					11.6	1.35							12.2	
41007	3 Dec 1960	35.5	27	99.71	21.2	12.41	0.0	1.9	126.9	30.9	87.1	86.8	14.0	#
41007	26 Jan 1961	55.0	67	95.17	37.2	1.58	0.4	0.5	125.1	49.6	90.2	87.4	—	
41007	27 Feb 1961	18.8	41	61.19	21.0	12.88	0.0	6.1	131.1	12.5	66.4	64.8	25.1	#
41007	3 May 1961	27.3	27	65.82	32.4	0.33	8.2	2.7	119.5	21.5	78.9	80.4	32.2	#
41007	17 Nov 1963	60.3	58	103.65	18.1	13.29	0.0	3.8	128.8	53.5	88.8	84.4	21.7	#
41007	13 Mar 1964	58.8	49	97.56	23.5	1.69	6.2	0.2	119.0	43.3	73.6	71.6	33.5	#
41007	31 May 1964	55.0	62	77.80	27.2	0.32	44.5	0.0	80.5	37.6	68.4	76.5	—	
41007	28 Nov 1965	29.4	21	66.90	29.6	0.01	0.0	1.9	126.9	20.3	69.1	68.6	32.1	#
41007	22 Oct 1966	33.2	21	82.56	27.4	0.06	39.7	2.4	87.7	26.9	81.1	90.6	26.3	#
41007	14 Sep 1968	105.9	54	298.73	15.5	6.81	19.3	5.1	110.8	81.1	76.6	71.8	—	
41007	15 Dec 1968	49.5	73	79.35	37.7	2.31	0.1	0.0	124.9	42.2	85.3	83.3	—	
41007	11 Mar 1969	35.1	46	76.44	26.2	0.22	8.9	7.4	123.5	25.9	73.8	74.2	—	
a mean												78.4		
g mean					25.5	1.02							25.5	
41015	30 Oct 1967	17.2	12	0.33	4.7	0.05	12.9	5.1	117.2	0.1	0.8	2.4	4.3	#
41015	17 Dec 1968	34.5	19	2.70	3.1	0.87	10.2	8.0	122.8	1.0	2.8	3.0	3.7	#
41015	21 Dec 1969	16.1	14	0.26	5.6	0.05	9.8	4.9	120.1	0.1	0.9	1.8	4.8	#
41015	6 Nov 1970	30.1	20	0.32	8.4	0.03	48.3	2.5	79.2	0.2	0.8	11.9	3.3	#
41015	22 Nov 1970	19.8	16	0.48	6.4	0.08	0.7	5.7	130.0	0.3	1.7	0.1	4.2	#
41015	6 Feb 1972	16.2	14	0.34	3.6	0.07	0.0	4.8	129.8	0.2	1.2	—	3.1	#
41015	15 Sep 1974	19.8	15	0.26	3.3	0.05	51.3	1.2	74.9	0.1	0.7	12.9	3.6	#
41015	19 Oct 1974	13.8	8	0.53	2.2	0.16	9.8	13.1	128.3	0.2	1.1	—	2.4	#
41015	26 Sep 1975	37.5	16	0.41	5.1	0.06	37.7	11.8	99.1	0.2	0.6	6.7	2.2	#
41015	28 Nov 1975	14.6	9	0.35	4.2	0.06	21.4	5.0	108.6	0.2	1.2	4.9	4.4	#
a mean												5.4		
g mean					4.4	0.08							3.5	
41020	14 Dec 1969	16.1	5	9.03	12.2	0.52	11.0	3.0	117.0	11.3	70.1	72.1	—	
41020	14 Jan 1970	15.2	15	8.44	13.9	1.09	0.0	5.7	130.7	10.5	69.2	67.8	—	
41020	12 Feb 1970	25.0	12	8.65	12.6	0.59	0.2	0.9	125.7	12.5	50.1	49.8	—	
41020	23 Jan 1971	29.1	20	14.08	10.3	1.01	0.0	6.8	131.8	22.5	77.3	75.7	—	
41020	18 Jun 1971	36.2	13	11.88	12.7	0.35	19.4	4.4	110.0	17.5	48.4	52.0	—	
41020	19 Oct 1971	20.0	8	11.00	9.2	0.56	65.2	6.4	66.2	11.7	58.7	73.3	—	
41020	29 Apr 1972	27.4	20	5.77	11.2	0.21	21.2	0.1	103.9	8.1	29.4	34.4	—	
41020	4 Sep 1974	59.6	25	10.66	10.5	0.30	66.9	8.8	66.9	19.0	31.9	42.5	—	
41020	17 Nov 1974	18.8	16	11.96	10.9	1.96	0.0	12.5	137.5	13.5	71.7	68.6	—	
41020	21 Nov 1974	46.3	19	19.50	8.8	4.80	0.0	13.8	138.8	19.8	42.8	37.5	—	
41020	20 Jan 1975	34.8	14	16.51	9.7	0.92	0.0	10.0	135.0	23.4	67.1	64.6	—	
41020	18 Apr 1975	24.4	10	11.63	8.3	0.52	2.4	4.2	126.8	15.1	61.7	61.2	—	
41020	1 Dec 1975	28.2	18	10.98	11.6	0.93	10.2	4.1	118.9	17.4	61.8	63.3	—	
a mean												58.7		
g mean					10.8	0.73							—	
41021	14 Dec 1969	15.3	19	1.53	9.2	0.11	11.2	2.2	116.0	10.3	67.4	69.7	—	
41021	4 Mar 1970	20.0	13	1.02	7.6	0.07	0.9	0.4	124.5	7.8	39.2	39.3	—	
41021	18 Nov 1970	23.0	22	1.78	6.1	0.29	0.8	10.4	134.6	9.4	40.9	38.5	—	
41021	14 Jun 1971	72.7	32	1.68	12.1	0.03	31.4	4.1	97.7	21.2	29.1	30.8	—	

Catch	Date	P mm	D h	Q_p m^3s^{-1}	LAG h	BF m^3s^{-1}	SMD mm	API5 mm	CWI mm	R/O mm	PR %	SPR %	Tp(0) h	
41021	10 Jan 1972	28.9	27	1.91	9.5	0.06	3.7	1.0	122.3	14.1	48.7	49.4	—	
41021	24 Jan 1972	14.0	11	1.43	6.8	0.06	0.6	4.4	128.8	8.9	63.6	62.7	—	
41021	5 Mar 1972	13.7	5	1.15	18.3	0.11	0.3	4.0	128.7	7.7	56.0	55.1	—	
41021	8 Dec 1972	26.8	16	2.42	9.6	0.36	4.3	21.7	142.4	12.7	47.3	43.0	—	
41021	12 Feb 1973	13.4	16	0.77	10.1	0.05	0.1	0.9	125.8	6.3	46.8	46.6	—	
a mean												48.3		
g mean					9.4	0.09							—	
41022	29 Nov 1970	25.5	19	9.99	9.5	0.62	0.0	1.0	126.0	13.3	52.0	51.7	11.5	#
41022	6 Mar 1972	11.9	8	6.79	8.4	1.28	0.0	12.1	137.1	6.0	50.2	47.1	7.0	#
41022	13 Dec 1972	14.7	3	8.64	8.6	2.16	9.7	5.0	120.3	6.3	43.0	44.1	9.3	#
41022	22 Nov 1974	25.0	14	27.45	7.8	9.29	0.0	13.2	138.2	11.6	46.6	43.3	7.1	#
41022	20 Jan 1975	34.3	18	29.84	7.2	1.62	35.6	5.1	94.5	21.8	63.6	71.2	7.1	#
41022	8 Mar 1975	14.3	10	10.09	5.2	1.64	0.4	5.6	130.2	6.6	46.5	45.2	4.3	#
41022	18 Apr 1975	20.7	15	10.38	7.9	0.77	3.5	2.9	124.4	10.3	49.8	49.9	3.5	#
41022	1 Dec 1975	32.7	18	16.49	6.4	0.69	12.4	3.3	115.9	14.0	42.7	44.9	4.1	#
a mean												49.7		
g mean					7.5	1.48							6.3	
41025	10 Jan 1972	22.2	14	11.71	20.9	0.73	0.0	1.5	126.5	13.1	58.8	58.4	—	
41025	10 Feb 1972	14.6	38	8.62	17.9	1.19	0.2	1.9	126.7	7.9	53.9	53.4	—	
41025	4 Mar 1972	20.6	19	17.50	22.8	1.12	0.0	5.1	130.1	13.1	63.6	62.3	—	
41025	5 Dec 1972	33.3	49	22.29	21.7	3.00	0.0	15.8	140.8	17.6	53.0	49.0	—	
41025	13 Dec 1972	13.5	17	11.99	21.9	3.86	0.0	7.2	132.2	5.9	43.9	42.0	—	
41025	14 Feb 1974	25.6	30	23.68	15.1	2.30	0.1	5.0	129.9	16.9	66.2	65.0	—	
41025	26 Sep 1974	24.7	29	21.48	19.6	0.83	16.6	4.2	112.6	19.4	78.7	81.8	—	
41025	25 Dec 1974	23.4	26	20.14	20.5	1.94	0.0	4.1	129.1	14.5	61.9	60.8	—	
41025	1 Dec 1975	26.8	17	21.90	19.2	0.81	14.1	3.8	114.7	16.5	61.4	63.9	—	
a mean												59.6		
g mean					19.8	1.48							—	
41028	13 Jan 1965	20.1	13	5.39	10.2	0.47	2.9	3.0	125.1	10.6	52.8	52.6	9.0	#
41028	19 Nov 1965	43.6	16	8.93	7.1	0.55	0.0	3.3	128.3	17.6	40.4	38.3	6.3	#
41028	28 Nov 1965	27.4	21	6.59	6.9	0.45	0.0	3.0	128.0	13.1	47.8	46.9	7.1	#
41028	8 Dec 1965	35.3	26	10.40	11.1	0.39	0.2	1.4	126.2	20.1	56.8	56.4	7.1	#
41028	22 Dec 1965	23.8	14	7.50	6.8	0.82	0.0	2.1	127.1	12.8	53.7	53.1	7.1	#
41028	19 Feb 1966	33.3	35	6.19	11.9	0.65	0.0	4.7	129.7	19.6	58.8	57.5	6.0	#
41028	20 Feb 1967	16.0	9	6.17	8.0	0.50	0.0	8.4	133.4	8.7	54.4	52.2	8.0	#
41028	27 Feb 1967	26.8	17	5.63	7.4	0.37	0.0	2.4	127.4	13.7	51.2	50.5	8.2	#
41028	3 Nov 1967	45.5	24	7.70	12.0	0.72	1.4	12.1	135.7	21.6	47.4	43.1	9.5	#
41028	6 Feb 1968	19.1	11	6.29	8.6	0.57	0.0	8.4	133.4	10.2	53.5	51.3	8.5	#
41028	11 Oct 1968	26.2	13	6.79	6.8	0.84	0.6	7.0	131.4	12.5	47.8	46.0	8.5	#
41028	12 Mar 1969	19.5	23	6.65	10.4	0.71	0.0	12.6	137.6	9.9	50.8	47.5	8.6	#
41028	21 Nov 1969	19.4	20	3.69	9.0	0.18	26.2	5.9	104.7	9.3	48.0	52.9	7.0	#
41028	12 Feb 1970	25.2	12	3.90	9.0	0.29	0.4	0.9	125.5	8.6	34.3	33.9	—	
41028	23 Jan 1971	29.3	18	6.11	8.2	0.75	0.2	5.9	130.7	13.9	47.6	46.0	9.9	#
41028	10 Jan 1972	31.2	15	4.27	11.8	0.16	0.0	2.5	127.5	11.6	37.3	36.4	10.8	#
41028	10 Feb 1974	42.9	19	8.48	9.1	0.69	0.0	5.9	130.9	23.1	53.9	51.4	9.6	#
41028	21 Nov 1974	40.9	18	13.62	5.5	3.08	0.0	10.9	135.9	14.5	35.4	32.0	5.8	#
41028	20 Jan 1975	31.7	26	8.27	8.5	0.66	0.0	10.0	135.0	16.3	51.5	48.9	7.5	#
a mean												47.2		
g mean					8.7	0.54							7.9	
41801	19 Feb 1969	19.9	26	0.81	8.2	0.02	0.0	2.0	127.0	12.4	62.4	59.1	—	
41801	12 Mar 1969	18.2	17	0.94	5.3	0.07	0.0	6.5	131.5	7.0	38.3	25.2	5.1	
41801	31 May 1969	19.7	5	1.62	2.5	0.03	41.8	1.2	84.4	3.5	18.0	9.3	—	
41801	6 Jul 1969	43.4	19	1.74	4.3	0.01	94.6	0.0	30.4	7.1	16.3	19.4	3.5	
41801	28 Jul 1969	31.2	13	0.75	3.4	0.01	106.5	0.0	18.5	4.5	14.5	21.0	1.7	
41801	1 Aug 1969	15.3	5	1.31	1.9	0.02	92.1	1.6	34.5	2.7	17.6	21.2	2.7	
41801	2 Aug 1969	19.8	9	0.77	4.7	0.02	80.3	9.4	54.1	3.8	19.3	18.6	3.1	
41801	13 Nov 1970	55.6	30	2.76	5.6	0.06	52.5	3.0	75.5	42.6	76.6	88.3	—	
41801	16 Nov 1970	10.3	7	1.77	3.2	0.18	17.6	11.7	119.1	8.5	82.5	88.5	3.1	
41801	13 Jun 1971	59.8	34	2.93	6.8	0.02	59.0	4.7	70.7	19.9	33.2	29.8	3.6	
41801	18 Jun 1971	30.8	12	1.48	4.1	0.05	15.1	6.6	116.5	12.9	41.8	33.7	2.6	
41801	22 Aug 1971	21.1	5	2.82	3.6	0.04	61.7	12.5	75.8	9.1	43.1	45.6	—	
41801	9 Nov 1969	23.3	7	1.24	3.1	0.00	98.6	4.9	31.3	4.0	17.3	21.6	3.8	

Catch	Date	P	D	Q_p	LAG	BF	SMD	API5	CWI	R/O	PR	SPR	Tp(0)	
		mm	h	m^3s^{-1}	h	m^3s^{-1}	mm	mm	mm	mm	%	%	h	
41801	6 Dec 1972	12.5	9	2.48	4.1	0.06	44.3	8.8	89.5	5.2	41.9	40.6	3.6	
41801	21 May 1973	29.1	6	2.44	2.3	0.03	23.1	1.2	103.1	5.9	20.3	7.7	—	
41801	21 Nov 1974	30.2	17	3.02	3.8	0.15	0.0	11.6	136.6	17.3	57.2	49.6	2.8	
41801	28 Nov 1975	29.5	8	2.84	3.5	0.14	14.4	8.7	119.3	10.7	36.2	25.3	3.0	
a mean												35.6		
g mean					3.9	0.04							3.1	
45002	25 Aug 1963	23.3	16	57.80	10.2	10.14	2.9	3.9	126.0	4.6	19.8	19.5	—	
45002	18 Nov 1963	50.7	35	163.30	9.2	50.58	0.0	17.4	142.4	26.5	52.2	45.5	—	
45002	31 Jan 1964	20.8	10	47.92	7.1	7.35	0.0	1.9	126.9	3.0	14.3	13.8	7.5	#
45002	13 Nov 1964	30.8	24	69.96	7.4	6.04	29.9	1.9	97.0	4.5	14.7	21.7	—	
45002	12 Dec 1964	29.0	17	167.45	8.1	41.80	0.0	7.5	132.5	13.6	47.0	45.1	—	
45002	15 Jan 1965	51.2	44	155.56	11.8	45.47	0.0	13.1	138.1	27.6	54.0	48.3	—	
45002	23 Nov 1965	20.9	6	70.71	6.8	13.87	0.2	0.5	125.3	3.4	16.2	16.1	—	
45002	28 Nov 1965	26.0	21	102.84	5.9	31.17	0.0	6.1	131.1	6.5	25.0	23.5	6.5	#
45002	8 Dec 1965	66.2	47	188.51	14.7	32.22	0.1	3.7	128.6	37.1	56.1	50.8	—	
45002	14 Oct 1966	25.5	13	61.53	7.8	11.03	1.0	8.7	132.7	4.7	18.3	16.4	7.5	#
45002	9 Dec 1966	34.9	26	109.80	8.9	23.14	0.0	3.6	128.6	11.6	33.3	32.4	7.1	#
45002	12 Dec 1966	47.5	44	133.76	12.2	40.20	0.0	6.9	131.9	18.5	38.9	35.3	—	
45002	30 Dec 1966	28.9	19	147.10	8.8	41.89	0.0	10.2	135.2	11.2	38.9	36.3	—	
45002	20 Feb 1967	32.8	21	148.83	9.9	36.45	0.0	21.6	146.6	17.3	52.6	47.2	—	
45002	27 Feb 1967	34.8	21	134.16	6.4	26.51	0.0	3.2	128.2	10.2	29.3	28.5	7.3	#
45002	8 Jan 1968	51.0	21	168.66	13.5	29.95	0.0	5.2	130.2	27.3	53.6	49.9	—	
45002	9 Jul 1968	55.1	29	169.32	10.8	16.44	10.5	3.4	117.9	15.7	28.5	27.3	6.5	#
45002	28 Jul 1969	100.3	29	74.02	10.4	3.74	88.6	0.0	36.4	8.6	8.6	22.8	6.5	#
45002	18 Sep 1969	36.8	10	90.38	5.8	6.63	15.8	5.4	114.6	4.6	12.4	15.0	—	
45002	16 Dec 1965	106.9	54	224.34	8.9	36.42	0.0	8.1	133.1	65.3	61.1	50.5	—	
45002	1 Nov 1970	47.2	16	171.42	13.0	36.40	0.0	3.8	128.8	24.1	51.1	48.4	—	
a mean												33.1		
g mean					9.1	20.64							7.0	
45003	5 Jul 1963	40.5	14	21.85	13.1	2.86	51.7	2.1	75.4	4.9	12.1	24.1	—	
45003	10 Nov 1963	23.2	19	26.62	13.4	6.19	30.1	5.0	99.9	7.0	30.2	36.4	12.8	#
45003	15 Jan 1965	24.2	31	31.35	8.1	7.81	0.0	9.0	134.0	7.9	32.7	30.4	12.1	#
45003	19 Jan 1965	25.3	23	60.84	9.6	5.03	0.0	4.2	129.2	11.7	46.1	45.0	—	
45003	28 Nov 1965	25.3	19	62.01	9.2	6.05	2.4	4.9	127.5	11.2	44.3	43.6	10.0	#
45003	8 Dec 1965	29.7	44	39.12	14.3	5.97	0.1	2.6	127.5	11.6	39.1	38.4	10.9	#
45003	1 Jan 1966	21.2	25	50.24	8.4	9.27	0.0	8.1	133.1	8.7	40.9	38.8	10.0	#
45003	22 Oct 1966	28.8	8	47.48	12.2	3.54	46.8	1.4	79.6	10.5	36.4	47.7	11.9	#
45003	28 Dec 1966	24.4	36	34.29	13.1	4.71	0.0	3.1	128.1	8.9	36.4	35.5	11.1	#
45003	16 Feb 1967	25.6	17	65.01	10.0	3.27	0.0	16.0	141.0	15.2	59.2	55.2	10.5	#
45003	20 Feb 1967	21.3	25	53.63	11.6	9.21	0.0	11.2	136.2	8.9	42.0	39.1	9.7	#
45003	30 Oct 1967	29.4	16	48.43	13.2	5.07	22.1	6.9	109.8	12.1	41.1	44.8	14.7	#
45003	8 Jan 1968	31.7	24	71.59	11.0	4.86	0.0	4.1	129.1	16.0	50.4	49.3	11.5	#
45003	10 Jul 1968	51.6	18	201.86	8.4	3.66	42.0	4.2	87.2	30.2	58.6	65.5	—	
45003	24 Dec 1968	28.8	39	37.77	16.9	6.07	0.0	4.9	129.9	12.3	42.6	41.3	9.0	#
45003	28 Jul 1969	110.8	30	115.31	14.7	1.43	120.5	0.1	4.6	19.4	17.5	38.6	11.1	#
45003	30 Sep 1976	58.4	45	44.13	9.4	12.28	39.3	16.1	101.8	10.5	17.9	20.1	—	
45003	30 Nov 1976	29.5	14	81.62	11.6	9.82	0.0	9.4	134.4	12.6	42.8	40.4	—	
45003	21 Feb 1977	33.9	37	44.79	8.2	13.45	0.0	11.1	136.1	14.1	41.5	38.7	9.5	#
45003	2 May 1977	28.4	16	25.88	9.9	2.34	28.0	2.0	99.0	4.9	17.4	23.8	9.5	#
45003	24 Mar 1979	34.3	24	35.25	10.8	5.70	0.0	1.8	126.8	12.0	35.1	34.6	9.5	#
45003	26 Dec 1979	53.0	25	142.81	13.9	4.55	3.4	1.1	122.7	32.0	60.3	58.1	—	
45003	20 Jan 1980	31.8	25	65.33	7.4	5.84	0.0	4.1	129.1	13.1	41.2	40.1	9.5	#
45003	30 Mar 1980	34.6	48	33.34	12.3	5.48	0.5	3.4	127.9	13.4	38.6	37.8	7.9	#
45003	15 Oct 1980	30.0	16	41.05	13.0	4.45	57.7	5.0	72.3	11.4	37.9	51.0	11.8	#
45003	16 Nov 1980	28.7	20	134.01	8.4	4.70	15.6	7.1	116.5	18.4	64.1	66.2	—	
45003	8 Mar 1981	47.5	65	49.95	11.4	5.92	0.0	6.6	131.6	23.7	49.9	46.4	11.1	#
45003	21 Mar 1981	22.9	28	38.73	13.9	4.49	0.0	2.3	127.3	8.7	38.1	37.5	11.7	#
45003	9 Mar 1982	22.3	27	40.69	10.3	7.14	0.5	5.6	130.1	8.0	35.8	34.4	11.5	#
45003	6 Nov 1982	29.3	18	46.16	13.9	5.76	0.0	10.2	135.2	12.6	42.9	40.3	14.0	#
45003	11 Nov 1982	29.1	9	69.27	10.6	5.71	0.0	4.3	129.3	12.2	41.8	40.7	—	
45003	30 Jan 1983	36.7	28	63.65	11.3	4.64	0.0	4.8	129.8	17.6	48.0	46.7	—	
45003	16 May 1983	26.4	24	29.60	12.1	3.92	2.5	2.6	125.1	8.0	30.3	30.2	—	
45003	14 Dec 1983	28.5	14	51.12	11.4	4.58	59.1	5.9	71.8	11.7	41.0	54.2	10.5	#
45003	18 Dec 1983	59.6	59	62.07	16.8	6.58	37.4	8.0	95.6	29.6	49.6	53.3	10.3	#

Catch	Date	P mm	D h	Q_p m^3s^{-1}	LAG h	BF m^3s^{-1}	SMD mm	API5 mm	CWI mm	R/O mm	PR %	SPR %	Tp(0) h	
45003	16 Jan 1984	24.5	37	42.17	7.8	6.70	3.9	6.3	127.4	9.0	36.6	35.9	11.0	#
45003	25 Jan 1984	64.2	40	109.96	13.0	7.66	0.0	7.2	132.2	37.2	57.9	51.9	—	
45003	6 Apr 1985	28.9	38	31.32	9.7	4.61	0.0	3.6	128.6	10.4	36.1	35.1	10.0	#
45003	25 Dec 1985	60.8	33	130.17	9.2	11.04	21.7	10.5	113.8	32.7	53.8	52.8	8.5	#
45003	1 Dec 1976	18.4	21	39.48	11.5	11.80	0.0	20.6	145.6	6.6	35.9	30.7	11.5	#
a mean												41.9		
g mean					11.1	5.56							10.7	
45004	16 Feb 1967	35.6	30	62.95	9.3	7.75	0.0	8.2	133.2	12.2	34.3	32.1	9.2	#
45004	3 May 1967	48.4	28	42.02	12.7	2.24	39.6	0.0	85.4	8.4	17.3	25.1	9.8	#
45004	16 Oct 1967	29.4	32	60.66	13.1	8.80	35.9	8.2	97.3	12.8	43.4	50.2	11.7	#
45004	8 Jan 1968	30.8	27	69.60	7.6	5.19	0.0	3.3	128.3	13.1	42.4	41.5	6.3	#
45004	27 Jun 1968	27.3	10	71.61	10.4	2.86	34.6	9.0	99.4	13.8	50.6	56.9	9.9	#
45004	27 Oct 1968	38.9	35	44.22	16.9	2.36	7.0	0.3	118.3	13.6	34.9	36.5	9.5	#
45004	25 Nov 1968	27.3	28	47.58	13.9	4.74	0.1	2.6	127.5	10.7	39.2	38.5	8.5	#
45004	16 Dec 1968	23.9	14	64.65	8.8	6.25	0.0	10.8	135.8	10.9	45.7	42.9	7.5	#
45004	17 Dec 1968	15.6	11	73.00	7.8	7.68	0.0	23.1	148.1	10.5	67.2	61.4	—	
45004	21 Dec 1968	23.1	23	71.01	4.4	8.64	0.0	8.1	133.1	10.6	45.8	43.7	4.8	#
45004	24 Dec 1968	30.6	31	60.59	13.5	8.35	0.0	4.8	129.8	12.9	42.1	40.8	10.3	#
45004	12 Mar 1969	25.7	24	78.35	7.0	9.04	0.6	14.0	138.4	11.3	44.1	40.7	6.5	#
45004	28 Jul 1969	83.4	26	73.34	15.7	1.37	120.1	0.2	5.1	12.0	14.4	37.9	—	
45004	9 Jul 1968	56.9	31	217.91	6.3	4.19	43.2	2.4	84.2	21.6	37.9	44.8	—	
45004	6 Mar 1972	59.9	47	89.32	11.3	10.88	0.0	12.6	137.6	31.0	51.8	44.9	—	
45004	25 Dec 1985	71.7	36	154.36	10.3	10.22	21.1	12.0	115.9	39.3	54.8	52.0	7.3	#
a mean												43.1		
g mean					10.0	5.39							8.2	
45009	12 Dec 1966	49.0	27	42.21	8.3	16.75	0.0	12.7	137.7	16.2	33.0	27.7	—	
45009	30 Dec 1966	33.0	19	44.67	6.1	18.01	0.0	15.6	140.6	8.0	24.1	20.2	—	
45009	20 Feb 1967	40.4	25	51.82	6.2	15.10	0.0	15.5	140.5	16.0	39.7	35.6	4.3	#
45009	27 Feb 1967	31.8	11	37.23	6.4	9.21	0.0	3.5	128.5	7.0	22.1	21.2	—	
45009	4 Nov 1967	46.2	13	46.24	6.8	12.82	0.0	8.3	133.3	12.0	26.0	22.3	—	
45009	22 Dec 1967	30.2	20	33.43	6.4	5.82	0.0	5.9	130.9	6.7	22.1	20.6	5.1	#
45009	8 Jan 1968	49.5	21	48.18	9.6	12.37	0.0	6.9	131.9	19.9	40.3	36.4	—	
45009	9 Jul 1968	56.5	23	43.53	9.5	5.78	11.5	2.7	116.2	9.5	16.9	15.9	3.9	#
45009	28 Oct 1968	33.7	13	21.56	7.9	5.32	0.0	3.8	128.8	4.7	13.8	12.8	—	
45009	18 Sep 1969	24.9	10	13.38	4.6	1.52	2.8	4.7	126.9	1.2	4.9	4.4	—	
45009	22 Nov 1970	27.3	19	22.67	5.3	10.69	0.0	4.1	129.1	3.4	12.3	11.3	—	
45009	25 Jan 1971	25.1	14	32.00	5.0	16.41	0.0	11.6	136.6	4.1	16.2	13.3	—	
45009	18 Oct 1971	39.3	17	28.34	8.5	5.15	56.8	9.2	77.4	7.2	18.4	30.3	—	
45009	6 Jun 1972	25.8	9	19.88	6.4	4.95	0.0	5.8	130.8	3.4	13.2	11.7	5.7	#
45009	11 Nov 1972	52.7	29	33.00	8.6	4.09	0.1	9.7	134.6	10.6	20.2	15.1	6.6	#
45009	1 Apr 1973	41.6	15	14.81	8.7	1.28	13.2	1.4	113.2	3.2	7.8	10.1	6.0	#
45009	11 Nov 1974	17.7	13	20.30	5.9	5.71	0.0	5.1	130.1	3.4	19.3	18.0	—	
45009	19 Jan 1975	28.3	23	33.90	5.9	6.59	0.0	4.0	129.0	4.9	17.2	16.2	4.5	#
45009	21 Jan 1975	36.5	22	41.88	6.7	14.19	0.0	12.6	137.6	9.5	26.1	22.9	4.5	#
45009	28 Jan 1975	22.1	12	42.62	5.3	13.21	0.0	9.6	134.6	5.4	24.6	22.2	5.2	#
a mean												19.4		
g mean					6.8	7.48							5.0	
45011	9 Dec 1966	43.9	24	70.29	8.1	8.62	0.0	8.6	133.6	19.9	45.4	42.1	4.0	#
45011	12 Dec 1966	57.5	29	81.96	6.7	12.03	0.0	14.5	139.5	29.5	51.3	44.3	—	
45011	30 Dec 1966	41.2	19	100.57	4.6	13.83	0.0	21.8	146.8	23.2	56.3	50.3	—	
45011	27 Feb 1967	42.7	19	88.69	4.5	10.16	0.0	6.8	131.8	15.3	35.9	33.3	5.6	#
45011	1 Apr 1967	36.7	23	49.28	7.4	2.59	2.4	2.2	124.8	11.2	30.4	30.4	—	
45011	10 Jul 1968	48.0	16	131.99	3.8	5.57	3.6	4.2	125.6	14.4	30.0	27.9	2.7	#
45011	28 Jul 1969	100.7	28	27.18	10.1	1.09	87.2	0.5	38.3	8.4	8.3	22.0	5.5	#
45011	1 Nov 1970	62.0	17	120.71	5.8	11.44	0.0	19.1	144.1	38.3	61.8	53.1	5.1	#
45011	21 Apr 1970	37.7	16	40.68	5.5	3.20	0.0	0.3	125.3	9.9	26.3	26.2	3.2	#
45011	19 Oct 1971	44.8	20	85.98	5.4	7.52	18.1	7.2	114.1	16.8	37.5	38.9	—	
45011	12 Nov 1972	56.6	27	78.93	4.9	9.52	0.5	10.2	134.7	21.6	38.2	32.6	4.5	#
45011	1 Apr 1973	46.2	14	47.11	5.6	1.84	11.7	1.9	115.2	8.1	17.6	18.4	2.5	#
45011	18 Oct 1974	36.1	18	54.82	4.9	4.51	0.0	2.0	127.0	12.9	35.8	35.3	3.3	#
45011	15 Dec 1974	23.5	27	61.42	7.8	7.65	0.0	3.1	128.1	11.7	49.7	48.9	5.5	#
a mean												36.0		
g mean					5.9	5.70							4.0	

Catch	Date	P	D	Q_p	LAG	BF	SMD	API5	CWI	R/O	PR	SPR	Tp(0)	
		mm	h	m^3s^{-1}	h	m^3s^{-1}	mm	mm	mm	mm	%	%	h	
46003	16 Aug 1963	21.7	24	73.30	4.2	8.31	6.4	8.8	127.4	4.9	22.6	21.9	3.7	#
46003	4 Sep 1963	27.1	30	68.65	8.2	9.75	0.2	5.5	130.3	6.7	24.7	23.3	—	
46003	3 Nov 1963	31.2	8	130.03	4.4	16.80	0.0	16.7	141.7	9.3	29.8	25.5	4.7	#
46003	4 Nov 1963	32.7	16	128.02	2.3	32.47	0.0	23.1	148.1	5.7	17.3	11.4	2.3	#
46003	18 Mar 1964	28.4	13	115.69	5.8	28.72	0.0	16.6	141.6	10.0	35.3	31.1	6.0	#
46003	14 Jul 1964	30.7	15	69.26	3.8	5.90	17.0	3.5	111.5	6.6	21.6	24.9	—	
46003	13 Nov 1964	36.1	15	100.34	4.2	3.43	0.0	9.6	134.6	9.1	25.3	22.8	3.5	#
46003	12 Dec 1964	29.6	15	127.17	5.0	20.85	0.0	12.0	137.0	12.0	40.7	37.6	5.1	#
46003	13 Jan 1965	50.5	15	195.84	4.4	17.55	0.0	7.7	132.7	19.0	37.6	33.3	4.0	#
46003	2 Aug 1965	39.6	46	97.38	6.5	8.60	1.2	4.2	128.0	11.0	27.7	26.9	4.5	#
46003	28 Nov 1965	39.6	13	190.45	5.1	18.09	0.0	12.7	137.7	15.5	39.2	36.0	4.4	#
46003	10 Jan 1966	49.8	28	129.34	6.5	14.48	0.3	0.4	125.1	15.4	31.0	28.7	—	
46003	24 Jan 1966	51.9	20	145.14	8.8	11.27	0.0	2.1	127.1	19.2	36.9	33.8	—	
46003	2 Mar 1966	43.7	12	163.16	5.4	19.60	0.0	4.7	129.7	18.7	42.8	40.4	—	
46003	1 Dec 1966	24.4	12	85.58	4.6	9.92	0.0	9.0	134.0	7.6	31.2	28.9	4.3	#
46003	9 Dec 1966	29.6	19	94.45	5.1	9.66	0.0	4.0	129.0	10.3	34.8	33.7	—	
46003	25 Jan 1967	29.1	16	118.99	3.2	16.95	0.0	10.9	135.9	11.7	40.2	37.4	2.9	#
46003	20 Feb 1967	34.5	17	139.35	5.0	21.30	0.0	21.4	146.4	14.1	40.8	35.4	4.9	#
46003	16 Oct 1967	59.9	22	165.31	9.1	23.52	0.0	13.2	138.2	25.0	41.8	34.8	—	
46003	21 Jun 1968	52.2	23	116.75	8.2	6.01	9.2	7.1	122.9	15.0	28.7	26.5	4.2	#
46003	24 Jun 1968	41.4	17	188.19	6.1	9.94	3.0	12.7	134.7	14.6	35.3	32.2	3.9	#
46003	27 Oct 1968	44.2	16	137.09	7.9	16.62	0.0	9.1	134.1	17.6	39.8	36.2	6.0	#
46003	28 Jul 1969	121.7	31	192.44	6.1	4.71	78.6	0.2	46.6	22.1	18.2	27.9	2.5	#
a mean												30.0		
g mean					5.4	12.53							4.0	
46005	13 Nov 1964	38.1	15	24.81	4.8	0.48	0.0	9.6	134.6	24.5	64.4	62.0	3.0	#
46005	13 Jan 1965	58.4	17	44.89	3.1	0.93	0.0	7.7	132.7	37.8	64.8	59.4	—	
46005	28 Nov 1965	39.9	13	38.15	3.2	1.28	0.0	12.5	137.5	25.4	63.6	60.5	2.7	#
46005	24 Feb 1966	84.3	17	39.68	2.6	1.55	0.0	11.5	136.5	68.0	80.7	71.4	—	
46005	14 Oct 1966	23.1	8	25.26	2.2	1.01	1.0	10.4	134.4	15.9	68.8	66.5	—	
46005	28 Dec 1966	48.3	20	31.69	5.2	3.00	0.0	6.4	131.4	28.0	57.9	54.3	5.1	#
46005	25 Jan 1967	38.9	16	37.96	2.2	1.63	0.0	10.9	135.9	26.8	68.8	66.1	—	
46005	27 Feb 1967	67.9	21	37.24	0.0	1.34	0.0	4.9	129.9	46.6	68.6	62.7	—	
46005	22 Jul 1967	93.6	12	60.64	3.4	0.43	55.6	1.9	71.3	36.3	38.8	44.9	—	
46005	27 Jun 1968	38.6	10	39.42	2.7	1.46	0.0	22.5	147.5	35.4	91.6	86.0	—	
46005	21 Dec 1968	34.4	17	30.38	1.0	0.98	0.0	8.5	133.5	22.8	66.4	64.3	3.0	#
46005	13 Dec 1969	49.2	18	31.43	5.1	0.75	0.0	0.7	125.7	29.0	59.0	56.7	3.9	#
46005	8 Sep 1970	32.6	9	38.34	3.7	2.13	0.0	12.6	137.6	24.2	74.2	71.0	2.6	#
46005	12 Nov 1972	44.6	14	8.66	3.1	0.21	0.0	13.3	138.3	9.8	21.9	17.3	4.0	#
46005	4 Aug 1973	109.9	43	50.79	9.0	0.35	50.8	2.2	76.4	93.9	85.4	88.8	2.5	#
46005	13 Sep 1975	49.2	15	25.69	2.4	0.50	28.2	8.7	105.5	25.4	51.7	54.4	3.5	#
46005	10 Nov 1974	48.5	19	43.92	3.6	1.20	0.0	8.3	133.3	38.6	79.6	75.5	3.1	#
46005	3 Aug 1974	43.6	21	13.28	4.0	0.46	28.7	0.9	97.2	13.5	30.9	36.7	2.0	#
46005	12 Feb 1976	51.4	29	23.35	3.2	0.94	0.0	6.7	131.7	39.9	77.7	73.6	—	
46005	5 Oct 1976	56.6	29	17.38	5.3	1.01	0.2	16.2	141.0	27.8	49.1	41.9	3.5	#
46005	14 Oct 1976	104.1	34	17.73	5.8	1.48	0.0	6.3	131.3	50.8	48.8	38.9	3.3	#
a mean												59.7		
g mean					3.4	0.92							3.2	
46802	9 Mar 1963	59.1	13	19.20	6.0	1.14	0.0	6.4	131.4	36.8	62.3	57.2	—	
46802	17 Nov 1963	45.2	9	23.91	1.9	2.28	0.0	8.0	133.0	36.2	80.1	76.7	—	
46802	13 Nov 1964	45.8	13	14.33	4.2	0.15	0.0	0.4	125.4	25.3	55.2	53.6	1.8	#
46802	13 Jan 1965	48.1	11	17.38	2.1	0.68	0.0	9.5	134.5	30.2	62.8	58.5	—	
46802	16 Nov 1965	47.6	11	24.54	2.7	0.88	0.0	19.8	144.8	27.1	56.9	50.1	—	
46802	28 Nov 1965	36.4	9	22.01	3.5	0.37	0.0	9.7	134.7	26.9	74.0	71.6	2.7	#
46802	29 Dec 1965	38.4	13	13.56	4.3	0.09	0.0	1.9	126.9	24.6	64.1	63.6	1.5	#
46802	24 Jan 1966	45.4	15	16.03	5.2	0.10	0.0	3.7	128.7	33.1	73.0	70.6	2.5	#
46802	24 Feb 1966	62.2	16	17.57	1.6	0.79	0.0	18.4	143.4	44.9	72.2	63.7	—	
46802	2 Mar 1966	49.3	15	16.28	3.6	0.22	0.0	9.0	134.0	34.9	70.7	66.3	2.3	#
46802	18 Jan 1967	50.1	15	15.03	6.8	0.07	5.5	1.9	121.4	33.7	67.2	65.8	—	
46802	27 Feb 1967	57.0	20	20.11	0.6	0.69	0.0	6.3	131.3	36.4	63.9	59.1	—	
46802	21 May 1967	38.4	8	17.92	2.7	0.17	3.6	4.6	126.0	19.4	50.6	50.3	—	
46802	4 Sep 1967	35.0	7	20.05	1.8	0.37	0.0	10.2	135.2	20.6	58.9	56.4	—	
46802	10 Oct 1967	60.5	38	17.69	7.3	0.21	0.0	3.9	128.9	41.4	68.5	63.8	2.5	#
46802	24 Jun 1968	45.1	17	22.00	3.8	0.09	1.1	17.3	141.2	33.2	73.7	68.2	2.3	#

Catch	Date	P mm	D h	Q_p m^3s^{-1}	LAG h	BF m^3s^{-1}	SMD mm	API5 mm	CWI mm	R/O mm	PR %	SPR %	Tp(0) h	
46802	27 Jun 1968	45.1	10	20.11	2.2	0.59	0.0	28.9	153.9	34.5	76.4	67.8	1.5	#
46802	21 Dec 1968	40.3	7	19.88	1.7	0.67	0.0	10.2	135.2	30.3	75.3	72.6	—	
a mean												63.1		
g mean					2.9	0.34							2.1	
46805	9 Dec 1961	26.8	10	5.79	1.7	0.51	0.0	14.0	139.0	14.0	52.3	48.8	1.8	#
46805	17 Nov 1963	56.4	9	12.76	1.9	0.59	0.0	9.3	134.3	29.7	52.7	47.2	1.2	#
46805	6 Jun 1964	21.7	14	4.61	1.2	0.49	2.9	4.2	126.3	11.1	51.0	50.7	—	
46805	12 Nov 1964	53.8	13	5.77	3.5	0.25	0.0	9.0	134.0	25.1	46.7	41.6	2.0	#
46805	13 Jan 1965	49.9	11	6.41	1.5	0.86	0.0	7.5	132.5	26.9	53.9	49.8	—	
46805	13 Jul 1965	52.1	17	7.64	2.9	1.05	0.0	50.3	175.3	23.5	45.2	30.0	1.1	#
46805	16 Nov 1965	23.2	7	5.34	1.7	0.57	0.0	9.0	134.0	11.3	48.8	46.5	1.5	#
46805	28 Nov 1965	44.1	9	7.75	3.0	0.65	0.0	11.4	136.4	19.8	44.8	40.7	1.8	#
a mean												44.4		
g mean					2.0	0.58							1.6	
47007	12 Jan 1965	28.2	19	20.08	4.8	2.44	0.0	4.6	129.6	9.0	31.8	30.4	4.1	#
47007	10 Nov 1965	38.5	17	18.79	4.2	1.75	0.0	10.6	135.6	8.1	21.1	18.1	5.7	#
47007	28 Nov 1965	35.9	22	25.06	4.3	3.70	0.0	7.7	132.7	11.6	32.3	30.1	—	
47007	17 Dec 1965	48.1	41	20.81	9.6	5.80	0.0	16.6	141.6	27.8	57.8	51.6	4.0	#
47007	22 Dec 1965	26.1	14	21.58	6.1	5.08	0.0	9.0	134.0	9.9	38.1	35.6	5.0	#
47007	28 Dec 1965	33.1	17	21.78	6.7	3.12	0.0	0.8	125.8	11.1	33.4	32.9	5.1	#
47007	24 Jan 1966	38.6	15	19.11	6.5	2.01	0.0	1.9	126.9	8.9	23.1	22.3	3.7	#
47007	24 Feb 1966	30.3	17	20.91	2.9	5.02	0.0	11.1	136.1	11.8	39.1	36.1	—	
47007	2 Mar 1966	26.7	14	21.88	6.0	3.80	0.0	9.4	134.4	10.4	39.0	36.4	4.3	#
47007	6 Aug 1966	53.5	21	21.95	4.7	0.91	2.6	4.8	127.2	9.4	17.5	13.8	5.5	#
47007	22 Oct 1966	44.1	11	22.00	5.7	2.96	0.8	3.0	127.2	10.0	22.7	20.6	5.5	#
47007	20 Feb 1967	24.5	11	20.48	4.3	4.37	0.0	19.3	144.3	8.4	34.4	29.3	4.9	#
47007	27 Feb 1967	36.9	20	19.46	3.5	2.95	0.0	2.9	127.9	12.3	33.4	32.4	—	
47007	24 Jun 1968	33.8	17	19.04	6.9	1.83	0.0	14.5	139.5	9.3	27.4	23.5	5.5	#
47007	27 Jun 1968	53.0	11	23.31	7.1	4.88	0.4	20.2	144.8	17.6	33.3	25.4	3.7	#
47007	12 Feb 1976	31.8	28	11.15	4.9	1.94	0.0	5.8	130.8	9.0	28.4	26.6	—	
47007	30 Nov 1976	30.7	15	13.49	5.4	3.54	0.0	14.1	139.1	7.0	22.9	19.0	3.0	#
a mean												28.5		
g mean					5.3	2.99							4.5	
47008	18 Jun 1971	31.2	14	58.33	11.9	1.60	41.9	4.6	87.7	19.6	62.9	72.2	—	
47008	12 Jan 1972	23.4	9	30.42	5.1	4.17	0.0	16.6	141.6	9.4	40.0	35.8	—	
47008	14 Feb 1972	22.1	11	30.32	6.5	4.05	0.0	3.1	128.1	8.3	37.6	36.8	—	
47008	1 Dec 1972	34.8	25	38.90	14.1	3.41	0.0	5.6	130.6	20.6	59.1	57.7	—	
47008	1 Apr 1973	24.5	15	14.20	7.4	0.94	8.6	2.0	118.4	3.8	15.5	17.1	—	
47008	22 May 1973	19.4	19	15.32	7.6	0.85	9.8	1.3	116.5	4.1	21.2	23.3	—	
47008	15 Dec 1973	10.1	18	11.07	8.0	2.78	0.0	2.6	127.6	2.7	26.3	25.6	—	
47008	29 Dec 1973	9.1	9	9.94	6.8	2.23	0.0	1.1	126.1	1.5	16.4	16.1	—	
47008	8 Jan 1974	19.2	9	37.45	3.7	6.99	0.0	11.4	136.4	9.0	46.8	44.0	—	
47008	25 Jan 1974	29.4	28	41.01	5.7	3.15	0.0	4.2	129.2	12.0	40.8	39.8	—	
47008	29 Jan 1974	53.9	28	50.84	9.8	5.31	0.0	9.7	134.7	29.9	55.5	50.2	—	
47008	8 Feb 1974	36.3	21	61.12	12.7	4.30	0.0	11.8	136.8	26.4	72.8	69.9	—	
47008	26 Sep 1974	39.6	22	75.43	6.7	4.97	0.8	12.5	136.7	25.3	64.0	61.1	—	
47008	13 Sep 1975	37.8	15	5.21	8.9	0.24	65.8	7.4	66.6	1.9	5.0	19.6	—	
47008	14 Oct 1976	62.8	47	55.67	10.3	3.06	8.4	2.6	119.2	35.2	56.1	53.5	6.7	#
47008	19 Nov 1977	19.9	38	17.73	8.0	3.25	9.6	3.8	119.2	6.1	30.5	31.9	—	
47008	23 Nov 1977	11.6	24	10.18	5.1	2.73	6.8	3.0	121.2	1.8	15.7	16.7	5.5	#
47008	31 Jul 1978	26.5	15	8.43	8.1	0.59	40.0	1.0	86.0	2.9	10.9	20.6	—	
47008	9 Dec 1979	32.4	34	31.31	5.6	4.19	0.0	3.9	128.9	11.5	35.4	34.4	—	
47008	26 Dec 1979	99.0	44	123.66	9.4	2.14	0.0	0.9	125.9	60.8	61.4	53.4	5.2	#
47008	28 Mar 1980	12.7	28	8.28	6.1	1.72	0.0	3.1	128.1	2.2	17.5	16.7	5.5	#
47008	30 Mar 1980	44.1	49	42.06	7.3	2.98	1.0	4.6	128.6	21.8	49.4	47.3	5.5	#
47008	27 Jun 1980	30.9	17	22.68	5.9	1.79	34.1	2.9	93.8	7.4	23.9	31.7	7.3	#
47008	20 Sep 1980	48.7	32	45.79	7.8	2.42	46.1	2.8	81.7	19.6	40.2	49.0	4.5	#
47008	15 Oct 1980	34.4	20	44.17	8.1	3.66	3.2	4.9	126.7	19.2	55.9	55.5	7.5	#
47008	9 Mar 1981	65.8	65	61.46	12.1	6.54	0.0	9.1	134.1	36.9	56.1	49.4	6.5	#
47008	21 Mar 1981	46.9	31	36.33	8.4	3.27	0.0	1.1	126.1	23.3	49.6	47.6	6.3	#
47008	19 Sep 1981	36.1	14	32.92	5.8	1.99	33.0	16.2	108.2	9.3	25.8	30.0	5.0	#
47008	1 Oct 1981	38.1	40	26.91	7.7	3.38	10.0	5.2	120.2	15.8	41.5	42.7	4.7	#
47008	13 Dec 1981	29.6	23	49.37	6.9	4.95	0.3	2.9	127.6	16.5	55.9	55.3	8.8	#

Catch	Date	P	D	Q_p	LAG	BF	SMD	API5	CWI	R/O	PR	SPR	Tp(0)	
		mm	h	m^3s^{-1}	h	m^3s^{-1}	mm	mm	mm	mm	%	%	h	
47008	3 Jan 1983	46.9	36	41.22	9.2	4.38	0.0	1.9	126.9	21.3	45.4	43.2	6.0	#
47008	14 Dec 1983	36.2	12	47.09	7.5	3.45	10.5	4.6	119.1	17.7	48.8	50.3	6.5	#
47008	18 Dec 1983	62.6	59	50.10	9.5	4.84	9.9	5.0	120.1	39.0	62.3	59.5	5.3	#
47008	27 Jan 1985	25.8	14	31.36	5.0	4.37	0.0	2.7	127.7	10.5	40.6	39.9	4.5	#
47008	11 Aug 1985	19.9	18	20.00	4.4	2.13	46.1	4.9	83.8	4.6	23.3	33.6	6.5	#
47008	23 Dec 1985	23.9	24	33.64	6.1	4.73	0.4	8.5	133.1	9.5	39.7	37.7	6.5	#
47008	25 Mar 1981	14.1	15	32.67	9.9	4.56	0.4	7.7	132.3	6.3	44.8	43.0	6.0	#
47008	12 Mar 1981	16.4	22	26.44	6.2	6.89	0.0	16.5	141.5	5.4	32.9	28.8	6.7	#
a mean												40.6		
g mean					7.4	2.86							6.0	
47011	17 Jun 1971	34.5	12	16.55	3.7	1.15	15.1	1.3	111.2	3.8	11.0	14.2	3.7	#
47011	15 Oct 1971	36.2	20	16.94	6.7	0.67	53.8	7.1	78.3	7.2	19.8	31.2	7.4	#
47011	18 Oct 1971	14.1	20	12.24	9.6	0.82	21.8	7.5	110.7	4.2	29.8	33.2	—	
47011	18 Dec 1971	38.3	31	18.46	4.9	1.46	0.0	0.2	125.2	6.1	15.9	15.6	—	
47011	23 May 1972	26.4	9	31.73	3.1	3.46	1.1	5.7	129.6	8.1	30.8	29.5	3.4	#
47011	5 Jun 1972	30.3	18	22.89	7.1	2.48	1.7	3.6	126.9	8.3	27.3	26.6	—	
47011	11 Nov 1972	35.1	21	27.46	4.1	2.15	0.0	4.9	129.9	8.3	23.6	22.2	4.1	#
47011	1 Apr 1973	30.4	13	13.65	6.5	1.20	2.6	1.5	123.9	5.2	17.0	17.0	7.0	#
47011	4 Aug 1973	70.4	43	26.55	10.1	0.99	27.9	2.3	99.4	21.4	30.4	31.7	—	
47011	19 Jan 1975	38.3	29	42.89	4.7	3.22	0.0	9.6	134.6	18.5	48.2	45.7	—	
47011	2 Nov 1975	17.0	11	7.28	4.8	1.03	0.0	4.9	129.9	2.2	12.9	11.4	6.2	#
47011	4 Jan 1974	46.7	27	40.40	3.2	4.69	0.0	5.1	130.1	25.3	54.2	51.1	—	
47011	3 Aug 1975	12.0	4	8.42	0.0	0.63	78.0	0.3	47.3	2.4	19.7	38.9	—	
47011	26 Sep 1974	39.1	22	22.25	4.9	3.40	0.0	12.3	137.3	8.9	22.7	19.4	—	
47011	18 Oct 1974	29.7	15	16.19	4.2	2.76	0.0	2.3	127.3	7.9	26.5	25.7	—	
47011	12 Nov 1974	29.5	21	27.10	6.8	4.09	0.0	9.0	134.0	14.7	49.7	47.4	5.9	#
47011	21 Dec 1974	19.4	10	26.13	5.2	3.64	0.0	5.1	130.1	9.4	48.2	46.8	—	
a mean												29.9		
g mean					5.3	1.83							5.2	
47013	28 Jan 1976	50.7	23	11.45	5.6	0.36	0.0	3.2	128.2	19.3	38.0	34.8	3.1	#
47013	24 Sep 1976	48.6	5	6.01	2.6	0.28	84.9	6.9	47.0	5.4	11.1	28.6	2.3	#
47013	23 Jan 1978	38.9	21	8.38	2.0	1.01	0.0	13.7	138.7	12.3	31.6	28.2	2.5	#
47013	31 Jan 1979	42.4	27	7.47	6.4	0.74	0.0	5.0	130.0	17.0	40.1	38.0	3.5	#
47013	24 Mar 1979	43.1	22	4.94	5.5	0.72	1.6	2.0	125.4	10.1	23.4	22.3	4.0	#
47013	26 Dec 1979	130.5	39	21.81	4.8	1.08	0.0	2.7	127.7	65.0	49.8	38.6	3.8	#
47013	3 Feb 1980	67.7	40	11.69	5.0	0.90	0.0	12.3	137.3	24.9	36.8	29.1	3.8	#
47013	20 Sep 1980	72.7	16	13.81	2.8	0.57	70.7	5.2	59.5	24.8	34.1	45.3	2.9	#
47013	14 Nov 1980	84.7	48	7.08	7.4	0.42	0.9	0.6	124.7	26.9	31.8	25.4	—	
47013	21 Mar 1981	68.7	30	6.82	8.9	0.76	0.0	2.1	127.1	24.5	35.7	30.5	11.2	#
47013	19 Sep 1981	51.3	20	11.18	5.0	0.29	49.8	21.4	96.6	17.9	34.8	39.4	3.3	#
47013	1 Oct 1981	69.1	38	8.58	5.4	0.63	8.5	10.9	127.4	31.4	45.5	40.1	4.0	#
47013	19 Dec 1981	70.6	19	20.54	3.7	1.00	0.6	2.9	127.3	33.2	47.0	41.5	2.3	#
47013	9 Mar 1982	37.3	20	7.99	7.6	1.09	0.0	14.8	139.8	15.4	41.3	37.6	4.5	#
47013	1 Oct 1982	52.2	18	9.00	6.5	0.35	9.7	3.4	118.7	16.9	32.3	31.3	3.5	#
47013	11 Nov 1982	39.6	16	9.10	4.4	1.13	0.0	6.6	131.6	14.3	36.1	34.4	4.0	#
47013	2 Jan 1983	84.6	39	10.53	6.3	0.75	0.0	5.2	130.2	32.4	38.3	30.6	3.5	#
47013	14 Dec 1983	52.2	28	7.34	5.3	0.62	9.0	6.1	122.1	14.7	28.1	26.2	—	
47013	27 Jan 1985	40.6	23	7.15	5.1	0.82	0.0	7.8	132.8	11.4	28.1	25.8	3.5	#
47013	11 Aug 1985	34.1	14	7.30	4.0	0.56	42.5	7.0	89.5	10.2	29.8	38.7	3.9	#
47013	23 Aug 1985	35.0	22	5.42	5.4	0.63	35.0	5.5	95.5	9.4	26.8	34.2	4.0	#
47013	21 Dec 1985	30.3	13	5.99	5.2	0.61	4.6	3.9	124.3	8.4	27.8	28.0	3.0	#
47013	7 Feb 1980	57.9	54	8.20	6.0	1.09	0.0	18.8	143.8	25.9	44.7	36.6	3.8	#
47013	23 Dec 1985	36.4	40	5.85	7.0	0.76	1.4	15.3	138.9	12.0	33.0	29.5	4.5	#
47013	4 Jan 1983	41.5	21	6.54	5.8	1.43	0.0	40.9	165.9	13.8	33.3	22.5	—	
a mean												32.7		
g mean					5.1	0.68							3.6	
48004	17 Jan 1970	36.2	22	14.00	8.2	2.05	0.0	13.2	138.2	17.1	47.3	44.0	3.5	#
48004	11 Feb 1970	28.9	14	8.03	6.9	1.48	0.0	3.2	128.2	11.6	40.1	39.3	6.3	#
48004	21 Aug 1970	46.4	27	7.23	13.8	0.56	35.6	12.1	101.5	12.3	26.6	30.8	8.0	#
48004	6 Nov 1970	31.0	24	4.26	10.3	0.52	0.0	5.7	130.7	7.3	23.4	21.9	9.3	#
48004	18 Jun 1971	39.8	50	3.24	5.2	0.29	28.6	1.7	98.1	6.1	15.3	22.0	8.5	#
48004	12 Jun 1972	38.0	35	6.01	13.6	0.69	3.4	3.1	124.7	10.6	27.9	27.9	7.5	#
48004	1 Dec 1972	34.6	30	5.88	7.0	1.05	0.0	5.2	130.2	10.1	29.3	28.0	5.5	#

Catch	Date	P	D	Q_p	LAG	BF	SMD	API5	CWI	R/O	PR	SPR	Tp(0)	
		mm	h	m^3s^{-1}	h	m^3s^{-1}	mm	mm	mm	mm	%	%	h	
48004	27 Nov 1973	61.8	31	14.85	11.1	0.59	0.0	1.9	126.9	21.0	34.0	29.6	7.3	#
48004	26 Sep 1974	40.8	23	14.77	10.2	1.33	0.7	11.1	135.4	19.4	47.5	44.5	7.0	#
48004	17 Oct 1974	40.4	20	7.68	8.9	1.01	0.0	3.2	128.2	13.1	32.5	31.4	5.7	#
48004	12 Nov 1974	30.2	14	12.32	6.4	1.57	0.0	9.5	134.5	15.4	51.1	48.7	7.2	#
48004	28 Jan 1976	78.8	47	13.81	8.6	0.65	0.0	4.7	129.7	25.5	32.4	25.4	11.3	#
48004	13 Oct 1976	48.7	30	4.59	10.4	0.88	13.2	4.2	116.0	11.8	24.2	24.4	14.9	#
48004	9 Dec 1977	44.7	10	9.86	6.0	1.16	1.8	9.0	132.2	11.5	25.8	22.6	6.0	#
48004	26 Dec 1979	95.3	28	23.12	5.9	2.16	0.0	2.3	127.3	46.1	48.4	40.3	—	
48004	3 Feb 1980	48.8	33	7.60	11.7	1.18	0.0	8.1	133.1	15.7	32.2	28.1	7.0	#
48004	20 Sep 1980	67.2	16	13.75	6.0	0.56	69.8	4.2	59.4	17.9	26.7	38.5	6.0	#
48004	17 Nov 1980	29.9	14	7.12	4.8	1.25	0.0	14.6	139.6	8.3	27.7	24.0	5.3	#
48004	9 Mar 1981	62.7	54	4.70	9.3	1.12	0.0	14.2	139.2	17.0	27.1	19.5	—	
48004	21 Mar 1981	44.8	32	3.87	9.3	1.07	0.3	1.7	126.4	7.6	17.0	15.3	4.7	#
48004	19 Sep 1981	40.5	18	3.58	8.4	0.33	49.7	14.0	89.3	6.3	15.5	24.1	5.5	#
48004	19 Dec 1981	61.1	19	8.31	2.5	1.74	0.0	3.5	128.5	8.5	13.9	9.2	4.9	#
48004	5 Mar 1982	42.4	32	3.27	9.2	1.11	0.0	2.6	127.6	8.1	19.1	17.6	—	
48004	15 Oct 1982	39.9	19	3.77	9.3	1.17	0.0	5.2	130.2	7.4	18.5	17.2	—	
48004	5 Nov 1982	67.3	30	5.69	4.8	0.94	0.0	8.3	133.3	11.0	16.3	9.6	4.7	#
48004	11 Nov 1982	27.7	11	4.60	5.7	1.63	0.0	5.1	130.1	4.5	16.4	15.1	5.7	#
48004	14 Dec 1982	27.0	15	4.32	4.3	1.65	0.3	5.6	130.3	4.5	16.7	15.3	4.5	#
48004	2 Jan 1983	47.9	40	4.19	6.6	1.11	0.0	3.2	128.2	10.0	20.8	18.0	4.3	#
48004	27 Jan 1985	36.4	13	3.79	5.9	1.11	0.0	5.3	130.3	5.5	15.1	13.7	4.5	#
48004	7 Feb 1980	43.8	46	6.53	10.7	1.84	0.0	14.2	139.2	16.7	38.1	33.4	6.5	#
48004	9 Mar 1982	22.5	21	3.62	11.9	1.57	0.0	11.4	136.4	4.5	19.9	17.0	7.0	#
a mean												25.7		
g mean					7.6	1.03							6.3	
48005	25 Apr 1969	23.7	13	2.29	6.2	0.19	0.0	3.0	128.0	2.3	9.5	7.6	4.5	#
48005	28 Jul 1969	86.1	15	2.71	7.5	0.16	3.6	0.1	121.5	5.1	5.9	—	7.6	#
48005	**18 Jun 1971*	17.1	8	0.55	4.7	0.13	28.6	0.7	97.1	0.5	3.1	8.8	—	
48005	**6 Aug 1971*	3.5	4	1.88	13.7	0.08	62.0	4.6	67.6	1.6	44.5	58.4	—	
48005	**8 Nov 1971*	12.6	15	0.58	5.6	0.11	28.7	7.1	103.4	0.7	5.9	10.0	5.3	#
48005	19 Dec 1971	17.5	7	1.56	5.1	0.31	0.0	1.1	126.1	1.1	6.4	4.9	3.9	#
48005	7 Aug 1972	22.6	6	1.28	2.0	0.15	44.6	6.3	86.7	0.9	3.8	12.1	2.5	#
48005	18 Jan 1973	42.0	30	4.26	5.3	0.78	0.0	2.2	127.2	8.4	20.0	17.7	4.3	#
48005	**1 Apr 1973*	15.4	10	0.59	3.8	0.20	9.2	1.2	117.0	0.6	3.6	4.3	—	
48005	10 Nov 1974	17.8	10	2.52	3.1	0.48	0.0	2.5	127.5	2.1	12.0	10.2	3.5	#
48005	**19 Jan 1975*	24.1	17	4.69	4.7	0.68	0.0	8.3	133.3	4.5	18.6	15.5	—	
48005	30 Jan 1975	12.4	11	4.42	4.3	1.17	0.0	7.0	132.0	2.4	19.1	16.4	3.1	#
48005	17 Apr 1975	16.4	7	2.85	1.6	0.29	0.0	2.9	127.9	1.8	11.1	9.2	2.6	#
48005	16 Aug 1975	20.3	10	1.19	4.0	0.13	96.2	10.1	38.9	1.3	6.4	26.7	3.9	#
48005	13 Sep 1975	53.0	20	3.69	3.2	0.15	76.8	4.4	52.6	4.4	8.3	22.5	2.8	#
a mean												16.0		
g mean					4.4	0.24							3.8	

* Note that the events of *18 Jun 1971, 6 Aug 1971, 8 Nov 1971, 1 Apr 1973* and *19 Jan 1975* were not used in deriving the unit hydrograph and losses model parameters for worked examples involving this catchment.

Catch	Date	P	D	Q_p	LAG	BF	SMD	API5	CWI	R/O	PR	SPR	Tp(0)	
48009	3 Aug 1971	42.2	20	2.46	28.3	0.54	66.0	4.8	63.8	7.7	18.3	32.7	—	
48009	29 Nov 1971	61.9	25	8.70	7.9	1.79	0.0	9.8	134.8	24.9	40.2	33.8	—	
48009	14 Jan 1972	25.8	19	6.70	9.3	1.49	0.0	9.7	134.7	13.3	51.5	49.0	—	
48009	25 Jan 1972	32.5	25	5.64	6.1	1.39	0.0	6.6	131.6	11.2	34.6	32.9	10.3	#
48009	31 Jan 1972	36.5	13	6.76	9.9	1.26	0.2	0.6	125.4	11.8	32.2	32.0	—	
48009	12 Jun 1972	39.8	36	4.83	18.8	0.75	5.3	3.0	122.7	15.1	37.9	38.4	9.3	#
48009	4 Aug 1973	80.3	43	5.53	18.0	0.27	81.6	7.5	50.9	21.8	27.2	39.7	9.3	#
48009	17 Oct 1974	42.6	21	7.47	8.9	0.97	0.0	3.3	128.3	15.7	36.8	35.0	9.0	#
48009	12 Nov 1974	32.3	19	10.55	8.4	1.68	0.0	10.3	135.3	16.4	50.7	48.1	10.8	#
48009	30 Jan 1975	22.3	27	5.45	8.4	2.01	0.0	10.8	135.8	6.8	30.4	27.6	6.8	#
48009	28 Jan 1976	57.4	24	7.84	6.8	0.82	0.0	5.0	130.0	15.6	27.1	22.4	8.2	#
48009	13 Oct 1976	51.6	30	5.78	14.5	1.25	13.0	4.5	116.5	22.4	43.5	43.1	—	
48009	9 Dec 1977	48.1	10	7.58	7.7	1.50	1.8	9.6	132.8	13.6	28.3	24.3	9.3	#
48009	28 Mar 1978	28.7	31	3.77	7.8	1.44	0.0	8.5	133.5	6.8	23.8	21.6	11.5	#
48009	26 Dec 1979	104.2	28	21.14	8.4	2.08	0.0	2.6	127.6	55.6	53.4	44.4	—	
48009	3 Feb 1980	49.5	33	7.47	12.7	1.36	0.0	8.7	133.7	23.7	47.9	43.5	10.0	#
48009	20 Sep 1980	66.4	16	8.50	8.3	0.99	69.8	3.6	58.8	19.2	28.9	40.9	10.2	#
48009	15 Oct 1980	25.8	17	4.88	12.7	1.13	1.5	5.6	129.1	10.7	41.6	40.5	11.3	#
48009	8 Mar 1981	65.3	67	7.31	9.8	1.90	0.5	12.8	137.3	27.9	42.7	35.2	9.3	#

Catch	Date	P	D	Q_p	LAG	BF	SMD	API5	CWI	R/O	PR	SPR	Tp(0)	
		mm	h	m^3s^{-1}	h	m^3s^{-1}	mm	mm	mm	mm	%	%	h	
48009	20 Mar 1981	42.7	32	5.32	11.8	1.13	0.3	1.6	126.3	16.0	37.5	36.2	9.0	#
48009	1 Oct 1981	48.2	20	4.83	7.7	1.07	7.7	8.2	125.5	12.6	26.2	24.0	—	
48009	19 Dec 1981	62.6	19	13.60	6.6	2.04	0.0	3.6	128.6	21.9	35.0	30.0	7.5	#
48009	7 Feb 1980	45.0	46	6.99	5.9	2.47	0.0	14.2	139.2	14.9	33.1	28.1	9.4	#
48009	30 Mar 1978	39.7	33	3.85	5.4	1.70	0.0	5.7	130.7	6.9	17.3	15.8	9.2	#
a mean												34.1		
g mean					9.6	1.25							9.4	
49003	28 Dec 1966	35.8	21	14.10	5.9	1.56	0.0	14.4	139.4	18.8	52.4	48.8	3.7	#
49003	22 Jan 1967	35.9	9	14.32	5.0	1.05	0.0	9.1	134.1	19.2	53.4	51.1	2.8	#
49003	27 Feb 1967	42.0	22	14.74	3.9	0.91	0.0	4.2	129.2	23.1	54.9	53.1	5.8	#
49003	16 Oct 1967	48.9	29	16.99	5.8	1.52	0.0	14.3	139.3	36.6	74.8	69.1	—	
49003	4 Nov 1967	26.1	12	11.38	6.7	1.96	0.0	23.4	148.4	12.3	47.3	41.5	—	
49003	18 Dec 1967	61.6	29	13.70	8.5	0.46	0.0	1.6	126.6	30.9	50.1	45.8	—	
49003	21 Dec 1968	27.8	19	10.14	5.6	0.78	0.0	4.9	129.9	13.5	48.6	47.4	7.2	#
49003	23 Dec 1968	77.8	42	18.93	10.9	0.56	0.0	9.1	134.1	53.3	68.5	60.5	6.1	#
49003	28 Jul 1969	113.5	26	11.52	9.1	0.17	93.8	0.1	31.3	18.2	16.0	30.3	6.2	#
49003	16 Jan 1970	47.5	29	17.72	9.0	0.87	0.0	12.8	137.8	24.7	51.9	46.9	4.5	#
49003	1 Nov 1970	46.9	16	16.52	6.6	0.47	0.0	7.2	132.2	23.7	50.5	47.0	3.7	#
49003	29 Nov 1971	64.6	25	13.00	3.6	4.79	0.0	9.8	134.8	10.5	16.3	9.6	6.3	#
49003	25 Jan 1972	36.4	26	11.43	5.9	0.19	0.0	6.6	131.6	18.9	52.0	50.3	7.2	#
49003	14 Jan 1972	26.9	21	10.32	6.0	0.59	0.0	10.0	135.0	17.2	64.0	61.5	5.3	#
49003	11 Nov 1972	34.8	24	10.25	5.8	0.31	0.0	6.1	131.1	16.4	47.1	45.6	3.7	#
49003	1 Apr 1973	36.0	14	5.78	7.8	0.08	11.9	2.3	115.4	9.3	25.9	28.3	5.7	#
49003	17 Aug 1974	19.5	7	2.90	5.9	0.16	66.0	2.5	61.5	4.4	22.4	38.3	5.7	#
49003	4 Sep 1974	30.5	15	10.99	7.1	0.42	43.3	17.4	99.1	17.7	57.9	64.4	5.1	#
49003	13 Sep 1975	52.9	14	8.13	6.7	0.11	90.2	6.9	41.7	10.6	20.1	38.2	4.9	#
49003	17 Oct 1974	45.8	18	15.79	5.8	0.32	0.0	2.3	127.3	27.8	60.7	58.6	3.5	#
a mean												46.8		
g mean					6.4	0.52							5.0	
51002	**28 Nov 1973*	18.8	14	2.11	5.4	0.38	17.0	7.0	115.0	2.8	15.0	17.5	—	
51002	4 Sep 1974	22.5	13	3.17	5.0	0.92	67.3	22.3	80.0	3.7	16.4	27.6	5.0	#
51002	22 Sep 1974	37.7	22	3.39	5.6	0.54	90.5	6.3	40.8	5.8	15.4	36.4	3.5	#
51002	26 Sep 1974	57.6	24	5.96	7.2	1.22	0.6	12.5	136.9	10.9	18.9	12.6	2.5	#
51002	11 Nov 1974	19.5	11	2.90	4.1	0.84	6.2	6.2	125.0	2.7	14.1	14.1	5.5	#
51002	19 Jan 1975	29.0	20	4.11	6.1	0.84	0.0	3.5	128.5	4.6	15.9	15.0	3.9	#
51002	**21 Jan 1975*	34.3	22	5.54	4.3	1.28	0.0	13.3	138.3	6.4	18.7	15.4	—	
51002	31 Jan 1975	13.2	6	3.97	3.0	1.70	0.0	11.7	136.7	1.9	14.7	11.8	3.0	#
51002	2 Apr 1975	14.8	16	1.25	5.1	0.38	68.0	0.6	57.6	1.3	9.1	26.0	5.0	#
51002	1 Dec 1975	51.6	18	7.67	3.7	1.19	15.7	6.1	115.4	8.9	17.3	17.2	—	
a mean												19.4		
g mean					4.8	0.83							3.9	

* Note that the events of *28 Nov 1973* and *21 Jan 1975* were not used in deriving the unit hydrograph and losses model parameters for worked examples involving this catchment.

Catch	Date	P	D	Q_p	LAG	BF	SMD	API5	CWI	R/O	PR	SPR	Tp(0)	
52004	22 Oct 1966	32.9	10	22.98	8.0	1.58	46.8	1.7	79.9	11.1	33.7	44.8	6.9	#
52004	20 Feb 1967	13.9	13	21.26	4.2	3.89	0.4	12.8	137.4	6.5	47.0	43.8	5.4	#
52004	16 Oct 1967	33.4	22	19.20	10.4	1.17	32.1	5.7	98.6	12.3	36.8	43.2	6.2	#
52004	30 Oct 1967	28.9	20	22.09	9.9	1.82	22.0	4.0	107.0	14.7	50.8	55.2	8.5	#
52004	27 Jun 1968	19.6	9	18.73	6.4	1.36	35.2	6.9	96.7	8.4	42.8	49.7	6.8	#
52004	10 Jul 1968	54.5	21	27.92	6.9	1.21	35.2	6.9	96.7	19.7	36.1	40.0	5.7	#
52004	21 Dec 1968	20.0	7	25.02	7.2	2.93	0.0	5.6	130.6	8.8	44.1	42.5	6.9	#
52004	24 Dec 1968	31.8	31	20.82	11.6	2.56	0.0	4.8	129.8	14.2	44.7	43.3	5.3	#
52004	21 Feb 1969	23.1	14	27.53	14.3	1.40	0.0	11.8	136.8	21.2	91.7	88.9	—	
52004	12 Mar 1969	19.8	15	20.74	6.4	3.07	0.6	11.0	135.4	7.4	37.3	34.5	4.0	#
52004	28 Jul 1969	84.5	21	21.82	11.9	0.55	115.9	4.3	13.4	13.2	15.6	36.8	—	
a mean												47.5		
g mean					8.4	1.72							6.1	
52005	19 Jan 1965	24.0	12	41.89	9.4	7.37	8.7	6.3	122.6	7.9	32.9	33.3	8.7	#
52005	28 Nov 1965	25.5	19	30.66	8.1	5.74	2.4	3.9	126.5	6.7	26.2	25.6	7.7	#
52005	8 Dec 1965	32.0	46	34.35	14.4	6.03	0.1	2.6	127.5	14.5	45.4	44.7	—	
52005	24 Feb 1966	24.5	21	37.31	11.2	6.12	0.0	6.2	131.2	8.3	34.0	32.3	10.5	#
52005	17 Apr 1966	39.1	53	45.99	13.4	8.27	1.2	6.8	130.6	15.6	39.9	38.4	—	
52005	20 Feb 1967	17.4	11	33.72	8.6	8.50	0.0	12.0	137.0	6.6	38.1	35.0	9.0	#

Catch	Date	*P*	*D*	Q_p	*LAG*	*BF*	*SMD*	*API5*	*CWI*	*R/O*	*PR*	*SPR*	*Tp*(0)	
		mm	*h*	m^3s^{-1}	*h*	m^3s^{-1}	*mm*	*mm*	*mm*	*mm*	*%*	*%*	*h*	
52005	30 Oct 1967	30.2	22	26.58	10.2	4.49	22.1	8.1	111.0	7.9	26.2	29.5	10.3	#
52005	8 Jan 1968	32.0	24	42.41	9.5	7.38	0.0	4.1	129.1	11.0	34.3	33.1	9.1	#
52005	9 Jul 1968	68.8	30	111.63	16.4	2.16	23.6	2.6	104.0	39.0	56.7	57.2	—	
52005	27 Jul 1969	111.8	29	74.10	15.7	1.16	120.5	0.0	4.5	16.0	14.3	35.2	9.3	#
a mean												36.4		
g mean					11.3	4.97							9.2	
52006	2 Aug 1965	38.6	17	29.67	10.3	1.12	32.7	1.9	94.2	8.8	22.8	29.9	9.4	#
52006	28 Nov 1965	33.7	26	41.82	8.4	6.15	0.1	3.8	128.7	12.2	36.3	35.0	10.1	#
52006	22 Dec 1965	18.2	13	33.11	10.6	5.32	0.0	1.6	126.6	7.2	39.5	38.7	—	
52006	29 Dec 1965	15.8	11	34.79	9.5	4.22	0.3	0.3	125.0	7.6	48.2	47.9	—	
52006	24 Feb 1966	33.0	21	45.37	12.4	9.37	0.0	6.9	131.9	13.2	39.9	37.8	11.1	#
52006	21 Oct 1966	30.6	8	32.65	12.7	4.38	1.6	2.3	125.7	10.4	33.9	33.3	10.8	#
52006	4 Nov 1966	58.5	20	46.43	9.9	5.39	4.7	0.1	120.4	20.1	34.4	31.7	11.4	#
52006	22 Jan 1967	20.3	24	31.91	11.0	6.08	0.0	5.1	130.1	10.1	49.7	48.2	13.5	#
52006	27 Feb 1967	20.0	21	32.90	11.4	4.18	0.0	3.3	128.3	9.9	49.3	48.2	12.8	#
52006	3 May 1967	48.2	18	38.27	10.8	1.96	32.3	0.0	92.7	9.0	18.7	24.2	8.3	#
52006	15 Oct 1967	34.0	36	37.35	18.1	6.22	1.0	10.6	134.6	9.6	28.2	25.3	10.4	#
52006	9 Jul 1968	53.7	29	35.75	8.4	1.85	25.6	2.8	102.2	10.0	18.7	21.0	8.9	#
52006	24 Dec 1968	29.1	29	35.98	14.2	7.01	0.0	4.7	129.7	11.8	40.4	38.9	11.8	#
52006	12 Mar 1969	19.7	10	39.81	11.1	6.72	0.0	8.9	133.9	6.4	32.4	29.7	12.0	#
a mean												35.0		
g mean					11.1	4.37							10.8	
52010	22 Oct 1966	26.0	9	40.51	9.7	2.60	1.6	2.8	126.2	11.6	44.7	44.3	9.5	#
52010	4 Nov 1966	63.4	19	75.59	11.9	1.15	4.7	0.0	120.3	33.4	52.7	49.7	10.5	#
52010	29 Dec 1966	18.3	14	29.82	10.0	3.13	0.0	4.2	129.2	7.9	42.9	41.7	10.2	#
52010	16 Oct 1967	32.0	39	23.24	14.7	3.06	5.2	12.7	132.5	14.2	44.3	42.3	—	
52010	8 Jan 1968	27.9	25	40.41	9.9	3.03	0.0	4.8	129.8	13.4	48.1	46.8	10.7	#
52010	27 Jun 1968	21.9	9	35.74	9.2	2.04	10.8	8.3	122.5	9.6	43.9	44.4	9.9	#
52010	10 Jul 1968	46.3	19	76.00	9.7	5.59	23.4	4.4	106.0	32.7	70.7	73.8	10.9	#
52010	24 Dec 1968	24.8	25	28.46	13.3	2.90	0.0	3.9	128.9	12.3	49.5	48.4	—	
52010	12 Mar 1969	21.4	23	21.99	11.0	2.88	0.0	8.1	133.1	7.7	36.1	33.9	9.9	#
a mean												47.3		
g mean					10.9	2.72							10.2	
52016	4 Aug 1974	47.2	19	0.58	4.5	0.09	106.9	0.1	18.2	0.9	1.9	26.8	2.5	#
52016	26 Sep 1974	40.1	24	1.54	8.2	0.23	64.7	6.8	67.1	4.4	11.0	25.4	3.5	#
52016	21 Nov 1974	12.8	12	1.59	3.9	0.52	0.0	7.3	132.3	1.9	14.5	12.7	4.3	#
52016	26 Dec 1974	15.9	8	1.13	3.7	0.39	0.0	7.0	132.0	1.5	9.3	7.6	3.1	#
52016	26 Jan 1975	11.9	14	1.20	3.5	0.45	0.0	3.5	128.5	1.1	9.5	8.6	2.8	#
52016	6 Mar 1975	8.9	5	0.78	4.0	0.26	0.2	3.2	128.0	0.7	7.6	6.8	4.5	#
52016	1 Dec 1975	28.8	27	0.64	6.1	0.09	27.9	7.3	104.4	1.2	4.3	9.4	6.0	#
a mean												13.9		
g mean					4.6	0.24							3.7	
52020	22 Oct 1966	31.9	9	18.32	2.7	0.57	1.6	2.3	125.7	19.2	60.1	59.9	2.7	#
52020	3 May 1967	69.4	29	27.25	5.6	0.20	32.3	0.0	92.7	29.8	43.0	46.3	—	
52020	14 Oct 1967	17.3	14	7.51	4.3	0.38	0.0	2.0	127.0	6.3	36.6	36.1	—	
52020	16 Oct 1967	32.6	20	13.22	7.0	0.69	0.0	9.9	134.9	19.5	59.8	57.3	3.2	#
52020	4 Feb 1968	19.1	9	6.68	3.6	0.34	0.2	0.3	125.1	5.4	28.5	28.5	—	
52020	10 Jul 1968	47.6	29	16.68	6.2	0.24	25.6	2.5	101.9	15.5	32.5	36.4	—	
52020	27 Oct 1968	31.5	17	9.95	1.8	0.42	0.0	3.3	128.3	14.4	45.6	44.8	—	
52020	21 Dec 1968	18.2	7	15.13	3.3	0.69	0.0	5.1	130.1	15.0	82.2	80.9	2.7	#
52020	24 Dec 1968	33.3	29	9.16	12.2	0.55	0.0	4.7	129.7	22.5	67.5	66.3	—	
a mean												50.7		
g mean					4.5	0.42							2.9	
53005	1 Aug 1965	27.1	21	15.41	9.4	3.86	7.1	8.8	126.7	4.1	15.3	13.8	8.4	#
53005	6 Nov 1965	31.0	27	7.38	13.3	1.32	1.0	0.0	124.0	2.9	9.4	8.5	9.2	#
53005	22 Oct 1966	21.2	8	8.61	8.7	2.13	21.9	1.6	104.7	2.1	10.0	13.9	7.7	#
53005	4 Nov 1966	55.0	18	30.91	12.4	1.06	7.9	0.0	117.1	15.7	28.6	26.8	11.6	#
53005	1 Apr 1967	18.4	21	5.81	11.5	2.07	4.0	0.4	121.4	1.5	8.3	8.0	—	
53005	8 Jan 1968	22.8	22	17.16	8.2	4.24	0.0	4.7	129.7	5.5	24.0	22.0	10.2	#
53005	10 Jul 1968	79.5	21	55.45	11.0	2.84	22.1	4.2	107.1	22.7	28.5	26.3	9.5	#
53005	28 Sep 1968	23.7	26	9.64	13.2	2.18	0.2	5.8	130.6	4.1	17.2	14.8	15.6	#

Catch	Date	P mm	D h	Q_p m^3s^{-1}	LAG h	BF m^3s^{-1}	SMD mm	API5 mm	CWI mm	R/O mm	PR %	SPR %	Tp(0) h	
53005	1 Nov 1968	13.5	8	8.07	7.1	3.48	0.0	5.1	130.1	1.4	10.7	8.3	8.7	#
53005	25 Nov 1968	21.8	22	10.19	14.4	2.38	0.0	3.4	128.4	3.9	18.1	16.3	7.0	#
53005	16 Dec 1968	15.4	27	9.16	8.1	3.14	0.0	8.1	133.1	2.5	16.3	13.3	—	
53005	21 Dec 1968	18.6	16	17.22	9.9	4.17	0.0	5.5	130.5	5.0	26.7	24.5	6.2	#
53005	24 Dec 1968	20.6	25	13.31	12.3	4.73	0.0	5.6	130.6	5.0	24.1	21.8	9.1	#
53005	28 Jul 1969	71.1	32	7.68	12.1	0.74	106.1	0.0	18.9	2.5	3.5	23.8	—	
a mean												17.3		
g mean					10.6	2.42							9.1	
53007	11 Nov 1963	27.4	24	36.51	3.2	9.21	0.0	3.1	128.1	7.0	25.5	24.3	—	
53007	31 May 1964	29.2	15	36.67	11.0	5.45	4.9	12.7	132.8	7.6	26.1	23.7	13.5	#
53007	29 Dec 1964	9.8	11	28.42	11.4	4.18	16.7	8.0	116.3	6.9	70.5	72.7	—	
53007	20 Jul 1965	17.0	13	25.46	4.4	2.82	32.8	1.8	94.0	3.3	19.3	26.5	—	
53007	2 Aug 1965	31.6	19	83.55	10.9	6.43	5.9	4.8	123.9	15.5	49.1	49.2	9.7	#
53007	7 Nov 1965	30.0	28	24.86	10.7	2.58	8.7	0.1	116.4	5.9	19.6	21.2	—	
53007	28 Nov 1965	25.8	27	43.65	8.8	6.38	0.1	2.9	127.8	8.5	32.9	31.8	10.2	#
53007	7 May 1966	22.0	19	26.16	10.4	3.75	10.3	6.2	120.9	5.4	24.6	25.2	10.9	#
53007	14 Oct 1966	22.1	10	25.14	10.3	2.99	26.0	2.8	101.8	4.3	19.4	24.7	9.6	#
53007	22 Oct 1966	21.5	8	33.38	11.6	4.83	1.6	2.3	125.7	6.3	29.1	28.5	10.9	#
53007	4 Nov 1966	56.7	21	86.92	10.1	2.08	4.5	0.1	120.6	21.1	37.2	34.7	10.5	#
53007	27 Feb 1967	23.7	21	32.54	6.5	7.52	0.0	2.8	127.8	7.0	29.5	28.4	—	
53007	2 Apr 1967	23.9	20	23.22	12.1	3.52	8.0	0.3	117.3	5.0	20.9	22.3	8.1	#
53007	3 May 1967	30.4	16	16.74	11.6	2.37	33.1	0.4	92.3	3.0	10.0	17.6	6.6	#
53007	30 May 1967	17.6	18	19.29	9.3	7.12	10.2	5.6	120.4	3.2	17.9	18.5	—	
53007	18 Dec 1967	15.4	15	22.38	14.6	3.67	0.0	0.8	125.8	4.7	30.3	29.7	—	
53007	8 Jan 1968	21.6	22	49.91	9.1	6.95	0.0	3.6	128.6	9.9	46.0	44.9	—	
53007	10 Jul 1968	64.8	20	116.31	8.0	5.07	22.9	6.7	108.8	22.7	35.0	34.4	7.8	#
53007	8 Oct 1968	25.4	17	24.63	10.8	3.08	5.1	0.0	119.9	4.6	18.0	18.7	10.1	#
53007	1 Nov 1968	14.9	14	24.63	11.2	5.17	0.0	5.1	130.1	3.7	24.5	22.8	10.3	#
53007	24 Dec 1968	21.9	24	37.62	10.3	7.27	0.0	4.0	129.0	8.2	37.4	36.1	9.3	#
a mean												30.3		
g mean					9.4	4.48							9.7	
53008	20 Jul 1965	41.0	17	18.77	20.9	3.47	45.5	0.0	79.5	4.8	11.7	22.3	—	
53008	28 Nov 1965	21.3	17	20.75	9.8	6.02	0.1	2.5	127.4	4.2	19.5	18.7	—	
53008	8 Dec 1965	29.0	32	32.63	18.9	7.26	0.0	1.5	126.5	7.0	24.0	23.4	—	
53008	16 Dec 1965	57.8	51	62.37	26.3	11.28	0.0	5.0	130.0	33.7	58.3	53.6	—	
53008	30 Dec 1966	14.9	14	19.47	9.9	6.37	0.0	5.7	130.7	3.3	22.1	20.4	—	
53008	20 Feb 1967	23.5	23	41.32	11.4	10.85	0.0	12.6	137.6	8.1	34.6	31.3	—	
53008	27 Feb 1967	30.7	20	42.75	14.6	7.45	0.0	1.8	126.8	9.6	31.3	30.7	—	
53008	10 Jul 1968	101.3	28	105.34	13.4	5.92	19.4	2.3	107.9	24.0	23.7	19.7	—	
53008	1 Nov 1968	12.2	14	19.04	10.1	6.81	0.0	3.7	128.7	2.6	21.6	20.4	—	
53008	24 Dec 1968	21.1	23	32.99	15.4	8.38	0.0	4.7	129.7	8.2	39.0	37.7	—	
53008	25 May 1969	35.2	23	50.54	10.2	5.01	3.6	4.6	126.0	10.9	30.9	30.5	—	
a mean												28.1		
g mean					13.8	6.82							—	
53009	22 Oct 1966	20.3	8	4.02	7.7	1.37	21.9	1.9	105.0	1.8	8.8	12.3	7.3	#
53009	4 Nov 1966	63.1	20	14.48	9.7	2.14	7.9	0.1	117.2	15.3	24.2	21.0	9.0	#
53009	1 Apr 1967	29.5	23	3.80	10.7	1.42	4.0	0.3	121.3	2.2	7.5	6.9	6.3	#
53009	8 Jan 1968	24.4	22	8.52	8.9	2.42	0.0	5.7	130.7	5.4	22.2	19.6	8.9	#
53009	10 Jul 1968	64.9	19	29.91	6.9	2.27	22.1	4.8	107.7	15.4	23.7	22.6	—	
53009	28 Sep 1968	23.0	26	4.02	12.5	1.53	0.2	7.5	132.3	3.4	14.8	11.6	—	
53009	1 Nov 1968	15.2	12	4.42	5.8	2.21	0.0	4.2	129.2	1.4	9.2	6.7	—	
53009	25 Nov 1968	21.9	23	4.73	14.2	1.63	0.0	5.4	130.4	3.8	17.5	14.9	7.0	#
53009	21 Dec 1968	15.0	6	9.16	6.7	2.69	0.0	5.1	130.1	3.2	21.4	19.0	5.3	#
53009	24 Dec 1968	18.3	25	6.66	12.0	2.94	0.0	3.4	128.4	4.2	23.0	21.0	—	
a mean												15.6		
g mean					9.1	1.99							7.2	
54004	24 Jan 1960	38.4	17	45.78	15.2	6.06	0.0	3.8	128.8	14.7	38.2	34.4	10.8	#
54004	27 Jan 1960	32.1	28	38.09	11.3	7.24	0.0	17.9	142.9	14.4	44.9	38.2	12.1	#
54004	17 Nov 1960	17.8	9	22.40	13.8	5.10	0.0	1.3	126.3	7.9	44.5	41.9	11.0	#
54004	3 Dec 1960	34.7	21	45.36	18.4	3.19	0.0	0.5	125.5	19.1	55.0	53.5	13.0	#
54004	9 Dec 1965	23.8	27	29.83	10.7	5.49	0.0	2.3	127.3	10.0	42.2	39.1	9.8	#
54004	22 Dec 1965	20.1	20	23.65	16.8	5.47	0.0	1.4	126.4	10.0	49.6	47.4	12.5	#

Catch	Date	P	D	Q_p	LAG	BF	SMD	API5	CWI	R/O	PR	SPR	Tp(0)	
		mm	h	m^3s^{-1}	h	m^3s^{-1}	mm	mm	mm	mm	%	%	h	
54004	18 Feb 1966	40.5	63	32.18	20.2	4.23	1.0	0.3	124.3	22.0	54.3	52.8	—	
54004	29 Aug 1966	42.4	19	25.33	8.2	5.58	62.2	6.0	68.8	7.4	17.5	26.0	—	
54004	9 Dec 1966	15.7	15	24.36	12.8	7.25	0.0	4.0	129.0	6.5	41.3	37.7	12.5	#
54004	8 Mar 1967	23.8	22	22.88	12.1	4.23	0.0	2.0	127.0	8.8	37.1	33.6	10.5	#
54004	10 Jul 1968	54.4	15	42.35	19.0	3.36	10.7	4.8	119.1	21.1	38.7	34.4	—	
54004	12 Mar 1969	29.2	26	35.85	17.1	3.04	5.0	3.3	123.3	16.3	55.9	55.1	12.5	#
54004	5 May 1969	36.2	12	34.19	13.6	3.55	20.4	0.5	105.1	12.9	35.7	37.6	14.5	#
54004	3 Aug 1969	31.1	6	20.35	7.0	2.60	74.2	3.5	54.3	3.6	11.6	24.0	—	
a mean												39.7		
g mean					13.4	4.51							11.8	
54006	10 Jul 1968	36.4	21	19.37	30.4	2.82	10.0	5.8	120.8	5.8	15.8	11.2	—	
54006	12 Mar 1969	28.3	25	20.07	24.5	2.88	0.0	2.4	127.4	6.7	23.7	18.3	24.2	#
54006	5 May 1969	35.7	13	21.61	20.0	2.83	19.4	4.5	110.1	6.1	17.0	15.2	20.5	#
54006	2 Aug 1969	28.7	22	18.04	19.3	2.95	65.8	9.9	69.1	5.2	18.1	26.7	—	
54006	27 Jan 1960	44.9	25	30.57	24.0	5.80	0.2	5.8	130.6	13.1	29.1	22.1	25.7	#
a mean												18.7		
g mean					23.3	3.30							23.4	
54010	21 Jan 1959	22.1	26	37.02	19.7	9.54	0.0	8.7	133.7	9.2	41.6	39.2	—	
54010	23 Jan 1960	34.0	35	49.61	18.6	5.06	0.0	4.8	129.8	13.1	38.6	37.1	—	
54010	27 Jan 1960	27.0	28	47.64	15.3	5.28	0.0	3.9	128.9	11.0	40.6	39.4	—	
54010	17 Nov 1960	18.8	9	34.49	19.3	4.88	0.0	1.9	126.9	7.8	41.4	40.7	—	
54010	3 Dec 1960	30.2	24	52.81	17.5	5.26	0.0	1.7	126.7	13.9	46.0	45.4	—	
54010	9 Jan 1961	15.3	19	33.51	22.7	4.91	0.0	2.4	127.4	6.6	43.2	42.4	—	
54010	14 May 1967	29.3	32	43.56	14.1	1.92	7.3	6.4	124.1	13.1	44.8	44.8	—	
54010	10 Jul 1968	85.2	48	82.66	12.7	1.89	45.9	1.3	80.4	20.9	24.5	28.7	—	
54010	12 Mar 1969	24.9	33	33.86	21.0	3.52	1.2	3.3	127.1	9.8	39.4	38.6	20.8	#
a mean												39.6		
g mean					17.6	4.20							20.8	
54011	20 Jul 1965	21.9	22	7.51	11.5	0.92	68.4	1.7	58.3	2.8	12.9	27.8	—	
54011	8 Sep 1965	34.8	15	8.69	15.0	1.10	47.1	1.4	79.3	4.2	12.2	21.8	12.9	#
54011	25 Sep 1965	25.3	37	11.83	21.8	2.70	0.0	5.2	130.2	5.8	22.9	20.1	—	
54011	28 Nov 1965	18.5	15	15.07	15.6	1.09	0.0	2.1	127.1	7.1	38.2	36.7	13.5	#
54011	8 Dec 1965	20.2	19	30.27	11.9	2.05	0.0	1.8	126.8	11.0	54.5	53.6	—	
54011	22 Dec 1965	15.5	22	11.70	14.9	1.62	0.0	1.4	126.4	4.9	31.4	29.8	10.8	#
54011	31 Dec 1965	17.7	51	16.37	12.8	2.19	0.0	2.4	127.4	7.1	40.0	38.5	12.0	#
54011	8 May 1966	20.8	31	12.96	22.9	0.96	6.4	4.3	122.9	4.1	19.5	18.4	11.8	#
54011	20 Feb 1967	11.0	7	15.29	13.8	1.11	0.0	6.8	131.8	4.9	44.6	42.1	13.5	#
54011	8 Mar 1967	27.0	30	18.17	14.2	1.02	0.0	2.1	127.1	9.0	33.2	31.5	11.0	#
54011	27 May 1967	13.2	10	16.11	14.3	2.68	0.0	7.9	132.9	4.4	33.0	29.9	—	
54011	10 Jul 1968	51.0	26	36.97	16.8	1.53	53.2	2.7	74.5	15.2	29.8	38.7	16.0	#
54011	5 May 1969	31.3	13	38.04	12.4	0.97	26.0	2.0	101.0	11.8	37.7	42.7	11.5	#
54011	25 May 1969	16.6	6	34.16	10.3	3.31	3.6	16.0	137.4	10.8	65.1	61.8	—	
54011	28 Nov 1970	27.6	37	14.61	11.1	0.66	1.1	1.8	125.7	7.5	27.0	25.5	10.8	#
54011	12 Jan 1972	22.2	26	19.99	12.4	1.01	0.0	5.9	130.9	8.5	38.2	35.7	13.5	#
54011	3 Feb 1972	21.6	45	18.76	15.9	3.92	0.0	2.9	127.9	4.4	20.2	17.9	10.5	#
a mean												33.7		
g mean					14.2	1.48							12.2	
54016	21 Apr 1962	13.6	16	10.16	22.5	2.94	0.4	2.8	127.4	3.4	25.2	24.3	22.0	#
54016	29 Mar 1963	12.7	22	7.42	24.6	1.92	4.9	3.0	123.1	3.2	25.2	25.4	—	
54016	25 Nov 1963	29.0	36	11.31	31.6	2.13	47.5	1.6	79.1	7.1	24.6	35.8	30.0	#
54016	12 Dec 1964	25.2	20	6.98	25.1	1.03	42.3	1.6	84.3	3.4	13.6	23.4	23.0	#
54016	8 Mar 1967	21.5	34	10.01	28.1	2.50	3.2	0.2	122.0	6.0	27.8	28.3	—	
54016	16 Oct 1967	36.8	48	10.25	27.1	1.76	43.8	3.5	84.7	7.0	19.1	28.8	24.0	#
54016	27 May 1968	15.5	28	11.30	19.7	3.56	9.1	18.3	134.2	3.7	23.8	21.2	—	
a mean												26.7		
g mean					25.3	2.12							24.6	
54019	29 Mar 1963	31.7	38	36.55	33.1	2.34	10.1	3.8	118.7	14.4	45.3	46.3	—	
54019	17 Nov 1963	35.0	44	12.72	38.2	1.19	6.5	0.3	118.8	7.7	22.1	22.6	—	
54019	23 Mar 1964	18.1	26	16.81	37.5	2.66	1.4	1.2	124.8	7.7	42.6	42.0	—	
54019	29 Nov 1965	20.8	34	20.65	40.5	4.65	0.0	2.6	127.6	5.3	25.5	23.9	—	
54019	8 Dec 1965	21.3	32	22.08	40.4	3.11	0.0	1.9	126.9	9.2	43.1	42.0	41.0	#

Catch	Date	P mm	D h	Q_p m^3s^{-1}	LAG h	BF m^3s^{-1}	SMD mm	API5 mm	CWI mm	R/O mm	PR %	SPR %	Tp(0) h	
54019	22 Dec 1965	22.4	48	24.35	36.3	6.14	0.0	1.3	126.3	8.1	36.0	34.9	—	
54019	18 Feb 1966	24.8	62	24.69	51.1	1.89	1.3	0.3	124.0	21.1	85.0	85.6	—	
54019	29 Aug 1966	64.9	34	16.13	59.6	0.61	75.2	0.1	49.9	9.7	15.0	28.3	—	
54019	12 Oct 1966	43.7	92	20.16	50.5	1.38	12.2	0.9	113.7	19.4	44.4	45.5	—	
54019	9 Dec 1966	21.6	56	24.84	36.8	5.60	0.0	2.7	127.7	11.1	51.3	50.2	42.5	#
54019	27 Feb 1967	18.2	17	22.25	37.0	2.98	0.0	1.3	126.3	8.2	45.2	44.3	39.5	#
54019	8 Mar 1967	23.1	49	17.78	41.7	2.03	2.4	1.7	124.3	9.8	42.3	41.9	46.0	#
54019	14 May 1967	36.2	50	39.04	36.1	2.15	1.6	6.1	129.5	16.7	46.2	44.6	—	
54019	27 May 1967	18.9	26	20.24	45.9	4.05	1.3	4.0	127.7	7.1	37.8	36.4	—	
54019	10 Jul 1968	74.3	24	98.59	29.0	2.09	28.8	2.2	98.4	28.8	38.7	39.3	—	
54019	1 Nov 1968	36.7	18	35.05	34.5	7.87	0.0	3.9	128.9	8.7	23.8	21.8	—	
54019	12 Mar 1969	27.2	36	32.29	36.2	2.92	1.0	4.3	128.3	14.0	51.6	50.4	—	
54019	5 May 1969	36.2	12	38.90	31.4	1.46	33.7	1.0	92.3	13.1	36.1	43.5	—	
a mean												41.3		
g mean					39.1	2.56							42.2	
54020	25 Nov 1963	22.5	22	9.22	17.0	2.85	33.0	4.6	96.6	4.4	19.4	26.2	—	
54020	23 Mar 1964	26.5	26	10.46	13.8	2.54	0.0	1.3	126.3	6.1	23.0	22.4	—	
54020	8 Mar 1967	30.5	34	9.07	20.8	2.30	3.2	0.6	122.4	6.7	22.0	22.4	—	
54020	15 Oct 1967	41.3	56	7.49	17.0	1.76	35.2	4.4	94.2	6.9	16.6	23.5	—	
54020	5 May 1969	32.6	52	10.61	18.7	2.54	5.2	5.3	125.1	9.4	28.9	28.7	—	
a mean												24.6		
g mean					17.3	2.37							—	
54022	12 May 1968	52.9	11	8.07	3.7	0.50	3.6	9.3	130.7	25.2	47.6	43.5	2.0	#
54022	24 May 1968	34.2	17	1.56	3.8	0.14	12.7	0.0	112.3	3.6	10.5	13.7	—	
54022	25 Jun 1968	20.1	4	4.52	2.5	0.53	0.0	12.2	137.2	6.2	30.6	27.6	—	
54022	26 Jun 1968	39.6	14	7.65	2.1	0.77	0.0	18.4	143.4	18.3	46.2	41.6	2.0	#
54022	2 Jul 1968	31.4	18	3.44	2.7	0.46	0.8	13.3	137.5	10.6	33.6	30.5	1.5	#
54022	19 Sep 1968	68.9	32	7.46	4.9	0.21	1.0	1.2	125.2	23.6	34.3	29.5	2.0	#
54022	28 Sep 1968	39.7	26	6.58	1.8	0.76	0.3	13.4	138.1	14.3	35.9	32.6	—	
54022	2 Oct 1968	40.0	17	6.95	1.6	0.98	0.0	12.5	137.5	21.1	52.8	49.7	1.4	#
54022	22 Nov 1968	34.1	15	4.56	3.8	0.27	0.0	5.3	130.3	11.9	35.0	33.7	1.5	#
54022	26 Nov 1968	30.0	24	3.53	3.2	0.53	0.0	10.6	135.6	10.7	35.8	33.1	2.3	#
54022	19 Dec 1968	33.6	29	5.10	4.1	0.40	0.0	6.1	131.1	18.3	54.6	53.1	1.2	#
54022	19 Jan 1969	31.5	13	7.36	4.0	0.76	0.0	14.5	139.5	24.5	77.8	74.2	—	
54022	30 Mar 1969	42.5	9	8.05	3.9	1.16	0.0	17.9	142.9	19.9	46.8	41.5	—	
54022	10 Apr 1969	39.8	11	5.54	3.5	0.54	0.0	15.2	140.2	16.3	40.9	37.1	1.5	#
54022	14 Apr 1969	28.0	13	4.19	3.9	0.46	0.0	8.5	133.5	10.0	35.6	33.5	—	
54022	25 Apr 1969	33.5	13	3.60	2.7	0.46	0.0	9.3	134.3	8.8	26.3	24.0	1.5	#
54022	2 Jun 1969	32.8	13	4.31	3.6	0.42	6.7	1.9	120.2	10.5	32.0	33.2	1.5	#
54022	10 Sep 1969	31.2	20	2.56	1.8	0.13	28.3	1.0	97.7	3.3	10.5	17.3	1.5	#
54022	21 Sep 1969	19.3	7	5.46	2.7	0.40	0.0	8.3	133.3	5.8	29.8	27.7	2.5	#
54022	19 Feb 1970	32.1	16	5.73	4.5	1.14	0.0	16.7	141.7	18.6	57.9	53.7	3.5	#
54022	5 Apr 1970	36.3	15	4.61	2.5	0.33	1.2	3.8	127.6	8.5	23.3	22.6	—	
54022	22 Apr 1970	51.5	19	9.04	3.5	1.15	0.0	31.3	156.3	29.3	56.9	46.6	—	
54022	15 Aug 1970	54.5	23	8.71	4.0	0.33	2.0	3.2	126.2	19.1	35.0	31.8	1.3	#
54022	10 Sep 1970	49.0	21	9.26	2.7	0.74	0.0	14.6	139.6	21.6	44.0	38.3	1.8	#
54022	27 Oct 1970	61.5	23	9.90	5.3	1.10	0.0	22.5	147.5	34.9	56.8	47.3	2.7	#
54022	1 Nov 1970	60.5	16	11.24	3.8	0.79	0.0	31.1	156.1	29.8	49.3	37.8	1.8	#
a mean												36.7		
g mean					3.2	0.51							1.8	
54027	29 May 1979	39.4	12	19.18	5.8	4.34	2.9	5.8	127.9	3.0	7.6	5.9	3.8	#
54027	27 Dec 1979	59.2	23	16.99	8.4	2.16	0.0	2.2	127.2	3.7	6.3	1.2	3.0	#
54027	23 Mar 1986	15.3	8	4.52	4.0	3.02	6.0	2.5	121.5	0.4	2.3	2.2	3.0	#
54027	30 Jul 1986	15.5	13	3.56	4.4	2.17	93.9	4.3	35.4	0.3	1.8	23.2	—	
54027	25 Aug 1986	42.5	12	7.25	3.2	1.50	73.2	2.9	54.7	1.0	2.4	18.1	—	
54027	13 Sep 1986	17.9	11	2.35	1.3	1.40	59.2	0.3	66.1	0.1	0.7	14.4	1.5	#
54027	19 Oct 1986	22.8	6	3.51	1.8	1.25	76.4	2.9	51.5	0.2	1.0	18.3	1.5	#
54027	4 Apr 1987	26.0	15	9.31	6.5	4.49	0.0	3.1	128.1	1.2	4.7	3.0	5.0	#
54027	5 Jun 1987	23.9	8	4.82	2.3	2.29	60.7	6.9	71.2	0.4	1.8	14.2	—	
54027	8 Jun 1987	12.9	11	3.23	5.3	2.19	46.6	7.7	86.1	0.2	1.8	10.5	4.5	#
54027	30 Dec 1987	8.3	3	4.06	2.4	2.96	0.0	6.2	131.2	0.2	2.2	—	2.5	#
54027	1 Sep 1988	21.1	9	3.10	2.8	1.29	66.5	7.7	66.2	0.3	1.2	14.9	1.5	#
54027	18 Oct 1988	21.3	7	5.04	1.3	1.83	35.7	2.7	92.0	0.4	1.8	9.0	—	

Catch	Date	P mm	D h	Q_p m^3s^{-1}	LAG h	BF m^3s^{-1}	SMD mm	API5 mm	CWI mm	R/O mm	PR %	SPR %	Tp(0) h	
54027	7 Nov 1989	28.0	17	4.75	3.0	1.54	57.7	1.2	68.5	0.7	2.4	15.5	2.5	#
54027	20 Jun 1990	14.2	9	2.51	3.1	1.14	95.8	5.4	34.6	0.2	1.3	22.9	1.5	#
54027	28 Apr 1991	30.4	26	3.52	6.8	2.10	19.0	0.9	106.9	0.4	1.4	4.9	2.0	#
54027	30 Jul 1991	24.5	9	3.44	2.6	1.32	46.3	0.8	79.5	0.3	1.1	11.4	2.5	#
54027	3 Apr 1993	12.6	8	2.76	2.9	1.95	13.9	3.8	114.9	0.1	0.9	2.4	2.5	#
54027	4 Apr 1993	15.0	7	3.95	2.3	2.07	5.8	6.7	125.9	0.2	1.5	0.3	3.0	#
54027	9 May 1993	10.7	5	3.33	1.7	2.01	27.0	2.8	100.8	0.1	1.0	6.0	2.5	#
54027	25 May 1993	17.2	5	4.20	2.8	1.90	22.2	2.2	105.0	0.3	1.5	5.5	3.0	#
54027	8 Jul 1993	23.0	10	4.49	0.2	1.80	53.2	0.0	71.8	0.2	0.9	13.2	—	
54027	19 Nov 1987	29.0	11	10.75	5.7	3.78	0.2	1.3	126.1	1.6	5.4	4.2	7.5	#
a mean												10.1		
g mean					2.9	2.04							2.7	
54034	2 Feb 1972	23.5	45	8.52	7.1	0.80	0.0	2.4	127.4	10.8	46.1	45.4	—	
54034	15 Feb 1972	20.4	23	3.79	11.0	0.73	0.2	0.5	125.3	7.4	36.5	36.3	—	
54034	8 Sep 1972	45.8	17	2.22	12.2	0.12	94.4	1.6	32.2	3.0	6.6	28.1	—	
54034	3 May 1973	20.3	39	3.60	6.1	0.68	15.7	2.0	111.3	5.4	26.8	30.1	—	
54034	5 Aug 1973	20.1	16	2.47	11.2	0.20	65.8	2.7	61.9	1.6	8.1	23.7	—	
54034	14 Feb 1974	12.9	13	3.50	11.6	1.06	0.2	2.5	127.3	4.6	35.9	35.2	—	
a mean												33.1		
g mean					9.5	0.46							—	
54090	18 Oct 1973	88.2	17	2.41	2.8	0.06	0.0	5.6	130.6	55.8	63.3	55.1	0.6	
54090	14 Nov 1973	41.8	14	1.98	1.7	0.09	0.0	22.4	147.4	21.8	52.2	45.9	—	
54090	14 Jan 1974	72.0	28	2.02	2.8	0.08	0.0	10.3	135.3	55.9	77.7	70.0	—	
54090	16 Jun 1974	28.4	11	2.15	0.6	0.04	58.3	11.0	77.7	11.4	40.0	51.8	0.4	
54090	4 Sep 1974	42.5	22	1.61	5.9	0.08	69.2	16.3	72.1	30.5	71.8	84.2	1.5	
54090	21 Dec 1974	33.2	18	1.54	2.8	0.15	0.0	26.5	151.5	16.3	49.0	42.4	0.6	
54090	21 Jan 1975	103.4	24	2.14	2.5	0.10	0.0	22.9	147.9	75.9	73.4	59.5	0.6	
54090	24 Sep 1975	89.9	34	1.57	3.1	0.05	94.7	10.1	40.4	60.2	67.0	81.2	0.8	
54090	30 Nov 1975	116.6	31	1.94	1.7	0.07	4.4	7.2	127.8	88.5	75.9	65.8	1.0	
54090	30 Dec 1975	88.9	28	1.73	5.2	0.04	0.2	1.3	126.1	59.5	66.9	59.8	1.4	
54090	11 Feb 1976	84.4	25	1.75	2.1	0.06	0.0	5.3	130.3	64.1	75.9	68.2	0.7	
54090	5 Jul 1976	30.3	7	1.18	0.8	0.01	97.1	2.8	30.7	4.2	13.7	37.3	0.9	
54090	15 Aug 1977	97.6	4	4.40	1.9	0.07	80.1	4.9	49.8	33.6	34.4	45.5	1.4	
54090	9 Sep 1977	73.6	17	1.50	2.8	0.07	0.0	4.1	129.1	47.1	64.0	57.7	1.2	
54090	30 Sep 1977	77.9	22	1.74	2.5	0.05	55.8	2.0	71.2	35.4	45.4	53.1	—	
54090	1 Nov 1977	76.9	23	2.51	3.1	0.12	0.3	27.4	152.1	51.9	67.5	55.1	—	
54090	23 Nov 1977	48.7	19	1.68	3.2	0.07	0.0	10.1	135.1	23.1	47.5	42.9	0.6	
a mean												57.4		
g mean					2.4	0.06							0.8	
54999	25 Dec 1990				—								4.1	
54999	26 Dec 1990				—								3.2	
54999	24 Sep 1992				—								6.2	
54999	3 Oct 1992				—								2.9	
54999	20 Oct 1992				—								5.1	
54999	25 Oct 1992				—								2.9	
g mean													3.89	
55008	19 Sep 1968	62.9	30	8.91	5.5	0.32	2.4	1.0	123.6	21.3	33.9	30.2	2.2	#
55008	2 Oct 1968	45.7	17	8.92	1.8	1.40	0.0	14.8	139.8	26.3	57.5	52.3	2.0	#
55008	22 Nov 1968	31.6	13	5.23	4.5	0.37	0.0	4.4	129.4	13.2	41.9	40.8	1.5	#
55008	20 Jan 1969	24.5	16	8.99	2.3	1.93	0.0	29.1	154.1	17.2	70.4	63.1	—	
55008	29 Mar 1969	41.5	25	8.24	2.9	0.38	5.9	0.9	120.0	21.3	51.4	52.1	—	
55008	30 Mar 1969	42.3	9	13.34	3.4	1.14	0.0	20.8	145.8	26.1	61.6	55.6	—	
55008	10 Apr 1969	42.0	11	13.19	2.2	0.79	0.0	9.2	134.2	17.9	42.6	39.6	1.5	#
55008	25 May 1969	59.1	25	10.07	3.9	0.46	2.8	4.7	126.9	22.2	37.5	33.5	—	
55008	2 Jun 1969	34.4	13	7.91	2.8	0.54	6.7	1.9	120.2	14.0	40.8	42.0	1.2	#
55008	11 Aug 1969	104.4	41	17.24	7.5	0.37	24.4	0.4	101.0	29.5	28.3	26.0	—	
55008	8 Nov 1969	47.6	25	11.42	0.1	1.29	0.0	14.6	139.6	21.9	46.0	40.5	—	
55008	11 Nov 1969	30.8	9	14.66	1.8	2.67	0.0	34.6	159.6	15.0	48.7	40.0	—	
55008	20 Feb 1970	106.4	28	15.82	4.8	1.24	0.0	20.1	145.1	65.6	61.7	48.2	2.2	#
55008	5 Apr 1970	36.4	14	10.03	2.9	0.55	0.3	3.5	128.2	16.1	44.2	43.4	1.8	#
55008	21 Apr 1970	28.3	10	13.53	0.7	2.05	0.5	38.0	162.5	14.8	52.3	42.9	1.1	#
55008	15 Aug 1970	40.0	10	11.71	1.5	1.14	0.0	9.3	134.3	15.8	39.6	37.3	1.5	#

Catch	Date	*P*	*D*	Q_p	*LAG*	*BF*	*SMD*	*API5*	*CWI*	*R/O*	*PR*	*SPR*	*Tp*(0)	
		mm	*h*	m^3s^{-1}	*h*	m^3s^{-1}	*mm*	*mm*	*mm*	*mm*	*%*	*%*	*h*	
55008	27 Oct 1970	88.1	32	13.42	6.0	0.90	0.0	17.9	142.9	51.1	58.0	46.8	2.2	#
55008	1 Nov 1970	62.8	15	23.42	2.7	1.39	0.0	28.6	153.6	35.8	57.0	45.8	1.2	#
55008	4 Nov 1970	26.2	8	13.93	2.6	1.37	0.0	23.0	148.0	16.1	61.3	55.5	—	
55008	11 Feb 1971	81.4	22	16.10	4.0	0.46	2.6	0.0	122.4	45.5	55.9	50.5	—	
55008	21 Jan 1969	19.2	18	7.72	0.7	2.24	0.0	43.3	168.3	9.6	50.1	39.3	—	
a mean												44.1		
g mean					2.3	0.90							1.6	
55012	13 Dec 1969	36.0	16	145.94	6.3	12.67	0.0	1.7	126.7	15.7	43.6	43.2	—	
55012	18 Oct 1971	64.3	40	227.79	2.9	15.54	48.8	7.5	83.7	32.5	50.6	56.7	—	
55012	9 Nov 1972	33.3	23	92.81	4.1	7.32	24.8	1.5	101.7	11.9	35.7	41.5	—	
55012	5 Aug 1973	78.8	19	298.03	9.4	14.06	23.8	10.5	111.7	44.5	56.5	54.0	8.5	#
55012	9 Feb 1974	79.2	44	192.67	5.5	29.29	0.0	15.5	140.5	47.2	59.6	49.9	6.5	#
55012	12 Nov 1974	40.0	27	139.67	8.3	20.12	0.0	13.4	138.4	19.7	49.3	45.9	5.5	#
55012	19 Jan 1975	27.4	18	111.89	5.2	15.84	0.0	5.2	130.2	13.2	48.3	47.0	3.5	#
55012	12 Feb 1976	43.6	24	120.75	6.7	10.41	0.0	6.4	131.4	25.9	59.4	56.7	4.1	#
55012	13 Oct 1976	57.1	54	94.07	10.5	12.28	15.7	5.7	115.0	30.7	53.7	52.9	5.5	#
a mean												49.8		
g mean					6.1	14.25							5.4	
55021	20 Dec 1969	26.2	36	33.02	29.0	6.23	0.0	6.9	131.9	14.9	57.0	55.2	30.0	#
55021	6 Nov 1970	38.8	18	24.01	20.0	5.23	0.8	1.7	125.9	7.5	19.3	18.9	30.0	#
55021	22 Jan 1971	24.2	29	37.21	9.1	16.80	0.0	7.1	132.1	6.1	25.1	23.2	7.5	#
55021	16 Jan 1974	19.4	13	32.01	14.0	17.04	0.0	3.5	128.5	4.5	23.2	22.2	15.5	#
55021	5 Dec 1972	41.5	48	45.16	14.9	18.36	0.0	9.8	134.8	16.4	39.5	36.4	—	
55021	11 Feb 1974	35.7	33	45.96	14.3	27.13	0.0	7.7	132.7	7.4	20.8	18.7	—	
55021	13 Nov 1974	19.8	24	23.82	18.4	8.21	45.7	6.9	86.2	7.5	37.9	47.5	—	
55021	1 Dec 1975	26.8	18	11.88	25.6	3.36	72.8	1.7	53.9	4.2	15.8	33.4	—	
55021	14 Oct 1976	20.8	22	26.34	20.8	12.68	0.0	5.5	130.5	6.0	29.0	27.5	26.5	#
a mean												31.4		
g mean					17.5	10.55							19.4	
55022	14 Jan 1970	19.0	15	34.64	15.7	8.76	0.0	8.8	133.8	9.2	48.6	46.4	—	
55022	20 Jan 1971	14.3	17	32.28	13.3	9.37	0.0	4.6	129.6	8.3	58.2	57.0	14.0	#
55022	17 Mar 1971	31.5	31	26.50	7.4	1.94	0.0	4.2	129.2	13.6	43.1	42.0	14.5	#
55022	12 Jan 1972	28.6	33	26.16	4.7	4.02	0.0	7.5	132.5	12.9	45.1	43.2	13.1	#
55022	15 Feb 1972	39.5	29	33.99	12.4	2.43	0.3	0.6	125.3	18.3	46.3	46.2	11.5	#
55022	16 Jan 1974	23.5	16	33.46	7.6	4.23	0.0	5.4	130.4	12.1	51.5	50.1	12.5	#
55022	29 Jan 1974	24.6	36	25.26	13.6	3.26	0.0	11.1	136.1	11.2	45.7	42.9	6.5	#
55022	13 Nov 1974	28.1	17	40.60	11.4	2.68	0.0	8.8	133.8	15.3	54.6	52.4	14.0	#
a mean												47.5		
g mean					10.1	3.94							11.9	
55025	6 Nov 1970	33.3	20	22.23	11.1	2.10	0.0	2.3	127.3	8.5	25.5	24.9	6.2	#
55025	11 Dec 1972	19.7	13	43.23	6.7	7.93	0.0	8.4	133.4	6.3	32.1	30.0	5.3	#
55025	8 Jan 1974	13.0	8	32.01	6.4	6.35	0.0	8.5	133.5	5.2	39.9	37.7	5.1	#
55025	13 Nov 1974	32.0	19	41.54	7.8	5.09	0.0	6.1	131.1	10.9	34.1	32.5	—	
55025	26 Dec 1974	19.6	11	28.39	3.4	6.17	0.0	6.8	131.8	4.8	24.4	22.7	5.5	#
55025	11 Feb 1973	20.3	16	22.39	8.4	2.78	0.0	2.2	127.2	5.6	27.4	26.8	4.6	#
55025	14 Oct 1976	35.0	29	27.49	9.6	4.31	0.0	2.8	127.8	10.9	31.0	30.3	5.5	#
a mean												29.3		
g mean					7.2	4.54							5.3	
55026	20 Feb 1970	58.0	28	153.75	6.6	18.79	0.0	16.2	141.2	41.4	71.4	63.9	—	
55026	1 Apr 1973	60.9	23	113.77	8.4	3.36	14.1	2.0	112.9	20.5	33.6	32.8	—	
55026	5 Aug 1973	74.8	17	251.95	6.0	9.07	25.1	9.7	109.6	41.6	55.6	54.0	—	
55026	18 Oct 1973	49.7	18	91.05	7.5	7.57	1.8	2.4	125.6	20.3	40.9	38.5	—	
55026	1 Dec 1975	71.1	28	113.20	4.2	12.07	8.9	6.3	122.4	38.1	53.6	49.2	4.6	#
55026	12 Feb 1976	50.3	24	108.44	7.2	8.30	0.0	6.5	131.5	31.4	62.4	58.5	6.0	#
a mean												49.5		
g mean					6.5	8.70							5.3	
55034	18 Oct 1973	76.3	17	5.43	3.4	0.14	0.0	3.1	128.1	47.5	62.2	55.9	0.9	#
55034	28 Nov 1973	43.2	13	3.16	3.1	0.09	0.0	1.9	126.9	21.8	50.4	48.9	1.6	#
55034	15 Dec 1973	44.4	19	4.59	2.5	0.27	0.0	15.1	140.1	25.2	56.7	51.7	0.9	#
55034	14 Jan 1974	57.8	21	5.37	2.8	0.23	0.0	10.5	135.5	36.0	62.2	56.2	1.1	#

Catch	Date	P mm	D h	Q_p m^3s^{-1}	LAG h	BF m^3s^{-1}	SMD mm	API5 mm	CWI mm	R/O mm	PR %	SPR %	Tp(0) h	
55034	8 Feb 1974	51.9	13	5.04	1.9	0.17	0.0	5.3	130.3	32.5	62.6	58.7	0.9	#
55034	16 Jun 1974	31.8	7	4.62	1.3	0.17	61.3	9.6	73.3	13.6	42.7	55.6	0.9	#
55034	18 Oct 1974	60.0	18	4.55	3.6	0.09	0.0	1.4	126.4	40.2	67.0	63.0	—	
55034	21 Jan 1975	80.3	23	5.33	3.0	0.24	0.0	17.8	142.8	58.4	72.7	62.3	0.6	#
55034	30 Dec 1975	85.0	26	4.74	4.9	0.11	0.2	0.9	125.7	57.6	67.8	61.2	1.0	#
55034	12 Feb 1976	101.9	22	5.67	1.5	0.27	0.0	6.9	131.9	67.8	66.5	56.7	0.9	#
55034	30 Jun 1977	99.5	23	3.81	5.9	0.13	29.2	3.7	99.5	53.9	54.2	52.7	1.1	#
55034	9 Sep 1977	80.8	18	4.29	3.6	0.27	0.0	3.8	128.8	45.2	55.9	48.9	1.3	#
55034	30 Sep 1977	67.0	9	3.92	2.5	0.24	1.6	9.9	133.3	27.9	41.6	35.0	1.1	#
55034	19 Nov 1977	65.1	23	4.41	2.0	0.31	0.0	5.4	130.4	39.5	60.7	55.1	1.2	#
a mean												54.4		
g mean					2.8	0.18							1.0	
56002	18 Oct 1971	53.4	31	89.57	6.0	8.83	6.0	16.0	135.0	15.4	28.9	22.3	—	
56002	12 Nov 1972	35.3	13	42.62	5.9	5.71	19.9	4.7	109.8	6.4	18.1	20.2	—	
56002	11 Jan 1974	13.0	10	59.73	2.5	20.80	0.0	21.5	146.5	2.9	22.6	15.7	—	
56002	14 Feb 1974	37.4	15	71.16	4.2	22.73	0.0	8.8	133.8	9.9	26.4	22.8	5.5	#
a mean												20.3		
g mean					4.4	12.43							5.5	
56003	8 Dec 1965	34.2	50	34.51	8.3	3.23	0.0	2.2	127.2	26.0	76.0	75.5	—	
56003	16 Dec 1965	50.8	50	32.52	7.4	3.93	0.0	7.3	132.3	48.1	94.7	90.5	—	
56003	24 Feb 1966	41.7	13	17.76	4.8	3.78	0.0	4.4	129.4	7.9	19.0	17.2	—	
56003	3 Oct 1966	17.1	8	10.50	5.7	1.13	0.0	4.7	129.7	3.4	20.1	18.9	3.4	#
56003	9 Dec 1966	28.3	21	17.72	3.2	3.56	0.0	2.1	127.1	11.7	41.2	40.7	—	
56003	26 Feb 1967	47.3	19	24.39	7.1	3.57	0.0	5.9	130.9	14.9	31.4	28.1	—	
56003	15 Oct 1967	65.9	57	40.07	5.6	4.05	0.2	6.8	131.6	26.8	40.6	34.6	3.7	#
56003	23 Dec 1967	11.2	13	18.24	3.5	4.75	0.0	9.0	134.0	4.1	36.5	34.2	2.6	#
56003	26 Jun 1968	17.9	20	10.99	4.8	1.30	23.6	4.1	105.5	4.4	24.4	29.3	—	
56003	10 Feb 1974	23.3	24	19.53	12.6	6.65	0.0	14.8	139.8	10.7	45.8	42.1	—	
56003	16 Jun 1974	24.2	7	15.47	2.6	0.67	43.2	1.9	83.7	3.3	13.8	24.1	3.0	#
56003	13 Nov 1974	40.9	28	20.29	8.9	3.93	0.0	9.2	134.2	12.7	31.0	28.3	—	
56003	30 Jan 1975	20.8	14	18.67	4.4	4.08	0.0	6.0	131.0	6.1	29.4	27.9	3.0	#
56003	24 Sep 1975	32.1	24	5.49	5.2	0.41	106.9	1.6	19.7	3.1	9.8	36.1	2.5	#
56003	11 Feb 1976	23.4	23	9.51	6.8	1.66	0.0	2.9	127.9	7.8	33.4	32.7	—	
a mean												37.3		
g mean					5.6	2.48							3.0	
56004	6 Jan 1971	49.2	43	177.72	12.7	11.57	0.0	0.4	125.4	15.9	32.4	30.1	—	
56004	3 Dec 1972	39.8	34	252.03	19.8	40.58	0.0	21.8	146.8	19.5	49.0	43.5	—	
56004	5 Dec 1972	25.8	13	310.92	22.4	64.83	0.0	21.7	146.7	25.7	99.5	94.1	—	
56004	10 Feb 1974	45.1	26	324.63	6.5	90.74	0.0	17.3	142.3	22.5	49.9	44.1	4.9	#
56004	12 Nov 1974	58.0	20	360.25	10.8	36.53	0.0	9.2	134.2	31.6	54.5	48.8	7.5	#
56004	24 Sep 1975	57.8	31	118.39	6.9	6.45	106.9	1.6	19.7	9.5	16.4	39.3	7.3	#
56004	12 Feb 1976	31.2	18	142.03	7.5	16.86	0.0	2.9	127.9	11.3	36.1	35.3	9.1	#
56004	5 Dec 1972	77.8	40	310.92	14.9	64.74	0.0	21.7	146.7	35.9	46.1	34.9	—	
a mean												46.3		
g mean					11.5	30.30							7.0	
56005	2 Jul 1968	24.3	5	27.18	3.2	6.93	5.2	11.0	130.8	5.3	22.0	18.1	—	
56005	10 Jul 1968	55.0	14	51.95	6.4	4.60	1.0	7.1	131.1	16.7	30.3	23.8	6.8	#
56005	26 Oct 1968	87.8	52	41.55	13.5	3.40	2.0	0.5	123.5	37.2	42.4	34.6	—	
56005	26 Nov 1968	35.1	25	24.94	6.1	3.69	0.0	3.9	128.9	9.2	26.2	23.0	4.1	#
56005	21 Dec 1968	34.9	23	32.32	4.6	7.85	0.0	16.7	141.7	12.4	35.5	29.6	—	
56005	6 Jan 1971	42.5	24	36.86	9.6	3.44	0.0	0.3	125.3	17.2	40.5	38.1	3.8	#
56005	6 Nov 1970	57.3	20	31.32	4.8	5.43	1.2	1.8	125.6	15.0	26.1	20.4	5.7	#
56005	24 Jan 1975	31.7	11	34.86	5.8	6.97	0.0	10.8	135.8	9.6	30.3	25.6	3.6	#
56005	14 Feb 1974	42.5	14	36.35	4.8	9.44	0.0	10.3	135.3	11.9	28.0	22.4	4.5	#
56005	10 Oct 1976	30.6	11	46.86	4.1	7.58	14.3	6.3	117.0	12.5	40.7	41.2	—	
56005	13 Oct 1976	30.9	14	40.33	6.0	8.10	6.4	7.1	125.7	15.4	49.8	48.6	—	
56005	17 Oct 1976	41.7	17	49.59	6.8	9.93	2.9	5.8	127.9	18.9	45.4	42.8	—	
a mean												30.7		
g mean					5.8	6.04							4.6	
56006	11 Dec 1964	81.7	39	193.65	8.2	12.40	0.0	9.1	134.1	52.6	64.4	56.0	—	
56006	13 Jan 1965	44.8	16	226.53	2.8	18.70	0.0	13.7	138.7	28.6	63.9	59.1	4.0	#

Catch	Date	*P*	*D*	Q_p	*LAG*	*BF*	*SMD*	*API5*	*CWI*	*R/O*	*PR*	*SPR*	*Tp*(0)	
		mm	*h*	m^3s^{-1}	*h*	m^3s^{-1}	*mm*	*mm*	*mm*	*mm*	*%*	*%*	*h*	
56006	8 Dec 1965	69.1	48	148.38	4.8	8.76	0.0	3.2	128.2	35.1	50.8	45.2	—	
56006	16 Dec 1965	144.6	52	223.56	6.5	11.02	0.0	9.2	134.2	106.9	73.9	59.9	—	
56006	24 Feb 1966	53.0	15	193.12	3.3	16.18	0.0	8.1	133.1	30.5	57.5	52.8	3.0	#
56006	26 Feb 1967	64.0	18	239.32	5.3	13.57	0.0	8.2	133.2	42.0	65.6	59.4	5.5	#
56006	16 Oct 1967	81.0	18	242.66	3.7	17.05	0.0	14.2	139.2	48.0	59.3	49.7	5.3	#
56006	10 Feb 1974	57.8	25	142.60	3.5	33.30	0.0	19.7	144.7	27.2	47.1	38.8	3.0	#
56006	12 Nov 1974	68.9	29	160.68	6.5	14.95	0.0	16.7	141.7	33.9	49.2	40.3	3.2	#
56006	24 Sep 1975	74.9	32	78.31	2.8	6.22	105.7	2.0	21.3	14.4	19.2	39.7	3.1	#
56006	12 Feb 1976	41.1	21	76.95	6.7	6.53	0.0	2.6	127.6	15.9	38.7	37.6	—	
56006	2 Feb 1977	40.3	20	89.41	3.7	14.38	0.0	3.6	128.6	11.8	29.2	28.1	5.3	#
56006	9 Feb 1974	30.6	15	108.61	4.1	22.99	0.0	14.6	139.6	12.9	42.2	38.5	4.1	#
a mean												46.5		
g mean					4.5	13.63							3.9	
56011	30 Nov 1975	47.8	26	26.33	9.4	1.14	0.0	2.4	127.4	19.2	40.2	36.8	3.5	#
56011	11 Feb 1976	24.8	18	10.94	8.9	1.50	0.0	3.8	128.8	7.7	31.0	28.9	10.0	#
56011	25 Sep 1976	57.7	22	42.95	6.2	2.79	62.2	17.4	80.2	15.0	26.0	32.6	7.1	#
56011	14 Mar 1977	40.3	31	25.08	2.8	3.14	0.0	7.8	132.8	9.6	23.9	20.4	3.7	#
a mean												29.7		
g mean					6.1	1.97							5.5	
57004	1 Dec 1966	57.3	37	34.88	9.4	4.48	0.0	10.0	135.0	25.4	44.3	37.9	5.1	#
57004	9 Dec 1966	48.0	36	27.70	8.0	3.25	0.0	3.1	128.1	19.0	39.5	36.1	4.1	#
57004	30 Dec 1966	45.5	17	41.95	8.2	8.63	0.0	12.1	137.1	18.5	40.7	35.5	6.0	#
57004	20 Feb 1967	39.6	24	34.19	10.9	7.31	0.0	15.9	140.9	16.8	42.4	37.8	7.7	#
57004	26 Feb 1967	79.6	20	76.87	7.2	8.18	0.0	7.9	132.9	42.8	53.8	45.5	—	
57004	4 Sep 1967	47.9	21	30.26	8.3	1.55	0.0	12.4	137.4	17.6	36.8	31.0	5.2	#
57004	30 Sep 1967	44.8	23	40.29	8.1	5.81	0.0	10.8	135.8	18.2	40.7	35.9	5.7	#
57004	16 Oct 1967	89.0	26	93.80	9.0	10.10	0.0	15.9	140.9	52.8	59.3	48.2	9.1	#
57004	22 Dec 1967	63.9	32	38.51	9.8	4.47	0.0	4.6	129.6	30.0	46.9	41.0	—	
57004	22 Mar 1968	100.6	45	49.69	7.9	4.07	0.0	5.6	130.6	53.9	53.6	43.8	—	
57004	1 Jul 1968	37.0	15	31.43	3.6	5.61	0.0	7.2	132.2	10.0	27.1	24.3	—	
57004	9 Jul 1968	37.4	22	29.32	6.0	2.69	8.1	1.8	118.7	9.5	25.4	25.9	4.7	#
57004	10 Oct 1968	39.5	21	31.25	9.3	4.43	0.0	10.0	135.0	12.7	32.1	28.7	6.9	#
57004	26 Oct 1968	79.0	46	33.52	11.8	3.30	1.6	0.0	123.4	34.3	43.4	37.3	6.8	#
57004	21 Dec 1968	37.6	23	30.37	6.7	6.43	0.0	15.0	140.0	15.8	42.0	37.6	5.1	#
57004	25 Apr 1969	37.9	31	25.11	7.5	2.18	0.0	7.3	132.3	11.9	31.4	28.6	4.7	#
57004	10 Aug 1969	64.9	20	32.07	8.1	2.37	5.7	2.7	122.0	19.5	30.1	25.6	4.6	#
a mean												35.3		
g mean					8.0	4.41							5.7	
57005	22 Mar 1968	97.9	44	218.87	7.6	29.05	0.0	7.3	132.3	49.6	50.7	40.7	—	
57005	12 May 1968	33.1	14	120.80	6.1	16.26	2.4	4.3	126.9	10.1	30.4	28.9	5.9	#
57005	26 Jun 1968	39.1	20	142.59	9.4	24.60	1.4	13.9	137.5	15.5	39.6	35.7	7.7	#
57005	2 Jul 1968	41.2	15	156.64	6.8	46.74	0.0	16.7	141.7	9.0	21.8	15.9	—	
57005	10 Oct 1968	49.1	37	159.05	9.7	22.63	0.0	10.4	135.4	22.4	45.7	40.4	4.0	#
57005	26 Oct 1968	83.8	47	199.89	9.7	19.40	1.6	0.2	123.6	41.7	49.8	43.3	5.1	#
57005	17 Jan 1969	42.7	39	155.60	6.6	32.66	0.0	9.7	134.7	22.2	51.9	48.1	—	
57005	11 Nov 1969	40.7	12	154.03	5.5	23.40	0.0	11.6	136.6	12.0	29.6	25.3	4.0	#
57005	15 Jan 1970	53.2	34	217.51	10.5	38.92	0.0	20.1	145.1	25.7	48.3	40.0	—	
57005	1 Nov 1970	51.1	17	224.03	6.2	40.53	0.0	43.3	168.3	23.9	46.8	33.0	4.2	#
57005	18 Oct 1971	64.7	31	236.23	10.5	16.61	0.0	13.6	138.6	33.8	52.3	44.2	7.1	#
57005	5 Dec 1972	62.3	23	281.29	10.2	69.39	0.0	19.9	144.9	31.4	50.4	41.0	7.3	#
57005	5 Aug 1973	79.2	25	211.00	5.8	14.39	19.6	10.5	115.9	18.3	23.1	18.3	—	
a mean												35.0		
g mean					7.8	27.34							5.5	
57006	11 Oct 1968	43.7	12	65.38	4.4	10.67	0.0	11.6	136.6	17.6	40.3	35.2	1.3	#
57006	22 Apr 1970	40.2	18	61.30	4.0	12.57	0.6	16.0	140.4	15.4	38.4	33.2	1.2	#
57006	1 Nov 1970	63.8	15	93.76	3.7	18.50	0.0	28.4	153.4	35.2	55.1	43.3	2.2	#
57006	6 Jan 1971	71.5	23	89.18	5.1	4.01	0.0	2.7	127.7	23.4	32.7	25.6	1.6	#
57006	17 Oct 1971	97.0	39	82.37	6.4	5.64	0.0	10.2	135.2	47.3	48.8	37.8	3.2	#
57006	14 Feb 1972	95.6	31	73.51	5.4	8.21	0.0	2.3	127.3	42.4	44.4	35.4	2.5	#
57006	8 Sep 1972	68.2	22	61.93	6.0	1.63	33.7	3.7	95.0	11.2	16.4	17.2	1.5	#
57006	12 Nov 1972	64.8	18	97.35	2.8	9.62	0.0	8.3	133.3	27.0	41.7	34.3	1.5	#
57006	30 Nov 1972	68.3	30	74.46	5.3	9.32	0.0	17.8	142.8	40.0	58.6	49.0	1.5	#

Catch	Date	*P*	*D*	Q_p	*LAG*	*BF*	*SMD*	*API5*	*CWI*	*R/O*	*PR*	*SPR*	*Tp*(0)	
		mm	h	m^3s^{-1}	h	m^3s^{-1}	mm	mm	mm	mm	%	%	h	
57006	3 Dec 1972	48.4	19	62.46	3.8	14.44	0.0	24.5	149.5	19.2	39.6	30.3	1.5	#
57006	4 Dec 1972	75.0	21	91.75	4.0	22.58	0.0	32.4	157.4	37.4	49.9	35.6	1.5	#
57006	12 Dec 1972	57.1	12	94.37	3.9	19.11	0.0	22.7	147.7	26.2	45.9	36.0	1.9	#
57006	1 Apr 1973	66.7	19	60.08	6.1	2.91	0.6	1.2	125.6	19.0	28.5	22.3	2.9	#
57006	5 Aug 1973	83.1	26	79.11	4.3	6.28	0.0	16.8	141.8	24.5	29.5	17.5	2.0	#
57006	10 Jan 1974	40.9	9	76.32	3.4	10.98	0.0	12.4	137.4	15.3	37.4	32.6	2.4	#
57006	10 Nov 1974	42.4	17	64.47	2.8	10.28	0.0	15.9	140.9	14.2	33.4	27.2	1.5	#
57006	13 Nov 1974	61.7	24	87.94	2.0	15.26	0.0	22.3	147.3	27.6	44.7	34.3	—	
57006	19 Jan 1975	57.2	21	98.89	4.6	9.43	0.0	6.7	131.7	26.3	46.0	40.1	2.5	#
57006	21 Jan 1975	75.2	20	108.52	6.5	14.21	0.0	25.0	150.0	45.6	60.6	48.6	2.5	#
57006	24 Jan 1975	51.6	13	91.33	3.9	14.71	0.0	25.6	150.6	22.7	44.0	34.1	1.5	#
57006	30 Jan 1975	37.9	20	63.25	5.0	13.92	0.0	19.7	144.7	15.0	39.5	33.4	—	
57006	30 Nov 1975	91.4	21	113.07	3.5	10.23	0.0	4.7	129.7	47.1	51.5	42.5	1.5	#
57006	5 Oct 1976	64.3	26	69.27	7.4	8.26	0.0	16.1	141.1	36.8	57.2	48.5	4.1	#
57006	15 Mar 1977	42.0	13	62.04	3.7	7.41	0.4	15.1	139.7	16.8	40.0	34.5	—	
57006	30 Oct 1977	58.9	24	64.26	4.9	5.46	0.1	3.2	128.1	23.1	39.2	33.7	1.6	#
57006	31 Oct 1977	94.0	23	146.06	7.6	12.48	0.0	26.1	151.1	64.6	68.7	54.8	2.2	#
a mean												35.3		
g mean					4.4	9.31							1.9	
58001	26 Jan 1961	31.6	14	59.43	3.8	8.44	0.5	0.1	124.6	6.7	21.3	20.2	—	
58001	11 Sep 1962	66.7	29	114.48	5.3	6.33	0.0	2.8	127.8	18.5	27.8	21.6	—	
58001	17 Nov 1963	55.4	16	107.34	4.9	16.31	0.0	15.4	140.4	11.4	20.6	12.5	6.0	#
58001	18 Nov 1963	48.5	29	127.72	5.3	39.52	0.0	53.3	178.3	13.1	27.0	10.6	3.5	#
58001	14 Jul 1964	56.8	27	48.84	3.8	8.28	5.5	15.3	134.8	12.4	21.8	14.9	—	
58001	13 Nov 1964	53.1	12	62.44	5.3	3.60	0.0	6.9	131.9	9.9	18.7	13.0	—	
58001	12 Dec 1964	50.3	24	101.06	4.9	18.51	0.0	23.1	148.1	20.1	40.0	31.2	—	
58001	15 Jan 1965	50.6	25	63.51	5.4	17.80	0.0	17.0	142.0	19.5	38.5	31.1	3.5	#
58001	25 Jun 1965	28.8	15	45.76	5.1	8.85	0.0	13.6	138.6	9.0	31.1	26.7	—	
58001	11 Jul 1965	74.1	48	45.54	5.7	6.68	31.8	19.5	112.7	24.2	32.6	29.4	3.5	#
58001	8 Dec 1965	82.5	36	99.57	6.4	15.27	0.0	3.6	128.6	33.7	40.9	33.1	3.7	#
58001	16 Dec 1965	161.2	51	149.06	8.4	18.72	0.0	15.6	140.6	123.2	76.4	59.7	—	
58001	19 Oct 1966	64.7	28	103.34	5.2	13.13	0.0	16.2	141.2	23.5	36.3	27.2	—	
58001	30 Dec 1966	46.0	17	119.87	4.1	23.17	0.0	21.5	146.5	20.7	45.1	37.5	3.8	#
58001	27 Feb 1967	48.3	21	94.42	3.0	11.58	0.0	4.9	129.9	15.2	31.4	27.2	—	
58001	28 Jul 1967	78.6	29	112.62	8.6	8.73	19.6	19.7	125.1	35.8	45.5	39.1	3.7	#
58001	16 Oct 1967	61.8	20	115.92	6.1	17.61	0.0	16.5	141.5	32.8	53.0	44.6	4.9	#
58001	26 Jun 1968	40.9	19	110.87	5.1	14.81	1.7	25.2	148.5	13.1	32.1	24.9	2.8	#
58001	27 Oct 1968	49.8	29	69.68	5.1	14.73	0.0	15.8	140.8	24.3	48.7	42.0	—	
58001	1 Nov 1970	64.7	15	143.82	5.6	27.62	0.0	30.8	155.8	39.7	61.3	49.1	—	
a mean												29.8		
g mean					5.2	12.99							3.8	
58002	11 Dec 1964	118.8	35	241.49	5.1	12.23	0.0	11.9	136.9	77.5	65.2	52.6	—	
58002	8 Dec 1965	89.6	33	201.75	6.5	6.16	0.0	3.7	128.7	54.8	61.2	53.3	3.5	#
58002	16 Dec 1965	202.0	54	272.92	4.7	8.36	0.0	9.9	134.9	171.1	84.7	66.4	2.9	#
58002	30 Dec 1966	43.0	17	184.61	4.1	15.50	0.0	17.6	142.6	28.9	67.2	61.8	3.3	#
58002	26 Feb 1967	71.6	19	260.23	5.9	11.60	0.0	9.7	134.7	58.2	81.3	73.9	4.6	#
58002	30 Sep 1967	43.0	17	201.61	4.3	14.94	0.0	12.9	137.9	28.3	65.9	61.7	3.8	#
58002	2 Oct 1967	43.5	37	183.26	4.5	13.89	0.0	27.8	152.8	25.3	58.2	50.1	3.4	#
58002	16 Oct 1967	97.6	25	307.86	6.6	7.67	0.0	16.8	141.8	84.7	86.8	75.0	—	
58002	11 Nov 1969	38.4	12	160.13	5.6	2.17	0.0	11.9	136.9	19.4	50.5	47.4	4.5	#
58002	1 Nov 1970	52.8	17	154.68	4.6	2.51	0.0	20.3	145.3	26.0	49.3	41.5	6.9	#
58002	6 Jan 1971	69.7	24	141.22	7.6	0.52	0.0	1.1	126.1	18.0	25.8	20.5	4.1	#
58002	9 Aug 1971	67.2	18	128.04	6.9	4.96	4.6	2.0	122.4	24.6	36.6	32.6	4.5	#
58002	18 Oct 1971	71.7	33	141.13	4.7	11.78	0.0	14.5	139.5	28.2	39.4	30.6	2.9	#
58002	12 Nov 1972	50.3	26	130.97	3.1	9.77	0.0	8.3	133.3	16.3	32.4	27.9	4.3	#
58002	5 Aug 1973	78.1	24	156.82	5.4	7.79	19.6	22.1	127.5	28.1	36.0	29.5	3.5	#
a mean												48.3		
g mean					5.2	6.66							3.9	
58003	15 Jan 1965	40.5	26	18.16	10.0	3.10	0.0	10.9	135.9	18.2	44.9	41.3	7.2	#
58003	1 Dec 1965	17.4	10	18.09	6.2	3.59	0.0	7.2	132.2	7.1	40.7	38.2	6.2	#
58003	8 Dec 1965	49.3	32	20.12	7.2	3.26	0.0	2.5	127.5	20.6	41.7	38.3	8.5	#
58003	16 Dec 1965	92.3	51	20.97	9.4	4.31	0.0	9.0	134.0	47.8	51.8	41.9	—	
58003	2 Mar 1966	27.9	13	17.88	6.8	2.58	0.0	8.8	133.8	9.4	33.8	30.7	4.8	#

Catch	Date	*P* mm	*D* h	Q_p m^3s^{-1}	*LAG* h	*BF* m^3s^{-1}	*SMD* mm	*API5* mm	*CWI* mm	*R/O* mm	*PR* %	*SPR* %	*Tp*(0) h	
58003	21 Apr 1966	35.6	25	17.77	5.7	2.64	1.0	3.4	127.4	12.5	35.1	33.7	3.3	#
58003	19 Feb 1967	38.3	45	19.19	11.0	1.69	0.0	9.8	134.8	11.5	30.1	26.7	—	
58003	18 Dec 1967	35.2	17	18.30	8.6	1.37	0.0	2.0	127.0	11.7	33.1	31.7	7.8	#
58003	22 Dec 1967	35.2	20	18.50	6.7	1.91	0.0	8.2	133.2	12.1	34.5	31.6	7.9	#
58003	8 Jan 1968	36.4	23	18.55	5.9	1.85	0.0	5.5	130.5	11.2	30.9	28.6	5.3	#
58003	10 Jul 1968	38.4	25	19.45	8.5	1.57	8.1	2.8	119.7	10.2	26.5	26.8	5.8	#
a mean												33.6		
g mean					7.6	2.38							6.1	
58006	9 Aug 1971	70.7	23	67.32	9.7	3.17	71.2	3.1	56.9	40.4	57.1	69.2	4.7	#
58006	18 Oct 1971	74.4	33	65.43	6.2	4.90	6.0	15.2	134.2	46.2	62.1	54.4	4.5	#
58006	9 Nov 1972	46.7	19	42.53	2.5	2.78	20.9	5.5	109.6	12.9	27.6	29.7	—	
58006	12 Nov 1972	51.1	21	59.28	5.5	3.94	15.6	9.8	119.2	23.4	45.7	44.7	2.4	#
58006	1 Apr 1973	54.7	27	45.34	6.8	1.76	10.9	3.4	117.5	18.2	33.3	32.2	2.7	#
58006	5 Aug 1973	88.4	23	66.76	4.1	3.48	41.3	22.1	105.8	34.0	38.5	36.5	2.3	#
a mean												44.5		
g mean					5.3	3.18							3.2	
58008	19 Dec 1971	20.8	10	20.80	4.4	0.92	0.0	0.8	125.8	8.9	42.7	42.3	3.6	#
58008	15 Feb 1972	55.8	30	26.00	7.4	1.73	0.1	1.7	126.6	30.9	55.3	51.7	3.5	#
58008	6 Jun 1972	34.0	21	24.97	7.8	2.27	5.3	7.6	127.3	11.6	34.2	33.4	4.6	#
58008	9 Nov 1972	20.4	17	29.08	3.8	2.19	41.7	4.2	87.5	14.5	70.9	80.3	2.6	#
58008	12 Nov 1972	47.9	27	47.04	2.2	2.56	17.1	2.5	110.4	23.1	48.3	49.9	3.6	#
58008	30 Nov 1972	51.6	39	32.25	11.1	2.13	0.0	14.8	139.8	37.2	72.0	65.8	5.0	#
58008	12 Dec 1972	33.3	24	33.45	3.5	4.07	0.0	18.5	143.5	22.4	67.4	62.8	—	
a mean												55.2		
g mean					5.0	2.09							3.7	
58009	11 Nov 1972	38.2	25	17.04	5.3	1.83	16.9	3.1	111.2	9.9	26.0	28.4	4.0	#
58009	12 Dec 1972	15.7	12	15.25	5.1	4.72	0.0	12.9	137.9	4.4	28.0	23.8	4.5	#
58009	22 Jan 1973	14.6	16	8.99	4.9	1.53	0.0	3.8	128.8	4.0	27.5	25.6	—	
58009	11 Feb 1973	24.2	19	12.49	6.7	2.07	0.0	2.9	127.9	7.3	30.2	28.5	4.9	#
58009	1 Apr 1973	31.2	16	10.20	9.6	0.89	11.1	1.3	115.2	5.8	18.7	20.0	5.9	#
58009	27 Sep 1973	41.2	19	9.41	4.8	0.73	42.9	3.2	85.3	6.4	15.5	23.6	4.8	#
a mean												25.0		
g mean					5.9	1.62							4.8	
60002	8 Dec 1965	47.1	39	125.89	13.1	33.04	0.0	13.0	138.0	24.1	51.2	46.2	—	
60002	16 Dec 1965	100.3	49	155.00	12.6	26.12	0.0	14.8	139.8	70.5	70.3	58.7	—	
60002	27 Feb 1967	56.6	20	163.03	5.6	18.71	0.0	4.9	129.9	22.6	40.0	35.6	5.5	#
60002	1 Oct 1967	55.1	14	166.04	9.1	27.42	1.6	15.9	139.3	28.6	51.9	45.3	8.5	#
60002	16 Oct 1967	56.5	18	151.68	5.8	36.73	0.0	15.1	140.1	25.8	45.7	38.7	3.9	#
60002	15 Jan 1968	39.7	21	111.70	7.3	24.50	0.0	7.1	132.1	18.1	45.7	43.9	7.8	#
60002	19 Jan 1969	81.1	44	139.77	11.1	24.49	0.0	8.6	133.6	47.4	58.4	50.2	—	
60002	12 Dec 1972	32.1	11	130.46	8.8	38.96	0.0	14.9	139.9	17.2	53.5	49.8	—	
60002	5 Aug 1973	86.5	17	183.46	9.7	14.49	2.7	14.9	137.2	39.4	45.6	35.9	—	
60002	29 Jan 1974	56.8	38	133.35	12.3	21.95	0.0	11.1	136.1	44.4	78.2	72.2	—	
60002	20 Dec 1974	61.5	40	150.01	9.3	20.50	0.0	8.4	133.4	38.9	63.2	57.2	—	
60002	10 Feb 1974	66.0	35	141.60	10.5	30.09	0.0	13.1	138.1	42.9	65.0	57.3	—	
60002	30 Jan 1975	31.6	19	132.02	7.7	23.91	0.0	9.5	134.5	20.7	65.6	63.2	—	
a mean												50.3		
g mean					9.1	25.35							6.1	
60003	21 Apr 1966	41.8	25	68.89	13.5	12.88	0.9	7.2	131.3	18.6	44.5	42.2	13.5	#
a mean												42.2		
g mean					13.5	12.88							13.5	
60006	7 Aug 1972	34.0	13	61.65	3.1	4.71	3.5	9.1	130.6	9.9	29.2	27.8	—	
60006	12 Nov 1972	36.3	10	75.06	1.9	7.86	0.0	6.4	131.4	10.7	29.4	27.8	—	
a mean												27.8		
g mean					2.5	6.08							—	
60007	2 Jul 1968	28.0	15	151.64	3.2	35.47	0.9	19.8	143.9	13.9	49.8	45.1	2.1	#
60007	10 Nov 1969	62.9	33	235.14	1.7	18.01	0.0	16.1	141.1	39.4	62.7	54.6	3.0	#
60007	13 Dec 1969	39.0	20	203.04	7.8	20.91	0.0	1.4	126.4	26.8	68.6	68.2	—	
60007	1 Nov 1970	27.5	14	177.11	4.1	50.24	0.0	10.5	135.5	16.3	59.4	56.8	—	

Catch	Date	P mm	D h	Q_p m^3s^{-1}	LAG h	BF m^3s^{-1}	SMD mm	API5 mm	CWI mm	R/O mm	PR %	SPR %	Tp(0) h	
60007	19 Oct 1971	57.3	26	193.28	7.1	22.22	0.8	5.9	130.1	21.8	38.1	33.5	—	
60007	20 Nov 1971	38.7	21	115.47	7.3	8.99	0.0	6.2	131.2	22.6	58.4	56.8	—	
60007	5 Aug 1973	72.2	17	294.05	6.6	8.66	30.4	11.5	106.1	48.9	67.7	67.3	—	
60007	10 Mar 1970	26.5	20	115.72	14.2	9.17	0.0	3.6	128.6	24.3	91.6	90.7	—	
60007	6 Jan 1971	41.8	25	156.91	4.3	5.30	0.0	0.1	125.1	21.4	51.1	50.4	—	
a mean												58.2		
g mean					5.3	15.65							2.5	
61001	11 Sep 1962	42.6	38	19.64	9.4	1.68	0.0	5.1	130.1	5.4	12.6	10.4	9.3	#
61001	29 Sep 1962	40.6	29	26.47	6.3	1.62	0.0	6.5	131.5	6.3	15.5	13.5	—	
61001	17 Nov 1963	34.0	26	41.98	10.1	8.54	0.0	7.0	132.0	11.4	33.6	31.8	8.5	#
61001	28 Nov 1963	26.0	46	35.48	5.8	7.80	0.0	4.3	129.3	5.9	22.8	21.7	—	
61001	13 Jan 1965	21.4	20	34.63	4.6	7.29	0.0	7.3	132.3	5.1	23.6	21.7	3.8	#
61001	17 Nov 1965	39.3	46	33.97	10.9	5.09	0.0	0.5	125.5	4.6	11.8	11.6	—	
61001	28 Nov 1965	30.7	32	43.17	4.8	9.81	0.0	4.6	129.6	8.3	27.0	25.8	5.5	#
61001	16 Dec 1965	34.3	31	52.48	9.4	15.90	0.0	10.4	135.4	13.1	38.1	35.5	7.9	#
61001	21 Apr 1966	35.7	25	48.11	9.1	11.88	1.8	9.2	132.4	11.6	32.4	30.5	7.5	#
61001	12 Aug 1966	36.5	35	41.20	6.9	4.78	0.0	6.9	131.9	8.0	22.0	20.2	8.0	#
61001	27 Feb 1967	38.7	43	53.00	6.9	13.93	0.0	7.8	132.8	12.1	31.2	29.2	6.3	#
61001	29 Sep 1967	37.3	35	43.88	8.0	8.37	0.0	4.1	129.1	8.5	22.8	21.7	5.7	#
61001	1 Oct 1967	37.3	11	53.10	8.1	11.58	1.2	10.8	134.6	10.3	27.6	25.2	5.8	#
61001	4 Nov 1967	30.7	22	54.27	8.0	14.39	0.2	4.4	129.2	12.2	39.7	38.6	—	
61001	26 Jun 1968	24.8	22	25.31	6.6	3.22	25.6	6.8	106.2	3.8	15.3	20.0	5.3	#
61001	16 Dec 1968	33.1	29	34.03	3.9	8.10	0.0	5.5	130.5	7.5	22.8	21.4	5.0	#
61001	20 Dec 1968	25.8	22	36.15	6.2	10.77	0.0	8.9	133.9	5.0	19.4	17.1	5.8	#
61001	21 Dec 1968	15.4	25	40.14	4.7	13.56	0.0	20.9	145.9	4.4	28.4	23.1	5.0	#
61001	24 Dec 1968	26.3	28	44.75	8.2	12.44	0.0	7.1	132.1	9.2	35.0	33.2	6.2	#
61001	17 Nov 1970	22.3	13	50.97	8.3	13.64	0.0	11.9	136.9	7.7	34.4	31.4	7.3	#
61001	18 Nov 1970	24.0	11	53.35	6.0	19.03	0.0	20.0	145.0	7.6	31.5	26.5	8.2	#
61001	20 Nov 1971	34.4	11	54.45	8.6	4.59	0.0	11.1	136.1	11.9	34.7	31.9	7.5	#
61001	29 Nov 1971	41.7	22	59.33	7.9	11.39	0.1	2.8	127.7	14.5	34.8	33.4	—	
a mean												25.0		
g mean					7.1	8.08							6.4	
61003	16 Jun 1969	56.1	32	9.99	7.8	0.44	42.5	4.0	86.5	14.9	26.5	33.0	6.0	#
61003	13 Dec 1969	44.5	21	17.97	6.8	1.17	0.1	3.6	128.5	16.1	36.1	33.9	3.5	#
61003	9 Aug 1971	65.3	27	20.15	5.5	1.03	62.0	5.3	68.3	26.0	39.8	49.7	—	
61003	20 Nov 1971	45.0	20	28.11	7.2	1.25	0.0	10.5	135.5	22.9	51.0	47.0	6.3	#
61003	14 Feb 1972	40.6	23	14.86	6.9	1.72	0.2	2.5	127.3	19.2	47.3	46.4	5.7	#
61003	7 Jun 1972	70.4	32	18.63	9.1	2.05	3.6	7.0	128.4	25.8	36.6	30.8	—	
61003	12 Nov 1972	35.8	15	13.06	5.3	1.18	0.0	6.7	131.7	10.2	28.5	26.8	4.3	#
61003	5 Aug 1973	75.5	17	21.91	1.6	0.63	74.5	11.5	62.0	20.3	26.9	37.2	—	
61003	30 Jan 1975	23.4	16	16.75	4.2	2.52	0.0	10.4	135.4	12.5	53.6	51.0	3.5	#
61003	10 Jan 1974	26.6	7	21.67	5.0	2.99	0.0	16.4	141.4	13.3	49.9	45.8	4.5	#
61003	12 Nov 1974	42.7	20	17.48	6.8	1.48	0.0	6.6	131.6	18.3	42.8	40.2	5.9	#
a mean												40.2		
g mean					5.6	1.31							4.8	
62002	14 Feb 1972	45.1	40	88.35	14.4	23.22	0.0	2.0	127.0	27.8	61.6	59.7	—	
62002	6 Jun 1972	53.9	83	86.29	25.0	13.86	0.0	9.2	134.2	31.5	58.4	53.2	—	
62002	11 Dec 1972	37.6	36	97.99	14.4	32.74	0.0	5.6	130.6	25.0	66.4	65.0	—	
62002	4 Aug 1973	93.9	65	82.35	33.7	2.21	22.9	1.2	103.3	28.7	30.6	28.7	—	
62002	4 Jan 1974	83.4	73	172.86	5.7	35.77	0.0	5.0	130.0	45.7	54.8	47.2	—	
62002	9 Feb 1974	52.6	64	141.91	16.1	47.16	0.0	9.6	134.6	28.9	55.0	49.9	—	
a mean												50.6		
g mean					15.9	18.44							—	
63998	29 Aug 1990				—								2.6	
63998	19 Sep 1990				—								2.2	
63998	23 Sep 1990				—								1.9	
63998	12 Nov 1990				—								2.9	
63998	19 Nov 1990				—								1.1	
63998	20 Nov 1990				—								1.0	
63998	31 Dec 1990				—								0.9	
63998	1 Jan 1991				—								1.3	
63998	9 Jan 1991				—								0.9	
g mean													1.49	

Catch	Date	P	D	Q_p	LAG	BF	SMD	API5	CWI	R/O	PR	SPR	Tp(0)	
		mm	h	m^3s^{-1}	h	m^3s^{-1}	mm	mm	mm	mm	%	%	h	
63999	19 Aug 1990				—								1.8	#
63999	8 Jan 1991				—								3.8	#
63999	24 Jun 1991				—								3.1	#
63999	26 Sep 1991				—								3.7	#
63999	28 Sep 1991				—								3.1	#
63999	9 Oct 1991				—								3.9	#
63999	16 Oct 1991				—								4.3	#
63999	31 Oct 1991				—								2.5	#
g mean													3.17	
64001	14 Sep 1966	24.0	13	203.55	4.9	23.44	1.2	10.3	134.1	11.6	48.4	46.1	4.8	#
64001	29 Nov 1966	31.9	21	204.98	6.8	34.36	0.0	12.2	137.2	17.2	53.8	50.7	—	
64001	30 Nov 1966	71.5	49	213.95	6.4	53.78	0.0	20.5	145.5	34.0	47.5	37.3	—	
64001	8 Dec 1966	79.5	48	269.13	8.6	38.30	0.0	8.7	133.7	46.8	58.9	50.8	4.4	#
64001	26 Feb 1967	60.0	20	310.90	5.8	39.22	0.0	7.1	132.1	37.7	62.9	57.5	3.5	#
64001	17 Aug 1967	36.4	35	168.82	4.5	27.48	2.7	9.0	131.3	17.8	48.9	47.3	—	
64001	16 Oct 1967	63.2	41	289.13	7.3	59.64	0.0	15.2	140.2	41.3	65.4	57.5	—	
64001	22 Dec 1967	99.3	62	270.15	7.0	35.39	0.0	5.6	130.6	56.4	56.8	47.6	4.7	#
64001	22 Mar 1968	83.3	55	287.81	8.9	28.40	0.0	8.7	133.7	71.8	86.2	77.7	—	
a mean												52.5		
g mean					6.5	36.22							4.3	
65001	1 Apr 1962	111.7	26	50.76	6.9	0.95	0.0	4.8	129.8	48.6	43.5	33.3	5.1	#
65001	25 Aug 1962	75.0	12	51.32	5.3	2.46	5.2	16.8	136.6	29.2	38.9	30.6	4.3	#
65001	29 Oct 1962	64.7	12	44.45	4.4	1.81	0.8	13.2	137.4	19.5	30.2	22.8	4.2	#
65001	10 Dec 1962	74.6	16	39.10	7.5	1.70	0.0	8.9	133.9	29.5	39.6	32.0	5.5	#
65001	14 Apr 1963	89.4	20	53.63	3.7	2.02	0.0	9.0	134.0	32.4	36.2	27.0	—	
65001	24 Jun 1963	53.6	14	48.65	5.2	3.45	3.6	22.3	143.7	21.4	39.9	32.4	3.4	#
65001	20 Nov 1963	83.2	14	54.12	2.1	5.97	0.0	6.3	131.3	22.8	27.4	19.5	—	
65001	10 May 1964	98.4	30	46.38	5.2	1.86	3.2	10.8	132.6	36.2	36.8	27.1	2.9	#
65001	12 Nov 1964	72.7	13	49.74	5.3	1.82	0.0	7.6	132.6	24.0	33.0	25.9	3.2	#
65001	8 Dec 1964	105.9	17	61.50	5.9	4.04	0.0	50.9	175.9	49.2	46.5	25.3	2.3	#
65001	11 Dec 1964	205.3	34	62.39	5.0	3.28	0.1	15.7	140.6	95.3	46.4	26.4	1.9	#
65001	9 Jan 1965	180.6	47	63.57	9.1	2.09	0.0	17.3	142.3	98.2	54.4	35.7	5.7	#
65001	14 Sep 1965	123.3	28	52.79	9.1	0.35	3.2	4.5	126.3	52.9	42.9	32.6	2.9	#
65001	28 Dec 1965	71.6	17	43.81	5.0	1.32	0.0	0.7	125.7	25.3	35.3	30.1	3.2	#
65001	26 Jun 1966	106.8	24	51.09	8.2	0.80	2.4	7.7	130.3	45.2	42.3	32.4	3.4	#
65001	15 Jan 1968	64.7	22	50.33	2.7	5.50	0.0	29.7	154.7	28.7	44.3	32.6	—	
65001	22 Mar 1968	117.2	34	56.63	11.0	1.52	0.0	12.5	137.5	65.6	56.0	43.4	—	
65001	1 Jul 1968	99.5	51	34.28	11.1	0.53	8.3	2.5	119.2	44.2	44.4	38.0	—	
65001	18 Aug 1968	136.9	23	58.69	10.9	0.45	54.2	4.6	75.4	60.0	43.8	45.1	—	
65001	19 Sep 1968	103.9	32	42.76	8.2	0.98	0.4	0.1	124.7	35.3	34.0	25.8	—	
65001	19 Jan 1969	177.9	48	66.35	8.0	2.36	0.2	17.3	142.1	99.8	56.1	37.7	—	
a mean												31.2		
g mean					6.1	1.67							3.5	
65801	30 Mar 1972	89.6	24	16.00	6.1	0.64	0.0	3.2	128.2	52.8	58.9	51.2	—	
65801	28 Apr 1972	86.3	17	17.00	4.0	0.46	20.0	0.9	105.9	38.9	45.1	43.3	1.6	#
65801	2 Jun 1972	48.2	11	21.00	3.8	0.91	4.7	3.4	123.7	34.7	71.9	70.3	—	
65801	3 Jul 1972	178.2	38	33.00	5.9	0.71	5.3	1.6121.3171.8		96.4	83.1	—		
65801	5 Aug 1972	62.1	23	14.00	4.4	0.79	12.2	8.7	121.5	52.2	84.0	80.9	—	
65801	29 Oct 1972	100.9	27	19.00	5.5	0.77	23.0	8.4	110.4	76.6	75.9	71.6	—	
65801	12 Nov 1972	65.0	25	23.50	5.9	0.86	0.0	11.9	136.9	53.8	82.8	75.5	6.2	#
65801	19 Nov 1972	75.4	22	13.00	5.2	1.22	0.0	5.3	130.3	57.9	76.8	70.0	—	
65801	27 Nov 1972	21.4	13	15.00	3.8	0.90	0.0	3.9	128.9	19.2	89.8	88.8	—	
65801	9 Dec 1972	23.9	7	12.00	2.5	1.54	0.0	9.8	134.8	13.6	56.8	54.3	—	
65801	11 Dec 1972	79.1	14	33.00	2.9	1.60	0.0	10.7	135.7	65.0	82.2	73.7	—	
65801	12 Dec 1972	55.8	10	28.00	3.1	1.99	0.0	36.5	161.5	44.2	79.3	67.1	1.9	#
a mean												69.2		
g mean					4.2	0.95							2.7	
66002	22 Mar 1968	48.2	36	124.11	7.6	9.79	0.0	6.9	131.9	40.0	83.0	79.3	8.5	#
66002	24 May 1968	40.5	32	36.44	10.7	3.36	14.0	0.1	111.1	7.9	19.6	22.8	—	
66002	30 Jun 1968	66.3	51	58.51	9.1	3.44	40.0	2.8	87.8	11.9	18.0	22.8	4.3	#
66002	10 Feb 1969	21.7	36	52.43	7.1	9.48	0.0	2.3	127.3	15.3	70.5	69.9	—	
66002	5 May 1969	29.9	21	35.71	5.2	4.82	3.6	3.7	125.1	4.6	15.4	15.4	6.9	#

Catch	Date	*P* mm	*D* h	Q_p m^3s^{-1}	*LAG* h	*BF* m^3s^{-1}	*SMD* mm	*API5* mm	*CWI* mm	*R/O* mm	*PR* %	*SPR* %	*Tp(0)* h	
66002	19 Aug 1970	70.7	28	50.46	16.2	3.02	102.7	3.9	26.2	22.6	32.0	51.7	—	
66002	20 Mar 1971	61.1	38	53.77	29.2	3.08	0.6	9.9	134.3	24.4	39.9	33.8	—	
66002	3 Jul 1971	51.6	4	54.26	7.2	2.34	39.5	0.2	85.7	7.6	14.7	22.0	—	
66002	15 Jul 1973	76.8	25	42.74	10.3	0.05	102.7	21.0	43.3	8.1	10.5	25.3	1.3	#
a mean												38.1		
g mean					10.0	2.61							4.3	
66004	19 Aug 1970	57.7	31	2.54	9.2	0.57	102.7	4.3	26.6	2.7	4.6	25.8	—	
66004	11 Jun 1971	21.5	10	1.38	5.5	0.54	54.4	8.0	78.6	0.6	2.7	14.2	2.1	#
66004	25 Jul 1971	9.4	9	2.64	3.0	0.57	66.6	13.0	71.4	0.6	6.9	20.2	—	
66004	9 Aug 1971	56.7	26	3.68	11.0	0.64	77.6	0.7	48.1	2.6	4.6	20.5	4.6	#
66004	22 Nov 1971	22.2	8	2.63	1.2	1.47	7.7	7.6	124.9	0.6	2.5	2.4	—	
66004	15 Jul 1973	61.2	34	2.37	10.9	0.52	83.3	7.7	49.4	1.7	2.8	17.8	—	
a mean												16.8		
g mean					5.3	0.66							3.1	
66006	15 Jul 1973	74.4	25	63.92	13.8	3.19	101.9	18.6	41.7	17.6	23.6	39.1	6.0	#
66006	19 Oct 1973	30.7	28	55.13	29.0	10.48	52.5	8.4	80.9	10.8	35.2	46.2	—	
66006	10 Nov 1974	23.4	16	50.57	6.2	6.21	0.3	2.6	127.3	7.7	33.1	32.5	3.9	#
66006	1 Feb 1974	24.3	22	48.56	6.8	10.40	0.1	4.7	129.6	8.7	35.9	34.7	—	
66006	22 Jan 1975	32.5	23	75.34	11.2	9.39	0.0	5.3	130.3	21.5	66.0	64.7	—	
66006	25 Jan 1975	26.2	15	68.81	23.0	9.81	0.0	5.7	130.7	14.0	53.5	52.1	—	
66006	2 Jan 1976	30.4	13	81.79	6.2	16.47	8.3	17.9	134.6	12.8	42.2	39.8	—	
66006	13 Sep 1976	44.7	26	43.02	7.4	7.34	75.2	38.5	88.3	10.0	22.4	30.2	—	
66006	13 Oct 1976	84.6	48	141.17	12.3	8.90	8.7	5.4	121.7	57.8	68.3	62.7	8.8	#
a mean												44.7		
g mean					11.1	8.43							5.9	
66011	6 Jul 1964	71.6	15	236.74	5.4	6.51	44.4	0.1	80.7	19.3	27.0	33.0	—	
66011	12 Nov 1964	41.2	13	241.45	5.5	10.39	0.0	8.1	133.1	21.4	51.9	49.4	3.8	#
66011	11 Dec 1964	191.5	34	535.23	5.9	26.01	0.0	22.3	147.3	147.5	77.0	56.3	—	
66011	8 May 1965	42.6	10	333.01	4.2	20.64	2.0	9.8	132.8	22.5	52.7	49.9	—	
66011	14 Sep 1966	40.6	17	301.86	5.2	15.83	0.0	13.1	138.1	23.2	57.2	53.6	—	
66011	30 Nov 1966	76.4	43	335.68	1.6	27.90	0.0	11.0	136.0	45.0	58.9	50.6	3.0	#
66011	22 Feb 1967	61.8	17	399.48	5.9	17.49	0.0	4.6	129.6	38.9	63.0	58.0	4.7	#
66011	27 Feb 1967	71.8	19	520.77	4.8	35.88	0.0	7.6	132.6	57.9	80.6	73.6	2.2	#
66011	1 Oct 1967	56.8	14	442.82	5.7	25.15	0.3	9.8	134.5	42.1	74.1	68.5	4.5	#
66011	16 Oct 1967	71.4	23	396.79	3.8	43.22	0.2	16.5	141.3	55.3	77.4	68.3	4.1	#
66011	22 Dec 1967	57.9	18	376.91	6.6	19.00	0.0	2.8	127.8	44.9	77.6	73.5	—	
66011	13 Jan 1968	97.1	42	412.15	5.6	7.09	0.2	0.2	125.0	96.5	99.4	91.8	—	
66011	22 Mar 1968	122.9	38	449.58	6.1	19.93	0.0	15.9	140.9	110.9	90.2	76.3	—	
a mean												61.7		
g mean					4.9	18.48							3.6	
67003	22 Mar 1968	50.2	35	13.39	2.8	1.60	0.0	10.3	135.3	38.0	75.7	70.8	—	
67003	19 Aug 1970	47.1	30	13.31	3.8	0.54	101.1	1.2	25.1	31.2	66.2	89.4	6.3	#
67003	1 Mar 1971	17.7	19	7.42	7.7	0.52	1.4	2.2	125.8	11.8	66.5	66.3	4.3	#
67003	9 Aug 1971	45.8	24	14.81	10.2	0.27	74.0	1.0	52.0	24.5	53.5	70.2	4.3	#
67003	31 Jul 1972	46.2	27	21.80	7.4	0.17	62.5	0.6	63.1	35.2	76.1	90.0	4.5	#
67003	16 Jul 1973	28.1	8	14.37	3.7	1.10	71.9	0.6	53.7	11.5	41.0	58.8	4.5	#
a mean												74.3		
g mean					5.3	0.53							4.7	
67005	15 Jan 1962	27.4	46	40.00	10.5	6.16	0.2	2.8	127.6	23.6	86.0	85.4	—	
67005	8 Dec 1965	37.0	35	65.40	4.8	10.75	0.0	13.2	138.2	27.7	74.9	71.6	—	
67005	21 Feb 1967	40.7	21	36.14	6.2	7.73	0.0	7.1	132.1	12.3	30.1	27.9	5.3	#
67005	26 Feb 1967	48.2	28	30.85	6.8	7.97	0.0	5.4	130.4	14.5	30.1	26.7	4.5	#
67005	14 Oct 1967	53.8	50	27.28	3.7	5.89	0.0	9.6	134.6	15.0	27.9	22.6	—	
67005	28 Oct 1967	26.4	13	24.47	3.4	9.20	0.8	13.9	138.1	6.7	25.5	22.2	4.9	#
a mean												42.7		
g mean					5.5	7.78							4.9	
67008	12 Jan 1968	9.9	31	27.06	10.7	6.24	0.2	0.8	125.6	9.8	99.1	99.3	—	
67008	24 May 1968	38.6	30	16.69	8.2	2.06	14.0	0.3	111.3	6.0	15.5	18.2	—	
67008	1 Jul 1968	57.5	50	16.61	2.0	2.69	40.0	2.6	87.6	4.3	7.4	12.6	—	
67008	1 Nov 1968	24.7	20	12.17	12.6	2.20	0.0	3.1	128.1	4.9	19.8	18.4	9.3	#

Catch	Date	P mm	D h	Q_p m^3s^{-1}	LAG h	BF m^3s^{-1}	SMD mm	API5 mm	CWI mm	R/O mm	PR %	SPR %	Tp(0) h	
67008	10 Feb 1969	20.7	29	29.54	11.6	5.04	0.0	3.7	128.7	13.6	65.6	64.6	—	
67008	25 Apr 1969	19.4	11	12.13	7.8	2.54	5.7	1.5	120.8	2.4	12.2	12.5	6.9	#
67008	29 May 1969	23.3	19	21.23	5.2	6.00	5.6	3.5	122.9	3.9	16.8	16.6	5.6	#
67008	21 Jan 1970	3.9	11	15.07	0.9	4.30	0.0	7.2	132.2	1.7	43.1	40.9	—	
67008	5 Apr 1970	18.7	14	17.59	7.9	4.98	1.4	1.7	125.3	3.3	17.4	16.6	5.5	#
67008	9 Aug 1971	59.0	31	17.44	13.9	1.14	29.3	0.6	96.3	6.4	10.8	13.7	—	
67008	20 Nov 1971	28.5	21	29.84	12.0	2.92	0.1	5.3	130.2	9.5	33.5	31.7	5.5	#
a mean												31.4		
g mean					6.7	3.24							6.4	
67010	26 Jun 1966	58.4	18	11.46	4.6	0.34	3.6	5.3	126.7	37.2	63.7	59.8	2.8	#
67010	13 Sep 1966	50.7	15	12.61	2.7	0.86	0.0	11.6	136.6	23.5	46.3	41.0	2.2	#
67010	29 Nov 1966	52.2	24	11.87	2.3	0.51	0.0	6.4	131.4	24.5	46.9	42.7	3.9	#
67010	22 Feb 1967	72.9	21	11.16	5.1	0.32	0.0	6.7	131.7	33.6	46.1	39.2	3.3	#
67010	26 Feb 1967	77.9	19	18.02	2.7	0.70	0.0	10.0	135.0	35.6	45.7	37.5	1.1	#
67010	4 Sep 1967	67.3	21	11.74	3.2	0.57	0.0	15.8	140.8	40.4	60.0	51.5	3.2	#
67010	1 Oct 1967	54.7	13	13.60	2.8	0.73	0.0	16.8	141.8	25.6	46.8	39.6	2.2	#
67010	16 Oct 1967	78.6	22	12.30	6.7	0.95	0.0	23.7	148.7	49.2	62.6	50.9	—	
67010	22 Dec 1967	75.0	14	14.52	4.5	0.77	0.0	6.8	131.8	44.6	59.5	52.4	2.2	#
67010	18 Mar 1968	103.0	29	15.01	7.6	0.36	0.0	6.4	131.4	60.5	58.7	48.9	—	
67010	19 Sep 1968	94.5	31	10.53	7.3	0.23	4.1	0.1	121.0	42.9	45.4	39.0	—	
67010	2 Oct 1968	31.5	10	11.29	2.4	1.17	0.0	25.1	150.1	20.3	64.5	58.2	2.0	#
a mean												46.7		
g mean					3.9	0.56							2.4	
68006	8 May 1965	30.3	12	92.81	6.0	4.69	2.6	5.4	127.8	13.0	42.8	41.7	5.0	#
68006	7 Sep 1965	48.1	19	122.98	4.3	6.81	0.0	11.4	136.4	24.0	50.0	44.9	5.5	#
68006	8 Dec 1965	35.1	23	104.96	8.2	4.06	0.0	7.5	132.5	24.4	69.4	67.5	—	
68006	14 Sep 1966	25.1	7	70.82	7.2	3.19	0.0	6.8	131.8	10.0	39.8	37.6	5.7	#
68006	3 Oct 1967	20.6	19	54.53	4.5	4.35	0.0	7.3	132.3	6.6	32.0	29.6	4.3	#
68006	1 Jul 1968	29.2	11	84.48	5.7	1.32	3.4	4.1	125.7	10.9	37.2	36.5	—	
a mean												43.0		
g mean					5.8	3.65							5.1	
68010	21 Sep 1973	31.6	16	8.89	0.4	0.39	91.0	3.9	37.9	5.4	17.1	31.3	—	
68010	17 Aug 1974	3.4	14	1.79	3.0	0.07	88.8	0.3	36.5	0.7	19.4	34.3	—	
68010	4 Mar 1975	16.7	17	4.63	3.2	0.29	0.9	1.6	125.7	4.8	29.0	22.9	—	
68010	1 May 1974	13.2	17	1.82	0.6	0.06	38.6	0.2	86.6	0.7	5.5	5.9	—	
68010	21 Mar 1975	14.1	8	0.94	2.2	0.09	5.4	0.1	119.7	1.3	9.0	1.6	—	
68010	20 Nov 1974	31.4	22	5.65	5.7	0.68	0.0	0.6	125.6	16.1	51.2	48.4	3.5	#
68010	7 Jun 1974	14.8	9	1.33	1.8	0.10	84.2	4.7	45.5	0.7	4.8	15.3	—	
a mean												22.8		
g mean					1.7	0.16							3.5	
68014	12 Dec 1964	87.9	33	1.39	5.5	0.09	4.2	1.3	122.1	21.9	24.9	18.6	—	
68014	8 Dec 1965	31.9	23	1.41	4.2	0.12	0.0	3.6	128.6	16.5	51.8	50.8	2.0	
68014	14 May 1967	19.3	13	1.25	4.1	0.17	3.2	8.0	129.8	9.2	47.7	46.4	2.3	
68014	18 May 1967	17.2	18	1.03	5.8	0.05	6.0	2.7	121.7	8.0	46.4	47.1	1.6	
68014	1 Jul 1968	31.6	11	1.78	4.9	0.20	0.1	12.8	137.7	16.3	51.5	48.2	5.7	
68014	1 Nov 1968	29.8	12	1.75	5.4	0.11	0.0	7.1	132.1	15.7	52.8	50.9	—	
68014	5 May 1969	32.2	13	1.50	3.3	0.11	9.7	2.5	117.8	13.2	41.1	42.7	2.3	
68014	30 May 1969	15.0	3	1.32	1.6	0.21	2.8	8.3	130.5	4.2	28.3	26.6	1.5	
a mean												41.4		
g mean					4.1	0.12							2.3	
69008	27 Feb 1967	14.2	17	3.60	5.1	1.21	0.0	2.8	127.8	3.0	21.3	19.5	6.3	
69008	11 May 1967	16.9	5	4.41	2.7	0.46	19.4	0.6	106.2	1.5	8.7	12.1	—	
69008	24 Jun 1967	42.8	30	7.21	9.8	0.16	60.1	1.6	66.5	6.0	14.1	26.6	—	
69008	13 Jul 1967	22.4	15	3.71	5.4	0.22	41.6	0.0	83.4	2.2	9.9	19.0	—	
69008	16 Oct 1967	31.3	40	7.28	9.0	0.96	0.4	7.1	131.7	13.9	44.4	42.2	9.5	
69008	1 Jul 1968	33.0	21	10.69	4.6	2.34	0.0	6.5	131.5	10.6	32.2	29.8	—	
69008	14 Apr 1969	27.5	21	23.13	11.0	6.10	2.0	2.1	125.1	25.6	93.2	93.7	—	
69008	18 Oct 1971	45.6	24	28.23	12.0	4.50	66.6	13.9	72.3	31.4	68.8	80.4	7.5	
a mean												40.4		
g mean					6.7	1.02							7.7	

Catch	Date	P	D	Q_p	LAG	BF	SMD	API5	CWI	R/O	PR	SPR	Tp(0)	
		mm	h	m^3s^{-1}	h	m^3s^{-1}	mm	mm	mm	mm	%	%	h	
69011	1 Jul 1968	18.7	3	24.09	3.3	5.02	11.3	2.5	116.2	8.5	45.7	46.1	—	
69011	1 Oct 1968	40.6	23	21.18	5.1	2.89	0.0	7.5	132.5	11.9	29.2	23.9	4.1	
69011	10 Feb 1969	14.1	27	10.47	10.1	0.68	0.6	2.1	126.5	10.7	75.7	75.8	—	
69011	14 Apr 1969	26.8	22	16.58	8.1	0.58	2.0	2.3	125.3	9.4	35.0	32.3	4.4	
a mean												44.5		
g mean					6.1	1.55							4.2	
69012	2 Jul 1968	24.0	11	41.33	5.6	10.58	0.0	6.6	131.6	13.4	56.0	53.7	4.8	#
69012	1 Oct 1968	22.5	15	27.60	3.9	11.69	0.0	6.9	131.9	9.3	41.2	38.1	3.6	#
69012	2 Nov 1968	16.9	15	34.94	4.5	11.39	0.0	7.8	132.8	10.9	64.3	62.1	4.5	#
69012	20 Dec 1969	11.8	11	25.24	7.4	11.61	0.0	4.5	129.5	10.5	88.9	88.7	—	
a mean												60.6		
g mean					5.2	11.31							4.3	
69013	26 Sep 1971	13.0	10	4.81	3.2	0.26	41.1	0.7	84.6	1.5	11.5	13.2	3.5	#
69013	7 Jun 1974	14.4	6	2.51	2.1	0.29	70.9	2.5	56.6	0.9	6.3	14.3	—	
69013	22 Jul 1972	24.7	13	4.14	2.6	0.51	54.9	1.7	71.8	2.2	8.8	13.3	4.0	#
69013	21 Jul 1973	31.2	19	13.07	2.0	1.53	27.9	12.6	109.7	8.0	25.6	23.1	—	
69013	9 Aug 1975	7.3	3	1.74	2.9	0.25	116.8	2.5	10.7	0.4	5.0	24.3	3.2	#
69013	25 Sep 1975	30.0	20	6.22	1.3	0.26	130.2	1.0	-4.2	3.0	9.9	33.6	—	
69013	22 Jan 1975	21.2	13	10.47	5.9	1.20	0.0	3.5	128.5	8.9	41.9	37.0	—	
69013	8 Aug 1974	15.9	19	6.25	1.1	0.31	93.0	0.0	32.0	1.5	9.6	24.2	1.3	#
a mean												22.9		
g mean					2.3	0.44							2.8	
69018	17 Nov 1970	22.5	18	10.51	9.3	0.64	9.1	2.3	118.2	13.8	61.4	62.2	—	
69018	18 Oct 1971	44.6	21	11.35	10.7	0.37	66.9	4.8	62.9	20.9	46.8	58.7	—	
69018	12 Nov 1972	24.0	21	10.76	11.0	1.63	35.5	11.4	100.9	11.9	49.5	53.5	—	
a mean												58.2		
g mean					10.3	0.73							—	
69019	16 Jun 1974	9.7	13	2.96	3.7	0.31	74.3	1.0	51.7	1.8	18.6	27.6	—	
69019	2 Jul 1974	18.6	12	2.66	4.5	0.25	91.9	2.7	35.8	3.0	15.9	28.3	—	
69019	1 May 1975	23.4	11	3.58	2.4	0.48	9.1	1.4	117.3	4.6	19.7	12.5	—	
69019	4 Jul 1975	41.1	8	3.98	1.4	0.45	113.8	0.1	11.3	3.2	7.7	24.3	—	
69019	14 Jul 1975	19.3	15	3.42	2.9	0.23	103.6	2.2	23.6	3.8	19.7	35.9	1.2	#
69019	9 Aug 1975	9.4	6	2.18	2.3	0.27	124.7	1.0	1.3	0.9	9.8	29.8	2.1	#
69019	2 Nov 1975	11.1	6	1.85	2.7	0.25	75.0	1.9	51.9	1.5	13.2	21.1	2.4	#
a mean												25.6		
g mean					2.7	0.31							1.8	
69020	18 Oct 1971	73.0	23	38.77	13.6	0.88	0.0	9.1	134.1	31.0	42.5	30.0	—	
69020	26 Jan 1973	19.4	7	15.97	4.0	0.97	0.2	1.8	126.6	5.9	30.5	22.9	—	
69020	3 Apr 1973	22.0	10	15.91	4.1	1.15	0.0	8.5	133.5	6.2	28.4	18.7	—	
69020	16 Jul 1973	35.1	12	32.20	4.8	1.77	37.0	14.6	102.6	10.7	30.4	28.7	—	
69020	5 Aug 1973	45.8	23	37.04	1.9	1.12	19.7	28.3	133.6	15.7	34.3	24.1	—	
69020	1 May 1975	33.0	15	18.45	3.3	1.28	5.9	2.3	121.4	8.9	27.0	20.0	—	
69020	24 Sep 1975	40.0	26	14.79	3.4	0.88	2.9	0.6	122.7	7.0	17.6	8.6	—	
a mean												21.8		
g mean					4.2	1.12							—	
69027	31 Mar 1972	27.9	27	39.50	4.9	8.13	0.7	14.4	138.7	11.6	41.7	36.3	—	
69027	15 Jul 1973	62.3	24	78.03	11.5	2.04	89.4	9.0	44.6	19.9	31.9	45.4	6.4	#
69027	15 Dec 1973	16.6	17	19.30	7.6	3.14	0.0	2.3	127.3	4.7	28.3	24.8	7.4	#
69027	12 Aug 1974	17.1	9	21.61	5.4	2.61	75.9	7.4	56.5	4.0	23.3	37.2	7.1	#
69027	2 Sep 1974	36.7	24	43.04	9.2	3.02	81.4	4.7	48.3	10.5	28.5	44.8	5.3	#
69027	7 Sep 1974	25.6	14	24.44	5.0	4.18	67.1	7.5	65.4	5.2	20.2	31.6	—	
69027	5 Aug 1973	44.2	15	69.93	7.7	3.61	94.3	8.7	39.4	19.1	43.3	61.6	8.5	#
a mean												40.2		
g mean					7.0	3.48							6.9	
69031	17 Nov 1970	22.4	19	12.16	4.4	1.59	9.1	2.7	118.6	10.7	47.9	45.8	4.6	#
69031	20 Nov 1971	24.3	17	12.99	6.4	0.50	13.5	2.5	114.0	11.1	45.5	44.2	5.3	#
69031	15 Jul 1973	35.9	28	13.90	7.3	0.60	79.9	6.4	51.5	12.1	33.6	45.9	4.9	#
69031	7 Dec 1973	27.3	25	16.70	4.9	0.82	0.0	0.2	125.2	13.9	51.0	47.8	3.6	#
69031	8 Jan 1974	14.3	6	14.12	5.3	1.36	0.0	4.3	129.3	7.2	50.0	45.6	5.6	#

Catch	Date			P mm	D h	Q_p m^3s^{-1}	LAG h	BF m^3s^{-1}	SMD mm	API5 mm	CWI mm	R/O mm	PR %	SPR %	Tp(0) h	
69031	4	Jul	1974	30.7	21	12.38	3.1	0.36	85.9	6.9	46.0	8.2	26.7	39.2	—	
69031	20	Nov	1974	22.0	20	13.48	4.8	0.89	0.0	1.2	126.2	11.9	53.9	50.9	4.3	#
69031	18	Apr	1975	15.4	10	9.89	3.9	0.92	3.2	2.1	123.9	5.8	37.5	32.3	—	
69031	1	Jan	1976	19.4	22	17.50	4.6	2.07	27.8	13.4	110.6	10.3	53.0	53.8	4.5	#
a mean														45.0		
g mean							4.8	0.88							4.6	
69034	18	Apr	1968	25.5	9	0.51	3.4	0.03	17.0	1.7	109.7	3.1	12.0	15.8	3.7	#
69034	26	Nov	1968	21.5	16	1.39	2.9	0.11	0.0	5.8	130.8	8.8	40.8	39.3	1.1	#
69034	26	Apr	1969	24.5	24	0.84	1.7	0.05	2.0	2.6	125.6	5.4	22.0	21.9	1.2	#
69034	2	Jun	1969	38.0	13	2.31	3.3	0.11	7.5	2.4	119.9	16.1	42.4	43.7	1.2	#
69034	11	Sep	1969	19.1	14	0.32	3.6	0.02	61.9	1.7	64.8	1.4	7.1	22.2	0.9	#
69034	18	Jan	1972	31.0	23	3.88	3.6	0.08	0.0	5.6	130.6	21.4	69.1	67.7	1.4	#
69034	23	Jul	1972	10.4	3	1.63	0.5	0.16	7.0	12.3	130.3	3.1	30.0	28.7	0.9	#
69034	10	Nov	1974	24.2	22	2.28	3.5	0.07	0.0	6.0	131.0	12.3	50.7	49.2	1.1	#
69034	1	Jan	1976	35.2	10	5.41	1.4	0.09	0.0	14.4	139.4	17.7	50.3	46.7	0.7	#
a mean														37.2		
g mean							2.3	0.07							1.2	
69802	21	Jan	1970	16.1	8	6.65	3.5	0.41	0.0	2.7	127.7	7.5	46.6	45.9	4.1	
69802	13	Aug	1971	16.3	12	7.65	3.8	0.57	9.1	12.7	128.6	10.8	66.4	65.5	2.5	
a mean														55.7		
g mean							3.6	0.48							3.2	
70006	4	Feb	1970	10.2	8	3.42	4.4	0.63	0.0	4.5	129.5	3.4	32.9	28.9	3.5	#
70006	23	Mar	1970	12.0	11	4.94	3.8	0.54	0.8	3.3	127.5	3.1	26.0	22.0	4.0	#
70006	5	Apr	1970	11.5	12	3.11	4.5	0.36	3.6	0.4	121.8	2.0	17.1	13.8	4.1	#
70006	1	Nov	1970	15.5	9	5.92	4.5	0.82	0.0	7.8	132.8	4.3	27.7	22.5	3.5	#
70006	6	May	1971	13.2	8	4.35	4.5	0.23	71.4	0.1	53.7	1.3	10.2	23.4	1.5	#
70006	10	Aug	1971	52.7	24	23.79	5.0	0.60	85.9	10.5	49.6	17.7	33.5	46.9	3.3	#
70006	13	Aug	1971	18.4	13	8.15	4.3	1.05	76.0	12.5	61.5	6.9	37.4	50.7	3.4	#
70006	20	Nov	1971	20.6	20	8.11	6.7	0.42	31.1	2.5	96.4	10.4	50.6	56.2	3.6	#
70006	7	Dec	1973	3.2	22	2.41	11.6	0.15	0.0	0.2	125.2	1.7	54.4	53.1	—	
a mean														35.3		
g mean							5.2	0.46							3.2	
71003	5	Jul	1960	109.0	27	9.56	6.8	0.20	76.4	7.9	56.5	48.1	44.1	52.5	—	
71003	1	Nov	1960	46.7	13	10.32	3.8	0.55	0.0	9.5	134.5	22.6	48.3	44.2	3.2	#
71003	3	Aug	1961	61.2	18	20.36	3.3	0.24	45.9	1.5	80.6	26.5	43.3	50.6	2.2	#
71003	16	Oct	1961	48.1	13	15.07	4.4	0.36	0.0	3.5	128.5	34.2	71.2	68.4	2.0	#
71003	30	Oct	1961	37.6	21	10.37	2.3	0.71	0.0	6.5	131.5	27.9	74.1	72.5	2.0	#
71003	29	Nov	1961	53.9	15	10.48	4.3	0.60	0.0	10.2	135.2	36.9	68.5	63.1	2.3	#
71003	1	Apr	1962	74.1	22	7.46	6.7	0.28	0.0	2.5	127.5	37.3	50.4	44.5	2.8	#
71003	6	Apr	1962	49.9	25	8.67	4.6	0.36	0.9	8.7	132.8	40.8	81.7	77.5	—	
71003	23	Aug	1962	52.2	22	12.64	2.3	0.57	20.6	10.0	114.4	24.8	47.6	47.7	3.2	#
71003	25	Sep	1963	56.3	25	14.57	3.4	0.36	0.0	18.4	143.4	27.5	48.9	41.1	1.1	#
71003	2	Oct	1963	35.1	11	12.08	3.4	0.65	0.0	6.3	131.3	28.2	80.4	78.8	—	
71003	7	Jul	1964	56.4	19	6.12	3.2	0.18	32.5	0.2	92.7	15.1	26.7	31.6	3.0	#
71003	8	Dec	1964	76.2	14	12.22	3.2	0.66	0.0	27.1	152.1	33.6	44.1	31.8	2.7	#
71003	11	Dec	1964	115.3	38	11.83	7.7	0.42	0.0	12.2	137.2	65.6	56.9	44.6	2.2	#
71003	8	Dec	1965	43.6	16	13.89	5.2	2.23	0.0	11.2	136.2	29.3	67.1	63.2	2.2	#
71003	19	Dec	1966	70.0	20	13.31	4.3	0.52	0.0	7.4	132.4	51.9	74.2	67.5	—	
71003	22	Feb	1967	45.3	10	11.59	4.1	0.43	0.0	5.0	130.0	22.1	48.8	46.1	—	
71003	27	Feb	1967	61.9	17	12.69	4.9	0.53	0.0	7.0	132.0	44.4	71.7	66.0	—	
71003	8	Aug	1967	53.1	5	29.64	2.5	0.64	4.8	4.0	124.2	30.8	58.0	55.5	1.8	#
71003	16	Oct	1967	72.6	23	11.82	5.1	0.60	0.0	22.8	147.8	28.5	39.3	28.4	2.5	#
71003	2	Jul	1968	26.5	15	4.49	3.2	0.38	0.0	5.5	130.5	7.5	28.4	27.0	1.8	#
71003	29	Sep	1968	21.6	10	10.22	1.8	0.82	0.0	12.8	137.8	14.0	64.9	61.7	2.2	#
71003	30	Mar	1969	47.9	18	8.68	2.1	0.67	0.6	4.5	128.9	27.9	58.2	55.3	2.8	#
71003	2	Jul	1968	24.4	15	11.08	2.3	0.82	0.0	19.0	144.0	20.1	82.3	77.6	—	
a mean														54.0		
g mean							3.7	0.50							2.3	
71004	21	Jan	1970	18.3	25	81.83	3.1	15.78	0.0	1.7	126.7	8.1	44.2	42.6	3.9	#
71004	12	Apr	1970	27.5	18	97.80	5.8	12.00	4.7	0.4	120.7	11.8	43.0	42.8	—	
71004	24	Apr	1970	15.6	23	70.13	11.1	17.23	1.5	6.8	130.3	7.9	50.5	48.3	—	

Catch	Date	*P* mm	*D* h	Q_p m^3s^{-1}	*LAG* h	*BF* m^3s^{-1}	*SMD* mm	*API5* mm	*CWI* mm	*R/O* mm	*PR* %	*SPR* %	*Tp(0)* h	
71004	11 Jun 1970	18.7	3	92.42	3.2	12.02	92.3	0.1	32.8	4.0	21.4	42.2	—	
71004	11 Aug 1974	16.8	22	60.90	5.2	5.42	36.4	12.9	101.5	5.6	33.4	37.6	4.5	#
71004	23 Nov 1974	30.9	46	105.58	4.9	9.48	0.0	1.7	126.7	12.7	41.1	39.3	4.6	#
71004	24 Jan 1975	16.6	11	70.82	6.1	11.63	0.0	6.3	131.3	6.7	40.4	37.4	—	
71004	30 Apr 1975	29.9	26	87.73	5.9	3.61	7.3	1.9	119.6	9.8	32.7	32.3	4.4	#
71004	15 Nov 1975	20.1	34	29.91	5.4	3.30	2.2	0.0	122.8	4.6	22.9	21.2	5.9	#
71004	30 Nov 1975	51.2	24	110.59	6.8	8.84	0.0	6.2	131.2	26.9	52.5	47.7	—	
a mean												39.1		
g mean					5.4	8.69							4.6	
71008	20 Dec 1969	32.0	40	97.26	4.3	6.23	0.0	10.4	135.4	22.7	70.9	68.3	—	
71008	17 Jan 1970	14.7	18	58.12	7.3	5.04	0.0	1.5	126.5	6.7	45.9	45.5	4.5	#
71008	22 Apr 1970	54.5	31	176.45	5.9	10.34	0.0	6.1	131.1	35.4	64.9	60.4	4.3	#
71008	25 Jan 1972	28.2	31	88.37	2.3	8.72	0.0	6.1	131.1	10.6	37.5	36.0	—	
71008	28 Apr 1972	33.4	32	37.83	4.2	2.64	22.7	0.0	102.3	4.8	14.4	20.1	3.4	#
71008	26 Jan 1973	27.2	12	162.65	4.0	8.27	0.1	3.9	128.8	14.2	52.3	51.3	3.5	#
71008	1 Oct 1974	20.5	11	71.25	5.9	4.70	2.2	0.7	123.5	6.0	29.1	29.5	4.8	#
71008	30 Apr 1975	30.1	23	54.92	7.6	2.68	9.7	2.1	117.4	7.8	25.9	27.8	4.7	#
71008	14 Nov 1975	24.3	34	56.98	5.6	2.57	1.8	0.5	123.7	7.8	32.3	32.6	4.6	#
71008	30 Nov 1975	64.7	36	125.46	4.3	7.75	0.0	3.1	128.1	29.7	45.9	40.9	4.1	#
a mean												41.2		
g mean					4.9	5.24							4.2	
71802	19 Dec 1966	38.4	26	131.85	7.5	8.67	0.0	8.5	133.5	31.0	80.8	78.7	6.6	#
71802	17 Aug 1967	62.2	30	125.62	6.1	8.55	3.6	9.3	130.7	43.5	70.0	64.6	6.3	#
71802	16 Oct 1967	52.5	35	148.31	5.7	14.96	0.0	17.4	142.4	37.2	70.8	63.8	5.7	#
71802	19 Mar 1968	62.0	34	122.02	4.8	12.27	0.0	6.4	131.4	41.7	67.3	61.8	6.9	#
71802	22 Mar 1968	90.4	35	154.85	2.4	20.55	0.0	11.0	136.0	60.7	67.2	57.4	—	
71802	31 Mar 1968	44.5	38	138.39	6.7	5.92	0.6	2.4	126.8	39.6	88.9	87.2	—	
71802	12 Sep 1968	48.7	10	127.17	10.3	6.38	7.8	13.6	130.8	29.3	60.1	56.6	—	
71802	30 Oct 1968	54.0	50	133.47	5.8	9.64	1.0	7.9	131.9	36.7	68.0	63.4	8.1	#
71802	31 Mar 1969	52.0	23	142.41	7.9	6.26	0.0	5.0	130.0	29.8	57.3	53.5	—	
a mean												65.2		
g mean					5.9	9.51							6.7	
71804	5 Jul 1960	108.5	39	25.16	1.9	0.53	79.4	7.2	52.8	64.4	59.4	68.8	1.8	#
71804	3 Aug 1961	63.1	18	33.13	2.4	0.43	45.9	1.1	80.2	21.0	33.3	40.4	1.2	#
71804	23 Aug 1962	60.5	23	27.47	0.5	1.06	20.0	9.2	114.2	18.4	30.4	29.4	1.2	#
71804	25 Sep 1963	63.4	25	24.15	2.4	0.57	0.0	16.0	141.0	18.6	29.4	21.3	1.5	#
71804	20 Nov 1963	59.3	15	21.85	1.6	0.87	0.0	10.6	135.6	11.6	19.6	13.4	1.5	#
71804	8 Dec 1964	73.7	29	22.84	3.3	0.98	0.0	32.5	157.5	27.6	37.4	24.0	2.0	#
a mean												32.9		
g mean					1.7	0.70							1.5	
72002	14 Dec 1962	27.0	24	99.48	6.9	4.69	0.0	3.4	128.4	15.7	58.1	57.2	5.3	#
72002	25 Sep 1963	38.2	14	131.13	6.0	8.42	0.0	13.6	138.6	16.8	44.1	40.6	5.3	#
72002	2 Oct 1963	31.5	11	138.87	6.1	10.21	0.0	6.4	131.4	17.2	54.5	52.8	5.1	#
72002	21 Nov 1963	31.2	13	118.24	5.8	9.83	0.0	6.9	131.9	16.5	52.9	51.1	5.1	#
72002	10 May 1964	36.8	18	134.79	6.0	5.87	3.6	6.7	128.1	20.7	56.3	55.5	4.3	#
72002	8 Dec 1964	39.8	15	142.71	8.1	13.60	0.0	16.8	141.8	24.6	61.7	57.5	5.8	#
72002	9 Jan 1965	61.4	43	120.75	8.7	9.09	0.0	11.3	136.3	41.6	67.8	61.1	6.5	#
72002	9 Sep 1965	29.6	18	145.56	6.4	12.33	0.0	10.2	135.2	22.4	75.8	73.3	5.5	#
72002	8 Dec 1965	38.0	41	117.36	8.1	6.32	0.0	6.6	131.6	25.0	65.9	64.2	5.3	#
72002	16 Dec 1965	41.9	47	121.86	4.9	8.14	0.0	3.3	128.3	27.0	64.5	63.0	5.7	#
72002	26 Jun 1966	44.4	22	139.03	5.1	6.81	9.9	6.2	121.3	25.6	57.7	57.3	3.9	#
72002	1 Oct 1968	68.9	41	164.74	9.1	14.45	0.0	10.8	135.8	59.4	86.2	78.8	4.4	#
72002	20 Jan 1969	35.1	21	89.24	5.8	7.83	0.0	1.8	126.8	19.5	55.6	55.1	5.9	#
72002	2 Jun 1969	44.1	14	166.64	6.6	6.77	8.3	1.1	117.8	26.5	60.1	60.7	4.5	#
72002	23 Sep 1968	18.8	11	93.04	3.6	31.84	0.0	21.4	146.4	8.9	47.4	42.0	—	
a mean												58.0		
g mean					6.3	9.23							5.1	
72006	16 Sep 1970	37.8	14	280.68	7.3	10.09	20.4	1.9	106.5	18.9	50.0	54.6	6.5	#
72006	31 Oct 1970	15.0	8	258.90	7.8	28.63	0.0	24.3	149.3	11.3	75.3	69.2	7.4	#
72006	11 Feb 1971	51.6	26	285.25	11.1	7.62	0.8	0.6	124.8	32.0	62.0	59.5	—	
72006	20 Nov 1971	25.5	16	181.98	8.6	12.04	0.3	2.3	127.0	12.1	47.6	47.1	5.4	#

Catch	Date	P mm	D h	Q_p m^3s^{-1}	LAG h	BF m^3s^{-1}	SMD mm	API5 mm	CWI mm	R/O mm	PR %	SPR %	Tp(0) h	
72006	18 Jan 1972	26.7	17	274.96	6.7	14.29	0.0	2.5	127.5	16.3	61.0	60.4	4.8	#
72006	3 Jul 1972	54.2	36	207.83	6.8	13.68	8.6	0.8	117.2	28.1	51.9	51.0	—	
72006	11 Feb 1973	17.8	26	152.69	7.7	14.31	0.0	2.7	127.7	14.3	80.6	79.9	—	
72006	15 Dec 1973	24.7	32	182.58	5.5	17.41	0.0	4.3	129.3	15.7	63.7	62.6	—	
72006	30 Apr 1975	19.9	13	162.83	6.6	14.87	0.9	4.4	128.5	12.2	61.4	60.5	—	
72006	24 Sep 1975	64.6	28	492.98	6.8	28.72	0.7	4.9	129.2	53.3	82.5	77.2	5.6	#
a mean												62.2		
g mean					7.4	14.93							5.9	
72818	26 Jan 1973	20.8	9	12.94	7.8	0.69	0.0	2.6	127.6	6.0	28.7	27.8	7.3	#
72818	3 Apr 1973	23.1	7	17.13	5.3	0.87	0.0	9.7	134.7	6.3	27.3	24.6	4.6	#
72818	7 Dec 1973	17.7	10	8.04	8.0	0.49	0.0	0.6	125.6	4.3	24.4	23.9	8.0	#
72818	19 Dec 1973	17.6	15	9.58	5.8	1.23	0.0	4.0	129.0	6.1	34.9	33.7	3.9	#
72818	24 Sep 1974	17.5	14	7.31	9.6	0.54	0.7	3.8	128.1	5.4	30.8	29.8	8.3	#
72818	6 Jan 1975	17.9	8	6.88	6.9	0.55	0.0	0.6	125.6	3.3	18.5	18.0	7.5	#
72818	12 Jan 1975	11.9	6	6.96	6.2	0.75	0.0	2.5	127.5	2.7	22.9	22.0	5.7	#
72818	17 Feb 1975	13.4	6	10.83	5.9	0.77	0.0	2.2	127.2	3.8	28.4	27.6	5.7	#
72818	18 Apr 1975	11.8	11	6.57	7.3	0.62	1.6	3.9	127.3	2.7	22.6	21.7	4.4	#
a mean												25.4		
g mean					6.9	0.70							5.9	
72820	4 Apr 1973	66.1	16	0.54	4.9	0.04	0.5	7.7	132.2	28.6	43.3	—	—	
72820	4 Aug 1973	16.1	11	0.07	4.0	0.00	54.5	5.2	75.7	2.3	14.5	—	3.3	
72820	5 Aug 1973	49.2	22	0.42	3.2	0.03	28.7	9.6	105.9	19.9	40.4	—	1.4	
72820	9 Nov 1973	77.0	23	0.67	4.6	0.05	22.5	3.3	105.8	37.7	48.9	—	0.4	
72820	12 Nov 1973	53.5	26	0.34	2.7	0.05	10.8	30.8	145.0	18.9	35.3	—	—	
72820	15 Dec 1973	28.8	11	0.19	3.2	0.05	0.0	4.5	129.5	5.5	19.0	—	4.2	
72820	2 Jul 1974	18.6	5	0.07	4.4	0.03	79.0	4.5	50.5	-0.4	-2.0	—	—	
72820	15 Jul 1974	20.4	13	0.45	1.9	0.06	51.2	2.4	76.2	7.6	37.5	—	0.6	
72820	8 Aug 1974	29.4	6	0.33	1.8	0.06	68.0	0.4	57.4	1.9	6.5	—	—	
72820	7 Sep 1974	24.6	12	0.40	1.9	0.11	62.9	17.4	79.5	10.8	43.7	—	0.6	
a mean												—		
g mean					3.1	0.05							1.2	
73005	19 Feb 1970	33.4	18	86.82	4.6	10.23	0.0	23.1	148.1	16.3	48.7	42.8	6.0	#
73005	16 Jun 1972	54.8	15	72.00	6.4	5.95	15.4	0.8	110.4	12.7	23.2	23.5	6.7	#
73005	3 Jul 1972	77.1	39	92.13	10.7	7.94	7.6	0.3	117.7	27.8	36.0	31.9	5.0	#
73005	28 Nov 1972	45.2	18	84.92	6.2	9.34	0.0	5.0	130.0	19.1	42.3	39.4	6.5	#
73005	9 Nov 1973	28.4	21	56.72	9.9	7.12	0.0	3.1	128.1	15.1	53.1	52.2	6.5	#
73005	17 Oct 1974	30.3	17	34.42	5.4	5.46	0.3	1.8	126.5	5.8	19.1	18.4	6.6	#
73005	10 Nov 1974	33.7	14	87.69	10.9	14.29	0.0	10.6	135.6	13.5	40.0	37.1	—	
73005	21 Jan 1975	64.9	23	148.25	7.6	18.53	0.0	8.2	133.2	29.8	45.9	39.4	6.4	#
73005	16 Feb 1975	30.1	23	52.55	7.2	5.14	0.1	3.6	128.5	8.4	27.8	26.6	4.2	#
73005	20 Apr 1975	36.2	24	47.10	10.8	8.95	0.6	6.3	130.7	22.6	62.5	61.0	—	
73005	21 Jul 1975	82.3	33	74.29	10.9	3.97	73.1	2.9	54.8	22.6	27.5	38.6	3.5	#
73005	23 Sep 1975	64.7	18	118.44	7.1	5.23	1.1	5.6	129.5	26.5	41.0	35.4	5.5	#
a mean												37.2		
g mean					7.8	7.71							5.6	
73007	30 Aug 1970	38.4	9	13.22	3.5	0.70	89.4	0.1	35.7	10.2	26.6	48.9	—	
73007	18 Jan 1972	53.1	20	23.34	5.3	1.42	0.0	11.3	136.3	19.1	36.0	30.5	3.8	#
73007	8 Nov 1972	89.2	19	38.81	4.9	1.05	1.5	1.7	125.2	47.6	53.4	46.5	3.1	#
73007	17 Oct 1974	42.3	13	10.77	0.2	1.42	0.6	1.7	126.1	7.4	17.4	16.3	—	
73007	28 Dec 1974	44.1	14	30.67	2.4	2.77	0.0	14.2	139.2	25.4	57.5	52.7	3.5	#
73007	16 Feb 1975	40.9	24	15.75	7.0	0.59	0.1	2.1	127.0	16.6	40.7	39.8	3.1	#
a mean												39.1		
g mean					2.6	1.16							3.4	
73008	21 Apr 1970	66.2	30	46.38	10.4	5.79	0.5	3.2	127.7	32.2	48.6	43.5	—	
73008	23 Nov 1970	38.3	23	27.26	7.2	8.00	0.0	6.9	131.9	12.4	32.5	30.7	—	
73008	20 Nov 1971	27.8	18	19.90	9.7	2.80	0.3	2.6	127.3	6.9	24.7	24.1	—	
73008	17 Jun 1972	36.7	14	23.97	1.3	3.89	17.2	1.4	109.2	5.6	15.2	19.1	—	
73008	3 Jul 1972	50.8	37	25.54	15.8	3.53	8.2	0.5	117.3	20.9	41.2	40.7	—	
73008	1 Dec 1972	27.4	12	26.12	5.9	8.74	0.0	14.0	139.0	6.2	22.8	19.2	4.1	#
73008	12 Dec 1972	18.6	7	26.13	5.8	10.94	0.0	14.0	139.0	4.0	21.6	18.0	5.1	#
73008	3 Apr 1973	29.9	9	25.04	5.2	3.79	0.4	8.4	133.0	7.1	23.9	21.8	3.7	#

Catch	Date	P	D	Q_p	LAG	BF	SMD	API5	CWI	R/O	PR	SPR	Tp(0)	
		mm	h	$m^3 s^{-1}$	h	$m^3 s^{-1}$	mm	mm	mm	mm	%	%	h	
73008	21 Jan 1975	46.4	30	40.97	5.0	8.80	0.0	5.0	130.0	16.6	35.8	32.8	4.3	#
a mean												27.8		
g mean					6.2	5.63							4.3	
73803	27 Nov 1976	25.4	7	6.06	5.9	1.75	0.0	14.5	139.5	13.0	51.2	47.6	—	
73803	1 Jan 1976	18.5	24	6.32	3.5	1.08	0.0	10.5	135.5	16.9	91.5	88.9	—	
73803	21 Jan 1975	56.4	43	9.73	5.6	1.75	0.0	10.7	135.7	35.6	63.2	57.3	—	
73803	21 Dec 1974	31.4	13	7.24	10.1	2.07	0.0	14.0	139.0	21.8	69.4	65.9	9.4	#
73803	6 Sep 1974	42.4	38	7.26	14.3	1.91	0.0	20.6	145.6	32.7	77.1	71.1	—	
a mean												66.2		
g mean					7.0	1.67							9.4	
73804	3 Feb 1966	95.7	43	50.54	10.1	3.37	0.0	13.2	138.2	70.7	73.9	63.1	6.4	#
73804	25 Feb 1966	50.7	9	51.87	6.5	8.22	0.0	26.3	151.3	32.0	63.2	54.3	6.5	#
73804	21 May 1966	95.6	55	54.91	11.1	3.23	3.6	8.7	130.1	81.6	85.4	76.6	—	
73804	13 Aug 1966	65.7	26	73.92	11.3	3.65	8.3	8.2	124.9	59.5	90.5	86.2	—	
73804	3 Sep 1966	100.8	24	89.73	7.5	2.51	0.0	21.2	146.2	64.7	64.2	50.9	5.6	#
73804	29 Nov 1966	62.9	26	44.35	6.1	3.69	0.0	9.2	134.2	40.5	64.4	58.1	7.7	#
73804	1 Dec 1966	86.2	34	46.26	5.6	7.17	0.0	39.4	164.4	53.4	62.0	45.6	8.3	#
73804	26 Feb 1967	69.7	17	60.43	6.7	6.71	0.0	10.6	135.6	53.9	77.3	69.8	—	
73804	29 Jul 1967	103.6	41	53.76	12.3	3.13	6.9	3.9	122.0	83.0	80.1	72.6	9.1	#
73804	2 Oct 1967	72.6	37	54.98	7.7	8.54	0.0	40.9	165.9	41.8	57.6	42.2	8.5	#
73804	6 Oct 1967	71.3	33	53.61	7.7	2.57	0.8	17.0	141.2	46.4	65.1	56.0	5.0	#
73804	8 Oct 1967	135.9	28	128.72	11.6	3.08	0.0	24.8	149.8	133.9	98.5	81.3	—	
73804	13 Oct 1967	60.6	18	54.32	8.0	4.56	0.0	15.3	140.3	38.7	63.9	56.3	—	
73804	16 Oct 1967	74.7	18	65.41	7.2	6.69	0.8	23.5	147.7	49.8	66.6	55.5	5.4	#
73804	22 Mar 1968	109.5	34	59.50	7.3	5.04	0.0	12.2	137.2	83.2	76.0	64.2	—	
73804	20 Jan 1969	97.0	43	54.41	12.6	3.22	0.2	3.8	128.6	72.4	74.6	66.1	—	
73804	13 Dec 1969	78.0	21	65.39	8.4	3.68	0.2	1.9	126.7	63.0	80.8	74.6	—	
a mean												63.1		
g mean					8.4	4.29							6.8	
74001	1 Jul 1968	87.5	59	90.74	11.4	1.96	15.8	0.9	110.1	48.6	55.6	52.6	—	
74001	19 Sep 1968	77.4	31	47.68	10.5	2.03	6.3	0.0	118.7	49.4	63.8	59.7	—	
74001	9 Oct 1968	34.6	6	47.72	3.2	4.15	1.8	0.1	123.3	11.7	33.7	34.1	—	
74001	23 Nov 1968	30.6	12	48.79	3.2	6.61	0.0	11.8	136.8	13.5	44.0	41.0	—	
74001	19 Dec 1968	45.1	16	59.77	5.4	3.96	0.0	4.3	129.3	28.5	63.2	60.7	—	
74001	20 Jan 1969	85.6	43	119.12	6.1	5.04	0.2	3.6	128.4	66.1	77.2	69.8	—	
74001	13 Dec 1969	60.1	20	102.78	5.7	3.62	0.2	0.9	125.7	51.1	85.0	81.2	—	
74001	18 Jan 1972	55.7	19	154.82	4.2	6.34	0.0	14.6	139.6	39.1	70.2	63.5	—	
a mean												57.8		
g mean					5.6	3.87							—	
75006	10 Nov 1974	53.7	16	43.19	4.5	4.77	0.0	16.8	141.8	32.0	59.6	52.6	3.3	#
75006	19 Jan 1975	36.2	11	37.09	5.4	2.89	0.0	5.5	130.5	26.6	73.4	72.0	2.4	#
75006	13 Jan 1975	45.6	14	37.19	4.4	6.91	0.0	16.5	141.5	30.0	65.8	60.2	—	
75006	26 Jan 1975	58.2	25	43.05	4.8	4.76	0.0	23.5	148.5	55.1	94.7	85.4	—	
75006	30 Jan 1975	57.1	13	35.91	2.6	6.11	0.0	8.2	133.2	28.7	50.2	44.9	—	
75006	24 Sep 1975	71.4	14	33.02	10.6	2.47	19.0	8.4	114.4	65.5	91.7	89.3	—	
75006	2 Jan 1976	40.2	12	27.28	4.5	3.52	0.0	13.6	138.6	21.9	54.5	50.9	—	
75006	27 Nov 1976	35.9	8	42.15	3.7	6.21	0.0	22.4	147.4	22.7	63.3	57.7	2.5	#
a mean												64.1		
g mean					4.7	4.43							2.7	
75007	10 Jan 1974	28.0	14	40.86	3.7	4.52	0.0	11.2	136.2	12.5	44.8	42.0	3.3	#
75007	10 Nov 1974	44.1	17	60.16	5.8	4.22	0.0	18.6	143.6	27.4	62.2	56.3	3.5	#
75007	24 Nov 1974	48.6	24	61.20	4.5	3.03	0.0	5.1	130.1	31.3	64.4	61.1	3.4	#
75007	28 Dec 1974	31.6	12	45.82	3.7	4.72	0.0	10.5	135.5	16.8	53.1	50.5	2.4	#
75007	14 Jan 1975	37.5	16	53.26	5.1	6.34	0.0	10.2	135.2	19.1	50.9	48.3	3.5	#
75007	24 Jan 1975	41.3	13	43.03	3.5	3.42	0.0	9.3	134.3	17.5	42.3	39.4	—	
75007	24 Sep 1975	68.2	18	42.51	5.3	2.47	19.2	3.9	109.7	26.5	38.8	38.0	—	
75007	27 Sep 1975	34.4	15	42.39	4.1	4.01	13.8	15.2	126.4	18.3	53.3	52.9	4.5	#
75007	2 Jan 1976	37.4	11	51.39	5.2	3.22	0.0	13.0	138.0	25.7	68.6	65.3	—	
75007	27 Nov 1976	21.6	8	21.72	4.7	3.60	0.0	16.5	141.5	7.3	33.6	29.5	—	
a mean												48.3		
g mean					4.5	3.83							3.4	

Catch	Date	P mm	D h	Q_p m^3s^{-1}	LAG h	BF m^3s^{-1}	SMD mm	API5 mm	CWI mm	R/O mm	PR %	SPR %	Tp(0) h	
76005	23 Nov 1970	33.5	20	205.84	12.1	20.79	0.0	3.7	128.7	22.1	65.9	65.0	—	
a mean												65.0		
g mean					12.1	20.79							—	
76008	30 Oct 1970	23.7	13	131.92	4.2	16.19	0.0	12.5	137.5	12.4	52.4	49.3	5.0	#
76008	31 Oct 1970	28.5	26	189.99	7.4	14.05	0.0	20.5	145.5	18.5	64.8	59.7	6.5	#
a mean												54.5		
g mean					5.6	15.08							5.7	
76011	27 Feb 1967	29.8	23	2.12	10.2	0.08	0.0	2.0	127.0	22.9	77.0	76.5	—	
76011	11 Aug 1967	17.2	5	1.06	3.0	0.08	0.4	10.9	135.5	11.6	67.7	65.1	2.5	#
76011	1 Oct 1967	23.4	11	1.16	3.9	0.04	0.6	4.2	128.6	17.1	73.0	72.1	2.8	#
76011	2 Oct 1967	27.4	24	0.90	3.0	0.06	0.0	25.3	150.3	18.9	68.8	62.5	2.2	#
76011	6 Oct 1967	41.0	16	1.50	2.5	0.03	1.0	7.8	131.8	28.8	70.3	68.2	2.0	#
76011	8 Oct 1967	71.4	24	2.69	3.0	0.04	0.0	13.1	138.1	60.0	84.0	75.7	1.0	#
76011	16 Oct 1967	48.4	15	1.75	3.6	0.03	0.2	6.0	130.8	35.2	72.7	69.3	1.8	#
76011	1 Nov 1967	33.4	20	1.34	2.4	0.03	1.0	1.2	125.2	23.6	70.7	70.6	1.0	#
76011	18 Mar 1968	34.8	39	0.92	3.1	0.05	0.0	7.9	132.9	27.6	79.4	77.4	2.2	#
76011	22 Mar 1968	96.4	33	2.18	2.0	0.07	0.0	6.1	131.1	77.2	80.1	71.0	—	
76011	31 Mar 1968	28.6	15	1.24	3.8	0.16	0.0	10.8	135.8	20.2	70.7	68.0	2.0	#
76011	13 Aug 1968	66.0	16	0.87	4.7	0.04	45.1	3.6	83.5	20.4	30.9	36.9	4.2	#
76011	12 Sep 1968	33.9	16	1.37	3.1	0.05	11.2	6.9	120.7	26.0	76.7	77.8	2.2	#
76011	19 Dec 1968	22.4	14	1.08	4.2	0.03	0.0	4.0	129.0	20.8	92.9	91.9	—	
76011	19 Aug 1969	66.5	21	1.84	4.3	0.02	50.1	2.8	77.7	36.5	54.9	62.3	1.5	#
76011	20 Aug 1970	21.7	25	0.60	5.1	0.02	51.6	3.1	76.5	15.9	73.3	85.4	2.2	#
76011	16 Sep 1970	46.3	17	0.97	3.1	0.03	4.3	2.8	123.5	22.7	49.1	47.8	—	
76011	31 Oct 1970	34.6	26	2.11	2.7	0.07	0.0	18.4	143.4	23.9	69.1	64.5	1.8	#
76011	26 Aug 1974	18.6	8	1.14	1.5	0.05	0.4	4.2	128.8	6.7	35.9	35.0	0.9	#
76011	10 Nov 1974	30.6	19	1.92	2.3	0.10	0.0	13.3	138.3	24.5	80.1	76.8	1.2	#
76011	24 Nov 1974	21.1	23	1.14	2.7	0.10	0.0	11.1	136.1	16.3	77.1	74.3	—	
76011	21 Jan 1975	33.2	22	1.59	5.7	0.05	0.0	2.5	127.5	32.4	97.6	97.0	—	
76011	30 Aug 1975	74.4	14	5.98	3.3	0.04	45.4	1.0	80.6	59.9	80.5	86.2	1.0	#
76011	27 Sep 1975	30.4	23	1.22	3.3	0.05	0.0	10.2	135.2	20.4	67.0	64.4	1.6	#
76011	2 Jan 1976	27.2	13	2.32	2.0	0.06	0.0	3.4	128.4	24.4	89.6	88.8	—	
76011	23 Feb 1976	29.7	28	1.39	1.2	0.04	0.0	0.5	125.5	16.6	55.8	55.7	—	
76011	15 Oct 1976	34.6	20	1.85	2.4	0.15	0.0	13.1	138.1	27.5	79.5	76.2	2.2	#
76011	25 Jan 1975	22.6	12	1.43	4.8	0.06	0.0	11.1	136.1	21.7	96.1	93.3	1.6	#
76011	24 Sep 1975	34.5	20	1.26	3.3	0.04	0.4	2.2	126.8	26.3	76.1	75.7	1.1	#
76011	25 Jan 1977	24.0	29	1.47	0.0	0.20	0.0	4.0	129.0	23.9	99.7	98.7	—	
76011	6 Sep 1977	24.1	7	1.74	1.9	0.06	0.0	4.2	129.2	14.0	58.2	57.2	1.4	#
a mean												71.7		
g mean					3.1	0.05							1.7	
76014	28 Dec 1974	20.5	7	52.48	3.0	5.45	0.0	7.0	132.0	13.8	67.5	65.7	3.4	#
76014	10 Jan 1975	15.0	7	20.73	4.9	2.46	0.0	0.8	125.8	7.5	50.0	49.8	4.0	#
76014	25 Jan 1975	27.2	10	74.24	3.6	5.19	0.0	8.3	133.3	22.4	82.4	80.3	2.5	#
76014	27 Sep 1975	29.7	9	112.18	3.8	5.71	33.1	14.8	106.7	27.9	93.9	98.5	2.4	#
76014	2 Oct 1975	20.2	12	25.55	3.5	3.71	24.3	7.2	107.9	12.0	59.4	63.7	3.7	#
76014	10 Jan 1976	21.5	12	28.19	4.8	3.84	0.0	6.5	131.5	9.6	44.6	42.9	—	
76014	23 Feb 1976	28.4	16	31.57	6.4	1.66	0.3	2.7	127.4	18.8	66.2	65.6	—	
76014	3 Apr 1976	15.7	5	30.85	4.7	2.84	0.8	4.5	128.7	8.9	56.8	55.8	4.6	#
76014	17 Oct 1971	13.2	4	34.98	2.9	5.86	51.4	9.7	83.3	7.6	57.7	68.1	2.9	#
76014	7 Nov 1971	17.5	8	29.35	4.0	3.02	31.9	8.0	101.1	8.2	46.8	52.7	3.0	#
76014	18 Jan 1972	34.1	10	62.73	2.8	2.90	0.0	0.9	125.9	19.9	58.5	58.3	4.0	#
76014	26 Jan 1972	25.3	13	31.32	0.7	4.38	0.0	3.8	128.8	8.3	33.0	32.0	3.2	#
76014	2 Jun 1972	15.6	13	22.90	5.2	2.17	0.4	5.7	130.3	8.7	55.9	54.5	—	
76014	17 Jun 1972	32.0	12	43.99	5.1	1.54	3.6	0.2	121.6	17.9	55.9	56.7	—	
76014	9 Nov 1972	60.0	15	123.79	5.2	1.80	73.0	2.4	54.4	49.3	82.2	96.2	2.4	#
76014	1 Dec 1972	29.7	10	75.38	2.9	8.90	0.0	11.6	136.6	23.1	77.8	74.9	3.5	#
76014	5 Dec 1972	12.3	6	31.02	4.3	6.26	0.0	11.1	136.1	8.7	70.8	68.0	3.9	#
76014	26 Jan 1973	10.9	10	24.77	0.0	4.41	0.0	3.2	128.2	5.5	50.4	49.6	—	
76014	16 Jul 1973	15.1	3	30.31	3.0	3.47	70.7	7.5	61.8	6.4	42.5	58.2	3.3	#
76014	5 Aug 1973	49.8	10	108.35	3.8	2.38	74.7	5.4	55.7	32.8	65.9	81.0	3.3	#
a mean												63.6		
g mean					3.6	3.49							3.3	

Catch	Date	P mm	D h	Q_p $m^3 s^{-1}$	LAG h	BF $m^3 s^{-1}$	SMD mm	API5 mm	CWI mm	R/O mm	PR %	SPR %	Tp(0) h	
76805	5 Aug 1973	67.8	14	4.23	2.9	0.24	28.7	7.2	103.5	30.1	44.4	45.2	1.5	#
76805	12 Nov 1973	17.4	15	0.65	5.5	0.08	8.0	1.8	118.8	7.3	42.1	43.6	3.5	#
76805	29 Jan 1974	74.8	31	2.68	3.4	0.28	0.0	8.6	133.6	44.4	59.4	51.9	1.1	#
76805	8 Aug 1974	18.6	7	0.33	2.8	0.06	69.1	0.0	55.9	0.8	4.5	21.8	0.4	#
76805	10 Nov 1974	47.6	16	4.83	2.0	0.32	12.9	9.5	121.6	30.5	64.1	63.1	0.6	#
76805	13 Nov 1974	29.6	10	3.03	5.5	0.24	5.2	9.1	128.9	18.9	63.7	62.7	1.8	#
76805	21 Dec 1974	54.3	12	4.65	2.4	0.45	0.0	19.3	144.3	39.1	72.0	64.3	0.6	#
76805	19 Jan 1975	35.0	13	3.03	0.9	0.32	0.0	5.7	130.7	18.9	54.0	52.6	1.2	#
76805	21 Jan 1975	59.5	17	5.60	4.5	0.27	0.0	11.8	136.8	44.7	75.1	68.6	1.0	#
76805	25 Jan 1975	37.3	12	3.46	2.4	0.28	0.0	8.8	133.8	21.4	57.4	55.2	1.0	#
76805	30 Jan 1975	45.0	13	2.70	2.7	0.35	0.0	5.8	130.8	21.2	47.2	44.4	2.2	#
a mean												52.1		
g mean					2.9	0.23							1.1	
77002	13 Mar 1963	57.7	28	358.80	4.0	37.34	0.0	1.6	126.6	32.1	55.7	51.9	4.6	#
77002	17 Nov 1963	46.4	21	311.03	9.8	30.18	0.2	3.7	128.5	27.5	59.3	56.8	5.8	#
77002	5 Oct 1964	74.9	49	526.39	9.6	14.36	5.4	0.0	119.6	44.2	59.0	54.9	5.0	#
77002	29 Dec 1964	58.3	37	422.72	11.4	13.24	0.0	1.1	126.1	33.3	57.2	53.5	—	
77002	13 Aug 1966	39.9	22	343.92	9.4	18.89	6.0	8.3	127.3	23.5	58.9	58.3	—	
77002	3 Sep 1966	55.6	21	464.36	3.4	23.45	0.0	11.1	136.1	26.9	48.3	42.4	4.1	#
77002	31 Jul 1967	37.5	14	320.93	5.0	22.38	3.6	14.7	136.1	14.3	38.1	35.3	—	
77002	8 Oct 1967	79.6	23	566.37	4.2	39.62	0.0	11.3	136.3	52.9	66.5	57.8	5.0	#
77002	27 Sep 1977	38.6	39	223.98	12.3	8.99	6.6	3.0	121.4	16.1	41.7	42.6	7.9	#
77002	23 Oct 1977	40.2	27	164.20	10.7	11.35	0.0	3.8	128.8	16.9	42.1	41.0	9.1	#
77002	30 Oct 1977	98.8	50	617.76	8.4	23.54	0.0	3.2	128.2	62.1	62.9	54.3	7.1	#
77002	22 Dec 1977	79.3	53	361.60	6.8	16.05	0.0	2.3	127.3	46.2	58.2	51.7	4.9	#
77002	27 Sep 1978	25.8	22	150.84	7.3	11.33	0.0	10.8	135.8	12.2	47.4	44.7	6.5	#
77002	13 Nov 1978	94.3	70	383.94	6.9	25.00	0.0	9.0	134.0	53.3	56.5	46.9	5.3	#
77002	8 Mar 1979	40.1	44	196.08	7.8	24.49	0.2	10.7	135.5	18.3	45.7	43.0	6.6	#
77002	6 Aug 1979	27.7	25	159.21	11.5	17.27	1.9	13.9	137.0	10.9	39.5	36.5	9.4	#
77002	29 Oct 1979	46.5	46	245.45	11.2	12.19	0.0	2.8	127.8	22.0	47.4	45.0	6.7	#
77002	24 Nov 1979	68.3	28	352.46	8.5	26.14	0.0	5.0	130.0	40.2	58.8	52.9	5.8	#
77002	1 Dec 1979	28.0	29	224.00	6.5	25.96	0.0	5.8	130.8	11.7	41.8	40.3	5.7	#
77002	3 Jan 1980	29.5	17	256.60	6.1	13.82	0.0	0.0	125.0	16.4	55.5	55.5	5.5	#
77002	25 Dec 1979	77.1	46	228.99	8.1	16.57	0.0	1.5	126.5	40.6	52.6	46.6	6.3	#
77002	30 Jul 1980	26.0	5	92.06	8.5	8.63	28.6	10.4	106.8	6.9	26.5	31.0	9.3	#
77002	13 Aug 1980	30.5	17	186.68	6.4	26.04	1.6	15.0	138.4	18.5	60.7	57.3	6.5	#
77002	11 Sep 1980	36.4	29	293.45	5.4	24.67	0.0	14.5	139.5	18.7	51.4	47.8	5.6	#
77002	14 Nov 1980	33.6	18	240.50	6.1	10.96	0.0	1.5	126.5	13.6	40.5	40.1	5.8	#
77002	2 Feb 1981	43.3	46	269.21	4.7	15.61	0.0	4.3	129.3	23.6	54.6	52.5	5.5	#
77002	23 Sep 1981	43.8	32	308.87	8.7	13.76	2.4	11.1	133.7	20.1	46.0	42.7	6.5	#
77002	25 Sep 1981	77.8	53	426.97	6.3	28.86	0.0	20.2	145.2	48.9	62.8	52.0	4.5	#
77002	8 Oct 1981	58.8	37	313.53	6.8	30.52	0.0	9.6	134.6	34.4	58.5	52.6	5.9	#
77002	22 Nov 1981	41.6	20	382.31	6.4	26.57	0.0	6.8	131.8	22.4	53.9	51.6	4.0	#
77002	30 Sep 1982	31.3	17	59.68	8.4	12.77	0.0	8.3	133.3	5.4	17.2	15.1	7.0	#
77002	11 Nov 1982	33.1	33	263.38	6.3	26.81	0.0	11.0	136.0	17.2	52.1	49.3	5.5	#
77002	24 Jul 1983	21.6	3	66.14	8.2	2.81	45.1	10.1	90.0	2.3	10.7	19.4	8.5	#
77002	3 Oct 1983	43.2	33	175.83	6.8	10.52	19.6	4.4	109.8	16.2	37.4	40.2	7.9	#
77002	11 Oct 1983	37.7	25	226.34	8.2	27.06	0.0	9.0	134.0	18.3	48.6	46.3	6.8	#
77002	26 Nov 1984	46.0	30	273.82	10.2	25.55	0.0	4.4	129.4	25.9	56.2	53.5	5.5	#
77002	21 Mar 1986	47.7	52	249.11	5.8	28.31	0.0	8.5	133.5	25.5	53.5	49.5	5.0	#
77002	25 Aug 1986	24.2	18	85.15	11.2	8.01	6.4	1.2	119.8	7.0	29.0	30.3	11.0	#
77002	9 Mar 1981	29.3	18	247.50	6.7	27.83	0.0	8.2	133.2	14.5	49.4	47.3	5.5	#
77002	22 Nov 1982	47.3	23	361.33	7.3	39.70	0.0	12.1	137.1	27.5	58.1	53.3	8.5	#
77002	17 Jul 1985	38.7	12	317.15	7.2	17.83	0.0	5.7	130.7	15.5	40.1	38.7	6.5	#
77002	17 Sep 1985	66.3	27	315.29	7.7	22.86	0.0	6.5	131.5	36.1	54.4	48.3	6.5	#
77002	20 Sep 1985	99.3	76	527.44	7.7	33.34	0.0	17.8	142.8	74.8	75.3	63.0	5.4	#
77002	19 Dec 1985	88.2	71	408.62	12.4	25.84	0.0	6.7	131.7	63.1	71.5	63.0	6.0	#
77002	24 May 1986	56.2	34	267.49	4.9	24.90	2.8	3.6	125.8	28.8	51.3	47.9	6.7	#
77002	19 Oct 1984	50.1	39	184.34	5.5	24.02	0.0	13.4	138.4	17.2	34.3	28.7	5.5	#
a mean												46.4		
g mean					7.3	19.09							6.2	
79006	5 Jun 1980	23.2	9	17.72	11.8	1.70	94.1	2.8	33.7	2.0	8.5	31.3	13.5	#
79006	4 Oct 1980	78.5	73	253.15	12.1	16.81	0.0	9.4	134.4	45.5	58.0	49.8	3.5	#
79006	18 Nov 1980	60.6	87	206.82	7.4	21.15	0.0	13.2	138.2	25.6	42.3	35.2	3.2	#

Catch	Date	P mm	D h	Q_p m^3s^{-1}	LAG h	BF m^3s^{-1}	SMD mm	API5 mm	CWI mm	R/O mm	PR %	SPR %	Tp(0) h	
79006	11 Dec 1980	58.2	89	222.40	7.1	21.95	0.0	14.4	139.4	26.5	45.5	38.4	3.1	#
79006	5 Mar 1981	56.6	56	240.98	14.7	6.08	0.0	1.4	126.4	39.2	69.3	65.7	4.7	#
79006	19 Sep 1981	42.7	17	267.08	6.9	16.94	22.4	11.7	114.3	20.8	48.6	50.4	4.4	#
79006	23 Sep 1981	39.8	11	267.70	5.2	25.64	0.0	6.0	131.0	15.7	39.5	38.0	4.5	#
79006	1 Oct 1981	77.4	39	365.08	9.0	24.47	0.0	8.1	133.1	51.8	66.9	59.2	3.5	#
79006	22 Nov 1981	31.3	17	255.35	6.8	25.61	0.0	9.8	134.8	16.2	51.9	49.4	4.5	#
79006	11 Feb 1982	33.6	10	224.90	4.1	34.43	0.0	12.7	137.7	16.1	47.8	44.6	3.4	#
79006	23 Sep 1982	51.4	39	238.76	4.9	10.75	0.0	4.1	129.1	19.3	37.6	34.1	4.5	#
79006	27 Sep 1982	57.0	30	259.06	8.7	26.13	0.0	18.6	143.6	33.9	59.5	51.6	6.7	#
79006	30 Sep 1982	47.2	20	230.54	10.7	20.46	0.0	10.5	135.5	29.6	62.8	58.4	7.1	#
79006	15 Oct 1982	79.6	43	532.90	7.2	19.99	0.0	4.9	129.9	55.7	70.0	62.9	3.5	#
79006	4 Nov 1982	51.2	36	244.90	7.0	20.57	0.0	1.8	126.8	27.5	53.7	50.8	6.0	#
79006	22 Nov 1982	41.3	15	261.08	4.4	41.90	0.0	11.4	136.4	17.2	41.7	38.3	4.5	#
79006	2 Jan 1983	42.6	49	281.74	5.4	23.83	0.0	11.7	136.7	21.4	50.3	46.5	4.5	#
79006	14 Oct 1983	75.7	55	318.20	16.6	22.15	0.0	10.1	135.1	48.7	64.3	56.3	10.1	#
79006	29 Oct 1984	31.8	14	189.56	6.6	29.76	0.0	8.0	133.0	14.2	44.6	42.6	6.2	#
79006	26 Nov 1984	62.1	32	332.29	5.7	20.78	0.0	5.0	130.0	29.8	48.0	42.8	4.1	#
79006	10 Aug 1985	27.9	23	106.07	9.0	8.27	2.6	4.0	126.4	9.1	32.5	32.1	6.5	#
79006	18 Sep 1985	37.4	21	209.48	6.3	24.98	0.0	12.5	137.5	21.3	57.0	53.9	3.8	#
79006	9 Jan 1986	106.2	129	276.41	8.1	13.29	0.0	3.6	128.6	66.0	62.1	52.7	5.0	#
79006	8 Jun 1986	45.7	45	95.66	7.2	8.19	18.6	0.3	106.7	11.8	25.9	28.9	5.0	#
79006	20 Sep 1985	82.6	62	327.37	12.0	23.03	0.0	13.9	138.9	54.5	66.0	56.3	6.1	#
a mean												46.8		
g mean					7.7	17.54							4.9	
80003	19 Sep 1981	46.1	23	7.50	0.2	0.34	0.0	15.1	140.1	28.0	60.8	55.4	1.0	#
80003	23 Sep 1981	52.8	11	6.79	2.2	0.36	0.0	9.8	134.8	31.6	59.9	54.8	2.0	#
80003	18 Oct 1981	46.0	26	6.27	0.0	0.23	2.1	1.0	123.9	22.2	48.2	46.9	—	
80003	19 Nov 1981	33.7	27	6.09	5.1	0.17	0.0	4.5	129.5	20.3	60.2	59.1	4.2	#
80003	25 Feb 1982	32.9	17	6.44	0.8	0.32	0.0	14.2	139.2	17.6	53.4	49.9	0.2	#
80003	5 Mar 1982	36.7	22	4.72	1.8	0.23	0.0	5.5	130.5	22.8	62.0	60.6	0.9	#
80003	30 Jun 1982	33.3	7	7.76	2.3	0.28	5.0	6.4	126.4	19.4	58.2	57.9	2.2	#
80003	17 Oct 1982	49.6	23	5.81	4.7	0.28	0.0	11.0	136.0	37.3	75.2	70.3	3.0	#
80003	29 Oct 1982	80.3	58	6.59	7.1	0.21	0.4	1.9	126.5	63.0	78.5	72.1	2.8	#
80003	5 Nov 1982	53.4	34	5.48	3.4	0.25	0.0	6.5	131.5	41.4	77.6	73.2	1.1	#
80003	11 Nov 1982	35.0	21	7.06	2.8	0.39	0.0	11.2	136.2	26.6	76.0	73.2	1.5	#
80003	22 Nov 1982	51.0	16	6.31	3.7	0.29	0.0	10.4	135.4	36.8	72.1	67.1	2.5	#
80003	7 Dec 1982	63.6	22	4.53	5.1	0.22	0.0	6.8	131.8	37.1	58.3	52.5	2.8	#
80003	2 Jan 1983	29.0	9	6.52	1.7	0.36	0.0	11.2	136.2	18.7	64.5	61.7	0.2	#
80003	4 Jan 1983	24.4	10	6.62	0.6	0.65	0.0	16.4	141.4	16.6	68.1	64.0	0.6	#
80003	23 Jan 1983	34.7	10	6.58	2.6	0.20	0.0	1.1	126.1	17.4	50.2	49.9	1.8	#
80003	13 Jun 1983	24.9	26	6.46	0.9	0.21	1.4	5.4	129.0	20.6	82.8	81.8	0.6	#
80003	1 Jul 1983	43.4	14	6.28	0.6	0.22	21.3	2.6	106.3	18.4	42.5	46.1	0.8	#
80003	17 Sep 1983	31.1	17	7.66	2.3	0.42	2.1	17.7	140.6	19.4	62.3	58.4	1.6	#
80003	26 Nov 1984	58.0	45	6.46	1.3	0.22	0.0	3.3	128.3	42.0	72.4	68.2	1.2	#
80003	14 Aug 1985	34.8	19	7.65	1.4	0.49	0.0	15.1	140.1	26.0	74.7	70.9	1.5	#
80003	22 Aug 1985	68.8	48	7.51	4.3	0.28	1.1	18.6	142.5	59.7	86.8	77.7	1.5	#
80003	26 Aug 1985	56.4	26	6.88	4.0	0.28	2.8	12.2	134.4	43.2	76.6	71.1	1.5	#
80003	30 Aug 1985	54.8	25	5.67	4.3	0.23	2.3	8.1	130.8	34.7	63.3	58.9	1.5	#
80003	13 Nov 1985	30.6	14	5.85	2.6	0.17	0.4	1.3	125.9	17.3	56.5	56.3	1.1	#
80003	15 Nov 1985	38.3	21	7.18	2.6	0.26	0.0	15.3	140.3	21.8	56.8	53.0	1.0	#
80003	30 Nov 1985	92.8	21	7.31	1.2	0.30	0.1	0.8	125.7	57.4	61.9	54.5	0.9	#
80003	21 Jan 1986	30.3	10	4.92	0.6	0.43	0.0	7.6	132.6	14.3	47.2	45.3	1.5	#
80003	26 Jan 1986	24.1	9	5.68	1.5	0.23	0.5	1.6	126.1	15.9	66.1	65.8	0.8	#
80003	19 Apr 1986	50.7	31	5.93	5.6	0.14	2.8	1.9	124.1	40.8	80.5	78.4	1.5	#
80003	27 Apr 1986	23.5	9	3.85	2.6	0.19	0.0	2.6	127.6	13.5	57.3	56.7	2.0	#
80003	29 Apr 1986	32.0	27	5.74	3.6	0.21	0.6	9.7	134.1	18.4	57.4	55.1	2.8	#
80003	30 Jul 1986	36.8	31	6.24	4.4	0.23	9.6	10.2	125.6	28.6	77.6	77.4	3.5	#
80003	27 Sep 1982	38.8	11	7.31	2.1	0.45	0.0	5.7	130.7	24.9	64.3	62.9	3.2	#
80003	19 Aug 1985	35.4	22	6.17	2.1	0.34	0.0	17.7	142.7	24.7	69.9	65.5	1.5	#
a mean												62.1		
g mean					1.9	0.27							1.4	
83002	14 Sep 1965	59.0	28	67.18	7.6	1.67	1.2	1.4	125.2	46.7	79.2	75.7	—	
83002	8 Oct 1967	50.3	20	51.76	2.6	6.93	0.0	24.1	149.1	29.4	58.5	50.1	—	
a mean												62.9		
g mean					4.5	3.40							—	

Catch	Date	*P* mm	*D* h	Q_p m^3s^{-1}	*LAG* h	*BF* m^3s^{-1}	*SMD* mm	*API5* mm	*CWI* mm	*R/O* mm	*PR* %	*SPR* %	*Tp(0)* h	
84002	11 Dec 1964	48.7	11	14.94	2.5	0.73	0.0	6.9	131.9	27.6	56.7	52.9	2.9	#
84002	24 Jun 1965	35.7	12	14.59	3.0	0.78	0.0	15.6	140.6	22.1	62.0	58.1	2.5	#
84002	14 Sep 1965	60.4	32	15.48	2.6	0.23	3.0	0.2	122.2	44.0	72.8	69.8	2.0	#
84002	1 Mar 1971	28.6	10	9.98	4.0	0.44	0.0	6.4	131.4	17.9	62.7	61.1	2.3	#
a mean												60.5		
g mean					3.0	0.49							2.4	
84008	1 Oct 1967	19.5	8	20.12	3.2	2.53	0.0	4.4	129.4	9.0	46.1	44.1	2.8	#
84008	8 Oct 1967	37.3	19	28.16	5.0	2.47	0.0	12.2	137.2	27.9	74.7	71.8	—	
84008	25 Oct 1967	38.1	32	24.07	10.2	2.12	0.0	8.0	133.0	21.0	55.2	52.6	3.2	#
84008	22 Dec 1967	18.5	23	26.91	4.8	2.13	0.0	3.6	128.6	16.5	89.0	88.9	3.5	#
84008	4 May 1968	66.8	43	35.95	8.8	1.32	2.0	9.1	132.1	44.6	66.8	60.4	—	
84008	2 Jul 1968	47.7	23	24.20	3.2	1.38	53.5	13.3	84.8	16.0	33.6	40.3	3.9	#
84008	21 Dec 1968	19.6	21	17.03	4.3	1.20	0.0	2.4	127.4	10.0	50.9	49.5	3.5	#
a mean												58.2		
g mean					5.1	1.80							3.3	
84012	31 Oct 1965	59.5	37	122.82	6.3	13.78	0.2	13.4	138.2	33.4	56.2	48.1	4.9	#
84012	13 Aug 1966	48.4	19	113.19	6.4	6.33	18.1	4.1	111.0	23.4	48.4	48.1	4.7	#
84012	17 Dec 1966	48.8	22	166.93	9.1	10.34	0.0	3.2	128.2	33.7	69.0	66.1	6.8	#
84012	19 Dec 1966	29.6	18	112.44	6.9	14.67	0.0	18.8	143.8	18.8	63.4	58.1	5.9	#
84012	8 Oct 1967	42.5	19	116.29	12.1	10.92	0.0	15.4	140.4	32.6	76.7	72.6	—	
84012	4 May 1968	66.1	43	113.17	6.2	9.68	2.0	5.6	128.6	35.8	54.2	47.5	—	
a mean												56.8		
g mean					7.6	10.58							5.5	
84022	4 Nov 1971	24.2	15	31.82	6.2	2.76	0.0	2.2	127.2	9.4	38.7	38.2	3.8	#
84022	18 Dec 1971	17.9	12	21.56	4.0	2.19	0.1	0.3	125.2	4.2	23.2	23.1	2.7	#
84022	12 Jan 1972	24.0	10	50.82	4.2	6.80	0.0	14.7	139.7	10.8	45.0	41.3	—	
84022	11 Dec 1972	32.9	13	53.92	5.0	3.71	0.0	4.7	129.7	14.4	43.9	42.7	—	
84022	24 Nov 1973	16.6	5	19.48	2.9	2.13	0.0	0.6	125.6	2.7	16.2	16.1	2.8	#
84022	29 Jan 1974	76.5	37	52.59	5.3	3.95	0.0	5.7	130.7	33.7	44.1	37.1	—	
84022	12 Sep 1974	22.9	15	25.08	5.2	1.62	1.1	1.9	125.8	4.6	20.0	19.8	2.2	#
a mean												31.2		
g mean					4.6	2.98							2.8	
85002	13 Oct 1967	19.1	12	86.22	4.2	8.98	0.0	6.4	131.4	11.4	59.7	58.1	5.6	#
85002	4 May 1968	40.5	30	104.50	7.3	12.10	0.0	10.8	135.8	26.6	65.6	62.6	3.5	#
85002	9 Oct 1968	32.2	21	80.47	5.9	3.79	4.1	1.5	122.4	16.2	50.4	51.0	4.4	#
85002	11 Oct 1968	31.3	22	103.64	5.8	10.46	0.0	10.6	135.6	17.4	55.7	53.0	3.9	#
a mean												56.2		
g mean					5.7	8.10							4.3	
96001	8 Nov 1985	39.9	33	119.68	5.9	5.95	0.0	8.9	133.9	35.0	87.7	85.5	3.9	#
96001	10 Jun 1986	38.5	21	139.32	4.1	4.09	5.6	3.4	122.8	31.8	82.6	83.2	5.5	#
96001	9 Feb 1987	39.1	70	51.45	10.3	2.86	0.0	2.2	127.2	25.4	65.0	64.4	6.5	#
96001	6 Jun 1987	35.7	121	20.73	13.7	0.60	23.0	0.2	102.2	16.0	44.8	50.5	—	
96001	15 Jul 1987	34.9	52	44.24	16.6	1.35	8.4	0.8	117.4	18.9	54.1	56.0	8.5	#
96001	20 Nov 1987	37.3	85	46.65	7.3	4.57	0.0	5.2	130.2	25.6	68.7	67.4	5.7	#
a mean												67.8		
g mean					8.6	2.52							5.8	
202004	26 Nov 1995				1.35								0.25	
202004	8 Jan 1996				1.25								1.625	
202004	9 Feb 1996				1.5								2.875	
202004	24 Oct 1996				2.0								1.625	
202004	26 Oct 1996				2.0								1.875	
202004	3 Dec 1996				8.0								5.75	
202004	18 Jan 1997				4.5								4.375	
202004	1 Mar 1997				2.25								1.875	
g mean					2.31								1.90	
202005	26 Nov 1995				2.5								1.375	
202005	8 Jan 1996				3.0								3.625	
202005	9 Feb 1996				5.25								5.75	

Catch	Date	P	D	Q_p	LAG	BF	SMD	API5	CWI	R/O	PR	SPR	Tp(0)
		mm	h	m^3s^{-1}	h	m^3s^{-1}	mm	mm	mm	mm	%	%	h
202005	24 Oct 1996				2.0								2.375
202005	26 Oct 1996				1.25								1.125
202005	3 Dec 1996				7.5								4.125
202005	18 Jan 1997				6.5								3.125
202005	1 Mar 1997				2.0								1.125
g mean					3.15								2.40
202006	26 Nov 1995				2.1								0.5
202006	8 Jan 1996				2.25								1.25
202006	9 Feb 1996				1.0								2.5
202006	24 Oct 1996				0.25								0.125
202006	3 Dec 1996				8.5								6.5
202006	18 Jan 1997				2.75								2.125
202006	1 Mar 1997				2.5								2.125
g mean					1.83								1.28
203046	25 Aug 1986				6.6								6.5
203046	14 Nov 1986				3.7								4.5
203046	15 Nov 1986				5.5								3.5
203046	15 Aug 1987				5.0								4.5
203046	25 Oct 1988				6.0								5.5
203046	3 Dec 1988				1.56								2.5
203046	12 Aug 1989				2.87								3.5
203046	6 Feb 1990				6.5								4.5
203046	27 Oct 1990				3.62								5.5
203046	18 Mar 1991				6.7								2.5
203046	30 Oct 1991				4.0								5.5
203046	22 Dec 1991				3.1								3.5
203046	24 Oct 1992				6.7								5.5
203046	15 Jan 1993				2.3								2.5
203046	23 Jan 1993				4.66								4.5
203046	23 Jul 1993				3.03								2.5
203046	8 Dec 1993				5.34								7.5
g mean					4.21								4.14
203049	25 Aug 1986				3.35								3.5
203049	14 Nov 1986				4.49								3.5
203049	15 Nov 1986				5.0								2.5
203049	15 Aug 1987				5.5								4.5
203049	17 Aug 1987				6.0								3.5
203049	6 Feb 1990				6.25								3.5
203049	18 Mar 1991				4.0								3.5
203049	29 Oct 1991				4.25								4.5
203049	30 Oct 1991				8.5								8.5
203049	15 Jan 1993				3.1								3.5
203049	23 Jan 1993				3.9								3.5
203049	23 Jul 1993				5.0								5.5
203049	8 Dec 1993				7.1								8.5
g mean					4.91								4.21
203050	27 Dec 1977				3.75								5.5
203050	19 Jan 1978				3.65								3.25
203050	3 Feb 1978				4.25								4.75
203050	14 Mar 1978				5.75								4.625
203050	4 Dec 1978				4.35								3.5
203050	3 Nov 1979				4.30								2.5
203050	27 Jan 1980				2.75								2.5
203050	23 Oct 1980				5.25								3.25
203050	13 Dec 1980				4.35								3.5
203050	14 Dec 1980				3.45								3.5
203050	13 May 1981				3.25								2.5
203050	21 Jul 1981				8.0								4.75
203050	23 Sep 1981				6.05								3.5
203050	23 Nov 1981				3.1								1.325
203050	12 Mar 1982				2.85								1.5

Catch	Date	P mm	D h	Q_p $m^3 s^{-1}$	LAG h	BF $m^3 s^{-1}$	SMD mm	API5 mm	CWI mm	R/O mm	PR %	SPR %	Tp(0) h
203050	24 Dec 1984				4.45								2.75
203050	12 Nov 1994				4.0								2.5
203050	10 Jan 1995				5.0								1.5
203050	27 Jan 1995				4.7								1.5
g mean					4.23								2.84
203094	23 Dec 1984				4.0								3.5
203094	7 Sep 1985				4.6								0.5
203094	25 Aug 1986				4.9								1.5
203094	24 Nov 1986				3.0								0.5
203094	4 Dec 1986				4.0								2.5
203094	1 Mar 1987				2.4								3.5
203094	19 Aug 1987				5.0								0.5
203094	1 Sep 1987				2.5								2.5
203094	15 Sep 1987				2.0								2.5
203094	15 Feb 1988				3.25								2.5
203094	27 Nov 1988				4.0								5.5
203094	15 Oct 1990				4.4								2.5
203094	6 Mar 1992				4.57								4.5
203094	24 Sep 1992				6.0								4.5
203094	24 Oct 1992				4.6								3.5
203094	9 Nov 1992				2.25								4.5
g mean					3.66								2.24
203095	23 Dec 1984				3.75								3.5
203095	7 Sep 1985				6.87								1.5
203095	25 Aug 1986				7.11								6.5
203095	24 Nov 1986				4.5								2.5
203095	4 Dec 1986				4.8								2.5
203095	1 Mar 1987				2.4								2.5
203095	20 Aug 1987				7.26								2.5
203095	1 Sep 1987				5.5								4.5
203095	15 Sep 1987				6.5								4.5
203095	15 Feb 1988				4.25								2.5
203095	27 Nov 1988				3.25								2.5
203095	29 Jan 1990				4.25								7.5
203095	15 Oct 1990				5.4								6.5
203095	6 Mar 1992				4.8								5.5
203095	24 Sep 1992				5.4								4.5
203095	24 Oct 1992				2.85								2.5
203095	9 Nov 1992				3.25								4.5
g mean					4.60								3.55
204003	4 Oct 1995				4.75								3.25
204003	6 Oct 1995				4.25								4.5
204003	24 Nov 1995				5.5								4.625
204003	26 Nov 1995				3.5								6.5
204003	9 Feb 1996				3.5								0.625
204003	20 Aug 1996				1.5								0.75
204003	7 Dec 1996				5.5								3.875
204003	7 Mar 1997				3.0								2.25
204003	27 Mar 1997				7.5								8.375
g mean					3.98								2.91
204004	24 Nov 1995				1.75								0.875
204004	26 Nov 1995				1.75								0.875
204004	9 Feb 1996				8.25								8.625
204004	20 Aug 1996				1.5								1.875
204004	22 Aug 1996				1.75								1.125
204004	19 Feb 1997				6.5								5.875
204004	7 Mar 1997				2.25								1.375
204004	27 Mar 1997				4.25								3.875
g mean					2.83								2.14

Catch	Date	P mm	D h	Q_p $m^3 s^{-1}$	LAG h	BF $m^3 s^{-1}$	SMD mm	API5 mm	CWI mm	R/O mm	PR %	SPR %	Tp(0) h
205101	19 Mar 1991				1.5								0.625
205101	5 Mar 1992				1.25								0.875
205101	12 Apr 1992				0.75								0.125
205101	14 Apr 1992				1.0								0.125
205101	25 Oct 1992				2.75								1.625
205101	26 Jan 1993				0.5								0.125
205101	5 Oct 1995				1.25								0.125
205101	26 Nov 1995				1.5								0.875
205101	4 Nov 1996				1.25								1.375
205101	24 Nov 1996				0.75								1.375
g mean					1.13								0.45
205105	3 Jan 1994				2.25								0.125
205105	10 May 1994				1.5								0.125
205105	3 Dec 1994				0.5								0.625
205105	5 Dec 1994				0.75								0.875
205105	13 Dec 1994				1.75								1.125
205105	21 Jan 1995				1.75								0.625
205105	9 Feb 1995				3.0								2.125
205105	16 Oct 1996				1.0								1.125
205105	31 Oct 1996				1.25								1.325
205105	28 Nov 1996				1.75								2.125
g mean					1.38								0.73
206007	3 Oct 1995				3.5								1.25
206007	5 Oct 1995				3.0								1.625
206007	25 Nov 1995				1.25								0.325
206007	9 Feb 1996				2.25								0.825
206007	11 Feb 1996				2.0								0.125
206007	18 Mar 1996				2.75								0.625
206007	17 Oct 1996				2.75								1.875
206007	5 Nov 1996				2.25								0.125
206007	24 Nov 1996				2.25								2.375
206007	28 Nov 1996				2.5								0.625
g mean					2.37								0.66
236052	5 Oct 1995				5.7								5.125
236052	25 Nov 1995				5.0								4.5
236052	26 Nov 1995				5.25								4.125
236052	8 Feb 1996				4.85								4.75
236052	22 Aug 1996				6.0								3.625
236052	28 Nov 1996				2.0								3.25
236052	7 Mar 1997				2.5								2.125
g mean					4.17								3.79
236053	5 Oct 1995				4.0								4.25
236053	24 Nov 1995				3.0								3.45
236053	26 Nov 1995				2.5								4.375
236053	8 Feb 1996				3.5								2.5
236053	22 Aug 1996				2.0								7.25
236053	28 Nov 1996				2.25								8.125
236053	18 Jan 1997				2.5								0.125
236053	20 Feb 1997				2.25								7.875
236053	7 Mar 1997				2.5								2.25
g mean					2.66								3.02

Appendix B Background to the FSR rainfall-runoff method

B.1 Unit hydrograph and losses model

The 3-parameter unit hydrograph and losses model forms the core of the FSR rainfall-runoff method. It is therefore no surprise that most of the updates to the method over the past 25 years have been concerned with improving the model parameter estimation equations. Some equations have been revised several times. The most recent updates for the FEH were primarily to use catchment information available in digital form. Derivation of the new estimation equations for unit hydrograph time-to-peak are summarised in Section B.2. The new equation for percentage runoff originates from conversion of the percentage runoff model of FSSR16 (IH, 1985) to use *URBEXT* in place of $URBAN_{FSR}$.

Tables B.1 to B.3 present the recommended estimation equations for the three model parameters, together with a summary of earlier equations that users might encounter when interpreting past flood calculations.

B.2 Derivation of new unit hydrograph time-to-peak estimation equations

Prior to the FEH, the standard procedure for estimating unit hydrograph time-to-peak on ungauged catchments used a relationship linking *Tp*(0) to catchment characteristics abstracted manually from 1:25000 and 1:50000 OS maps and a map of average annual rainfall. Using the Institute of Hydrology's Digital Terrain Model (IHDTM) to define catchment boundaries allows catchment descriptors to be defined with greater subtlety, and to be calculated automatically, from digital data sets. The equation linking *Tp*(0) to catchment information was, therefore, reworked to use digital catchment descriptors (Marshall, submitted). The opportunity was also taken to revise the equations linking *Tp*(0) to catchment lag *LAG*, to give a single equation that would be applicable to all catchments.

B.2.1 Data

A data set of 204 British catchments was constructed consisting of *Tp*(0) values for 1822 flood events, 1786 of which had associated *LAG* values, and relevant catchment descriptors. The data set incorporated a greater variety of catchments than were used for previous analyses.

The *Tp*(0) and *LAG* values originated from several sources:

- Events from 102 gauging stations published in the FSR/FSSR16, converting *Tp*(1) values to *Tp*(0) values using Equation 2.5;
- Additional events from these gauging stations;
- Events from 87 further gauging stations;
- Events from 15 small catchments specifically instrumented for IH Report 124 (Marshall and Bayliss, 1994).

The catchment descriptors consisted of one area index, three drainage path length indices, two catchment slope indices, two rainfall indices, five catchment wetness indices and four land-use indices. The descriptors were all calculated within the IHDTM-derived catchment boundaries.

Table B.1 *Estimation equations for unit hydrograph time-to-peak, Tp*

Source	Equation	r²	fse	n
FSR (NERC, 1975) Formulated in terms of 1-hour unit hydrograph in FSR I.6.5.3; problems in application to small, permeable and/or part-urban catchments; FSSR6 (IH, 1978a) looking at small catchments and FSSR5 (IH, 1979a) looking at urbanised catchments failed to find better alternatives.	$Tp(1) = 46.6\ S1085^{-0.38}\ RSMD^{0.40}\ MSL^{0.14}\ (1+URBAN_{FSR})^{-1.99}$	0.78	1.41	130
	$Tp(1) = 0.9\ LAG$	0.96	1.15[(1)]	129
FSSR16 (IH, 1985) Standardised on *Tp*(0) following *IH Report 94* (Boorman, 1985); replaced *RSMD* with more easily-derived *SAAR*; problems remained with application to small, permeable and/or part-urban catchments.	$Tp(0) = 283\ S1085^{-0.33}\ SAAR_{4170}{}^{-0.54}\ MSL^{0.23}\ (1 + URBAN_{FSR})^{-2.2}$	0.74	1.48	175
	$Tp(0) = 0.604\ LAG^{1.144}$	0.93	1.23[(1)]	175
IH Report 124 **(Marshall and Bayliss, 1994)** From study aimed specifically at small catchments; data set chosen to include particular combinations of catchment characteristics to compensate for deficiencies in previous data sets; new equation effectively allows continued use of FSSR16 equation for completely rural catchments; effect of urbanisation is proportionally greater for catchments that naturally respond quickly.	$Tp(0) = Tp(0)_{RURAL}\ (1 + URBAN_{FSR})^{-b}$ where $Tp(0)_{RURAL} = 283\ S1085^{-0.33}\ SAAR_{4170}{}^{-0.54}\ MSL^{0.23}$ and $b = 1.0 + 3.0 \exp[-(Tp(0)_{RURAL}/7.0)^2]$	n/a	n/a	n/a
	$Tp(0) = LAG^{0.94}$ [for $AREA < 25\ km^2$]	0.98	1.12[(1)]	24
*** For use with digital data sets (Marshall, 1999)** Equation for *Tp*(0) from manually-derived catchment characteristics updated for use with digitally-derived catchment descriptors; equation for *Tp*(0) from *LAG* updated to give one equation applicable to all catchments.	$Tp(0) = 4.270\ DPSBAR^{-0.35}\ PROPWET^{-0.80}\ DPLBAR^{0.54}(1+URBEXT)^{-5.77}$	0.74	1.85	204
	$Tp(0) = 0.879\ LAG^{0.951}$	0.73	1.48	1786

* current recommendation

(1) not strictly comparable since *LAG* is itself to be estimated from gauged rainfall and level / flow data

B.2.2 Tp(0) from catchment lag

Linear regression was used to link *Tp*(0) to *LAG*, both of which were logarithmically transformed prior to the regression, leading to:

$$\ln Tp(0) = a + b \ln LAG \tag{B.1}$$

which, on exponentiation, yields:

$$Tp(0) = e^{a}\ LAG^{b} \tag{B.2}$$

The data were analysed as 1786 individual events, both in the form outlined above and in the reverse form, linking *LAG* to *Tp*(0). The two approaches yielded slightly different equations. Because both variables have estimation errors associated with them, a compromise equation was derived by averaging the two equations:

$$Tp(0) = 0.879\ LAG^{0.951} \tag{2.9}$$

with coefficient of determination $r^2 = 0.73$ and factorial standard error $fse = 1.48$. The value of *fse* means that 68% of *Tp*(0) estimates can be expected to lie within a factor of 1.48 of the true value.

Table B.2 *Estimation models for perecentage runoff PR and standard percentage runoff SPR*

Source	Equation	r^2	see	n
FSR (NERC, 1975) Given in FSR I.6.5.8; constant additive effect of urban; problems found with application to small, permeable and/or part-urban catchments.	$PR = SPR + DPR$ where: $DPR = 0.22\ (CWI - 125) + 0.10\ (P - 10)$ and: $SPR = 95.5\ SOIL + 12\ URBAN_{FSR}$	0.43 0.43	15.09 15.09	1447 1447
FSSR5 (IH, 1979a) Following from *IH Report 63* (Packman, 1980); urban adjustment applied after *SPR* (15-51%) and *DPR* calculated for rural catchment; provides more realistic allowance for increased response from urban areas.	$PR = PR_{RURAL}\ (1.0 - 0.3\ URBAN_{FSR}) + 70\ (0.3\ URBAN_{FSR})$ where $PR_{RURAL} = SPR + DPR$ and $DPR = 0.28\ (CWI - 125) + 0.10\ (P - 10) - 1.9$ and $SPR = 102.4\ SOIL$	0.39 0.39	15.40 15.40	1074 1447
FSSR13 (IH, 1983c)	$SPR = 78.0 - 79.2\ BFI$	0.69	9.01[(1)]	104
*** FSSR16 (IH, 1985)** Following from *IH Report 94* (Boorman, 1985); problems found in application to highly impermeable/permeable catchments where range of *SPR* (10-53%) too limited.	$PR = PR_{RURAL}\ (1.0 - 0.3\ URBAN_{FSR}) + 70\ (0.3\ URBAN_{FSR})$ where $PR_{RURAL} = SPR + DPR_{CWI} + DPR_{RAIN}$ and $DPR_{CWI} = 0.25\ (CWI - 125)$ **and** $DPR_{RAIN} = 0.45\ (P - 40)^{0.7}$ **[for $P > 40$ mm],** $= 0$ **[for $P \leq 40$ mm]** and $SPR = 10\ SOIL1 + 30\ SOIL2 + 37\ SOIL3 + 47\ SOIL4 + 53\ SOIL5$	0.46 0.46	14.90 14.90	1851 1851
	$SPR = 72.0 - 66.5\ BFI$	0.59	8.97[(1)]	166
**** IH Report 126* (Boorman *et al.*, 1995)** From study to derive HOST soil classification; better reflects variation in *SPR* (2-60%) between different soil types.	$SPR = SPRHOST = \Sigma_1^{29}\ SPR_i\ HOST_i$ i.e. $SPR = SPR_1 HOST_1 + SPR_2 HOST_2 + \ldots + SPR_{29} HOST_{29}$	n/a	10.00	170
*** For use with digital data sets (1999)** Manually-derived $URBAN_{FSR}$ substituted with digitally-derived *URBEXT* in FSSR16 PR model.	$PR = PR_{RURAL}\ (1.0 - 0.615\ URBEXT) + 70\ (0.615\ URBEXT)$ i.e. $URBAN_{FSR} = 2.05\ URBEXT$ (see **5** 6.5.3)	n/a	n/a	n/a

* current recommendation

(1) not strictly comparable, since *BFI* is itself to be estimated from gauged daily flow data

Table B.3 *Estimation equations for baseflow, BF*

Source	Equation	r^2	see	n
FSR (NERC, 1975) Given in FSR I.6.5.11.	$BF = \{0.000326\ (CWI - 125) + 0.00074\ RSMD + 0.003\}\ AREA$	0.45	0.02	1447
*** FSSR16 (IH, 1985)** Following from *IH Report 94* (Boorman, 1985); *RSMD* replaced with more easily-derived *SAAR*.	$BF = \{33\ (CWI - 125) + 3.0\ SAAR + 5.5\}\ 10^{-5}\ AREA$	0.42	0.03	1851

* current recommendation

B.2.3 Tp(0) from catchment descriptors

Multiple regression was used to link $Tp(0)$ to up to six catchment descriptors (represented here as X_1, X_2, ...). All the variables were logarithmically transformed prior to the regression, leading to:

$$\ln Tp(0) = a + b \ln X_1 + c \ln X_2 = d \ln X_3 + e \ln X_4 \; ... \qquad \text{(B.3)}$$

which, on exponentiation, yields:

$$Tp(0) = e^a X_1^{\,b} X_2^{\,c} X_3^{\,d} X_4^{\,e} ... \qquad \text{(B.4)}$$

Use of a logarithmic transform on an independent variable that can take a zero value is not possible, so the *URBEXT* values were replaced by 1+*URBEXT*. Furthermore, the *URBEXT* values were back-dated to the mean year in which the flood events were recorded using the urban growth model in §6.5.4 of Volume 5.

The data were analysed both as 1822 individual events and as 204 catchment-average values, which were computed as geometric means. The two approaches yielded slightly different best 4-variable equations: models with five or six variables were not found to give useful improvements. Arguments against both approaches can be made: an event-based approach biases the analysis towards catchments able to supply the most $Tp(0)$ values, whilst a catchment-average based analysis gives the same weight to a catchment with one $Tp(0)$ value as it does to one with many values. As a compromise, the final regressions were based on catchment-average $Tp(0)$ values weighted according to the square root of the number of events contributing to the respective values. The best 4-variable equation was:

$$Tp(0) = 4.270\, DPSBAR^{-0.35}\, PROPWET^{-0.80}\, DPLBAR^{0.54}\, (1+URBEXT)^{-5.77} \qquad \text{(2.10)}$$

with coefficient of determination $r^2 = 0.74$ and factorial standard error $fse = 1.85$.

The value of fse means that 68% of $Tp(0)$ estimates can be expected to lie within a factor of 1.85 of the true value. The residuals obtained by subtracting the modelled values from the observed values of $\ln Tp(0)$ show similar regional over- and underestimation patterns to the FSR (Marshall, 1999).

B.3 FSR rainfall statistics

Estimation of the T-year flood requires input of an appropriate design rainfall. Subsection 3.2.2 describes the procedure for assessing the point rainfall depth of the given duration and return period, with reference to the rainfall depth-duration-frequency relationships presented in Volume 2. This section presents the original FSR statistics, which may be of use when attempting to reproduce a past flood estimate.

The T-year D-hour point rainfall $MT\text{-}Dh$ is determined from the FSR rainfall depth-duration-frequency relationships, once the duration and return period of the design storm are known, by the following procedure:

i Calculate 5-year D-hour point rainfall $M5\text{-}Dh$;

ii Scale point $M5\text{-}Dh$ to point $MT\text{-}Dh$.

The steps in the procedure are discussed below, together with relevant comment on related topics. The procedure is illustrated in Example B.1.

B.3.1 Calculation of 5-year D-hour point rainfall M5-Dh

The point *M5*-Dh rainfall is calculated by scaling *M5*-2d (see Section 1 of Appendix C) to the appropriate duration. The scaling factor is read from Table B.4 which shows percentage values of (*M5-D*h/*M5*-2d) for given values of *r* (see §1 of Appendix C) and duration *D*. In manual calculations this should be done by logarithmic interpolation on duration. Thus:

$$M5\text{–}D\text{h} = \frac{M5\text{–}D\text{h}}{M5\text{–}2\text{d}}\ M5\text{–}2\text{d} \qquad \text{(B.5)}$$

B.3.2 Calculation of *T*-year *D*-hour point rainfall *MT-D*h

The point *M*5–*D*h rainfall is calculated by scaling the point *M5-D*h rainfall by an appropriate growth factor *MT*/M5. The growth factor is read from Table B.5 which shows growth factors for given values of *M5* and return period. In manual calculations this should be done by logarithmic interpolation on return period. Thus:

$$M5\text{–}D\text{h (point)} = \frac{MT}{M5}\ M5\text{–}D\text{h} \qquad \text{(B.6)}$$

In the FSR rainfall frequency estimation procedure, growth factors are independent of duration and vary only simply with location, there being different tables for England and Wales (Table B.5a) than for Scotland and Northern Ireland (Table B.5b).

B.4 Quick method for PMF

Following publication of the FSR, there was an urgent requirement to reassess the design floods of many existing reservoirs. Flood estimation software was not generally available, and estimation of the PMF by the FSR rainfall-runoff method required a laborious manual convolution of a triangular unit hydrograph with the PMP after subtraction of losses, and addition of a baseflow, with options for allowances for snowmelt and for increased runoff from frozen ground in the Winter. The quick method for PMF estimation was developed to provide a rapid and easy-to-use preliminary screening method. The quick method was not intended be used as an alternative to the FSR rainfall-runoff method. In particular, the quick method provides only the inflow peak, and does not take into account important effects caused by the presence of the reservoir. For complex or unusual catchment configurations e.g. reservoir cascades, the quick method was not recommended for even initial evaluation.

With flood estimation software readily accessible, the requirement for a quick method no longer exists. However, for completeness, Table B.6 summarises the now-redundant equations for the quick method for PMF, worked through in Example B.2.

Example B.1
Abstraction of T-year D-hour point rainfall *MT-Dh* from FSR rainfall statistics

Catchment: Almond at Craigiehall (19001) (Figure 1 of Appendix C)

Relevant manually-derived catchment characteristics and other information:
M5-2d = 57.0 mm, r = 0.25, D = 13.0 hours (§3.2.1), T_R = 81 years (§3.2.2)

Calculating 5-year D-hour point rainfall *M5-Dh*
M5-Dh(point) is calculated by scaling *M5*-2d to the appropriate duration *D*. The scaling factor (*M5-Dh* / *M5*-2d) appropriate to the storm duration and Jenkinson's *r* value is obtained from Table B.4:

M5-13h / *M5*-2d = 0.66

M5-Dh is calculated using Equation B.5:

M5-Dh = (*M5-Dh* / *M5*-2d) *M5*-2d

M5-13h = 0.66 (57.0)
= 37.6 mm

Calculating *T*-year *D*-hour point rainfall *MT-Dh*
MT-Dh(point) is calculated by scaling *M5-Dh* to the appropriate return period T_R. The growth factor (*MT/M5*) appropriate to the *M5-Dh* value and return period is obtained from Table B.5:

M81/M5 = 1.71

MT-Dh(point) is calculated using Equation B.6:

MT-Dh(point) = (*MT/M5*) *M5-Dh*

M81-13h(point) = 1.71 (37.6)
= 64.3 mm

Table B.4 *Relationship between percentage values of (M5-given duration)/(M5-2d) and r (M5-60min)/(M5-2d)*

r	Duration						
	60-min	*120-min*	*4-hour*	*6-hour*	*12-hour*	*24-hour*	*48-hour*
0.12	12	18	26	33	49	72	106
0.15	15	21	30	37	53	75	106
0.18	18	25	34	41	56	77	106
0.21	21	28	38	45	60	80	106
0.24	24	32	41	48	63	81	106
0.27	27	35	44	51	65	83	106
0.30	30	38	48	54	68	85	106
0.33	33	41	51	57	70	86	106
0.36	36	44	54	60	73	88	106
0.39	39	47	57	63	75	89	106
0.42	42	50	60	66	77	90	106
0.45	45	53	63	68	79	92	106

Table B.5 Growth factors (MT/M5) for (a) England and Wales (b) Scotland and Northern Ireland

(a) England and Wales

M5	Partial duration series		Annual maximum series						
mm	*2M*	*1M*	*M2*	*M10*	*M20*	*M50*	*M100*	*M1000*	*M10000*
0.5	0.52	0.67	0.76	1.14	1.30	1.51	1.70	2.52	3.76
2	0.49	0.65	0.74	1.16	1.32	1.53	1.74	2.60	3.94
5	0.45	0.62	0.72	1.18	1.35	1.56	1.79	2.75	4.28
10	0.43	0.61	0.70	1.21	1.41	1.65	1.91	3.09	5.01
15	0.46	0.62	0.70	1.23	1.44	1.70	1.99	3.32	5.54
20	0.50	0.64	0.72	1.23	1.45	1.73	2.03	3.43	5.80
25	0.52	0.66	0.73	1.22	1.43	1.72	2.01	3.37	5.67
30	0.54	0.68	0.75	1.21	1.41	1.70	1.97	3.27	5.41
40	0.56	0.70	0.77	1.18	1.37	1.64	1.89	3.03	4.86
50	0.58	0.72	0.79	1.16	1.33	1.58	1.81	2.81	4.36
75	0.63	0.76	0.81	1.13	1.27	1.47	1.64	2.37	3.43
100	0.64	0.78	0.83	1.12	1.24	1.40	1.54	2.12	2.92
150	0.64	0.78	0.84	1.11	1.21	1.33	1.45	1.90	2.50
200	0.64	0.78	0.84	1.10	1.30	1.30	1.40	1.79	2.30
500	0.65	0.79	0.85	1.09	1.15	1.20	1.27	1.52	–
1000	0.66	0.80	0.86	1.07	1.12	1.18	1.23	1.42	–

(b) Scotland and Northern Ireland

M5	Partial duration series		Annual maximum series						
mm	*2M*	*1M*	*M2*	*M10*	*M20*	*M50*	*M100*	*M1000*	*M10000*
0.5	0.55	0.68	0.76	1.14	1.30	1.51	1.71	2.54	3.78
2	0.55	0.68	0.76	1.15	1.31	1.54	1.75	2.65	4.01
5	0.54	0.67	0.76	1.16	1.34	1.62	1.86	2.94	4.66
10	0.55	0.68	0.75	1.18	1.38	1.69	1.97	3.25	5.36
15	0.55	0.69	0.75	1.18	1.38	1.70	1.98	3.28	5.44
20	0.56	0.70	0.76	1.18	1.37	1.66	1.93	3.14	5.12
25	0.57	0.71	0.77	1.17	1.36	1.64	1.89	3.03	4.85
30	0.58	0.72	0.78	1.17	1.35	1.61	1.85	2.92	4.60
40	0.59	0.74	0.79	1.16	1.33	1.56	1.77	2.72	4.16
50	0.60	0.75	0.80	1.15	1.30	1.52	1.72	2.57	3.85
75	0.62	0.77	0.82	1.13	1.26	1.45	1.62	2.31	3.30
100	0.63	0.78	0.83	1.12	1.24	1.40	1.54	2.12	2.92
150	0.64	0.79	0.84	1.10	1.20	1.33	1.45	1.90	2.50
200	0.65	0.80	0.85	1.09	1.18	1.30	1.40	1.79	2.30
500	0.66	0.80	0.86	1.08	1.14	1.20	1.27	1.52	–
1000	0.66	0.80	0.86	1.07	1.12	1.18	1.23	1.42	–

Example B.2
Quick method for PMF

Catchment: West Lyn at Lynmouth (IHDTM grid ref. 272400 149450)
(Figure 4 of Appendix C)

Relevant manually-derived catchment characteristics:
$AREA = 23.5\ \text{km}^2$, $S1085 = 29.7\ \text{m km}^{-1}$, $SOIL = 0.38$, $URBAN_{FSR} = 0.000$, $SAAR = 1500$ mm

The PMF is calculated by the quick method using the equation from IH Report 114 (Reed and Field, 1992):

$$PMF = 0.629\ AREA^{0.937}\ S1085^{0.328}\ SOIL^{0.471}\ (1 + URBAN_{FSR})^{2.04}\ SAAR_{4170}^{0.319}$$

$$PMF = 0.629\ (23.5^{0.937})(29.7^{0.328})(0.38^{0.471})(1.0)^{2.04}\ (1500^{0.319})$$

$$= 241\ \text{m}^3\ \text{s}^{-1}$$

Table B.6 *Estimation equations for quick method for PMF*

Source	Equation	r^2	see	n
Farquharson *et al.* (1975) Also presented in *IH Report 49* (Sutcliffe, 1978); derived by applying full method to 80 gauged catchments.	$PMF = 0.835 AREA^{0.878}\ RSMD^{0.724}\ SOIL^{0.533}\ (1+URBAN_{FSR})^{1.308}\ S1085^{0.162}$	0.45 0.42	0.02 0.03	1447 1851
ICE (1978) and ICE (1989) Rapid method based on Farquharson *et al.* (1975); composite graph summarising the range of flood peak intensity expected from impermeable, rural catchments, together with adjustment factors for different terrains or less rare floods.	GRAPH	–	–	–
***IH Report 114* (Reed and Field, 1992)** Following from Farquharson *et al.* (1975); RSMD replaced with more easily-derived SAAR; derived by applying full method to 187 reservoired catchments.	$PMF = 0.629\ AREA^{0.937}\ S1085^{0.328}\ SOIL^{0.471}\ (1+URBAN_{FSR})^{2.04}\ SAAR_{4170}^{0.319}$	0.42	0.03	1851
ICE (1996) Rapid method based on *IH Report 114* (Reed and Field, 1992); equation for flood peak expected from impermeable, rural catchments, together with adjustment factors giving design flood inflows as fractions of rapid method PMF.	$PMF = 0.454\ AREA^{0.937}\ S1085^{0.328}\ SAAR_{4170}^{0.319}$	–	–	–

Appendix C Catchment characteristics and descriptors

C.1 Manually-derived catchment characteristics

Table C.1 provides a summary of the manually-derived FSR catchment characteristics. The summary information includes, for each characteristic, a reference to the original page or figure in the relevant source document, the scale of the map used in the abstraction, and a description of the abstraction method. In deriving several of the catchment characteristics, it was necessary to identify the *main stream.* If there was no obvious main stream, the recommendation was to take the stream draining the largest area.

C.2 Digitally-derived catchment descriptors

Table C.2 provides a summary of the digitally-derived FEH catchment descriptors. The summary information includes, for each descriptor, a cross-reference to the relevant section in Volume 5, which should be referred to for a more detailed explanation.

For multiple reservoir systems and some disparate subcatchment applications, there may be difficulties in automatic derivation of some digital catchment descriptors, particularly those required for estimating catchment response time. For instance, in a two-reservoir cascade, catchment descriptors are readily available for the subcatchment to the upper reservoir, and for the entire catchment to the lower reservoir, but not for the direct subcatchment to the lower reservoir.

Direct subcatchment descriptors such as *AREA*, *URBEXT*, *HOST* classes, *SAAR*, *PROPWET* and *EMP*s can be quickly derived by simple area-weighting:

$$X_{DIRECT}\,AREA_{DIRECT} = X_{TOTAL}\,AREA_{TOTAL} - X_{UPPER}\,AREA_{UPPER} \qquad (C.1)$$

where X is the catchment descriptor; the subscripts *DIRECT*, *TOTAL* and *UPPER* refer to the direct subcatchment to the lower reservoir, the entire catchment to the lower reservoir and the subcatchment to the upper reservoir, respectively. However, *DPLBAR* and *DPSBAR* are more problematic. Therefore, for calculation of unit hydrograph time-to-peak, the recommended guidance is to take appropriate catchment descriptors for the main tributary or a *typical* tributary.

C.3 HOST classification

C.3.1 Background

The Hydrology Of Soil Types or HOST classification is the product of a collaboration between the Institute of Hydrology (IH), the Soil Survey and Land Research Centre (SSLRC), the Macauley Land Use Research Institute (MLURI), and the Department of Agriculture of Northern Ireland (DANI). Derivation of the classification is described in detail in *IH Report 126* (Boorman *et al.*, 1995). The classification is available as digital data sets in raster form at 1 km and 100 m resolution. Because the classification is series-based, many HOST classes may be present within each 1 km or 100 m cell. Therefore, although the classification can be represented as a map showing only the dominant HOST class (Plate C.1), this disguises the refinement of the parent data set.

Table C.1 *Manually-derived catchment characteristics*

Catchment characteristic (units)	**Reference**	**Map scale**	**Definition & method**
AREA (km^2)	FSR I (296)	1:25K or 1:50K	Catchment area Measure using sketched catchment boundary and planimeter.
MSL (km)	FSR I (296-299)	1:25K	Mainstream length Set dividers at 4 mm and work upstream on blue line denoting main channel (channel draining largest area); remember to calibrate dividers: MSL = 0.1 N, where N is no. of steps.
*S*1085 (m km^{-1})	FSR I (286-299)	1:25K	10-85% channel slope Determine *MSL*, then find heights h_{10} and h_{85} at contours 10% and 85% of MSL upstream from starting point: $S1085 = (h_{85} - h_{10}) / (0.75\ MSL)$.
$URBAN_{FSR}$	FSR I (305)	1:50K	Urban index, i.e. fraction of catchment in urban development Measure built-up areas (flesh-coloured) using planimeter: $URBAN_{FSR}$ = sum of built-up areas / *AREA*.
SOIL	FSR I (303-305, 312) FSR Fig I.4.18 FSSR7 (IH,1978b)	1:625K	Soil index i.e. the weighted sum of the individual soil class fractions *SOIL*1 to *SOIL*5 from WRAP map Measure fraction of catchment within each soil class using planimeter: *SOIL* = 0.15 *SOIL*1+ 0.30 *SOIL*2+ 0.40 *SOIL*3+ 0.45 *SOIL*4+ 0.50 *SOIL*5.
$HOST_{1,\ldots,29}$	IH Report 126 (Boorman *et al.*, 1995)	1:250K	Individual soil class fractions $HOST_1$ to $HOST_{29}$ Measure fraction of catchment within each soil map unit using squared paper overlay; collate HOST classes for each map unit; calculate fraction of catchment in each HOST class (see §C.3).
$SAAR_{4170}$ (mm)	FSR I (305-306) FSR Fig II.3.1	1:625K	Standard average annual rainfall for period 1941-70 Grid point sampling or weighted areas technique.
RSMD (mm)	FSR I (306-312)	–	5-year 1-day catchment rainfall less effective mean *SMD* Find *M*5-24h using *M*5-2d and *r* in Table 4 of Appendix B; convert *M*5-24h to *M*5-1d point rainfall by: *M*5-1d = *M*5-24h/1.11; calculate *ARF* by: $ARF = \exp(-0.020\ AREA)^{0.25}$; then: $RSMD = ARF\ (M5\text{-}1d) - SMDBAR_{FSR}$.
*M*5-2d (mm)	FSR Fig II.3.2	1:625K	2-day rainfall of 5-year return period Grid point sampling or weighted areas technique.
r	FSR Fig II.3.5	1:625K	Jenkinson's *r* — the ratio of *M*5-60min to *M*5-2d Grid point sampling or weighted areas technique.
$SMDBAR_{FSR}$ (mm)	FSR Fig I.4.19	1:2M	Effective mean soil moisture deficit Grid point sampling or weighted areas technique.
EM-2h (mm)	FSR Fig II.4.1	1:2M	Estimated maximum 2-hour rainfall Grid point sampling or weighted areas technique.
EM-24h (mm)	FSR Fig II.4.2	1:2M	Estimated maximum 24-hour rainfall Grid point sampling or weighted areas technique.
EM-25d (mm)	FSR Fig II.3.4 FSR Tab I.6.22	1:2M	Estimated maximum 25-day rainfall Find *M*5-25d, mapped as % of *SAAR* by grid point sampling or weighted areas technique; convert to *EM*-25d using *EM* growth factors.

Table C.2 Digitally-derived catchment descriptors

Catchment descriptor (units)	Reference	Definition
AREA (km^2)	FEH **5** 2	Catchment area Catchment drainage area derived using an IHDTM-derived boundary
DPLBAR (km)	FEH **5** 3.2.2	Mean drainage path length Mean of distances between each node (on 50 m grid) and catchment outlet
DPSBAR ($m\ km^{-1}$)	FEH **5** 3.4.1	Mean drainage path slope Mean of all internodal slopes
URBEXT	FEH **5** 6.5	Extent of urban and suburban land cover (see **5** 6.5.3)
$HOST_{1,.....29}$	FEH **5** 5.4	Individual soil class fractions $HOST_1$ to $HOST_{29}$ (see Section C.3)
SAAR (mm)	FEH **5** 5.2	Standard average annual rainfall for period 1961-90
PROPWET	FEH **5** 5.7.2	Proportion of time when SMD was below 6 mm during period 1961-90
EM-2h (mm)	FEH **4** Fig 4.1	Estimated maximum 2-hour rainfall
EM-24h (mm)	FEH **4** Fig 4.2	Estimated maximum 24-hour rainfall
EM-25d (mm)	FEH **4** Fig 4.3	Estimated maximum 25-day rainfall

In particular applications, especially on small catchments, users may wish to purchase the 100 m resolution data set (held by SSLRC, MLURI and DANI), or manually derive the HOST classes on the study catchment. It may also be worth investigating whether the soils in that region of the country have been mapped at a larger scale e.g. the 1:25K soil maps available for some regions of the UK.

C.3.2 Manual derivation of HOST classes

The procedure to determine the proportions of a catchment in each HOST class has three steps:

i Determine the fraction of the catchment in each map unit, by overlaying the catchment boundary on the appropriate sheet of the 1:250 000 national soil map. Sufficient accuracy is obtained by using a squared paper overlay or a planimeter;

ii Collate the component HOST classes for each of these map units from Table C.3. Table C.3 gives the typical percentages of HOST classes found in associations, and is split into separate lists for England and Wales, Scotland and Northern Ireland;

iii Calculate the overall fraction of each HOST class in the catchment by combining the information from (i) and (ii) above.

This procedure is illustrated in Example C.1 (below). Summing the HOST class fractions provides a check that no errors have crept into the arithmetic. Where the catchment contains an unclassified urban area or lake, it may be possible to guess the underlying association; otherwise it may be necessary to eliminate the subarea by adjusting the other association amounts e.g. by an area-weighted factor. HOST class fractions less than 0.5% can be ignored, but it is then necessary to adjust allocations to ensure that the total of 100% is met, e.g. by adding to the largest class fraction.

Example C.1
Manual derivation of HOST classes

Catchment: Rhymney at Gilfach Bargoed (IHDTM grid ref. 315050 200250) (Plate C.2)

Map unit	**Fraction of catchment** %	**Component HOST classes** (fraction in map unit)
92c + U	7.69	24 (100.00)
311d	0.65	4 (23.08), 15 (76.92)
611d	32.07	4 (55.56), 17 (33.33), 21 (11.11)
631a	2.00	4 (60.00), 15 (40.00)
654c	7.83	15 (100.00)
713f	6.9	6 (20.00), 21 (26.67), 24 (53.33)
721c	42.86	10 (11.11), 26 (88.89)
Total	100.00	

HOST class	**Components** (fraction of HOST class in map unit x fraction of map unit in catchment)	**Fraction of catchment** %
4	23.08 (0.0065) + 60.00 (0.0200) + 55.56 (0.3207)	19.17
6	20.00 (0.0690)	1.38
10	11.11 (0.4266)	4.71
15	76.92 (0.0065) + 40.00 (0.0200) + 100.00 (0.0783)	9.13
17	33.33 (0.3207)	10.69
21	26.67 (0.0690) + 11.11 (0.3207)	5.4
24	100.00 (0.0769) + 53.33 (0.0690)	11.37
26	88.89 (0.4266)	38.16
Total		100.00

Plate C.1 Dominant HOST class mapped on a 1 km grid

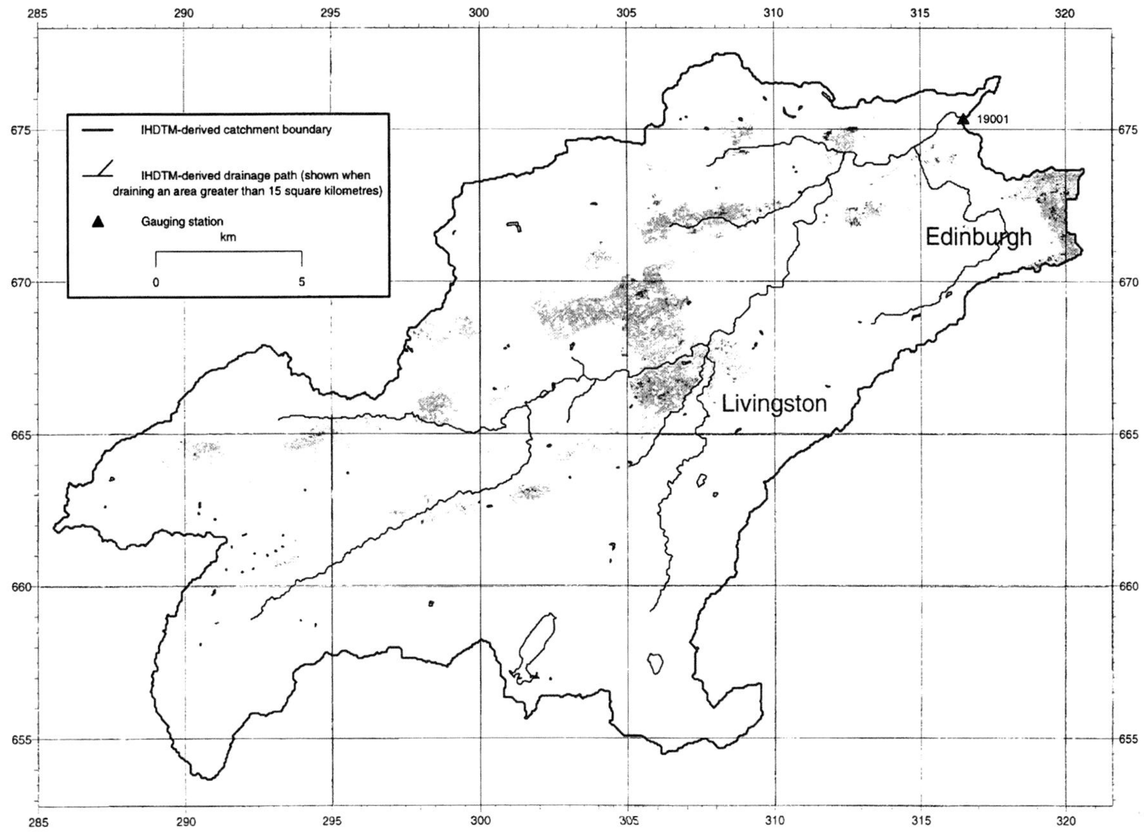

IHDTM-derived catchment boundary
IHDTM-derived drainage path (shown when draining an area greater than 15 square kilometres)
Gauging station
km
0
5
19001
Edinburgh
Livingston
285
290
295
300
305
310
315
320
675
670
665
660
655

Figure C.1 Almond at Craigiehall (19001)

631a
721c
92c
541g
721c
713f
611d

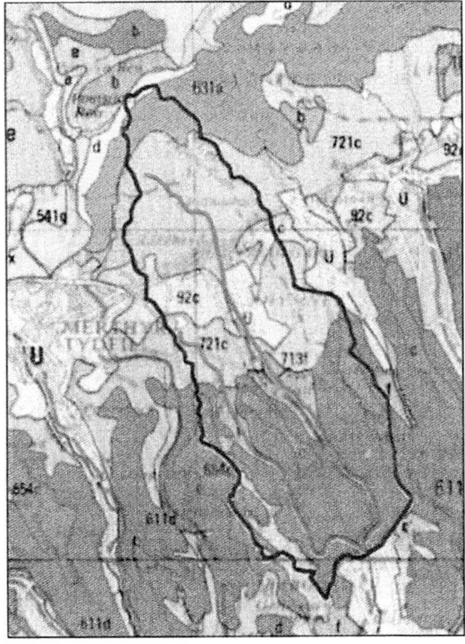

Plate C.2 *Overlay of catchment boundary on a soil map, shown at the actual size of the 1:250 000 map (with permission of the Soil Survey of England and Wales)*

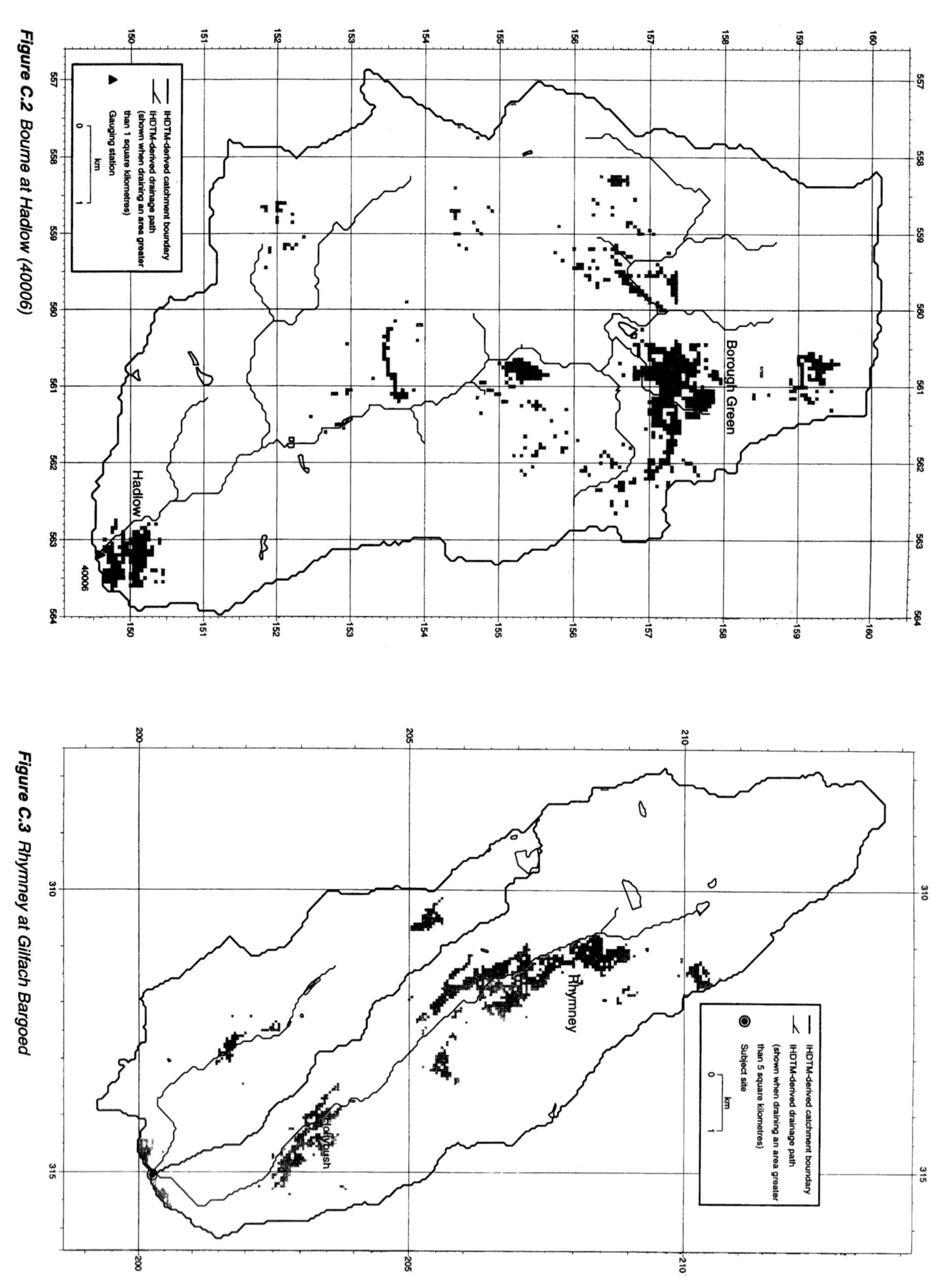

Figure C.2 *Bourne at Hadlow (40006)*

Figure C.3 *Rhymney at Gilfach Bargoed*

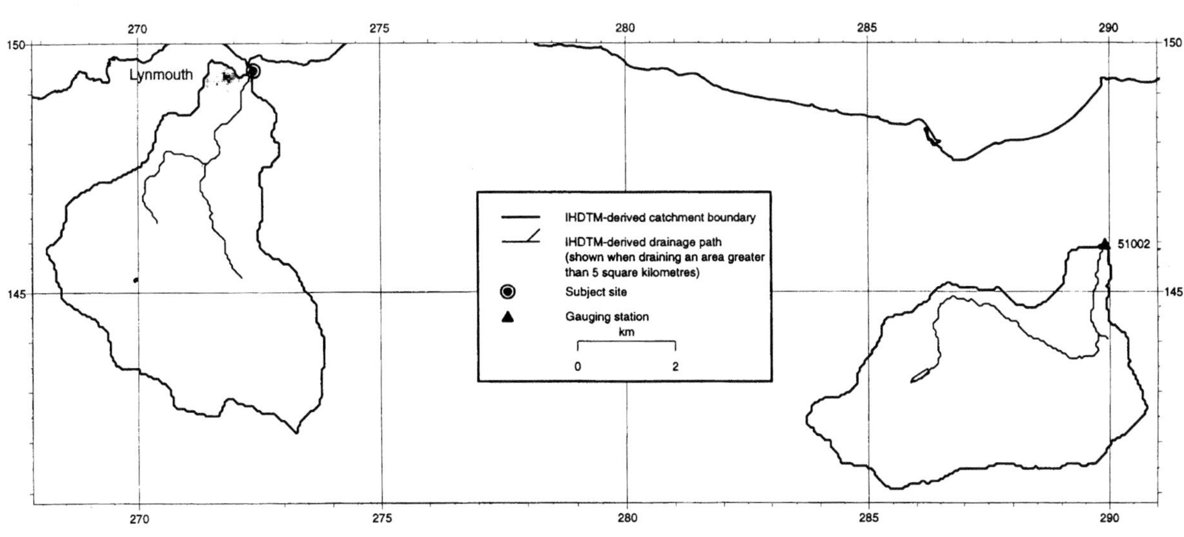

Figure C.4 *West Lyn at Lynmouth and Horner Water at West Luccombe (51002)*

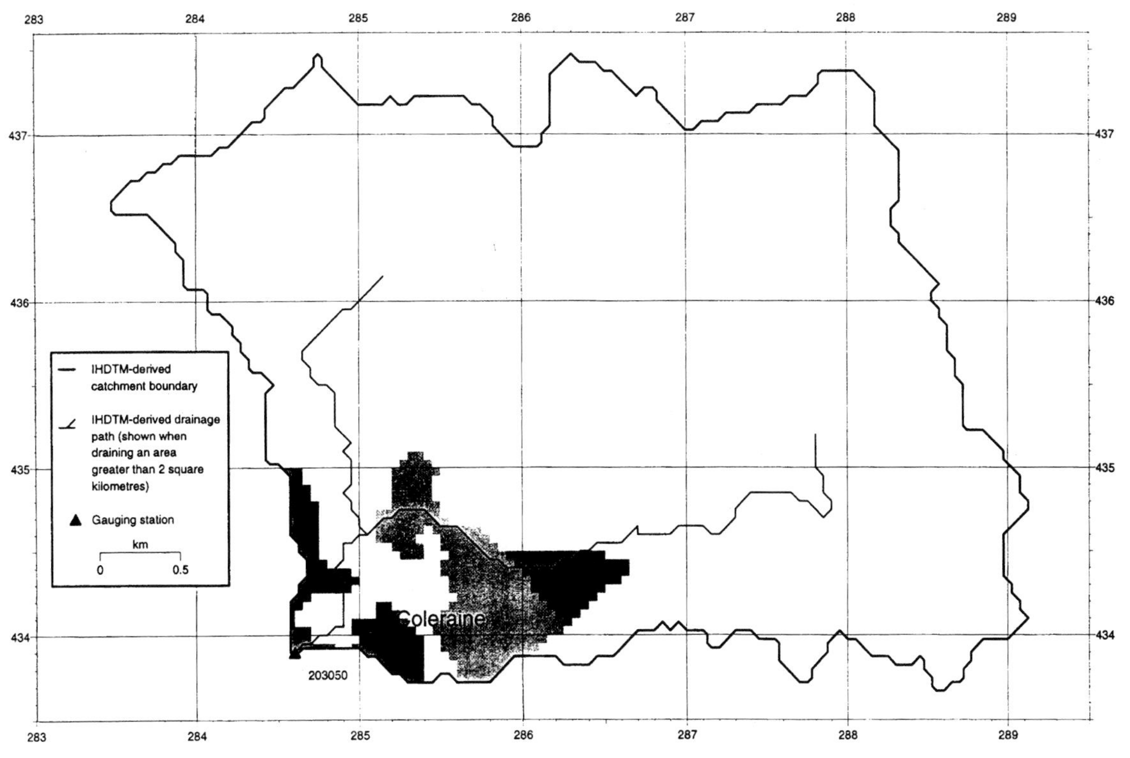

Figure C.5 *Ballysally Blagh at University of Ulster (203050)*

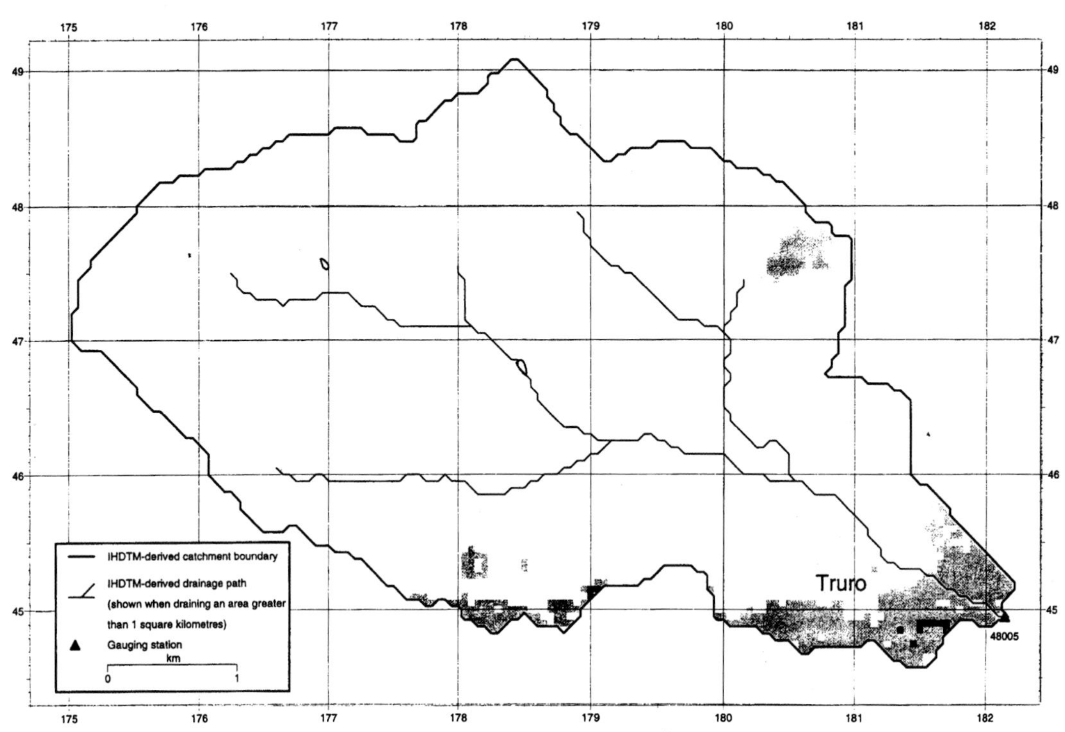

Figure C.6 *Kenwyn at Truro (48005)*

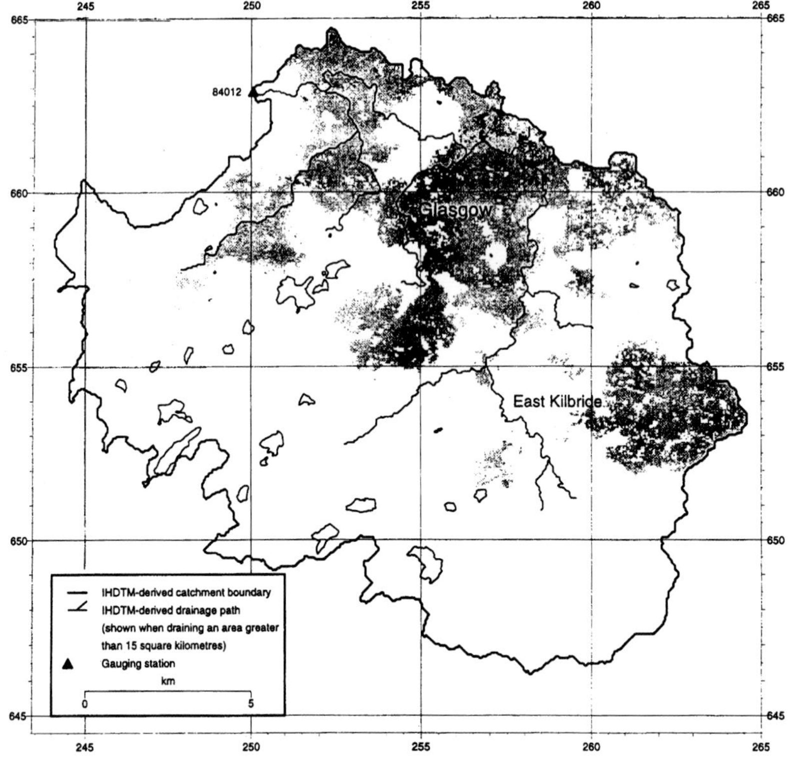

Figure C.7 *White Cart Water at Hawkhead (84012)*

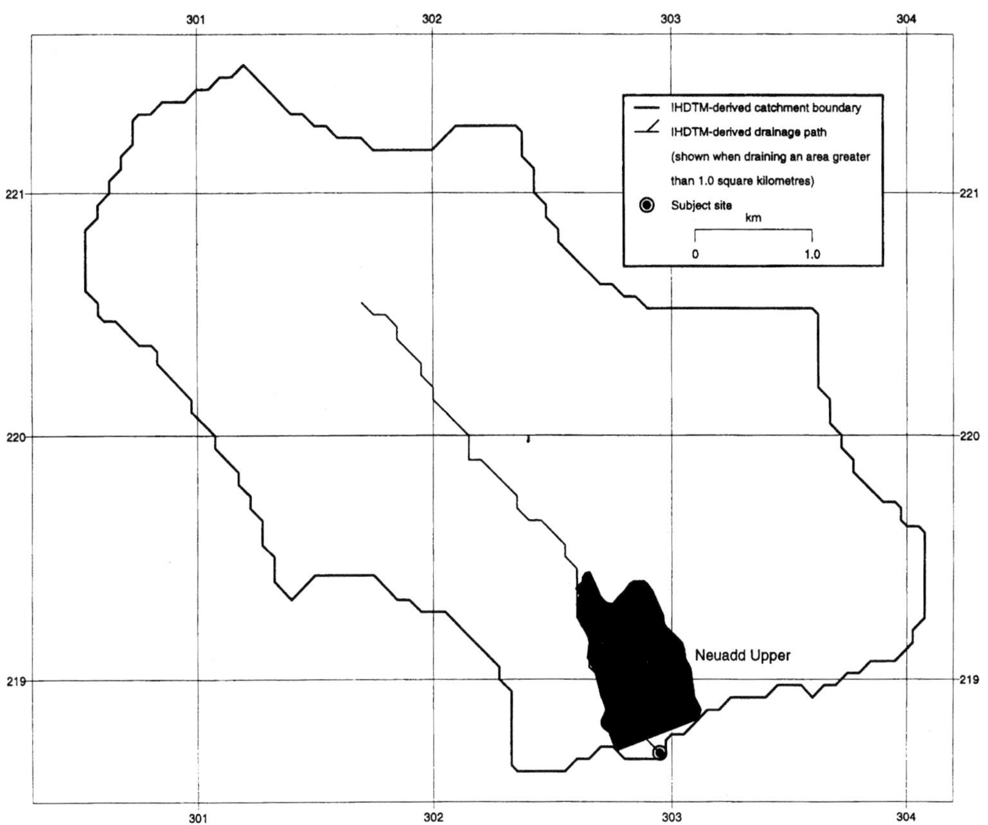

Figure C.8 *Upper Neuadd reservoir*

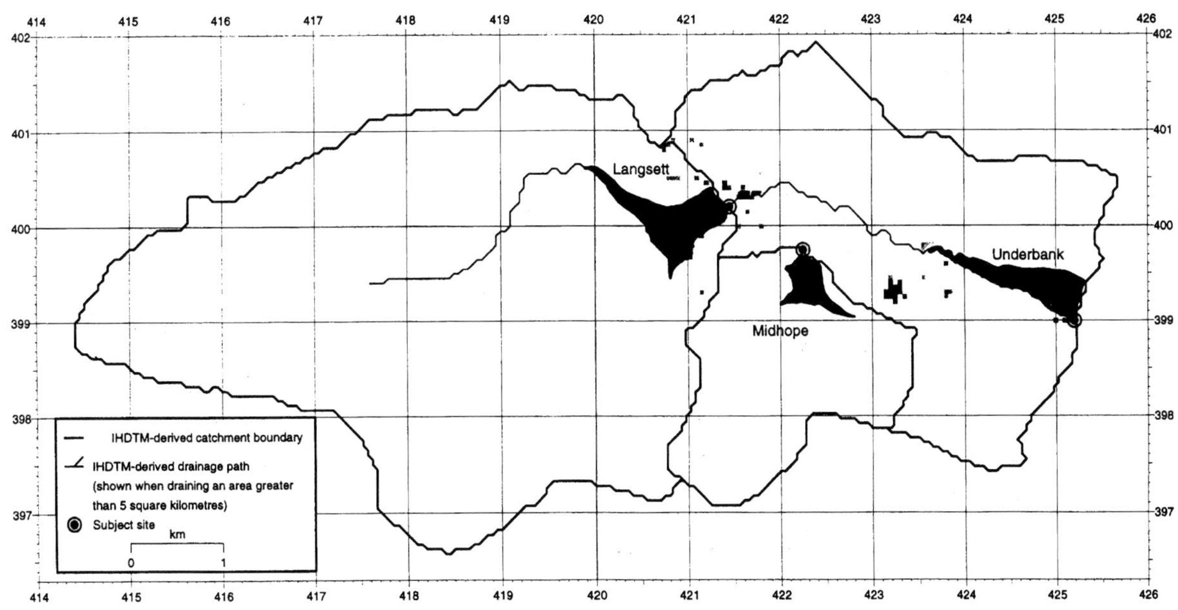

Figure C.9 *Langsett-Midhope-Underbank reservoir cascade*

Table C.3 *Assignment of HOST classes to map units*

The following lists give the typical percentages of HOST classes found in map units. The list for England and Wales map units starts overleaf; Scotland follows starting on page 261; Northern Ireland (where the assignment system is slightly different) follows starting on page 270.

Map units in England and Wales

Code	*Map unit*	*Class*	*%*
0C	China Clay Works	17	100.00
0l	Lake	98	100.00
0s	Sea	99	100.00
0u	Unsurveyed	97	100.00
22	Unripened Gley soils	9	100.00
92a	Disturbed soils 1	21	100.00
92b	Disturbed soils 2	21	100.00
92c	Disturbed soils 3	24	100.00
311a	Revidge	15	42.86
		29	57.14
311b	Skiddaw	15	33.33
		27	53.33
		29	13.33
311c	Wetton 1	4	41.86
		15	58.14
311d	Wetton 2	4	23.08
		15	76.92
311e	Bangor	27	57.14
		29	42.86
313a	Dunwell	19	38.89
		22	44.44
		27	16.67
313b	Powys	17	33.33
		22	66.67
313c	Crwbin	4	100.00
341	Icknield	1	94.74
		6	5.26
342a	Upton 1	1	100.00
342b	Upton 2	1	100.00
342c	Wantage 1	1	88.89
		6	11.11
342d	Wantage 2	1	69.23
		9	30.77
343a	Elmton 1	2	100.00
343b	Elmton 2	2	90.00
		4	10.00
343c	Elmton 3	2	56.25
		23	25.00
		25	18.75
343d	Sherborne	2	77.78
		23	22.22
343e	Marcham	2	100.00
343f	Newmarket 1	1	100.00
343g	Newmarket 2	1	84.21
		5	15.79
343h	Andover 1	1	90.00
		6	10.00
343i	Andover 2	1	85.00
		6	15.00
346	Reach	9	100.00
361	Sandwich	5	89.47
		10	10.53
372	Willingham	10	85.00
		11	15.00
411a	Evesham 1	2	29.41
		23	70.59
411b	Evesham 2	23	52.94
		25	47.06
411c	Evesham 3	20	23.08
		23	61.54
		25	15.38
411d	Hanslope	21	100.00
421a	Stow	16	16.67
		20	55.56
		21	16.67
		24	11.11
421b	Halstow	17	10.99
		21	45.05
		24	43.96
431	Worcester	21	100.00
511a	Aberford	2	89.47
		6	10.53
511b	Moreton	2	65.96
		23	34.04
511c	Panholes	1	90.00
		6	10.00
511d	Blewbury	1	68.75
		13	31.25
511e	Swaffham Prior	1	100.00
511f	Coombe1	1	77.78
		6	22.22
511g	Coombe2	1	100.00
511h	Badsey1	5	77.78
		7	11.11
		8	11.11
511i	Badsey2	5	78.95
		7	10.53
		10	10.53
511j	Stretham	18	50.62
		21	49.38
512a	Aswarby	2	17.65
		13	47.06
		23	17.65
		25	17.65
512b	Landbeach	5	13.79
		7	70.11
		8	16.09
512c	Ruskington	7	100.00
512d	Grove	8	41.18
		10	23.53
		20	23.53
		25	11.76

Code	Map unit	Class	%	Code	Map unit	Class	%
512e	Block	7	29.07	541p	Malham2	4	100.00
		8	30.23	541q	Waltham	4	55.56
		9	11.63			6	44.44
		10	29.07	541r	Wick1	5	75.00
512f	Milton	5	20.00			7	25.00
		8	80.00	541s	Wick2	5	37.50
513	Cannamore	18	70.00			6	15.63
		21	15.00			8	10.42
		24	15.00			13	36.46
521	Methwold	1	100.00	541t	Wick3	5	72.22
532a	Blacktoft	8	89.47			6	27.78
		9	10.53	541u	Ellerbeck	5	100.00
532b	Romney	8	100.00	541v	Rheidol	5	88.89
541a	Bearsted1	3	84.21			8	11.11
		8	15.79	541w	Newnham	5	71.43
541b	Bearsted2	3	52.94			8	28.57
		10	29.41	541x	East Keswick1	6	52.94
		19	17.65			7	11.76
541c	Newbiggin	6	65.00			21	35.29
		18	35.00	541y	East Keswick2	5	15.00
541d	Oglethorpe	5	77.78			6	65.00
		6	22.22			17	20.00
541a	Milford	6	10.53	541z	East Keswick3	4	37.50
		17	78.95			6	62.50
		21	10.53	542	Nercwys	21	62.50
541b	Bromsgrove	3	71.43			24	37.50
		4	14.29	543	Arrow	7	75.00
		18	14.29			10	25.00
541c	Eardiston1	3	14.93	544	Banbury	2	83.33
		4	67.16			20	16.67
		18	17.91	551a	Bridgnorth	3	89.47
541d	Eardiston2	4	100.00			5	10.53
541e	Crediton	2	22.22	551b	Cuckney1	3	55.00
		3	77.78			5	45.00
541f	Rivington1	4	66.67	551c	Cuckney2	3	52.94
		13	33.33			10	23.53
541g	Rivington2	4	83.33			16	23.53
		21	16.67	551d	Newport1	5	75.00
541h	Neath	17	25.00			10	12.50
		18	25.00			18	12.50
		21	50.00	551e	Newport2	3	26.67
541i	Munslow	4	100.00			5	73.33
541j	Denbigh1	4	13.33	551f	Newport3	5	60.00
		17	60.00			18	40.00
		18	13.33	551g	Newport4	5	100.00
		22	13.33	552a	Kexby	5	33.33
541k	Denbigh2	6	18.60			7	66.67
		8	17.44	552b	Ollerton	7	40.59
		9	17.44			13	19.80
		17	46.51			18	39.60
541l	Barton	4	83.33	554a	Frilford	3	89.47
		18	16.67			13	10.53
541m	South Petherton	3	80.00	554b	Worlington	1	50.00
		16	20.00			5	30.00
541n	Trusham	4	68.00			16	20.00
		17	20.00	555	Downham	5	21.05
		22	12.00			10	42.11
541o	Malham1	4	15.00			13	36.84
		15	85.00	561a	Wharfe	8	88.89

Code	Map unit	Class	%	Code	Map unit	Class	%
		10	11.11	571t	Efford2	5	36.05
561b	Teme	8	80.00			10	11.63
		9	20.00			18	34.88
561c	Alun	8	81.25			25	17.44
		10	18.75	571u	Sutton1	5	100.00
561d	Lugwardine	8	88.89	571v	Sutton2	5	77.78
		9	11.11			6	22.22
571a	Rowton	5	53.33	571w	Hucklesbrook	5	90.00
		18	33.33			7	10.00
		24	13.33	571x	Ludford	5	73.33
571a	Ston Easton	2	66.67			6	26.67
		4	16.67	571y	Hamble1	1	13.33
		23	16.67			6	40.00
571b	Bromyard	4	15.58			8	26.67
		18	84.42			18	20.00
571c	Malling	1	11.11	571z	Hamble2	6	53.33
		2	16.67			8	46.67
		3	16.67	572a	Yeld	2	22.22
		16	38.89			4	16.67
		18	16.67			18	61.11
571d	Fyfield1	3	66.67	572b	Middleton	18	85.88
		16	22.22			24	14.12
		18	11.11	572c	Hodnet	3	11.76
571e	Fyfield2	3	100.00			13	11.76
571f	Fyfield3	3	77.78			18	64.71
		15	22.22			21	11.76
571g	Fyfield4	3	70.00	572d	Whimple1	5	34.07
		18	20.00			6	29.67
		24	5.00			21	36.26
		25	5.00	572e	Whimple2	3	23.53
571h	Ardington	3	23.53			21	76.47
		16	64.71	572f	Whimple3	21	82.35
		24	11.76			24	17.65
571i	Harwell	4	10.00	572g	Dunnington Heath	18	71.43
		16	55.00			21	28.57
		24	35.00	572h	Oxpasture	20	52.50
571j	Frilsham	1	100.00			23	12.50
571k	Moulton	1	80.00			25	35.00
		5	20.00	572i	Curtisden	3	9.46
571l	Charity1	1	40.00			16	9.46
		6	60.00			18	54.05
571m	Charity2	1	58.82			24	27.03
		6	41.18	572j	Bursledon	10	17.24
571n	Tathwell	1	89.47			13	17.24
		18	10.53			18	34.48
571o	Melford	1	100.00			25	31.03
571p	Escrick1	6	62.50	572k	Bignor	4	11.24
		18	21.88			16	33.71
		24	15.63			18	32.58
571q	Escrick2	5	20.00			24	22.47
		6	60.00	572l	Flint	18	87.50
		18	20.00			24	12.50
571r	Hunstanton	1	68.42	572m	Salwick	5	25.00
		5	15.79			8	20.00
		6	15.79			18	55.00
571s	Efford1	5	39.60	572n	Burlingham1	5	37.50
		6	40.59			18	62.50
		8	14.85	572o	Burlingham2	6	15.79
		9	4.95			18	63.16

Code	Map unit	Class	%	Code	Map unit	Class	%
		24	21.05	611d	Withnell 1	4	55.56
572p	Burlingham 3	1	30.00			17	33.33
		5	30.00			21	11.11
		18	40.00	611e	Withnell 2	4	83.33
572q	Ashley	18	64.71			19	16.67
		21	23.53	612a	Parc	15	11.76
		24	11.76			17	70.59
572r	Ratsborough	18	37.50			26	17.65
		24	35.71	612b	Moor Gate	4	87.50
		25	26.79			15	12.50
572s	Bishampton 1	5	21.05	631a	Anglezarke	4	60.00
		6	26.32			15	40.00
		18	36.84	631b	Delamere	3	100.00
		24	15.79	631c	Shirrell Heath 1	3	44.44
572t	Bishampton 2	18	44.44			10	22.22
		20	11.11			13	16.67
		24	27.78			18	16.67
		25	16.67	631d	Shirrell Heath 2	3	100.00
573a	Waterstock	5	11.76	631e	Goldstone	3	78.57
		6	17.65			4	21.43
		7	23.53	631f	Crannymoor	5	72.94
		8	35.29			10	27.06
		9	11.76	633	Larkbarrow	4	50.55
573b	Wix	5	23.53			15	49.45
		7	64.71	634	Southampton	5	87.01
		25	11.76			24	12.99
581a	Nordrach	4	100.00	641a	Sollom 1	5	31.58
581b	Sonning 1	5	88.89			10	68.42
		18	11.11	641b	Sollom2	3	22.22
581c	Sonning 2	5	62.50			5	11.11
		18	12.50			10	50.00
		25	25.00			18	16.67
581d	Carstens	1	88.89	641c	Holme Moor	5	12.50
		6	11.11			7	66.25
581e	Marlow	1	73.33			10	21.25
		18	26.67	643a	Holidays Hill	3	23.53
581f	Barrow	1	55.00			10	11.76
		5	45.00			13	11.76
581g	Stone Street	1	27.78			18	29.41
		3	38.89			25	23.53
		5	33.33	643b	Poundgate	18	23.53
582a	Batcombe	1	18.75			24	64.71
		18	81.25			26	11.76
582b	Hornbeam 1	1	26.67	643c	Bolderwood	5	16.67
		5	40.00			24	83.33
		18	33.33	643d	Felthorpe	7	26.67
582c	Hornbeam 2	1	37.50			10	73.33
		18	62.50	651a	Belmont	4	18.75
582d	Hornbeam 3	18	70.59			15	81.25
		21	17.65	651b	Hexworthy	15	100.00
		24	11.76	651c	Earle	15	68.75
582e	Tendring	5	32.61			27	31.25
		8	45.65	652	Maw	15	100.00
		24	21.74	654a	Hafren	15	86.67
611a	Malvern	4	28.57			26	13.33
		19	71.43	654b	Lydcott	15	88.89
611b	Moretonhampstead	4	100.00			26	11.11
611c	Manod	17	87.50	654c	Gelligaer	15	100.00
		22	12.50	711a	Stanway	18	20.00

Code	Map unit	Class	%	Code	Map unit	Class	%
		24	80.00			25	90.00
711b	Brockhurst 1	21	20.00	712d	Hallsworth 1	24	100.00
		24	80.00	712e	Hallsworth 2	24	100.00
711c	Brockhurst 2	9	13.33	712f	Crewe	24	100.00
		24	86.67	712g	Ragdale	21	22.22
711d	Martock	24	100.00			24	77.78
711e	Wickham 1	20	11.76	712h	Foggathorpe 1	24	100.00
		24	17.65	712i	Foggathorpe 2	24	100.00
		25	70.59	713a	Bardsey	4	29.41
711f	Wickham 2	20	16.67			21	11.76
		23	11.11			24	58.82
		25	72.22	713b	Sportsmans	9	43.75
711g	Wickham 3	10	15.79			15	18.75
		18	10.53			21	18.75
		25	73.68			24	18.75
711h	Wickham4	25	100.00	713c	Fforest	21	10.53
711i	Wickham5	18	12.99			24	78.95
		20	12.99			26	10.53
		24	12.99	713d	Cegin	17	11.76
		25	61.04			18	11.76
711j	Kingston	3	17.65			24	76.47
		16	11.76	713e	Brickfield 1	24	68.75
		18	23.53			26	31.25
		24	47.06	713f	Brickfield 2	6	20.00
711k	Vernolds	9	21.43			21	26.67
		18	21.43			24	53.33
		24	57.14	713g	Brickfield 3	24	100.00
711l	Claverley	19	25.00	714a	Dunkeswell	18	10.53
		24	75.00			24	63.16
711m	Salop	18	18.75			26	26.32
		24	81.25	714b	Oak 1	24	100.00
711n	Clifton	10	10.53	714c	Oak 2	18	33.33
		18	21.05			24	66.67
		24	68.42	714d	Essenden	18	20.00
711o	Rufford	10	45.00			24	60.00
		24	55.00			25	20.00
711p	Dunkeswick	24	100.00	721a	Princetown	15	100.00
711q	Pinder	18	22.22	721b	Onecote	26	100.00
		24	77.78	721c	Wilcocks 1	10	11.11
711r	Beccles 1	24	100.00			26	88.89
711s	Beccles 2	10	15.79	721d	Wilcocks 2	15	11.11
		24	84.21			26	55.56
711t	Beccles 3	18	25.00			29	33.33
		21	15.00	721e	Wenallt	26	84.21
		24	60.00			29	15.79
711u	Holderness	18	32.61	811a	Enborne	8	21.05
		24	67.39			9	15.79
711v	Gresham	10	15.79			10	63.16
		14	63.16	811b	Conway	8	23.53
		24	21.05			9	76.47
711w	Croft Pascoe	4	10.00	811c	Hollington	8	11.11
		9	20.00			9	88.89
		13	20.00	811d	Rockcliffe	8	11.11
		14	50.00			9	55.56
712a	Dale	24	100.00			10	33.33
712b	Denchworth	20	14.29	811e	Tanvats	9	61.11
		23	14.29			10	38.89
		25	71.43	812a	Frome	10	95.00
712c	Windsor	23	10.00			11	5.00

Code	Map unit	Class	%	Code	Map unit	Class	%
812b	Wisbech	8	31.25	841e	Park Gate	8	22.22
		9	68.75			9	77.78
812c	Agney	9	100.00	851a	Downholland 1	9	64.71
813a	Midelney	9	83.33			10	17.65
		10	16.67			11	17.65
813b	Fladbury 1	8	15.00	851b	Downholland 2	9	71.43
		9	85.00			10	28.57
813c	Fladbury 2	8	23.53	851c	Downholland 3	9	50.00
		9	76.47			10	20.00
813d	Fladbury 3	9	88.89			11	30.00
		10	11.11	861a	Isleham 1	10	80.00
813e	Compton	9	100.00			29	20.00
813f	Wallasea 1	9	100.00	861b	Isleham 2	7	20.00
813g	Wallasea 2	8	12.77			10	50.00
		9	87.23			11	30.00
813h	Dowels	9	100.00	871a	Laployd	10	23.53
814a	Thames	8	8.89			12	64.71
		9	91.11			29	11.76
814b	Newchurch 1	8	25.32	871b	Hense	3	10.00
		9	74.68			10	70.00
814c	Newchurch 2	9	100.00			12	20.00
815	Normoor	9	100.00	871c	Hanworth	10	70.00
821a	Everingham	7	26.32			11	30.00
		10	73.68	872a	Peacock	9	15.00
821b	Blackwood	7	9.52			11	16.67
		10	90.48			25	68.33
831a	Yeollandpark	8	17.65	872b	Clayhythe	9	15.79
		9	70.59			10	63.16
		24	11.76			11	10.53
831b	Sessay	9	55.00			25	10.53
		10	15.00	873	Ireton	10	100.00
		24	30.00	1011a	Longmoss	12	100.00
831c	Wigton Moor	7	11.11	1011b	Winter Hill	29	100.00
		8	16.67	1013a	Crowdy 1	15	11.11
		9	44.44			26	16.67
		10	27.78			29	72.22
832	Kelmscot	7	12.50	1013b	Crowdy 2	29	100.00
		9	12.50	1021	Turbary Moor	11	80.00
		10	75.00			12	20.00
841a	Curdridge	10	80.00	1022a	Altcar 1	11	100.00
		25	20.00	1022b	Altcar 2	11	100.00
841b	Hurst	7	13.33	1024a	Adventurers' 1	11	100.00
		8	13.33	1024b	Adventurers' 2	10	20.00
		10	73.33			11	80.00
841c	Swanwick	10	100.00	1024c	Adventurers' 3	9	23.53
841d	Shabbington	7	13.33			10	23.53
		8	26.67			11	52.94
		9	46.67	1025	Mendham	9	38.89
		25	13.33	1025	Mendham	11	61.11

Map Units In Scotland

Code	Map unit	Class	%	Code	Map unit	Class	%
1	Alluvial soils	7	35.00	2	Alluvial soils	10	100.00
		8	15.00	3	Organic soils	12	100.00
		9	10.00	4	Organic soils	29	100.00
		10	20.00	5	Aberlour	14	70.00
		12	20.00			15	30.00

Code	Map unit	Class	%	Code	Map unit	Class	%
6	Aberlour	13	40.00	44	Balrownie	6	50.51
		17	60.00			13	49.49
7	Aberlour	15	50.51	45	Balrownie	15	100.00
		29	49.49	46	Balrownie	12	49.49
9	Aberlour	12	35.00			26	50.51
		15	65.00	47	Balrownie	24	100.00
10	Aberlour	15	50.51	48	Balrownie	26	100.00
		17	49.49	49	Balrownie	6	100.00
11	Aberlour	15	50.51	50	Balrownie	12	49.49
		29	49.49			26	50.51
12	Aberlour	17	100.00	51	Bargour	24	100.00
13	Aberlour	17	50.51	52	Barncorkrie	16	50.51
		29	49.49			24	49.49
14	Aberlour	17	100.00	53	Bemersyde	17	100.00
15	Aberlour	22	75.00	54	Bemersyde	17	100.00
		27	25.00	55	Bemersyde	15	100.00
16	Arbigland	18	25.00	56	Benan	6	100.00
		24	75.00	57	Benan	6	100.00
17	Ardvanie	5	100.00	58	Benan	24	100.00
18	Arkaig	17	100.00	59	Berriedale	6	100.00
19	Arkaig	14	50.51	60	Berriedale	14	100.00
		15	49.49	61	Berriedale	15	70.00
20	Arkaig	13	49.49			29	30.00
		17	50.51	62	Berriedale	12	49.49
21	Arkaig	15	100.00			15	50.51
22	Arkaig	15	50.51	63	Berriedale	6	100.00
		29	49.49	64	Berriedale	15	80.00
23	Arkaig	15	65.00			29	20.00
		29	35.00	65	Berriedale	15	100.00
24	Arkaig	15	100.00	66	Berriedale	4	34.34
25	Arkaig	17	100.00			6	35.35
26	Arkaig	12	35.00			17	30.30
		15	65.00	67	Berriedale	6	50.51
27	Arkaig	17	100.00			29	49.49
28	Arkaig	15	50.51	68	Blair	24	100.00
		17	49.49	69	Blair	24	35.35
29	Arkaig	12	49.49			26	34.34
		15	50.51			29	30.30
30	Arkaig	15	50.00	70	Bogtown	24	100.00
		22	25.00	71	Braemore	6	50.51
		27	25.00			13	49.49
31	Arkaig	15	70.00	72	Braemore	6	35.35
		27	30.00			13	34.34
32	Arkaig	12	30.30			14	30.30
		15	35.35	73	Braemore	14	100.00
		27	34.34	74	Braemore	6	100.00
33	Arkaig	19	100.00	75	Braemore	15	34.34
34	Arkaig	19	50.51			26	35.35
		29	49.49			29	30.30
35	Arkaig	19	100.00	76	Brightmony	16	100.00
36	Arkaig	22	49.49	77	Cairncross	6	50.51
		27	50.51			24	49.49
37	Arran	24	100.00	78	Canisbay	6	100.00
38	Arran	26	100.00	79	Canisbay	24	85.00
39	Ashgrove	24	100.00			26	15.00
40	Ashgrove	24	100.00	80	Canisbay	6	29.29
41	Balrownie	18	100.00			15	20.20
42	Balrownie	24	100.00			24	30.30
43	Balrownie	4	100.00			26	20.20

Code	Map unit	Class	%
81	Canisbay	15	100.00
82	Canisbay	26	100.00
83	Canisbay	24	100.00
84	Canonbie	16	50.51
		24	49.49
85	Canonbie	24	100.00
86	Canonbie	6	100.00
87	Canonbie	26	100.00
88	Canonbie	12	49.49
		26	50.51
89	Carpow	5	100.00
90	Carter	6	30.00
		14	70.00
91	Carter	14	30.00
		24	70.00
92	Carter	6	30.00
		24	70.00
93	Carter	15	100.00
94	Carter	24	49.49
		26	50.51
95	Carter	26	50.51
		29	49.49
96	Corby	17	100.00
97	Corby	5	100.00
98	Corby	5	70.00
		7	10.00
		8	5.00
		9	5.00
		10	5.00
		12	5.00
99	Corby	5	100.00
100	Corby	5	100.00
101	Corby	15	100.00
102	Corby	7	10.10
		8	5.05
		9	5.05
		10	5.05
		12	39.39
		15	35.35
103	Corby	5	50.51
		12	49.49
104	Corby	12	85.00
		15	15.00
105	Corby	5	50.51
		15	49.49
106	Corby	12	50.51
		15	49.49
107	Corriebreck	14	15.00
		17	85.00
108	Corriebreck	17	100.00
109	Corriebreck	12	30.00
		15	70.00
110	Corriebreck	15	100.00
111	Corriebreck	12	49.49
		15	50.51
112	Corriebreck	17	100.00
113	Countesswells	17	100.00
114	Countesswells	17	100.00
115	Countesswells	17	100.00
116	Countesswells	14	100.00
117	Countesswells	15	100.00
118	Countesswells	15	50.51
		29	49.49
119	Countesswells	15	50.51
		29	49.49
120	Countesswells	12	49.49
		15	50.51
121	Countesswells	17	70.00
		22	30.00
122	Countesswells	17	100.00
123	Countesswells	12	35.00
		15	65.00
124	Countesswells	12	85.00
		27	15.00
125	Countesswells	17	100.00
126	Countesswells	15	50.51
		17	49.49
127	Countesswells	12	49.49
		15	50.51
128	Countesswells	17	50.51
		22	49.49
129	Countesswells	15	49.49
		27	50.51
130	Countesswells	15	70.00
		29	30.00
131	Countesswells	15	70.00
		27	30.00
132	Countesswells	12	49.49
		15	50.51
133	Countesswells	27	100.00
134	Countesswells	17	100.00
135	Countesswells	17	50.51
		29	49.49
136	Countesswells	17	100.00
137	Countesswells	22	100.00
138	Craigdale	15	49.49
		17	50.51
139	Craigdale	24	50.51
		26	49.49
140	Craigellachie	18	100.00
141	Creetown	17	100.00
142	Creetown	17	100.00
143	Creetown	24	50.51
		26	49.49
144	Cromarty	13	100.00
145	Cromarty	18	100.00
146	Cromarty	14	49.49
		15	50.51
147	Darleith	17	100.00
148	Darleith	24	100.00
149	Darleith	24	100.00
150	Darleith	17	100.00
151	Darleith	19	100.00
152	Darleith	15	50.51
		19	49.49
153	Darleith	15	100.00
154	Darleith	15	70.00

Code	Map unit	Class	%	Code	Map unit	Class	%
		29	30.00	191	Durnhill	15	70.00
155	Darleith	15	50.51			27	30.00
		29	49.49	192	Durnhill	17	85.00
156	Darleith	15	49.49			27	15.00
		17	50.51	193	Durnhill	17	50.51
157	Darleith	12	35.00			29	49.49
		15	65.00	194	Durnhill	17	100.00
158	Darleith	19	100.00	195	Durnhill	22	100.00
159	Darleith	15	50.51	196	Eckford	5	100.00
		19	49.49	197	Eckford	5	70.00
160	Darleith	15	50.51			12	30.00
		29	49.49	198	Eckford	5	70.00
161	Darleith	17	100.00			7	10.00
162	Darleith	17	50.51			8	20.00
		29	49.49	199	Eckford	10	100.00
163	Darvel	5	100.00	200	Eckford	5	70.00
164	Darvel	5	70.00			10	30.00
		7	5.00	201	Elgin	14	50.51
		8	10.00			15	49.49
		9	5.00	202	Elgin	6	60.00
		10	5.00			13	40.00
		12	5.00	203	Elgin	15	100.00
165	Deecastle	4	100.00	204	Ethie	19	100.00
166	Deecastle	4	49.49	205	Ettrick	16	100.00
		15	50.51	206	Ettrick	17	100.00
167	Deecastle	4	100.00	207	Ettrick	19	100.00
168	Doune	5	100.00	208	Ettrick	17	100.00
169	Dreghorn	5	100.00	209	Ettrick	13	49.49
170	Dreghorn	10	100.00			24	50.51
171	Drongan	24	100.00	210	Ettrick	14	49.49
172	Dulsie	16	100.00			24	50.51
173	Dulsie	15	100.00	211	Ettrick	12	70.00
174	Dulsie	12	49.49			17	30.00
		15	50.51	212	Ettrick	12	49.49
175	Dulsie	15	100.00			15	50.51
176	Dunnet	15	100.00	213	Ettrick	12	70.00
177	Dunnet	15	100.00			15	30.00
178	Dunnet	17	100.00	214	Ettrick	12	35.00
179	Durisdeer	6	50.51			15	50.00
		18	49.49			17	15.00
180	Durisdeer	18	49.49	215	Ettrick	12	85.00
		24	50.51			27	15.00
181	Durnhill	14	50.51	216	Ettrick	15	70.00
		15	49.49			29	30.00
182	Durnhill	15	100.00	217	Ettrick	15	100.00
183	Durnhill	15	50.51	218	Ettrick	15	70.00
		29	49.49			29	30.00
184	Durnhill	15	50.51	219	Ettrick	12	25.00
		29	49.49			15	25.00
185	Durnhill	12	35.00			26	50.00
		15	65.00	220	Ettrick	15	25.00
186	Durnhill	17	100.00			26	25.00
187	Durnhill	15	70.00			29	50.00
		27	30.00	221	Ettrick	17	100.00
188	Durnhill	12	30.00	222	Ettrick	19	100.00
		15	70.00	223	Ettrick	19	70.00
189	Durnhill	27	100.00			22	30.00
190	Durnhill	15	70.00	224	Ettrick	17	34.34
		27	30.00			19	30.30

Code	Map unit	Class	%	Code	Map unit	Class	%
		22	35.35	268	Glenalmond	15	100.00
225	Ettrick	17	70.00	269	Glenalmond	15	34.34
		24	30.00			24	30.30
226	Ettrick	15	70.00			26	35.35
		17	30.00	270	Glenalmond	26	50.51
227	Ettrick	17	100.00			29	49.49
228	Ettrick	15	100.00	271	Glenalmond	6	100.00
229	Ettrick	15	100.00	272	Glenalmond	15	100.00
230	Ettrick	15	100.00	273	Gleneagles	5	100.00
231	Ettrick	15	100.00	274	Gourdie	6	30.00
232	Ettrick	14	50.51			18	70.00
		17	49.49	275	Gourdie	24	51.02
233	Ettrick	14	50.51			26	48.98
		15	49.49	276	Gourdie	6	100.00
234	Ettrick	15	65.00	277	Gourdie	6	49.49
		29	35.00			15	50.51
235	Ettrick	22	100.00	278	Gruline	5	100.00
236	Ettrick	17	100.00	279	Gruline	5	25.00
237	Forfar	16	45.00			12	75.00
		18	55.00	280	Gruline	12	30.00
238	Forfar	24	100.00			27	70.00
239	Forfar	16	50.51	281	Hatton	24	50.51
		18	49.49			26	49.49
240	Foudland	17	100.00	282	Hatton	6	100.00
241	Foudland	14	100.00	283	Hatton	15	100.00
242	Foudland	14	100.00	284	Hatton	15	50.51
243	Foudland	17	100.00			29	49.49
244	Foudland	15	100.00	285	Hatton	6	49.49
245	Foudland	15	50.51			15	50.51
		29	49.49	286	Hatton	15	100.00
246	Foudland	15	70.00	287	Hayfield	16	51.02
		29	30.00			24	48.98
247	Foudland	15	70.00	288	Hayfield	6	70.00
		29	30.00			24	30.00
248	Foudland	12	49.49	289	Hayfield	24	100.00
		17	50.51	290	Hayfield	15	100.00
249	Foudland	12	49.49	291	Hindsward	24	100.00
		15	50.51	292	Hindsward	24	100.00
250	Foudland	17	100.00	293	Hindsward	26	50.51
251	Foudland	17	100.00			29	49.49
252	Foudland	15	50.51	295	Hobkirk	16	100.00
		17	49.49	296	Hobkirk	6	100.00
253	Foudland	15	100.00	297	Hobkirk	6	70.00
254	Foudland	15	100.00			14	30.00
255	Foudland	17	100.00	298	Hobkirk	14	100.00
256	Foudland	17	70.00	299	Hobkirk	6	49.49
		29	30.00			15	50.51
257	Foudland	17	100.00	300	Hobkirk	6	49.49
258	Foudland	22	100.00			15	50.51
259	Fraserburgh	5	100.00	301	Hobkirk	15	100.00
260	Fraserburgh	5	100.00	302	Hobkirk	15	50.51
261	Fraserburgh	5	70.00			29	49.49
		10	30.00	303	Holywood	16	49.49
262	Fraserburgh	10	100.00			18	50.51
263	Fraserburgh	12	100.00	304	Holywood	18	50.51
264	Glenalmond	16	100.00			24	49.49
265	Glenalmond	24	100.00	305	Holywood	6	100.00
266	Glenalmond	24	100.00	306	Holywood	6	100.00
267	Glenalmond	6	100.00	307	Inchkenneth	6	100.00

Code	Map unit	Class	%
308	Inchkenneth	24	100.00
309	Inchkenneth	24	100.00
310	Inchkenneth	26	100.00
311	Inchkenneth	26	100.00
312	Inchkenneth	26	100.00
313	Inchkenneth	6	100.00
314	Inchnadamph	4	100.00
315	Inchnadamph	4	34.34
		15	35.35
		29	30.30
316	Insch	17	100.00
317	Insch	15	30.00
		24	70.00
318	Insch	17	100.00
319	Insch	15	100.00
320	Insch	15	50.51
		29	49.49
321	Insch	14	49.49
		17	50.51
322	Insch	12	30.00
		15	70.00
323	Insch	17	70.00
		22	30.00
324	Insch	17	100.00
325	Insch	15	70.00
		29	30.00
326	Insch	17	49.49
		22	50.51
327	Insch	12	49.49
		15	50.51
328	Insch	15	30.00
		17	70.00
329	Insch	17	50.51
		29	49.49
330	Insch	17	100.00
331	Kilmarnock	24	100.00
332	Kilmarnock	24	100.00
333	Kintyre	24	100.00
334	Kintyre	26	100.00
335	Kintyre	24	100.00
336	Kintyre	26	50.51
		29	49.49
337	Kippen	13	50.51
		17	49.49
338	Kippen	24	100.00
339	Kippen	6	100.00
340	Kippen	24	100.00
341	Kippen	6	100.00
342	Kippen	15	100.00
343	Kippen	15	65.00
		29	35.00
344	Kippen	15	50.51
		29	49.49
345	Kippen	15	100.00
346	Kippen	12	30.00
		15	70.00
347	Kippen	15	100.00
348	Kirkcolm	5	100.00
349	Kirkwood	6	50.51
		24	49.49
350	Kirkwood	24	50.51
		26	49.49
351	Knockskae	14	100.00
352	Knockskae	17	70.00
		22	30.00
353	Knockskae	17	100.00
354	Knockskae	15	100.00
355	Knockskae	12	35.00
		15	65.00
356	Knockskae	17	100.00
357	Knockskae	15	70.00
		29	30.00
358	Knockskae	15	70.00
		27	30.00
359	Lanfine	24	100.00
360	Lanfine	24	100.00
361	Lanfine	26	100.00
362	Lauder	6	100.00
363	Lauder	24	100.00
364	Lauder	6	100.00
365	Lauder	6	30.30
		15	35.35
		24	34.34
366	Lauder	6	50.51
		15	49.49
367	Lauder	15	50.51
		29	49.49
368	Laurencekirk	6	24.49
		17	24.49
		18	51.02
369	Leslie	17	100.00
370	Leslie	24	100.00
371	Leslie	17	100.00
372	Leslie	24	100.00
373	Leslie	22	30.00
		24	70.00
374	Lethans	6	100.00
375	Lethans	24	100.00
376	Lethans	6	49.49
		15	50.51
377	Lethans	15	100.00
378	Lethans	15	100.00
379	Linfern	12	49.49
		15	50.51
380	Links	5	100.00
381	Links	5	50.51
		10	49.49
382	Links	12	100.00
383	Links	5	100.00
384	Links	12	100.00
385	Lochinver	14	100.00
386	Lochinver	17	100.00
387	Lochinver	17	70.00
		22	30.00
388	Lochinver	14	65.00
		17	35.00
389	Lochinver	17	100.00
390	Lochinver	15	50.51

Code	Map unit	Class	%	Code	Map unit	Class	%
		29	49.49	426	North Mormond	15	100.00
391	Lochinver	12	49.49	427	Ordley	24	50.51
		15	50.51			26	49.49
392	Lochinver	15	50.51	428	Ordley	6	65.00
		29	49.49			13	35.00
393	Lochinver	14	15.00	429	Peterhead	24	100.00
		17	85.00	430	Peterhead	24	100.00
394	Lochinver	12	49.49	431	Rackwick	12	49.49
		15	50.51			15	50.51
395	Lochinver	12	34.34	432	Reppoch	6	100.00
		15	35.35	433	Reppoch	24	100.00
		27	30.30	434	Reppoch	6	49.49
396	Lochinver	15	70.00			15	50.51
		27	30.00	435	Reppoch	15	70.00
397	Lochinver	17	50.51			29	30.00
		29	49.49	436	Reppoch	15	50.51
398	Lochinver	17	80.00			29	49.49
		22	20.00	437	Rhins	17	100.00
399	Lynedardy	24	49.49	438	Rhins	24	100.00
		26	50.51	439	Rhins	19	49.49
400	Lynedardy	15	50.51			24	50.51
		26	49.49	440	Rhins	24	100.00
401	Mauchline	18	100.00	441	Rhins	19	85.00
402	Mauchline	24	100.00			22	15.00
403	Mauchline	26	100.00	442	Rhins	24	100.00
404	Mauchline	6	70.00	443	Rhins	17	100.00
		14	30.00	444	Rowanhill	18	100.00
405	Millbuie	14	100.00	445	Rowanhill	24	100.00
406	Millbuie	6	30.00	446	Rowanhill	24	100.00
		18	70.00	447	Rowanhill	6	100.00
407	Minto	24	100.00	448	Rowanhill	4	85.00
408	Minto	24	100.00			13	15.00
409	Minto	24	100.00	449	Rowanhill	15	100.00
410	Minto	15	49.49	450	Rowanhill	15	50.51
		24	50.51			29	49.49
411	Minto	15	70.00	451	Rowanhill	6	25.00
		29	30.00			14	25.00
412	Minto	15	100.00			15	50.00
413	Mountboy	16	100.00	452	Roy	5	50.51
414	Mountboy	6	30.00			24	49.49
		18	70.00	453	Roy	15	30.00
415	Mountboy	24	70.00			26	70.00
		26	30.00	454	Sabhail	4	49.49
416	Mountboy	6	100.00			13	50.51
417	Mountboy	15	100.00	455	Sabhail	15	100.00
418	Mountboy	6	50.51	456	Sabhail	15	50.51
		15	49.49			29	49.49
420	Nigg	5	100.00	457	Sabhail	13	49.49
421	Nigg	10	100.00			15	50.51
422	Nochty	5	70.00	458	Shawhill	6	100.00
		7	10.00	459	Skelberry	14	49.49
		8	5.00			15	50.51
		9	5.00	460	Skelberry	15	100.00
		10	5.00	461	Skelberry	15	100.00
		12	5.00	462	Skelmuir	24	100.00
423	North Mormond	24	100.00	463	Skelmuir	26	100.00
424	North Mormond	24	100.00	464	Smailholm	17	100.00
425	North Mormond	6	50.51	465	Sorn	18	100.00
		13	49.49	466	Sorn	24	100.00

Code	Map unit	Class	%	Code	Map unit	Class	%
467	Sorn	24	100.00	507	Strichen	12	49.49
468	Sorn	6	24.74			15	50.51
		15	24.74	508	Strichen	17	65.00
		24	25.77			22	35.00
		26	24.74	509	Strichen	15	49.49
469	Sorn	15	50.51			22	50.51
		26	49.49	510	Strichen	15	70.00
470	Sorn	14	49.49			27	30.00
		26	50.51	511	Strichen	12	30.30
471	Sorn	6	50.51			15	35.35
		14	49.49			27	34.34
472	Sourhope	17	100.00	512	Strichen	19	100.00
473	Sourhope	24	100.00	513	Strichen	19	30.00
474	Sourhope	19	100.00			29	70.00
475	Sourhope	17	100.00	514	Strichen	19	100.00
476	Sourhope	15	100.00	515	Strichen	22	75.00
477	Sourhope	15	50.51			27	25.00
		29	49.49	516	Symington	5	100.00
478	Sourhope	15	50.51	517	Tarves	13	49.49
		29	49.49			17	50.51
479	Sourhope	19	100.00	518	Tarves	15	49.49
480	Sourhope	15	65.00			24	50.51
		29	35.00	519	Tarves	14	50.51
482	Sourhope	22	100.00			17	49.49
483	Staffin	24	100.00	520	Tarves	17	100.00
484	Staffin	24	100.00	521	Tarves	15	100.00
485	Staffin	26	50.51	522	Tarves	15	50.51
		29	49.49			29	49.49
486	Staffin	26	50.51	523	Tarves	12	49.49
		29	49.49			15	50.51
487	Stirling	24	100.00	524	Tarves	12	30.00
488	Stirling	24	100.00			15	70.00
489	Stirling	26	100.00	525	Tarves	17	100.00
490	Stonehaven	6	30.00	526	Tarves	14	49.49
		18	70.00			17	50.51
491	Stonehaven	24	100.00	527	Tarves	15	49.49
492	Stonehaven	6	100.00			17	50.51
493	Stonehaven	6	49.49	528	Tarves	12	49.49
		13	50.51			15	50.51
494	Stonehaven	15	100.00	529	Tarves	17	49.49
495	Stonehaven	6	100.00			22	50.51
496	Stonehaven	6	100.00	530	Tarves	17	49.49
497	Strichen	14	49.49			22	50.51
		24	50.51	531	Tarves	15	50.51
498	Strichen	17	100.00			27	49.49
499	Strichen	15	100.00	532	Tarves	17	50.51
500	Strichen	15	50.51			29	49.49
		29	49.49	533	Tarves	17	49.49
501	Strichen	15	50.51			29	50.51
		29	49.49	534	Tarves	17	100.00
502	Strichen	15	50.51	535	Thurso	4	30.00
		29	49.49			6	70.00
503	Strichen	15	15.00	536	Thurso	24	100.00
		17	85.00	537	Thurso	24	100.00
504	Strichen	12	30.00	538	Thurso	24	100.00
		15	70.00	539	Thurso	6	100.00
505	Strichen	17	100.00	540	Thurso	12	49.49
506	Strichen	15	50.51			15	50.51
		17	49.49	541	Thurso	15	100.00

Code	Map unit	Class	%	Code	Map unit	Class	%
542	Thurso	15	100.00	563	Tynehead	24	100.00
543	Thurso	15	100.00	564	Tynehead	15	100.00
544	Thurso	12	49.49	565	Tynet	14	100.00
		15	50.51	566	Tynet	6	100.00
545	Tipperty	24	100.00	567	Tynet	15	100.00
546	Torosay	17	70.00	568	Walls	29	100.00
		22	30.00	569	Walls	14	49.49
547	Torosay	12	49.49			15	50.51
		15	50.51	570	Walls	15	100.00
548	Torosay	15	50.51	571	Walls	15	50.51
		29	49.49			29	49.49
549	Torosay	15	50.51	572	Walls	4	30.00
		17	49.49			15	70.00
550	Torosay	15	35.35	573	Walls	17	100.00
		27	34.34	574	Whitsome	16	30.00
		29	30.30			24	70.00
551	Torosay	19	50.51	575	Whitsome	24	100.00
		29	49.49	576	Yarrow	5	100.00
552	Torridon	14	100.00	577	Yarrow	5	100.00
553	Torridon	14	49.49	578	Yarrow	5	35.35
		17	50.51			12	64.65
554	Torridon	12	35.00	579	Yarrow	5	70.00
		15	65.00			7	10.00
555	Torridon	17	70.00			8	5.00
		22	30.00			9	5.00
556	Torridon	15	50.51			10	5.00
		29	49.49			12	5.00
557	Torridon	12	49.49	580	Yarrow	5	70.00
		15	50.51			12	30.00
558	Torridon	12	34.34	600	Built up area	97	100.00
		15	35.35	601	Lake	98	100.00
		27	30.30	602	Sea	99	100.00
559	Torridon	15	100.00	731	Organic soils - 3d	12	100.00
560	Torridon	19	50.51	732	Organic soils - 3e	28	100.00
		29	49.49	733	Organic soils - 3de	28	100.00
561	Torridon	17	25.00	741	Organic soils - 4d	29	100.00
		19	50.00	742	Organic soils - 4e	28	100.00
		22	25.00	743	Organic soils - 4de	28	100.00
562	Tynehead	6	50.51	800	Bare rock - X	17	40.00
		13	49.49			22	60.00

Map units in Northern Ireland

Profile descriptions

Brown earths

Be = brown earths
GBE = gleyed B-horizon brown earths
Sbe = shallow brown earths (40-60 cm deep)
Cbe = calcareous brown earths (alkaline)
Fbe = brown earths rich in ferric iron

Gleys

Pel = Pelosols (clay-rich, red, calcareous soils, with gley features masked)
Swg1/G1 = surface water gley (Swg1/G1) and groundwater gley (G1) (impeded drainage)
Swg2/G2 = surface water gley (Swg2) and groundwater gley (G2) (poor drainage)
Swg3/g3 = surface water gley (Swg3) and groundwater gley (G3) (very poor drainage)
Swhg/hg = surface water humic gley and groundwater humic gley

Podzols

Bp = brown podzolics
Pod = normal podzol (with ea and bs horizons)
Pp = peaty podzol (with peaty a/o horizon)
Sbp = shallow brown podzolics (40-60 cm deep)
Sp = stag(ranite)opodzol (gleyed above an iron pan middle horizon)

Rankers

Br = brown rankers (< 40 cm mineral soil)
Fr = ferric rankers (< 40 cm with high ferric iron content)
Gr = gleyed rankers (< 40 cm gleyed mineral soil)
Hr = humic rankers (< 40 cm mainly organic soil)
Pr = podzolic rankers (< 40 cm mineral soil with signs of leaching)
Rr = rock rankers (mostly rock outcrop)

Profile	*Origin*	*Class*
Be	Alluvium	8
G1	Alluvium	9
G2	Alluvium	9
G3	Alluvium	9
Hg	Alluvium	11
Br	Andesite	17
Sbe	Andesite	17
Be	Basalt	4
Bp	Basalt	4
Br	Basalt	4
Fr	Basalt	4
G3	Basalt	14
Gr	Basalt	14
Hr	Basalt	15
Pp	Basalt	15
Rr	Basalt	4
Sbe	Basalt	4
Swg1	Basalt	14
Swhg	Basalt	15
Br	Basalt/Chalk	1
Cbe	Basalt/Chalk	1
Be	Basalt/Chalk mixed till	18
Cbe	Basalt/Chalk mixed till	18
Swg1	Basalt/Chalk mixed till	24
Swg2	Basalt/Chalk mixed till	24
Swhg	Basalt/Chalk mixed till	26
Br	Basic igneous	4
Gr	Basic igneous	14
Hr	Basic igneous	15
Sbe	Basic igneous	4
Sbp	Basic igneous	4
Be	Basic igneous/ORS mixed till	18
Swg1	Basic igneous/ORS mixed till	24
Swg1	Basic igneous/Red Trias Sandstone mixed till	24
Be	Basic igneous till	18
Bp	Basic igneous till	18
Hg	Basic igneous till	26
Pod	Basic igneous till	18
Sbe	Basic igneous till	18
Sbp	Basic igneous till	18
Swg1	Basic igneous till	24
Swg2	Basic igneous till	24
Swhg	Basic igneous till	26
Swg2	Basalt/Lough Neagh Clay mixed till	24
Be	Basalt/Marl mixed till	18
Swg1	Basalt/Marl mixed till	24
Swg2	Basalt/Marl mixed till	24
Be	Basalt and Red Trias Sandstone mixed till	18
G1	Basalt and Red Trias Sandstone mixed till	24

Profile	Origin	Class
Swg1	Basalt and Red Trias Sandstone mixed till	24
Swg2	Basalt and Red Trias Sandstone mixed till	24
Be	Basalt/Shale mixed till	21
Swg1	Basalt/Shale mixed till	24
Swg2	Basalt/Shale mixed till	24
Be	Basalt till	18
Bp	Basalt till	26
Br_C	Basalt till	4
Fbe	Basalt till	18
G1	Basalt till	24
G2	Basalt till	24
G3	Basalt till	24
Gbe	Basalt till	21
Hg	Basalt till	26
Pp	Basalt till	26
Sbe	Basalt till	18
Swg1	Basalt till	24
Swg2	Basalt till	24
Swg3	Basalt till	24
Swhg	Basalt till	26
Swg1	Basalt till (stonefree)	24
Swg2	Basalt till (stonefree)	24
Swg2	Calp/Carboniferous Sandstone mixed till	24
Be	Calp	4
Br	Calp	4
Gr	Calp	14
Hr	Calp	15
Pp	Calp	15
Swg2	Calp	14
Swhg	Calp	15
Be	Calp till	18
G2	Calp till	24
Sbe	Calp till	18
Swg1	Calp till	24
Swg2	Calp till	24
Swg3	Calp till	24
Swhg	Calp till	26
Be	Chalk/Gravel	18
Be	Chalk	1
Br	Chalk	1
Cbe	Chalk	1
Hr	Chalk	15
Rr	Chalk	1
Sbe	Chalk	1
Be	Chalk/Marl	1
Br	Chalk/Marl	1
Swg1	Chalk/Mica Schist mixed till	24
Be	ORS Conglomerate	4
Bp	ORS Conglomerate	4
Br	ORS Conglomerate	4
Gr	ORS Conglomerate	14
Hr	ORS Conglomerate	15
Pr	ORS Conglomerate	4
Sbe	ORS Conglomerate	4
Sbp	ORS Conglomerate	4
Swg1	ORS Conglomerate/Andesite Mixed till	24
Be	ORS Conglomerate till	6
Bp	ORS Conglomerate till	6
G2	ORS Conglomerate till	14
Hg	ORS Conglomerate till	15
Sbe	ORS Conglomerate till	6
Sbp	ORS Conglomerate till	6
Swg1	ORS Conglomerate till	14
Swg2	ORS Conglomerate till	14
Swhg	ORS Conglomerate till	15
Be	Carboniferous Sandstone	4
Br	Carboniferous Sandstone	4
Gr	Carboniferous Sandstone	14
Hr	Carboniferous Sandstone	15
Sbe	Carboniferous Sandstone	4
Sbp	Carboniferous Sandstone	4
Be	Carboniferous Sandstone/ Conglomeratetill	18
Swg1	Carboniferous Sandstone/ Dolerite mixed till	24
Swg2	Carboniferous Sandstone/ Dolerite mixed till	24
Be	Carboniferous Sandstone/ Limestine mixed till	18
Swg1	Carboniferous Sandstone/ Limestone mixed till	24
Swg2	Carboniferous Sandstone/ Limestone mixed till	24
Swg3	Carboniferous Sandstone/ Limestone mixed till	24
Be	Carboniferous Sandstone/Red Trias Sandstone mixed till	18
G3	Carboniferous Sandstone/Red Trias Sandstone mixed till	24
Hg	Carboniferous Sandstone/Red Trias Sandstone mixed till	26
Swg1	Carboniferous Sandstone/Red Trias Sandstone mixed till	24
Swg2	Carboniferous Sandstone/Red Trias Sandstone mixed till	24
Swhg	Carboniferous Sandstone/Red Trias Sandstone mixed till	26
Be	Carboniferous Sandstone till	18
Bp	Carboniferous Sandstone till	18
G1	Carboniferous Sandstone till	24
G2	Carboniferous Sandstone till	24
G3	Carboniferous Sandstone till	24
Sbe	Carboniferous Sandstone till	18
Sbp	Carboniferous Sandstone till	18
Swg1	Carboniferous Sandstone till	24
Swg2	Carboniferous Sandstone till	24
Swhg	Carboniferous Sandstone till	26
Be	Carboniferous Sandstone/ Basalt mixed till	18
Swg1	Carboniferous Sandstone/ Basalt mixed till	24
Swhg	Carboniferous Sandstone/ Basalt mixed till	26

Profile	Origin	Class
Be	Chalk till	18
Cbe	Chalk till	18
Pel	Chalk till	21
Sbe	Chalk till	18
Swg1	Chalk till	24
Swg2	Chalk till	24
Br	Clogher Valley Limestone	4
Be	Clogher Valley Limestone till	18
Sbe	Clogher Valley Limestone till	18
Swg1	Clogher Valley Limestone till	24
Swg2	Clogher Valley Limestone till	24
G2	Diatomite	9
Br	Dungiven Limestone	4
Hr	Dungiven Limestone	15
Sbe	Dungiven Limestone	4
Swhg	Dungiven Limestone	15
Be	Dungiven Limestone till	18
Swg1	Dungiven Limestone till	24
Swg2	Dungiven Limestone till	24
Swhg	Dungiven Limestone till	26
Br	Dolerite	19
Gr	Dolerite	22
Hr	Dolerite	27
Rr	Dolerite	22
Be	Dolerite till	18
Swg2	Dolerite till	24
Br	Felsite	19
Hr	Felsite	27
Rr	Felsite	19
Pr	Granite	17
Be	Granite	17
Be	Granite (Mournes)	4
Bp	Granite (Mournes)	4
Br	Granite	17
Br	Granite (Mournes)	4
G2	Granite (Mournes)	14
Gr	Granite (Mournes)	14
Gr	Granite	17
Hr	Granite (Mournes)	15
Hr	Granite	27
Pod	Granite (Mournes)	4
Pp	Granite (Mournes)	15
Rr	Granite (Mournes)	4
Sbe	Granite	17
Sbe	Granite (Mournes)	4
Sbp	Granite	17
Sbp	Granite (Mournes)	4
Swg1	Granite	22
Be	Granite/Basic igneous mixed till	18
Sbp	Granite/Basic igneous mixed till	18
Swg1	Granite/Basic igneous mixed till	24
Swg2	Granite/Basic igneous mixed till	24
Swg1	Granite/ORS mixed till	24
Swg2	Granite/ORS mixed till	24
Be	Granite/Red Trias Sst till	18
Be	Granite till	18
Bp	Granite till	18
G2	Granite till	24
Pod	Granite till	18
Sbe	Granite till	18
Stp	Granite till	26
Swg1	Granite till	24
Swg2	Granite till	24
Swhg	Granite till	26
Be	Gravel	5
Bp	Gravel	5
Br	Gravel	5
G1	Gravel	10
G2	Gravel	10
G3	Gravel	10
Hg	Gravel	15
Pod	Gravel	5
Pp	Gravel	15
Swg1	Gravel	10
Swg2	Gravel	10
Swhg	Gravel	15
G1	Gravel/Basalt mixed till	24
Be	Gravel/Basalt mixed till	18
Swg1	Gravel/Basalt mixed till	24
Be	Gravel/Carboniferous Sandstone mixed till	18
Be	Gravel/Chalk mixed till	18
Swg1	Gravel/Chalk mixed till	24
Be	Gravel/Red Trias Sandstone mixed till	18
Be	Gravel/Shale mixed till	18
G2	Intake	9
G3	Intake	9
G2	Lake Shore Alluvium	9
G1	Lake Clay	9
G2	Lake Clay	9
Swg1	Lake Clay	9
Swg2	Lake Clay	9
Be	Limestone	4
Br	Limestone	4
Gr	Limestone	14
Hr	Limestone	15
Rr	Limestone	4
Sbe	Limestone	4
Swg3	Limestone	14
Be	Limestone Gravel	5
Be	Purer Limestone till	18
Cbe	Purer Limestone till	18
G2	Purer Limestone till	24
G3	Purer Limestone till	24
Sbe	Purer Limestone till	18
Swg1	Purer Limestone till	24
Swg2	Purer Limestone till	24
Swg3	Purer Limestone till	24
Swhg	Purer Limestone till	26
G2	Lough Neagh Clay till	24
Swg2	Lough Neagh Clay till	24
Be	Lake Sand	7
G2	Lake Sand	10

Profile	Origin	Class
G2	Marine Alluvium	9
G3	Marine Alluvium	9
Br	Marl	19
Be	Marl till	18
Hg	Marl till	26
Pel	Marl till	24
Swg1	Marl till	24
Swg2	Marl till	24
Hr	Millstone Grit	27
Rr	Millstone Grit	27
Be	Mica Schist	17
Bp	Mica Schist	17
Br	Mica Schist	17
Gr	Mica Schist	22
Hr	Mica Schist	27
Pr	Mica Schist	17
Rr	Mica Schist	19
Sbe	Mica Schist	17
Sbp	Mica Schist	17
Swg1	Mica Schist	22
Swhg	Mica Schist	27
Be	Mica Schist/Basalt till	18
Swg1	Mica Schist/Basalt till	24
Swg2	Mica Schist/Basalt till	24
Swhg	Mica Schist/Basalt till	26
Be	Mica Schist/Carboniferous Sandstone mixed till	18
Bp	Mica Schist/Carboniferous Sandstone mixed till	18
Hg	Mica Schist/Carboniferous Sandstone mixed till	26
Sbe	Mica Schist/Carboniferous Sandstone mixed till	18
Swg1	Mica Schist/Carboniferous Sandstone mixed till	24
Swg2	Mica Schist/Carboniferous Sandstone mixed till	24
Swg3	Mica Schist/Carboniferous Sandstone mixed till	24
Swhg	Mica Schist/Carboniferous Sandstone mixed till	26
Be	Mica Schist/Chalk mixed till	18
Swg2	Mica Schist/Chalk mixed till	24
Swg1	Mica Schist/Dungiven Limestone till	24
Pod	Mica Schist/Dungiven Limestone till	18
Pod	Mica Schist/Dungiven Limestone till	24
Pp	Mica Schist/Dungiven Limestone till	26
Bp	Mica Schist/Granite mixed till	18
Swg1	Mica Schist/Granite mixed till	24
Swg2	Mica Schist/Granite mixed till	24
Swhg	Mica Schist/Granite mixed till	26
Be	Mica Schist till	18
Bp	Mica Schist till	18
G1	Mica Schist till	24
G2	Mica Schist till	24
G3	Mica Schist till	24
Gbe	Mica Schist till	18
Hg	Mica Schist till	26
Pod	Mica Schist till	18
Pp	Mica Schist till	26
Sbe	Mica Schist till	18
Sbp	Mica Schist till	18
Swg1	Mica Schist till	24
Swg2	Mica Schist till	24
Swg3	Mica Schist till	24
Swhg	Mica Schist till	26
G1	Organic Alluvium	11
G2	Organic Alluvium	11
G3	Organic Alluvium	11
Be	ORS	4
Br	ORS	4
Gr	ORS	14
Hr	ORS	15
Pr	ORS	4
Rr	ORS	4
Sbe	ORS	4
Sbp	ORS	4
Swhg	ORS	15
Be	ORS/Carboniferous Sandstone mixed till	18
Swg1	ORS/Carboniferous Sandstone mixed till	24
Swg2	ORS/Carboniferous Sandstone mixed till	24
Swhg	ORS/Carboniferous Sandstone mixed till	26
Be	ORS/Limestone mixed till	18
Swg1	ORS/Limestone mixed till	24
Swg2	ORS/Limestone mixed till	24
Be	ORS/Mica Schist till	18
Swg2	ORS/Mica Schist till	24
Swhg	ORS/Mica Schist till	26
Be	ORS till	18
Bp	ORS till	16
Bp	ORS till	18
G2	ORS till	24
G3	ORS till	24
Hg	ORS till	26
Pod	ORS till	18
Sbe	ORS till	18
Sbp	ORS till	18
Swg1	ORS till	24
Swg2	ORS till	24
Swg3	ORS till	24
Swhg	ORS till	26
Br	Red Trias Sandstone	4
Hr	Red Trias Sandstone	15
Rr	Red Trias Sandstone	4
Sbe	Red Trias Sandstone	4
Be	Red Trias Sandstone/ Basalt mixed till	18
Swg1	Red Trias Sandstone/ Basalt mixed till	24

Profile	Origin	Class
Swg2	Red Trias Sandstone/ Basalt mixed till	24
Swhg	Red Trias Sandstone/ Basalt mixed till	26
Swg1	Red Trias Sandstone/Calp mixed till	24
Swg2	Red Trias Sandstone/Calp mixed till	24
Be	Red Trias Sandstone/Chalk mixed till	21
Swg1	Red Trias Sandstone/Chalk mixed till	24
Be	Rhyolite	4
Pp	Rhyolite	15
Sbe	Rhyolite till	18
Swg2	Rhyolite till	24
Swhg	Rhyolite till	26
Be	Red Trias Sandstone/ Limestone mixed till	18
Swg1	Red Trias Sandstone/ Limestone mixed till	24
Swg2	Red Trias Sandstone/ Limestone mixed till	24
Swg1	Red Trias Sandstone/LNC till	24
Be	Red Limestone till	21
G2	Red Limestone till	24
Swg1	Red Limestone till	24
Swg2	Red Limestone till	24
Be	Red Trias Sandstone/Shale mixed till	18
Gbe	Red Trias Sandstone/Shale mixed till	18
Swg1	Red Trias Sandstone/Shale mixed till	24
Swg2	Red Trias Sandstone/Shale mixed till	24
Be	Red Trias Sandstone till	6
G1	Red Trias Sandstone till	14
G2	Red Trias Sandstone till	14
Hg	Red Trias Sandstone till	15
Hr	Red Trias Sandstone till	15
Sbe	Red Trias Sandstone till	6
Swg1	Red Trias Sandstone till	14
Swg2	Red Trias Sandstone till	14
Swhg	Red Trias Sandstone till	15
Be	Shale	17
Bp	Shale	17
Br	Shale	17
G3	Shale	22
Gr	Shale	22
Hr	Shale	27
Pod	Shale	17
Pp	Shale	27
Rr	Shale	17
Sbe	Shale	17
Sbp	Shale	17
Swg1	Shale	22
Swg2	Shale	22
Be	Sand	5
Bp	Sand	5
Br	Sand	5
G1	Sand	10
G2	Sand	10
G3	Sand	10
Pod	Sand	5
Pp	Sand	15
Swg1	Sand	10
Swg2	Sand	10
Swhg	Sand	15
Be	Shale/Granite mixed till	18
Bp	Shale/Granite mixed till	18
G2	Shale/Granite mixed till	24
Swg1	Shale/Granite mixed till	24
Swg2	Shale/Granite mixed till	24
Be	Shale ORS mixed till	18
Swg1	Shale ORS mixed till	24
Swg2	Shale ORS mixed till	24
Be	Shale till	18
Bp	Shale till	18
G1	Shale till	24
G2	Shale till	24
G3	Shale till	24
Sbe	Shale till	18
Sbp	Shale till	18
Swg1	Shale till	24
Swg2	Shale till	24
Swhg	Shale till	26
Br	Yoredale Sandstone	4
Gr	Yoredale Sandstone	14
Hr	Yoredale Sandstone	15
Pp	Yoredale Sandstone	15
Swg3	Yoredale Sandstone	14
Swhg	Yoredale Sandstone	15
Swg1	Yoredale Sandstone/Clogher Valley Limestone mixed till	24
Swg2	Yoredale Sandstone/Clogher Valley Limestone mixed till	24
Be	Yoredale Sandstone till	18
Pod	Yoredale Sandstone till	18
Swg1	Yoredale Sandstone till	24
Swg2	Yoredale Sandstone till	24
Swg3	Yoredale Sandstone till	24
Swhg	Yoredale Sandstone till	26

Appendix D Reservoir routing

D.1 Formulation of routing problem

The underlying concepts of the reservoir routing problem and its solution, which are formulated in this appendix, are based on *IH Report 114* (Reed and Field, 1992). The routing problem is to determine the resulting outflow hydrograph q and the water level h during passage of a flood. The maximum water level, excluding wave effects, is of particular interest. A flood arrives in two forms: as an inflow hydrograph i at the reservoir edge, representing flood runoff from the gathering grounds, and as direct rainfall p onto the reservoir surface. The volume of flood water temporarily stored in the reservoir at time t is S, defined in terms of water level above a convenient datum h_0 (e.g. the sill of the lowest outflow device).

The modelling of the passage of a flood through a reservoir is relatively straightforward. Except for very special configurations, the passage is indifferent to hydraulic conditions at the inlet or approach conditions at the outlet. The moderating effect of the storage on an incoming flood can be represented by the geometrical relationship between storage and water level (the S-h relationship) and that by which the water level controls the discharge from the reservoir (the q-h relationship, sometimes referred to as the rating). This mathematical treatment is generally referred to as 'level-pool' flood routing. The assumption of a level pool is, of course, something of an approximation, as wind and seiche effects can produce pronounced differences.

The inflow i and outflow q are expressed in $m^3 s^{-1}$, with water level h in m and storage S in m^3. To keep the formulation simple, the lake area A is taken in m^2 and the rainfall p in m s^{-1}, although these are unfamiliar units for these variables.

The principle of conservation of mass yields the equation:

$$\frac{dS}{dt} = i + A\,p - q \qquad \text{(D.1)}$$

Since area is simply the rate of change of storage with level:

$$A = \frac{dS}{dh} \qquad \text{(D.2)}$$

Equation D.1 can be rewritten as:

$$A\left(\frac{dS}{dh}\right) = I + A\,p - q \qquad \text{(D.3)}$$

A preliminary to solving the routing problem is to eliminate A and q in favour of h, using an area-level equation $A = A(h)$ and the rating equation $q = q(h)$ respectively.

D.1.1 Area-level relationship

The area-level equation represents the bathometry of the lake and the topography of the lake shore. Where the shore is steep it may be adequate to treat the reservoir as having a fixed area regardless of water level. The next simplest treatment is to consider that the lake area A increases linearly with water level from some base area a_0 at datum level h_0, at a growth rate a_1:

$$A = a_0 + a_1\,(h - h_0) \qquad \text{(D.4)}$$

Only in exceptional cases will this equation fail to represent the area variation adequately, for example an engineered balancing pond where the slopes change abruptly and are better represented by an exponential relationship:

$$A = a_0 + a_1 (h - h_0)^{e_a} \qquad \text{(D.5)}$$

Some formulations of the reservoir routing problem prefer to work in terms of the storage-level relationship, rather than the area-level relationship. The main advantage of using an area-level formulation is that it simplifies the solution scheme, particularly when explicit allowance is to be made for rain falling directly on the reservoir. Furthermore, it is intuitively easier to check that an area-level relationship has been defined correctly.

D.1.2 Discharge-level relationship

The rating equation represents the various controls on discharge from the reservoir. In practice, there may be more than one overflow weir and, in some circumstances, a piped or culverted discharge may also need to be represented. The solution procedure adopts the following formulation:

$$q = C (h - h_0)^e \qquad [\text{for } h_{min} < h < h_{max}] \qquad \text{(D.6)}$$

where C is a rating coefficient. More usually, a set of equations is required to represent different behaviour in different water level ranges, or to represent more than one outlet device e.g. a main spillway and an auxiliary spillway. The formulation builds as a summation of several Equations D.6:

$$q = \Sigma \{C (h - h_0)^e\} \qquad [\text{for } h_{min} < h < h_{max}] \qquad \text{(D.7)}$$

The formulation can be used to represent one or more outflow devices with multi-stage ratings by appropriate choices of h_{min} and h_{max}.

In many situations h_{min} will be equal to the datum level h_0, and h_{max} will be unlimited i.e. infinite. The exponent e is commonly 1.5 for open structures with crest control, such as a broad-crested weir; for a drowned orifice it is 0.5. For a weir, the rating coefficient C would usually be the product of effective weir length (in m) and a discharge coefficient (a typical value of which is about 1.8 $m^{0.5} s^{-1}$). For a submerged orifice discharging freely, it would be the product of the cross-sectional area (in m^2) and another coefficient of discharge (a typical value of which is about 0.6 $m^{0.5} s^{-1}$); note that the water level is measured relative to the orifice centre. Flow behaviour in culverts is dependent on many factors, and to represent discharge performance in detail it is necessary to refer to a specialised text such as French's *Open-Channel Hydraulics*. The CIRIA guide to the design of flood storage reservoirs also discusses outlet controls and their rating equations (Hall *et al.*, 1993).

D.2 Solution scheme

Insertion of Equations D.4 and D.7 into Equation D.3, with appropriate limits retained on the terms in the summation, yields:

$$\{a_0 + a_1 (h - h_0)\} \left(\frac{dS}{dh}\right) = i + a_0 p - \Sigma \{C (h - h_0)^e\} \qquad \text{(D.8)}$$

Given knowledge of the inflow hydrograph i, the rainfall rate p and the initial water level, it is possible to solve Equation D.8 for successive time steps to obtain the water level graph during passage of the flood.

D.2.1 Standard case

Equation D.9 presents a finite difference representation of Equation D.8: h_1 and h_2 are the water levels at the start and end of the modelling interval Δt; i_1, i_2 and q_1, q_2 are the inflow and outflow rates at these times; a_f denotes the fixed area (m^2) for direct rainfall calculations.

$$\left\{a_0 + a_1 \frac{h_1+h_2}{2}\right\} \frac{h_2-h_1}{\Delta t} = \frac{i_1+i_2}{2} + a_f p - \frac{\Sigma C(h_1-h_0)^e + \Sigma C(h_2-h_0)^e}{2} \qquad \text{(D.9)}$$

On rearrangement, this gives Equation D.10, where $p\Delta t$ is denoted by P, and $0.5(i_1+i_2)\Delta t$ is denoted by I. This equation is solved for h_2 by an iterative solution, for which the Newton-Raphson method proves suitable. A suitable initial approximation for h_2 is $h_2 = h_1$.

$$(h_2-h_1)\{2a_0+a_1(h_1+h_2)\} = 2(I + a_f P) - \Delta t\{\Sigma C(h_1-h_0)^e + \Sigma C(h_2-h_0)^e\} \qquad \text{(D.10)}$$

D.2.2 Transition case

A difficulty in the solution process arises when the water level at the end of the time step is such that one or more terms in the summation cease to be active. This transition is tracked by checking that the water levels at the beginning and end of the time step lie within the same range of the q-h relationship. When such a condition is detected, a different numerical scheme is used to solve Equation D.8. This is formulated to seek not the water level at the end of the standard time step, but the time within the time step at which h transcends the current range of the q-h relationship.

A transition arises when the water level h_2 at the end of the modelling interval Δt lies outside the range of the rating relationship presently in force. In these circumstances, the finite difference representation of the routing equation is rewritten to determine the time T at which the transition water level h_T is reached within the modelling interval. The relevant equation is Equation D.11, where $i_T = i_1 + (i_2 - i_1)T/\Delta t$, which in turn yields a quadratic equation in terms of T (Equation D.12). The solution that lies between 0 and Δt is selected.

In the special case where $i_2 = i_1$, T is obtained from Equation D.13.

$$\frac{h_T-h_1}{T} = p + \frac{\dfrac{i_1 + i_T}{2} - \dfrac{\Sigma C(h_1 - h_0)^e + \Sigma C(h_T - h_0)^e}{2}}{a_0 + a_1 \dfrac{h_1 + h_T}{2}} \qquad \text{(D.11)}$$

$$\frac{i_2 - i_1}{\Delta t} T^2 + [2(i_1+a_f p) - \{\Sigma C(h_1-h_0)^e + \Sigma C(h_T-h_0)^e\}]\, T + [(h_1-h_T)\{2a_0+a_1(h_1+h_T)\}] = 0 \qquad \text{(D.12)}$$

$$T = \frac{(h_T - h_1)\{2a_0 + a_1(h_1 + h_T)\}}{2(i_1 + a_f p) - \{\Sigma C(h_1 - h_0)^e + \Sigma C(h_T - h_0)^e\}} \qquad \text{(D.13)}$$

The standard solution scheme is then restarted, in the new water level range, from part-way through the time step, using the q-h relationship which applies above (or below) the transition water level h_T.

D.3 ROUTER reservoir routing software

In IH Report 114, the solution scheme reproduced here is coded up as the FORTRAN program *ROUTER*. The reservoir routing module within the Micro-FSR (IH, 1991a; 1996) computer package is based on *ROUTER*, but differs from it in three respects:

- Micro-FSR provides user-friendly data entry screens which carry out some of *ROUTER*'s functions and checks, prior to execution of the hydrograph routing.
- *ROUTER* permits the reservoir area used for direct rainfall calculations to be specified independently from that used in the reservoir routing; in Micro-FSR, the reservoir area is defined only once.
- Micro-FSR uses the exponential form of the a-h relationship in order to provide additional flexibility for balancing pond design, where it is usual to leave undefined either the reservoir area or the rating coefficient of an outflow device, and to calculate the area or coefficient required to produce an outflow peak to match a specified target (see §9.3.4).

Index